S. U. Stroganov

CARNIVOROUS MAMMALS OF SIBERIA

TRANSLATED FROM RUSSIAN

Published for the Smithsonian Institution
and the National Science Foundation, Washington, D.C.
by the Israel Program for Scientific Translations

REFERENCE

AKADEMIYA NAUK SSSR. SIBIRSKOE OTDELENIE. BIOLOGICHESKII INSTITUT

Academy of Sciences of the USSR. Siberian Branch. Biological Institute

Novikov,

S.U. Stroganov

CARNIVOROUS MAMMALS
OF SIBERIA

(Zveri Sibiri: khishchnye)

Izdatel'stvo Akademii Nauk SSSR
Moskva 1962

Translated from Russian

Israel Program for Scientific Translations
Jerusalem 1969

TT 68-50349
Published Pursuant to an Agreement with
THE SMITHSONIAN INSTITUTION, U.S.A.
and
THE NATIONAL SCIENCE FOUNDATION, WASHINGTON, D.C.

Translated by Dr. A. Birron
Edited by IPST Staff

Printed in Jerusalem by IPST Press
Binding: Wiener Bindery, Jerusalem

Available from the
U.S. DEPARTMENT OF COMMERCE
Clearinghouse for Federal Scientific and Technical Information
Springfield, Va. 22151

TABLE OF CONTENTS

PREFACE

The book by Prof. S. U. Stroganov on the carnivores of Siberia is the second in a series of monographs published by the Biological Institute of the Siberian Branch of the Academy of Sciences of the USSR. The first monograph, on the insectivores of Siberia, was published in 1957.

The collected material on which this work is based was studied by Prof. Stroganov over many years. It includes the large collections of carnivores in the Zoological Institute of the Academy of Sciences of the USSR, in the Zoological Museum of Moscow State University, and in the Biological Institute of the Siberian Branch of the Academy of Sciences of the USSR, and in addition the carnivores collection in the zoological sections of the Chita Regional Branch of the Academy of Sciences and of the Irkutsk Antiplague Institute of Siberia and the Far East.

The Biological Institute sent special expeditions into various regions of Siberia for the collection of new material and for the study of the geographical distribution and biology of carnivores. These expeditions worked in the tundra in the northern Ob area, in the lower reaches of the Yenisei River, in the taiga of the Western Siberian plains, in the steppes of Kulunda, in forest steppes of Baraba, in the Altai, in the Eastern Sayans, on the Chukchi Peninsula and in the Maritime Territory.

Prof. Stroganov's untimely death has put an end to the tireless activity of this prominent zoologist of Siberia, but the present book has been completed and the manuscript prepared for print by Candidates of Biological Sciences K. T. Yurlov and B. S. Yudin, and by A. B. Markina, A. F. Potapkina, L. I. Galkina and V. I. Telegin of the staff of the vertebrates laboratory which Sergei Ul'yanovich Stroganov headed during his life. The technical preparation of the manuscript was handled by laboratory staff members O. V. Grigor'ev and N. P. Grigor'eva.

A few additions were made to the text according to draft notes of the author.

The monograph contains mainly original illustrations. The color plates* were made by the well-known painter V. A. Vatagin, and the line drawings by N. V. Lyakhov. The photographs were taken by the vertebrates laboratory staff members K. T. Yurlov, B. S. Yudin and V. I. Telegin.

Deep gratitude is hereby expressed by the management of the Biological Institute to all persons and institutions who assisted in the publication of this book.

_____

* [Reproduced in black and white in this translation.]

The series of monographs "Animals of Siberia" will be continued. Rodents will be described in the next monograph.

Professor A. I. Cherepanov
Doctor of Biological Sciences,
Director of the Biological Institute
of the Siberian Branch of the
Academy of Sciences of the USSR

Translation Editor's Note

The following names have been spelled in two ways throughout the book

Iohansen   — Ioganzen
Kastschenko — Kashchenko
Kuznetzov   — Kuznetsov

LIFE AND WORK OF SERGEI UL'YANOVICH STROGANOV

Sergei Ul'yanovich Stroganov died on 23 March 1960, in Novosibirsk. Soviet science has lost one of its major zoologists.

Stroganov was born into a peasant family on 29 September 1904, in the village Pogorelovo in the former Tver' Province (now Kalinin Region). He attended elementary school in his native village, continued his education in a workers' high school in Tver', and received his higher education in the Tver' Pedagogical Institute, from which he graduated in 1930. However, the teaching profession did not satisfy Stroganov and he continued to study, first at the law faculty and later at the faculty of biology of Moscow State University, completing his postgraduate course and defending his candidate's dissertation in March 1936 and his dissertation for the degree of Doctor of Biological Sciences in April 1943.

Stroganov belongs to a generation of men who reached maturity during the first years of the Soviet regime. In the complicated conditions of the first post-revolutionary years, Stroganov found an aim in life. He entered the Komsomol at the age of 15 and became an active fighter for the new life. The Komsomol cell which he organized took part in all measures of the Soviet regime to combat devastation and famine in Tver' Province. His lively mind, gift for organization, and principled behavior as a member of the Komsomol attracted the attention of his comrades and they elected him as delegate to the 3rd conference of the Komsomol, where he heard and saw V. I. Lenin giving his speech "Problems of Youth Associations." He was educated by the Komsomol, and in 1923 became a candidate and in 1925 a member of the Communist Party. He devoted the major part of his energy to party work and for several years headed the party organization of the faculty of biology of Moscow State University.

During the Second World War, Stroganov joined the ranks of those defending his country, becoming a member of the People's Volunteer Corps on 1 July 1941. He was wounded on the Leningrad front near Krasnoe Selo and was shell-shocked near Kolpino. He was decorated with the following medals: "For the defense of Leningrad," "For victory over Germany," "For valor in the Second World War."

Stroganov began his scientific work in Moscow State University under the guidance of Prof. S. I. Ognev. His first study, "Notes on the Game-Mammal Fauna of the Northeastern Part of the Western Region" was published in 1934. Several other publications appeared in print. At the same time Stroganov was engaged in educational activity as assistant in the Department of Vertebrate Zoology of Moscow State University.

In 1936 Stroganov completed his dissertation "Mammals of the Valdai Heights" and was given the degree of Candidate of Biological Sciences. Soon he was elected a member of the Moscow Society of Naturalists. He became a senior member of the Scientific Institute of Zoology of Moscow State University, but in April of the same year, according to the decision of the Central Committee of the Communist Party, he was sent to work for a doctor's degree at the Academy of Sciences of the USSR. He moved to Leningrad and worked for his degree in the Zoological Institute of the Academy of Sciences until the end of 1937.

In 1938 Stroganov was a senior member of the staff of the Institute, and in April 1939 became its acting director of science. When war broke out Stroganov left this post and went to the front as a volunteer. Shell-shocked in the battle of Kolpino, he was brought to Leningrad, which was already blockaded. Soon after recovery from a contusion, Stroganov embarked on scientific work. He worked on his dissertation in blockaded Leningrad, interrupting his studies only to take part in building the Ladoga ice route.

After the siege of Leningrad was raised, the Zoological Institute was evacuated to Tadzhikistan. Stroganov came to Dushanbe, where he lived until 1945, devoting himself to scientific research. In 1943 he defended his dissertation, "Monograph of Family Talpidae," at Moscow State University and this dissertation was published in 1948 under the name "Systematics of Talpidae." In Tadzhikistan Stroganov made numerous excursions and enthusiastically studied the local fauna. He made autecological and taxonomical studies of little-studied vertebrates in Central Asia (the Tugai deer, the tolai hare, and the black-golden pheasant) which were published later.

For his successful work in Tadzhikistan Stroganov was awarded a diploma of the Supreme Soviet of the Tadzhik Soviet Socialist Republic.

Stroganov was professor of the Karelo-Finnish University in 1946—1948, gave courses on zoology and biology of vertebrates, ecology of animals, and zoogeography, and trained postgraduate students. With the aid of his students, he studied the fauna of Karelia and prepared "A Key to Karelian Mammals," a summary of his studies and an outline of further tasks in the study of this region.

In June 1947 Stroganov was appointed Professor of Vertebrate Zoology.

In February 1949 Stroganov was appointed to the Chair of Zoology at Tomsk University. During his work in Tomsk University he made studies of the fauna in the taiga region of western Siberia and published some of his findings.

In October 1950 Stroganov moved to the University of Tadzhikistan. After a year, a throat disease forced him to give up lecturing and his Chair.

Stroganov went to the Western Siberian Branch of the Academy of Sciences of the USSR in Novosibirsk in autumn 1951. He directed the Biological Institute for some time but had to leave this post because of illness and became the Director of the Laboratory of Zoology, which he directed for nine years up to his death. This was the period of his most intensive scientific work.

Stroganov was a zoologist of great erudition, with a broad range of scientific interests. His outstanding abilities were shown mostly in the field of theriology.

He achieved great success in systematics, his main interest. He generally worked on the most difficult groups and attempted to carry out original research. The following papers are important in this respect: "Morphological Characters of the Auditory Ossicles of Recent Talpidae," the monograph on the systematics and geographical distribution of Talpidae, and two monographs of the series "Animals of Siberia" on insectivores and carnivores.

Stroganov displayed keen interest in the problem of the species and evolution of mammals, and published a number of papers on this subject, making numerous studies in faunistics and zoogeography.

The ecological studies of Stroganov are distinguished by thoroughness and depth.

Stroganov devoted much energy and time to collections. The collection of mammals of Siberia made under his guidance is one of the principal contributions to the zoological collections of the Biological Institute of the Siberian Branch of the Academy of Sciences. It is basic for the study of the fauna of Siberia.

Stroganov wrote in a precise, clear, lively style. He always prepared his work carefully, allowing time to read the text again and insert corrections, to select illustrations and to supervise the technical layout. Thus, his books and papers are a model of excellent work.

Stroganov was a distinguished teacher. He was a master of language and could explain complicated phenomena in a simple manner. This, combined with his broad erudition and lively mind, made him a perfect lecturer. Everyone who attended his lectures and academic appearances praised their form and content.

Stroganov was a man of single purpose. His main interest and aim in life was scientific creation. In his last years, even while suffering from a very serious disease (myocardial infarction), he occupied himself tirelessly with science. When he left the hospital (often against the advice of his doctors) he left his working table only for a few hours a day.

Stroganov was a strong-willed, vigorous, cheerful, witty and enthusiastic person.

His love of sports was second only to his scientific enthusiasm. His interests were dog breeding and hunting, and he always kept pedigree dogs. He took part in numerous exhibitions and field tests for dogs and was considered an expert of national standing.

Hunting capercaillies during their courtship was one of his special hobbies. He went on the hunt on every possible occasion. He also liked hunting with a setter for woodcock and hunting hares with greyhounds.

Toward the end of his life, Stroganov was awarded a sporting degree for shooting.

Stroganov lived a short but full life as a scientist. His great gifts, strong will and hard work enabled him to make an important contribution to zoology. He died at the height of his creative abilities.

PUBLICATIONS OF S. U. STROGANOV

Zametki po faune promyslovykh mlekopitayushchikh severo-vostochnoi chasti Zapadnoi oblasti (Notes on the Game-Mammal Fauna of the Northeastern Part of the Western Region).— Uchenye Zapiski Moskovskogo Universiteta, No. 2, pp. 292—310. 1934.

Fauna mlekopitayushchikh Valdaiskoi vozvyshennosti (The Mammalian Fauna of the Valdai Heights).— Zoologicheskii Zhurnal, Vol. 13, No. 4, pp. 714—730, 1934; Vol. 15, No. 1, pp. 128—142; No. 3, pp. 520—559. 1936.

Ob okhote i sostoyanii okhotkhozyaistva v Kalininskoi oblasti (Hunting and Hunting Trade in the Kalinin Region).— Boets-Okhotnik, No. 11, pp. 15—18. 1935.

O taksonomicheskom polozhenii Rattus rattus L. i o rasprostranenii ee v SSSR (The Taxonomic Position of Rattus rattus L. and Its Distribution in the USSR).— Sbornik Nauchno-Issledovatel'skogo Instituta Zoologii Moskovskogo Gosudarstvennogo Universiteta, No. 3, pp. 108—109. 1936.

Novye dannye po sistematike nekotorykh gryzunov (New Data on the Systematics of Some Rodents).— Sbornik Nauchno-Issledovatel'skogo Instituta Zoologii Moskovskogo Gosudarstvennogo Universiteta, No. 3, pp. 110—114. 1936.

Novyi podvid chernoi krysy (Rattus rattus ruthenus subsp. n.) (A New Subspecies of the Black Rat (Rattus rattus ruthenus subsp. n.)).— Sbornik Nauchno-Issledovatel'skogo Instituta Zoologii Moskovskogo Gosudarstvennogo Universiteta, No. 3, pp. 82—84. 1936. (In collaboration with S. I. Ognev.)

Novaya forma sadovoi soni Eliomys quercinus superans subsp. n. iz Vostochnoi Evropy (A New Form of the Garden Dormouse Eliomys quercinus superans subsp. n. from Eastern Europe).— Sbornik Nauchno-Issledovatel'skogo Instituta Zoologii Moskovskogo Gosudarstvennogo Universiteta, No. 3, pp. 84—85. 1936. (In collaboration with S. I. Ognev.)

Zametki po faune promyslovykh mlekopitayushchikh Zapadnoi oblasti (Notes on the Game-Mammal Fauna of the Western Region).— Sbornik Nauchno-Issledovatel'skogo Instituta Zoologii Moskovskogo Gosudarstvennogo Universiteta, No. 3, p. 108. 1936.

Metodika opredeleniya vozrasta i analiz vozrastnogo sostava populyatsii gornostaya (Mustela erminea L.) (Methods of Age Determination and Analysis of the Age Composition of Populations of the Ermine (Mustela erminea L.)).— Zoologicheskii Zhurnal, Vol. 16, No. 1, pp. 113—129. 1937.

Kratkii obzor issledovanii po mlekopitayushchim v. SSSR za 20 let (1917—1937) (A Brief Review of 20 Years of Mammal Study in the USSR, (1917—1937)).—Izvestiya AN SSSR, pp. 1503—1515. 1937. (In collaboration with Vinogradov, B. S., V. I. Gromova et al.).

O standartakh okhotnich'e-promyslovykh sobak (On the Standards of Hunting Dogs).— Sovetskii Okhotnik, No. 10, pp. 34—35. 1939.

Sovetskii akademik-aktivnyi uchastnik sotsialisticheskogo stroitel'stva (The Soviet Academician, an Active Participant in the Building of Socialism).— Za Bol'shevistskuyu Nauku, No. 1(11), p. 2. Leningrad, 1939.

Morfologicheskie osobennosti slukhovykh kostochek sovremennykh nasekomoyadnykh (Morphological Characteristics of the Auditory Ossicles of Recent Insectivores).— Zoologicheskii Zhurnal, Vol. 20, No. 3, pp. 375—381. 1941.

Nasekomoyadnye mlekopitayushchie fauny SSSR (Insectivores in the USSR Fauna).— Doklady AN SSSR, Vol. 23, No. 3, pp. 270—272. 1941.

Novye formy nasekomoyadnykh mlekopitayushchikh (New Forms of Insectivores).— Doklady AN SSSR, Vol. 11, Issue 4, No. 3, pp. 130—132. 1944.

Materialy po biologii zaitsa-peschanika v Yuzhnom Tadzhikistane (Data on the Biology of the Tolai Hare in Southern Tadzhikistan).— Referat Nauchno-Issledovatel'skikh Rabot za 1943 g. Otdelenie Biologicheskikh Nauk AN SSSR. 1944. (In collaboration with A. S. Stroganova.)

Materialy po ekologii zaitsa-peschanika (Lepus tibetanus buchariensis Ogn.) po nablyudeniyami v Yuzhnom Tadzhikistane (Data on the Ecology of the Tolai Hare (Lepus tibetanus buchariensis Ogn.) according to Observations in Southern Tadzhikistan). Izvestiya Tadzhikskogo Filiala AN SSSR, No. 5, pp. 161—188. 1944. (In collaboration with A. S. Stroganova.)

Tugainyi olen', ili gavas, v Tadzhikistane (The Tugai Deer* or Gavas of Tadzhikistan). Synopses of Reports.— Otchetnye sessii Zoologicheskogo instituta AN SSSR, pp. 34—35, Dushanbe. 1945.

Tugainyi olen', ili gavas (Cervus bactrianus Lydekker) (The Tugai Deer or Gavas (Cervus bactrianus Lydekker)).— Referat Nauchno-Issledovatel'skikh Rabot za 1944g. Otdelenie Biologicheskikh Nauk AN SSSR, p. 133, Izdatel'stvo AN SSSR. 1945.

Materialy po razmnozheniyu tadzhikskogo chernozolotogo fazana (Data on the Reproduction of the Black-Golden Pheasant (Phasianus chrysomelas bianchi Buturl.) in Tadzhikistan).— Ibid., p. 134.

Morphological Characters of the Auditory Ossicles of Recent Talpidae.— J. Mammal., Vol. 26, No. 4, pp. 413—420. 1945.

Materialy po razmnozheniyu tadzhikskogo chernozolotogo fazana (Phasianus chrysomelas bianchi Buturl.) (Data on the Reproduction of the Black-Golden Pheasant (Phasianus chrysomelas bianchi Buturl.) in Tadzhikistan).— Byulleten MOIP, otdel biologicheskii, Vol. 2, No. 1, pp. 73—86. 1946.

Osnovopolozhnik russkoi gidrobiologii (The Founder of Russian Hydrobiology) (In memoriam Academician S. A. Zernov).— Priroda, No. 2, pp. 94—96. 1946.

---

* [Generally known as Turkestan red deer.]

Gibel' fazana ot beskormitsy v mnogosnezhnuyu zimu 1945 g. v Gissarskoi doline (Death of Pheasants from Famine in the Snowy Winter of 1945 in the Gissar Valley).— Priroda, No. 3, pp. 68—69. 1946.

Sergei Ivanovich Ognev. K 60-letiyu so dnya rozhdeniya i 40-letiyu nauchnoi deyatel'nosti (Volume Dedicated to S. I. Ognev's 60th Birthday and 40 Years of Scientific Activity). Byulleten' MOIP, otdel biologicheskii, Vol. 1, Nos. 4/5, pp. 3—12. 1946.

Angliiskii setter. Obzor vedeniya porody za 15 let (The English Setter. A Review of 15 Years of Breeding).— In: Okhotnich'e sobaki Leningrada (edited by S. U Stroganov), pp. 285—288, Leningrad. Izd. Leningradskogo obshchestva krovnogo sobakovodstva. 1947.

Printsipy postroeniya standartov okhotnich'ikh i promyslovykh sobak (Principles for Establishing Standards for Hunting and Game Dogs).— Ibid., pp. 222—288.

Novye dannye po sistematike perevyazki (Vormela peregusna Gueld) (New Data on the Systematics of the Mottled Polecat (Vormela peregusna Gueld)).— Trudy Zoologicheskogo Instituta AN SSSR, Vol. 8, No. 3, pp. 129—131. 1948.

Sistematika krotovykh (Talpidae) (The Systematics of Talpidae).— Trudy Zoologicheskogo Instituta AN SSSR, Vol. 8, No. 2, pp. 289—406. 1948.

S. I. Ognev. Zveri SSSR i prilezhashchikh stran. T. 5, gryzuny (Animals of the USSR and Adjacent Countries, Vol. 5, Rodents). Review.— Zoologicheskii Zhurnal, Vol. 27, No. 4, pp. 381— 382. 1948.

Samyi malen'kii zver'. Ves 2,2 gramma (The Smallest Beast. Weight 2.2 grams).— Gazeta Smena, Leningrad, 8 August. 1948.

Novyi podvid ryzhei polevki (A New Subspecies of the Bank Vole).— Byulleten' MOIP, otdel biologicheskii, Vol. 53, No. 6, pp. 51—52. 1948. (In collaboration with V. V. Tur'eva.)

K sistematike i geograficheskomu rasprostraneniyu nekotorykh antilop Tsentral'noi Azii (The Systematics and Geographical Distribution of Some Antelopes in Central Asia).— Byulleten' MOIP, otdel biologicheskii, Vols. 1—4, No. 4, pp. 15—26. 1949.

Zadachi issledovaniya nazemnykh pozvonochnykh zhivotnykh Karelo-Finskoi SSR. Prirodnye resursy, istoriya i kul'tura Karelo-Finskoi SSR (The Aims of the Study of Terrestrial Vertebrates of the Karelo-Finnish SSR. Natural Resources, History and Culture of the Karelo-Finnish SSR).— Trudy Pervoi Nauchnoi Sessii Karelo-Finskogo Gosudarstvennogo Universiteta, No. 2, pp. 80—82, Petrozavodsk. 1949.

Opredelitel' mlekopitayushchikh Karelii (Key to the Mammals of Karelia). pp. 1—200, Petrozavodsk, Izd. Karelo-Finskogo Gosudarstvennogo Universiteta. 1949.

Obzor podvidov i geograficheskogo rasprostraneniya kroshechnoi burozubki (Sorex tscherskii Ognev) (Survey of Subspecies and Geographical Distribution of the Pigmy Shrew (Sorex tscherskii Ognev)). — Uchenye Zapiski Tomskogo Gosudarstvennogo Universiteta, No. 12, pp. 180—192. 1949.

K kharakteristike fauny gryzunov Tomskoi oblasti (Characteristics of the Rodent Fauna of the Tomsk Region).— Uchenye Zapiski Tomskogo Gosudarstvennogo Universiteta, No. 14, pp. 101—142. 1950. (In collaboration with A. F. Potapkina.)

O rabote diplomnikov (On Graduation Work of Students).— Za Sovetskuyu Nauku, Tomsk, 1 April. 1950.

K sistematike i rasprostraneniyu dvukh maloizuchennykh vidov burozubok Srednei i Tsentral'noi Azii (Systematics and Distribution of Two Little-Studied Species of Shrew in Central and Soviet Central Asia).— Byulleten' MOIP, otdel biologicheskii, Vol. 1—7, No. 5, pp. 21—22. 1952.

Vazhnaya zadacha uchenykh-zoologov. K XIX s"ezdu VKP(b) (An Important Task for Zoologists. XIX Congress of the All-Union Communist Party (B)).— Gazeta Sovetskaya Sibir', Novosibirsk, 2 October. 1952.

Mnimoe novatorstvo v nauke (On Imaginary Innovation in Science).— Gazeta Sovetskaya Sibir', Novosibirsk, 9 April.

Gryzuny. Otryad Glires (The Rodents. Order Glires).— Atlas Okhotnich'ikh i Promyslovykh Ptits i Zverei SSSR, Vol. 2, pp. 25—102, Moskva, Izdatel'stvo AN SSSR. 1953. (In collaboration with Argiropulo, A. I., B. S. Vinogradov, et al.).

Khishchnye. Otryad Carnivora (Order Carnivora).— Ibid., pp. 103—195. (In collaboration with Argiropulo, A. I., G. A. Novikov, et al.)

Parnokopytnye. Otryad Artiodactyla (Order Artiodactyla).— Ibid., pp. 196—267. (In collaboration with Novikov, G. A., V. V. Petrov, and K. K. Flerov.)

Vyvodka okhotnich'ikh sobak v Novosibirske (Breeding of Hunting Dogs in Novosibirsk).— Byulleten' Prezidiuma Oblastnogo Soveta Novosibirskogo obshchestva okhotnikov, pp. 21—24. 1954.

Polevye ispytaniya okhotnich'ikh sobak v Novosibirskoi oblasti v 1954g. (Field Tests of Hunting Dogs in Novosibirsk, 1954).— Katalog 5 Novosibirskoi oblastnoi vystavki okhotnich'ikh sobak, pp. 30—39, Novosibirsk. 1955.

Otchet o vyvode-vystavke okhotnich'ikh sobak v g. Tomske v 1955 godu (Report on the Exhibition of Hunting Dogs in Tomsk, 1955).— Katalog 1 oblastnoi vystavki-vyvodki okhotnich'ikh promyslovykh sobak, pp. 7 — 18, Tomsk. 1956.

Novyi dlya fauny Sibiri vid zemleroiki (A Species of Shrew New to Siberia).— Trudy Biologicheskogo Instituta Zapadno-Sibirskogo Filiala AN SSSR, No. 1, pp. 11—14, Novosibirsk. 1956.

Materialy po sistematike sibirskikh mlekopitayushchikh (Data on the Systematics of Siberian Mammals).— Ibid., pp. 3—10.

Materialy k poznaniyu teriofauny Sovetskogo Soyuza (Sistematicheskie i nomenklaturnye zametki) (Data on the Theriofauna of the Soviet Union (Systematic and Nomenclature Notes)).— Ibid., pp. 15—19.

K sistematike nekotorykh vidov gryzunov Zapadnoi Sibiri (The Systematics of Some Rodent Species in Western Siberia).— Trudy Tomskogo Gosudarstvennogo Universiteta, No. 142, pp. 291—294. 1956. (In collaboration with B. S. Yudin.)

O nekotorykh formal'nykh napravleniyakh v sistematike (On Some Formalistic Trends in Systematics).— Tezisy dokladov IX nauchnoi konferentsii Novosibirskogo sel'skokhozyaistvennogo instituta, pp. 5—8, Novosibirsk. 1957.

Fazan v Tadzhikistane (The Pheasant in Tadzhikistan).—Okhota i Okhotnich'e Khozyaistvo, No. 11, pp. 30—31, Moskva. 1957.

K voprosu o pustykh stoikakh (On the Problem of Hunting Checks).— Ibid.

K voprosu o proiskhozhdenii fauny nasekomoyadnykh Sibiri (On the Origin of the Insectivore Fauna of Siberia).— Izvestiya Vostochnykh Filialov AN SSSR, No. 2, pp. 96—103, Novosibirsk. 1957.

O vide i ego sistematicheskikh kriteriyakh v zoologii (The Species and Its Systematic Criteria in Zoology). — Izvestiya Vostochnykh Filialov AN SSSR, No. 6, pp. 116—127, Novosibirsk. 1957.

Obzor issledovanii zhivotnogo mira Sibiri za sovetskii period (1917—1957) i zadachi dal'neishego izucheniya ego (A Review of the Studies of the Animal World of Siberia during the Soviet Regime (1917—1957) and Problems of Its Further Study). — Tezisy dokladov soveshchaniya zoologov Sibiri, pp. 3—6, Novosibirsk. 1957. (In collaboration with A. I. Cherepanov.)

Zveri Sibiri. Nasekomoyadnye (Animals of Siberia. Insectivores). pp. 1—267, Moskva, Izdatel'stvo AN SSSR. 1957.

K rasprostraneniyu i taksonomii belozubki-malyutki Srednei Azii (Suncus etruscus bactrianus subsp. n.) (The Distribution and Taxonomy of Suncus etruscus bactrianus subsp. n. in Central Asia). — Izvestiya Sibirskogo Otdeleniya AN SSSR, No. 11, pp. 122—125. 1958.

Pamyati Nikolaya Petrovicha Krasinskogo (In Memoriam Nikolai Petrovich Krasinskii). — Trudy po Lesnomu Khozyaistvu Zapadnoi Sibiri, No. 4, pp. 448—450, Novosibirsk. 1958. (In collaboration with Z. N. Bryantseva.)

Obzor podvidov stepnogo khorya (Putorius eversm anni Lesson) Sibirskoi fauny (A Review of the Subspecies of the Steppe Polecat (Putorius eversm anni Lesson) in Siberia). — Izvestiya Sibirskogo Otdeleniya AN SSSR, No. 11, pp. 149—155. 1958.

Soveshchanie zoologov Sibiri (Conference of Siberian Zoologists). — Izvestiya Sibirskogo Otdeleniya AN SSSR, No. 1, pp. 149—155. 1958.

Kratkii obzor rabot po izucheniyu zhivotnogo mira Sibiri za sovetskii period (1917—1957) (Brief Review of Studies of the Animal World of Siberia during the Soviet Regime (1917—1957)). — Trudy Biologicheskogo Instituta Sibirskogo Otdeleniya AN SSSR, No. 5, pp. 3—13. 1959. (In collaboration with A. I. Cherepanov.)

Materialy k kharakteristike i ekologii tugainogo olenya (Data on the Characteristics and Ecology of the Tugai Deer). — Trudy Biologicheskogo Instituta Sibirskogo Otdeleniya AN SSSR, No. 5, pp. 15—84. 1959.

O gladkoiglom ezhe (Hemiechinus homalacanthus Stroganov) (The Smooth-Spined Hedgehog (Hemiechinus homalacanthus Stroganov)). — Ibid, pp. 231—233.

Okhotnich'i sobaki Sibiri (Hunting Dogs of Siberia). — In: Sbornik "Kniga okhotnika," Novosibirskoe knizhnoe izdatel'stvo, pp. 313—384, 1959.

Okhotnich'i sobaki. Porody, razvedenie, soderzhanie, obuchenie, vystavki i polevye ispytaniya (Hunting Dogs, Breeds, Breeding, Keeping, Training, Exhibitions and Field Tests). — Novosibirskoe knizhnoe izdatel'stvo, pp. 1—195. 1959.

Zametki po taksonomii nekotorykh vidov roda Crocidura (Soricidae) (Notes on the Taxonomy of Some Species of the Genus Crocidura (Soricidae)). — Trudy Biologicheskogo Instituta Sibirskogo Otdeleniya AN SSSR, No. 6, pp. 159—162. 1960.

Novye formy khishchnykh mlekopitayushchikh (Carnivora, Mammalia) Palearktiki (New Forms of Palaearctic Carnivores (Carnivora, Mammalia)). — Ibid., pp. 155—158.

Yaponskii kolonok, ili itatsi (Mustela itatsi Temminck) na Sakhaline (The Japanese Weasel or Itatsi (Mustela itatsi Temminck) in Sakhalin). — Izvestiya Sibirskogo Otdeleniya AN SSSR, No. 3, pp. 116—121. 1960.

The Vertebrate Laboratory of the Biological Institute of the Siberian Branch of the Academy of Sciences of the USSR

ORDER **CARNIVORA** — Terrestrial Carnivores

Diagnosis. The order of terrestrial carnivores includes mammals of varying size and habits, from the small, slender weasel to the huge, clumsy bear. Limbs are plantigrade, subplantigrade, or digitigrade. Feet have four or five digits, with claws varying in form and size. The claws are retractile or semiretractile in some species. The thumb is not opposable. The length of the tail varies from the short tail of the bear, hidden in the fur, to the long tail of most dogs, some cats and martens.

Clavicula rudimentary or absent. A character of the anterior legs is the fusion of the three carpals, scaphoideum, lunatum and centrale on which the radius is supported. Ulna and radius are separate.

Braincase and brain are well developed. Temporal fossa of the skull connected with the orbits, and tympanic bullae are well developed. Crests for the attachment of the strong masticatory musculature are well developed. The dental system is heterodont and rooted. Both upper and lower jaws possess three small incisors on each side with the exception of the sea otter (genus Enhydra), which has two incisors in the lower jaw. Canines well developed, sharp and slightly curved. Carnassial teeth (Pm^4 and M_1) are present. The size and development of their cutting cusps and the crests vary with food texture. The molars vary from tuberculosectorial, quadritubercular to multitubercular, with sharp or blunt cusps.

The testes lie behind the penis in the scrotum. Uterus bicornuate; placenta deciduate, discoidal. Mammary glands usually ventral. The number of teats varies from three pairs in most cats to six or seven pairs in the red dog (genus Cuon).

The skin contains alveolar glands which are also present in small numbers in dogs (the widely held opinion that these glands are absent in dogs is incorrect). The tubular and racemose anal glands are very characteristic. The anal glands form a highly developed complex, enveloped in a thin muscular layer in some Mustelinae (the American skunk genera Mephitis and Conepatus). The secretion of these glands is very malodorous and in some forms can be ejected as far as one meter.

The length, density and color of the fur are widely variable; spots and stripes are not rare. In some species there is a distinct difference in the color of the winter and the summer fur.

Systematics. The order is represented in the Soviet Union by 44 species belonging to five families. In Siberia, there are 33 species belonging to four families.

Geographical distribution. Carnivores are distributed from the poles to the equator. Only one species, the dingo (Canis dingo L.) can be found in Australia.

9

Biology. Carnivores are terrestrial, partly subterraneal, semi-arboreal or amphibious. There are diurnal, nocturnal and crepuscular carnivores. They live in burrows, temporary lairs, caves, tree hollows and other habitats.

The species of the order feed on animal food to a varying degree. The most specialized flesh eaters occur among the cats, many of which feed exclusively on animal food. The dog family feeds on plant as well as animal food. Bears and badgers feed mainly on vegetable food. The diet not only varies among various groups of carnivores, but may also vary within one group according to the season, locality and the biocenotic composition.

Carnivores breed only once a year. The young are born slightly developed and are helpless for some time. The litter contains from $1-2$ (bears) to $15-18$ young, sometimes even more (Arctic fox and other mustelids). Some Mustelidea have a prolonged gestation with a latent phase of egg development. Gestation lasts $1\frac{1}{2}-2$ months (small mustelids) to 9 months (sable and martens). They are either polygamous or monogamous.

The senses are well developed. If one of the senses is weak, this is compensated by the stronger development of another sense.

Practical importance. The pelts of carnivores are in high demand in the fur market. They constitute about 35 % of the total yield of furs by value and about 7 % by number. Some species cause damage to animal breeding (wolves), while others — Mustelidae and foxes — benefit agriculture by killing large numbers of harmful rodents.

The skull of terrestrial carnivores

Figures $1-3$ show the skull of a wolf (C a n i s l u p u s L.) ⅔ natural size. Bones and other elements are indicated by figures.

Key to the Families of Carnivores Found in Siberia

1 (2). Fur spotted. Hairs on tip of ears form tufts. Claws retractile. Three teeth in each side of lower jaw behind the canine . . . .
. . . . **Felidae** (p. 421). .

2 (1). Fur not spotted. No tufts on ear. Claws not retractile. More than three teeth in lower jaw behind the canine. . . . . 3.

3 (4). Adults very large: length of body and head at least 150 cm, length of skull at least 280 mm. Tail shorter than hind foot. Lower jaw provided with an alveolar process. Upper carnassial tooth double-rooted without additional lobe (talon) on the inner side. Two tubercular teeth behind upper carnassial tooth, the last upper molar not smaller than the first; longitudinal diameter of last upper molar markedly longer than transverse diameter . . . . **Ursidae** (p. 79).

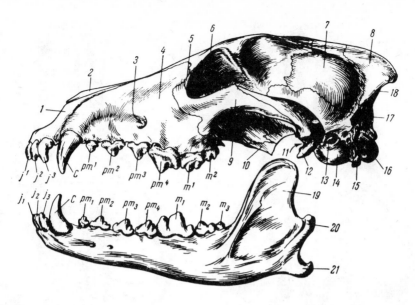

FIGURE 1. Skull of wolf (Canis lupus L.) lateral view, $^3/_5$ natural size (after S.U. Stroganov, 1949):

1 — premaxilla (intermaxillary); 2 — nasal bone; 3 — infraorbital foramen; 4 — maxilla; 5 — lachrymal; 6 — frontal bone; 7 — parietal bone; 8 — interparietal; 9 — jugal (= zygomaticum); 10 — pterygoid; 11 — glenoid fossa; 12 — postglenoid process; 13 — external auditory meatus; 14 — tympanic bullae; 15 — paroccipital process; 16 — occipital condyle; 17 — supraoccipital; 18 — supraoccipital crest; 19 — coronoid process; 20 — condylar process; 21 — angular process; I^1, I^2, I^3, first, second, and third upper incisors, I_1, I_2, I_3, lower incisors (Incisivi); C, canines: Pm^1, Pm^2, Pm^3, Pm^4, first to fourth upper premolars, Pm_1, Pm_2, Pm_3, Pm_4, lower premolars; M^1, M^2, first and second upper molars M_1, M_2, M_3, lower molars.

4 (5). Adults of medium or small size: length of body and head less than 150 cm, maximum length of skull less than 280 mm. Tail longer than hind foot. Lower jaw without alveolar process. Upper carnassial tooth with an additional lobe at the inner aspect (talon), tri-rooted. Usually one tubercular tooth behind carnassial tooth; if two tubercular teeth, the second is markedly smaller than the first; longitudinal diameter of last upper molar not longer than transverse diameter . . 6

6 (7). Hind feet with four toes. Posterior edge of bony palate usually on same level as posterior margin of last upper molars. At least six teeth behind upper canine and at least seven behind lower canine. Total number of teeth 42 . . . . **Canidae** (p. 12).

7 (6). Posterior feet with five toes. Posterior margin of bony palate markedly behind posterior margin of last upper molars. Less than six teeth behind upper canine and seven behind lower canine. Total number of teeth 34—48 . . . . **Mustelidae** (p. 154).

11

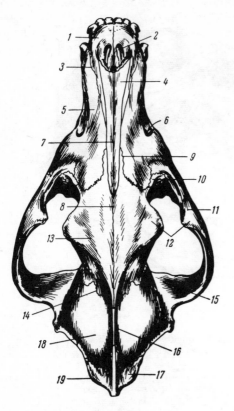 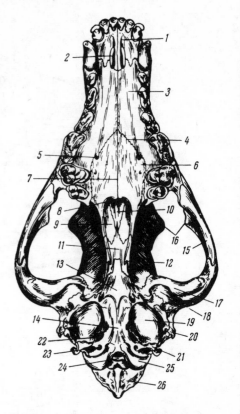

FIGURE 2. Skull of wolf (Canis lupus L.).
Dorsal view, $\frac{3}{5}$ natural size (after S.U. Stroganov, 1949):

1 — premaxilla (intermaxillary);
2 — anterior palatine foramen; 3 — maxillo-intermaxillary suture; 4 — nasal bone; 5 — maxilla;
6 — infraorbital foramen; 7 — internasal suture;
8 — sagittal suture; 9 — maxillo-frontal suture;
10 — lachrymal; 11 — jugal (= zygomaticum);
12 — postorbital process; 13 — frontal; 14 — coronal suture; 15 — zygomatic process; 16 — sagittal crest; 17 — interparietal; 18 — parietal;
19 — supraoccipital crest.

FIGURE 3. Skull of wolf (Canis lupus L.).
Ventral view, $\frac{3}{5}$ natural size (after S.U. Stroganov, 1949):

1 — premaxilla (intermaxillary); 2 — anterior palatine foramen; 3 — maxilla; 4 — palato-maxillary suture; 5 — palatine foramen;
6 — palatine; 7 — palatine suture; 8 — choanae;
9 — pterygoid fossa; 10 — vomer; 11 — presphenoid;
12 — hamular process; 13 — basisphenoid;
14 — basioccipital; 15 — jugal (= zygomaticum);
16 — postorbital process; 17 — glenoid fossa;
18 — postglenoid process; 19 — tympanic bullae;
20 — mastoid process; 21 — paroccipital process;
22 — jugular foramen (= for. lacerum posterius);
23 — anterior condyloid foramen; 24 — foramen magnum; 25 — occipital condyle;
26 — supraoccipital.

1. Family CANIDAE GRAY (1821) — Dogs

1821. Canidae. Gray. I. — London Medical Repository, XV, April 1, p. 301.

Diagnosis. Carnivores of small or moderate size, and of compact build. Body moderately or very elongated. Neck muscular but thin and well marked.

Head small, elongated with blunt nose. Legs slender with large feet. Most species have five toes on forefeet and four toes on hind feet. The exceptions are some domestic dogs having five toes on the hind feet, and the species of the African genus L y c a o n Brookes, which has four toes on all feet. Pollex shorter than other toes. Claws non-retractile, digitigrade. Tail very bushy, length varying from moderate to long. Color of fur varies from dull to bright.

Tympanic bullae more or less inflated, without internal septa.

Dental formula: $I\frac{3}{3}$; $C\frac{1}{1}$; $Pm\frac{4}{4}$; $M\frac{2}{2-3}$; 40 or 42 teeth.

Molars of tuberculosectorial type. Upper carnassial tooth possessing three roots. Internal lobe of this tooth small and situated at anterior internal margin.

Systematics. The geological history of family Canidae begins at the end of the Eocene. The first forms with the family characteristics are found in the Oligocene of Europe and North America. The oldest fossil dogs are the numerous species of genus C y n o d i c t i s (Bravard and Pomel 1850). They are related to V i v e r r a and derived from the creodonts. The family includes 12 contemporary genera. The fauna of the USSR contains 8 species of 5 genera, and of these 6 species of 5 genera occur in Siberia

Geographical distribution. Canidae are distributed throughout the world. Wild Canidae are absent only on the large islands Madagascar and New Zealand.

Biology. The species of the family Canidae are ecologically very plastic, occurring in all landscapes. They feed mainly on animal food and occasionally on carrion. Vegetable food is essential only in some cases. The nest is built in a burrow or in a lair. They are usually monogamous, and produce one litter per year, except for the domestic dog, which may have two litters per year. The litter may contain 12 — 15 young or more, in rare cases as many as 23. The young are born blind and helpless. Lactation lasts 4 — 6 weeks. Some species tend to live in packs or families during the winter. The raccoon dog hibernates in winter. All Canidae are able to run rapidly for long distances, and are indefatigable. They also swim well. Their senses are well developed, some having a very acute sense of smell and relatively weak sight, and their hearing is no less developed than that of cats.

Practical importance. Most species, particularly the Arctic foxes and the common fox, have a valuable fur which is in high demand. Small species of Canidae are beneficial because they kill harmful rodents and insects, and feed on carrion. Some species, e.g., wolves, cause serious damage to animal breeding and are dangerous epidemiologically.

Key to the Genera of Canidae in Siberia

1 (2). Lower jaw with two molars. Total number of teeth 40. Lower
    carnassial tooth (M_1) with a small denticle at the posterior margin
    (Figure 4, b) . . . . Genus **Cuon** — Red dog (p. 73).
2 (1). Lower jaw with three molars. Total number of teeth 42. Lower
    carnassial tooth (M_1) with two small denticles at posterior margin . 3.

3 (4). Cheeks black. Hair on cheek long, forming side whiskers. Bony
palate continuing beyond posterior margin of last molar by about a
third the width of the palate between these molars. Posterior margin
of lower jaw with large rounded projection below the angular process
(Figure 5). . . . . Genus **Nyctereutes** — raccoon dog (p. 65)

4 (3). Color of cheeks different. Hairs not forming side whiskers on
cheeks. Bony palate not or only slightly extending beyond the
posterior margin of the last molar. Posterior margin of lower jaw
without a rounded projection below angular process 5

5 (6). Tail shorter than half the length of body and head. Hind feet with a
large, rounded-triangular, bare heel callus. Postorbital processes
without fossae on upper side. Skull markedly elevated in the area of
the postorbital processes. Paroccipital processes projecting
markedly beyond the tympanic bullae . . . Genus **Canis** — dogs (p. 19)

6 (5). Tail not shorter than half the length of body and head. Soles of hind
feet without bare heel callus. Postorbital processes dorsally flat or
with fossae. Skull little elevated in area of postorbital processes.
Paroccipital process not projecting below tympanic bullae. 7

7 (8). Ears rounded and short; if drawn forward they do not reach the eyes.
Winter fur white or smoke-brown. Yellow or reddish brown tones
absent. Postorbital processes dorsally flat or slightly concave.
Lower margin of external auditory meatus slightly extended, its
opening visible from below. Upper carnassial tooth with weakly
developed anterior-external projection. Lower posterior molar
about as large as posterior half of the preceding molar (Figure 27).
Lower ridge of os penis with a small projection or tubercle near the
base . . . . — . . . . Genus **Alopex** — Arctic fox (p. 56)

9 (7). Ears long and pointed and, if drawn forward, they reached the eyes. Color
of winter fur different. Yellow or reddish brown tones present.
Postorbital processes with well-marked dorsal fossae. Lower
margin of external auditory meatus markedly extended, its opening
completely covered and not visible. Upper carnassial tooth with well-
developed anterior-external projection. Lower posterior molar
smaller than posterior half of the preceding molar (Figure 13).
Lower ridge of os penis without projection or tubercle near the base.
. . . . Genus **Vulpes** — fox (p. 31).

1. Genus CANIS Linnaeus (1758).   Dogs and wolves

1758. Canis Linnaeus C. Syst. Nat., ed. X, 1, p. 38; Blasius,
Säugethiere Deutschlands, p. 177. 1857; Miller, G. S. Catalogue of the
Mammals of Western Europe, p. 304, London. 1912; Ognev, S. I. Zveri
Vostochnoi Evropy i Severnoi Azii (Animals of Eastern Europe and
Northern Asia). Vol. 2, p. 161. 1931; Pocock, R. I. Fauna British India,
Mamm., II, p. 80. 1941.

1816. Lupus (Canis lupus Linnaeus). — Lehrb d. Naturgesch.,
Vol. 3, pt. 2. p. 1039.

Type of genus. Canis familiaris Linnaeus (1758).
Diagnosis. The largest representatives of the family. Body of
moderate length. Legs high, slender and strong. Head large, forehead

broad, muzzle long and tapering. Ears of moderate length and pointed. Papillae round. Tail shorter than half the body length and not very bushy. Soles of feet with five bare calluses: four oval-rounded calluses on the toes and a triangular-oval callus on posterior part of the sole. Number of teats 8—10.

Skull markedly elevated in the frontal region. Frontal area with a broad and deep longitudinal groove. Postorbital processes without dorsal fossae. Interorbital width about equal to width of rostrum above canines.

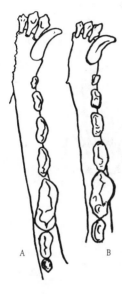

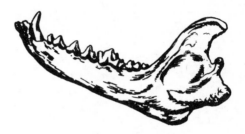

FIGURE 4. Right half of lower jaw of wolves:

A — Canis lupus L.;
B — Cuon alpinus
Pallas (after R. Pocock).

FIGURE 5. Lower jaw of Nyctereutes procyonoides Gray (original)

Anterior palatine foramina usually not longer than the longitudinal diameter of alveoli of upper canines. Paroccipital processes massive, projecting markedly above the surface of the tympanic bullae. Inner walls of tympanic bullae forming projecting angles. Lower margin of external auditory meatus so broad that it covers the meatus and this is not visible. Lower jaw without projection at posterior margin below the angular process.

Dental formula: $I\frac{3}{3}$; $C\frac{1}{1}$; $Pm\frac{4}{4}$; $M\frac{2}{3}$ = 42.

The lower canines do not reach the alveoli of the upper canines if the jaws are closed (Figure 6). Lower carnassial tooth (M_1) with an entoconid.

Geographical distribution. Coincides with the distribution of the family.

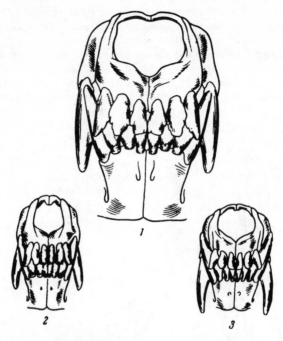

FIGURE 6. Teeth, front view:

1— Canis lupus L.; 2— Alopex lagopus L.;
3— Vulpes vulpes L. (after G.S. Miller, 1912, with
modifications).

Systematics. The number of species of this genus has not yet been determined. The genus is represented in the Soviet Union by two species, one of these in Siberia.

1. **Canis lupus** Linnaeus (1758). Gray wolf
(Figure 7, Map I).

1758. Canis lupus. Linnaeus, C. Systema Naturae, ed. X., p. 39; Pallas, P. Zoographia Rosso-Asiatica pp. 36 — 39. 1811 — 1831; Bogdanov, M.N. Okhotnich'i i promyslovye zveri i ptitsy Evropeiskoi Rossii i Kavkaza (Commercial and Hunting Animals and Birds of European Russia and the Caucasus).— Zhurnal Okhoty i Konnozavodstva, Nos. 11 — 12, pp. 236 — 240. Greeve, C. Die geographische Verbreitung der Raubtiere, pp. 104 — 113. 1894; Trouessart, E. L. Faune des Mammifères d'Europe, p. 90. 1910.

1792. Canis lupus flavus. Kerr, R. Animal Kingdom, p. 137; Selys-Longchamps. Edm. Études de Micromammalogie, p. 144. Paris. 1839.

1804. Canis lupus niger. Hermann, I. Observationes zoologicae, quibus novae complures, aliaeque animalium species describuntur et illustr. Parisiis et Argentorati, p. 32; Selys-Longchamps, Edm. Études de Micromammalogie, p. 144, Paris. 1839.

1839. Canis lupus canis. Selys-Longchamps, Edm. Études de Micromammalogie, p. 144, Paris.

1849. Lupus orientalis. Wagner, A. — In: I. Ch. Schreber's Säugethiere, Suppl. 2, p. 367.

1863. Canis lupus var. major. Ogerien. Histoire Natur. du Jura, 3, p. 59.

1863. Canis lupus var. minor. Ogerien. Histoire Natur. du Jura, 3, p. 69.

1876. The Wolf. Lazarevskii, V. M. Ob istreblenii volkom domashnego skota i dichi (. termination of Domestic Livestock and Game by the Wolf), Sankt-Peterburg; Sabaneev, L. P. — Priroda, pp. 227 — 331. 1877; Lorents, F. K. — Russkii Okhotnik, No. 6, pp. 85 — 89. 1890.

1910. Canis lupus lycaon. Trouessart, E. L. Faune des Mammifères d'Europe, p. 90.

Description. Size about that of a large dog, of powerful and compact build. Head large, forehead broad, frontal area distinctly elevated. Muzzle long and tapering, with powerful jaws. Ears pointed, projecting markedly from the fur; length of ears about half the length of head. Neck of moderate length, muscular.

Chest broad and deep, back powerful, croup sloping. Tail bushy, straight, reaching the calcareal joint; the animal always carries it low or between the legs and never raises it above the back. Legs high, slender, but strong and muscular. Toes long, feet oval (Figure 7).

Fur long, dense but not soft. Color of fur highly variable individually and geographically. Fur varies from light yellowish or grayish white to dark brown with an occasional mixture of reddish brown tones.

FIGURE 7. Canis lupus L. (original)

Skull (Figure 8) large. Maximum length 225 — 285 mm, distinctly elevated in the frontal area. Length of braincase about 3/4 of facial length.

17

Postglenoid process projecting beyond upper margin of the external auditory meatus by about half the diameter of the meatus. Distance between outer sides of the occipital condyles markedly greater than width of muzzle above canines.

Teeth strong and sharply cuspidate. Canines strong and long. The premolars increase in size from first to the last. Transverse diameter of first upper molar (M^1) almost 1.5 times as long as its longitudinal diameter. Longitudinal diameter of first lower molar (M_1) as long or longer than the length of the third and fourth premolars (Pm_3 and Pm_4) together. Cingulum on outer side of M^1 narrow and almost absent in the middle.

Length of body $110-160$ cm, length of tail $35-45$ cm. Weight $40-65$ kg, exceptionally 82 kg. The females are smaller than males of the same age and they weigh correspondingly less.

Geographical distribution. The range of the wolf extends almost throughout Eurasia (southwards to about $25-30°$ N lat.) and North America. The wolf has been exterminated in some countries in Europe (British Isles, Netherlands, Denmark, some regions of Germany and Switzerland). In the Soviet Union the wolf is distributed throughout the entire territory except the Crimea, where it has been exterminated. It can be found in Novaya Zemlya, the islands of Franz Josef Land, the Commander Islands, the Karagin Islands and on other islands.

The wolf occurs everywhere in Siberia (Map I), but its population density varies in different landscapes and in regions which differ in economical development, due to the presence or absence of sufficient animals for food (mainly wild ungulates and livestock, and depending on the availability of food during the year (depth and looseness of the snow).

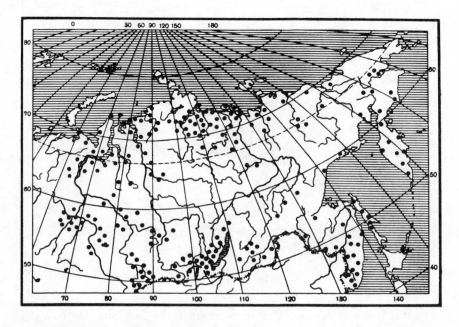

MAP I. Geographical distribution of Canis lupus L. in Siberia

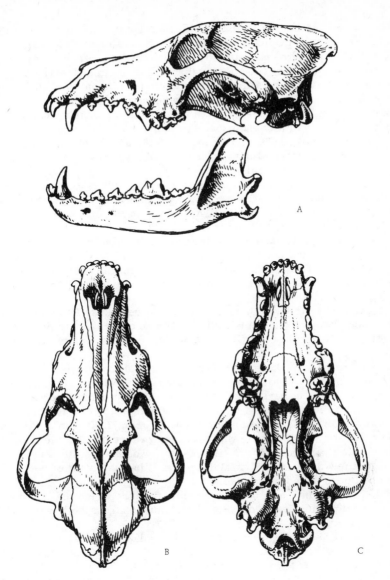

FIGURE 8. Skull of Canis lupus L. (original):

A — lateral; B — dorsal; C — ventral.

The wolf is found in large numbers in the tundra and in the krummholz zone and in even larger numbers in the forest steppe and steppe. It is rare in the taiga.

A. F. Middendorf (1869) associates the larger numbers of wolves in the tundra with the depth of the snow. The snow is less deep here and more compact, so that it is able to bear the weight of the wolf. In addition, deer breed here, creating very good food conditions. The quality of the snow is even more favorable in the forest steppe and steppe areas, and livestock breeding and wild ungulates (roe deer and elk in the forest steppe and antelopes in the steppe) provide food for the wolf.

The number of wolves is limited in the taiga by the depth and looseness of the snow, which limits food availability. In this region the wolf keeps to the river valleys more inhabited by man, where denser snow makes conditions for obtaining food better than in the depth of the area.

The size of wolf populations in the southern Siberian mountains depends on the constancy of the snow and the presence of ungulates.

The above pattern of distribution and population density has been reported by various authors (Middendorf, 1869; Polyakov, 1873; S. P. Naumov, 1931; N. P. Naumov, 1934; Dubrovskii, 1940, and others).

We give below detailed data on the distribution of the wolf in Siberia according to landscape regions.

In the tundra and in the krummholz region, wolves are generally numerous, occurring locally up to the seashore, and may pass to adjacent islands. Their presence has been recorded on the following islands: Belyi, Olen'ii, Nordenskjöld, Novosibirsk, Lyakhovskii and other Arctic islands near the mainland where they occur regularly in summer, returning to the mainland for the winter.

The number of wolves in each locality varies markedly because of seasonal migrations from south to north and vice versa. These migrations may be on a large scale.

Wolves are distributed throughout the entire Yamal Peninsula (Zhitkov, 1913; Sdobnikov, 1937; Dubrovskii, 1940 and others). They have been collected by T. N. Dunaeva (Zool. Mus. Moscow University) in the Khe-Yaga valley.

According to A. N. Dubrovskii (1940), the wolf occurs in large numbers in the tundra of the Ural area, in the lower Ob, Nadym, Pur and Taz. It moves south only in pursuit of deer. The highest density of wolves has been observed in the typical tundra where domestic deer are grazing. In February—April 1935, the author traveled about 2,000 km in tundra, and visited 30 Nenets huts. He was told everywhere about attacks of wolves on deer. It was reported in 6 villages that wolves had attacked reindeer in the last few days, and some villages still had the meat of deer which had been killed by wolves.

V. I. Telegin (in a personal communication) reported that a wolf pack was present on the Taz Peninsula in autumn 1952, in the lower reaches of the Nyd River.

Wolves are abundant in the tundra of the Gyda Peninsula and on the lower reaches of the Yenisei River. On his voyage to the Gyda, S. P. Naumov (1931) observed that wolves are very rare in the Yenisei valley and everywhere up to Turukhansk and that hunters sometimes do not find them at all. This is the case up to the beginning of the forest tundra (about 67° N lat.), where wolves are more common and begin to disturb the deer breeders. Wolves are occasionally so numerous here that herds of deer have to be inspected every night. V. I. Telegin observed two wolves in September 1958 on the banks of the Bol'shaya Kheta River where it joins the Solenaya River.

The wolf was found on the Taimyr by A. F. Middendorf (1869) near 74° N lat. It is rare in the western part of the Taimyr in the valley of the Pyasina River (Kolyushev, 1935), and on very rare occasions it appears in the winter on Dickson Island and the adjacent northwestern part of the Taimyr (Heptner, 1936). Two to three packs of 3—5 wolves may be observed in some years, but in other winters wolves are completely absent. The presence of wolves on Dickson Island depends on the presence of reindeer, wolves occurring here only when the deer remain for winter (as deer are the only food source). Small numbers of wolves stay on through the summer.

The wolf occurs everywhere in the tundra between the rivers Khatanga and Lena, but its presence is directly associated with the presence and numbers of the wild and domestic reindeer which are its principal food.

The most densely populated area of the tundra extends from the northern boundary of the tundra forest northwards to the seasshore, and includes the Begichev, Salkai, and other islands visited by wolves mainly in summer in pursuit of wild reindeer.

West of the Khatanga River and Khatanga Bay the most densely populated areas are the valleys of the rivers Bol'shaya Balakhna and Gusikha and the area around Lake Portnyaginskii. Numerous wolves follow herds of wild reindeer deep into the Taimyr Peninsula. In winter the majority of wolves migrate to the southern part of the tundra and to the northern part of the tundra forest in the Kheta River valley, where herds of wild and domestic reindeer pass the winter (Figure 9).

The number of wolves is relatively small in summer in the mountainous area of the upper and middle Popigai River, of the right tributaries of the Kotui, and of the left tributaries of the Anabar (above the mouth of the Doruokha River). They appear here in large numbers in October— November, with the arrival of the herds of reindeer from the Taimyr. They follow these herds in winter into the Staraya River valley, occasionally moving even further south. Many wolves spend the winter in the forests on the right bank of the Khatanga and the area of its tributaries Bludnaya, Nizhnaya, Zhdanikha and Kazachya, where reindeer breeders pass the winter with their herds. In March— April the wolves return to the western shore of Khatanga Bay.

Between the Khatanga and Anabar rivers, large numbers of wolves remain in summer in the plains of the tundra north of the Khara-Tas and the Syuryakh-Dzhyangy highlands. Even in winter the number of wolves in this area is large. The distribution of wolves varies seasonally in different biotopes: in summer they are more uniformly distributed in the tundra and in winter they concentrate near the winter stations of reindeer breeders.

There is a dense population of wolves between the Anabar and Olenek near the reindeer breeders spring-summer stations — the vicinities of lakes Ulakhan-Kyuel' and Boganidka, the lower reaches of the Yuel River, and the Pronchishchev Range. Most wolves keep in winter to the southern part of the tundra, and to the forest fringe near its edge in the area of the left tributaries of the Pura River and the right tributaries of the Udzha River. Wolves are absent in winter from the northern and central tundra between the Anabar and Olenek except for the right shores of Anabar Bay and the Anabar River, where they remain in large numbers hunting the reindeer of local nomads. They are rare throughout the year in the area south of the rivers Pura and Udzha.

The most densely populated areas are between the rivers Olenek and Lena, the northern end of the Chekanovskii Range and the mountains where the Lena passes into the Olenek valley. Large numbers of wild reindeer

In the Olenek-Lena watershed there is a dense summer population in the northern end of the Chekanovskii Range, and especially in the mountains between the Olenek and the Lena, where many wild reindeer

21

remain for calving. Wolves are more common in summer further south. The majority of them concentrate in winter in the forested valleys of the rivers Balagannakh, Tigiya, Ayakit, Kelimyar and Khorgukhuonka. Most wolves move southwest from the northern end of the Chekanovskii Range into the upper reaches of the Buolkalakha River and the area of the left tributaries of the Pura River, where reindeer breeders and herds of wild reindeer pass the winter.

The wolf occurs in small numbers on the islands in the Lena delta, mainly in the summer, arriving here together with herds of wild reindeer in early spring. The wolves keep mainly to the western part of the archipelago (Erge-Muora-Sige, Khagdang-Sige Islands etc.), and are rarer on the islands in the northern part of the delta. They migrate in October—November from the islands to the mainland with only a few individuals staying for the winter in places where some wild reindeer remain.

Dr. A. Bunge (1883) observed wolves in the mouth of the Lena even earlier.

Wolves are numerous throughout the year on the left bank of the Lena in the Kharaulakh Range, where numerous herds of domestic and wild reindeer breed, but particularly in the northeastern part of the range in summer and in the more southern part in winter (Romanov, 1941).

According to Bunge (1883), wolves breed some years in very large numbers on the lower reaches of the Yana River. He met Tungus in 1884 whose entire herd of reindeer had been killed by wolves.

According to A. I. Ivanov, wolves are locally very common in the tundra between the Lena and Yana, causing great damage to herds of wild and domestic reindeer. They are also common in the tundra between the Indigirka and Kolyma (Tugarinov, Smirnov and Ivanov, 1934).

FIGURE 9. Valley of the Bol'shaya Kheta River, Gyda Peninsula. Wolf biotope. Photo by V. I. Telegin

Wolves were observed by M. Brusnev (1904) in the middle of March on Malyi Lyakhov island.

N. P. Mikhel' informed me that the wolf is the most numerous species among the large animals of the local fauna in the tundra of the lower Indigirka, but is rare in the forests further south.

The wolf is not rare east of the lower Kolyma, in the Chukchi-Anadyr Region.

According to L. A. Portenko (1941$_2$) the wolf is common on the Anadyr but its numbers have been markedly reduced by the decrease of reindeer breeding in the area. The wolf occurs sporadically, mainly in localities with herds of domestic reindeer, i.e., in hilly and mountainous parts of the Anadyr area. Large numbers of wolves have been reported by various authors (Sokol'nikov, 1927 and others).

Wolves were reported in the 1930s in the Anadyr 50—60 km above the village Ust-Belaya, in the valley of the Belaya River, on the southern slope of the Russkii Range and near the River Chernaya north of Penzhino. According to S. D. Pereleshin, wolves were ranging widely in 1930 in the Penzhino area, mainly near the large herds of reindeer. Numerous wolves appeared at the end of 1932 near the village Anadyr and in the Anadyr estuary. According to local inhabitants, large numbers also appeared that winter on the Kanchalan River (Portenko, 1941$_2$).

According to A. V. Samorodov (1939) wolves were abundant in the Olyutorsk District, as they were not hunted. The author has seen tracks from packs of 7—15 individuals near herds of reindeer in the tundra, in the floodplain forests of the Apuka River, and in thickets of Japanese stone pine on mountain slopes.

The wolf occurs in the taiga of Siberia in markedly smaller numbers than in the tundra, and is usually found in river valleys and in areas where the forests are divided by open spaces and cultivated land.

The distribution of the wolf in the taiga can be described as follows. K. K. Flerov (1933) found wolves in the northern Transurals on the rivers Synya and Lyapin. They are common on the lower reaches of the Ob and on the Polui River, according to K. T. Yurlov, who reported that in July 1959 he had found a wolf den on Kui, an island on the left bank of the Ob River near the Atlymka River Station. Wolves are rare in the forests of the middle Ob; they occur in forests near Tobolsk, and are numerous on the middle reaches of the Irtysh River.

According to V. N. Skalon and V. V. Raevskii (in litt.) very few wolves breed in the former Konda-Sosva reserve; these authors give the following localities where packs of wolves have been found: the upper reaches of the rivers Syrym-Puze and Nyurukha, and the valley of the river Nekhsapr-Egan. The number of wolves grows in winters in which reindeer arrive in large numbers.

According to commercial statistics, wolves are moderately common in in Yamalo-Nenetsk and Khanty-Mansi national districts of the Tyumen Region.

Wolves are most abundant in the southern districts of the Tyumen Region with the densest populations: Abatsk, Armizonskoe, Golyshmanovo, and Uporovsk. The number of wolves is lower in the following districts: Berdyuzhsk, Vagaisk, Vikulovsk, Isetsk, Kozymsk, Omutinsk, Tyumensk, and Yalutorovsk. Wolves occur in small numbers in the following areas:

Baikalovo, Velizhany, Dubrovnoe, Maslyansk, Novo-Zaimka, Tobolsk, Uvatsk, Yurginskoe and Yarkovo.

Wolves are rare in the Surgutsk and Vasyugan taiga, according to V. P. Anikin (1902), S. M. Chugunov (1915), and others. V. N. Skalon (1928) writes that wolves occur on Vakh and Lar-Egan.

According to my data, wolves occur sporadically in the Narym taiga, in comparatively woodless cultivated areas inside the forest, (e. g., in the Narym, Kolpasheva, Belyi Yar, and certain other areas).

Wolves occur in the northern part of the Chulym taiga, according to G. E. Iohanzen (1923).

Wolves are present (according to P A. Baikov, 1949) in the Tomsk Region's southern districts of Zyryanskoe, Asino, Tuganskoe, and to an extent in Pyshkino-Troitskoe, Shegarka, and Kozhevnikovo. B. S. Yudin informed me that only a few wolves were observed in the last district. Observing from a plane in winter 1957, K. T. Yurlov saw only one wolf in the upper reaches of the Om River.

Wolves occur sporadically in the Altai and in other mountains in southern Siberia, and their numbers vary in different districts. They are very rare in the northeastern, more wooded parts of the Altai region (Savinov, 1953). Only a few stragglers were recorded in winter in the Sorokino and Zalesskii district. A. P. Razorenova (1039) observed wolves in the Ongudai, Chemal, Ulagan, Uimen, and Ust'-Kan districts. They are abundant in Ongudai, Elekmonar, Oya and Maima.

Wolves are rare in the central Altai, according to A. M. Nikol'skii (1883), but N. F. Kashchenko (1899) considered them common here. These contradictions may be due to a difference in wolf numbers during the visits of these authors. The numbers of wolves here are rather large according to A. A. Nasimovich (1949), V. N. Savinov (1953), and others.

FIGURE 10. Ukok Plateau, Altai. Wolf biotope. Photo by K. T. Yurlov

Wolves are most numerous in the mountain steppe of the Altai where livestock breeding is highly developed. Large numbers have been recorded in the Chuya steppe by various authors (Razorenova, 1939; Kolosov, 1939, and others), and this has been confirmed by my data. K. T. Yurlov found wolves in 1959 in numerous localities on the Ukok Plateau (Lake Kal'dzhin-Kul, Karachat, the Kalguta River, etc.), in the valleys of the Dzhazator and Ak-Alakha, and on the northern slopes of the Sailyugem Range between the upper reaches of the Sardzhimata River and the source of the Ulandryk (Figure 10).

Wolves were collected by Wache near Lake Teletskoe and on the Chulyshman area and part of the collection was examined by Noack (1910). Wolves are usually rare in the former Altai reserve (Yurgenson, 1938). Occasional occurrences of wolves have been recorded near the Lake Teletskoe and they are common in the valley of the Chulyshman River (particularly in its upper reaches), near the mouth of the Shavla, and in the Choodra and Yazumu areas. They have also been reported near Lakes Saigonysh, Iery-Kul, and Ity-Kul.

According to G. D. Dul'keit (1949), wolves came in 1941 from the valley of the Chulyshman River to the eastern shore of Lake Teletskoe and occur every year (on slopes with little snow and on terraces) from the Koksha River to the Kych River.

Wolves are rare in the Gornaya Shoriya, according to G. Gol'tsmaier (1936), entering from the adjacent steppe. They are common in the Krasnoyarsk Territory and skulls from the vicinity of Tvorogovo village and from the Sukhobuzimskoe area are in the collection of the Zoological Museum of Moscow University.

There are a few data on the distribution of the wolf from Western Sayan. A. I. Yanushevich and K. T. Yurlov (1949) recorded them in all landscapes except the alpine zone. V. N. Nadeev observed wolves on the Bol'shoi Arbat, in the basin of the upper Abakan, and in the upper reaches of the Dzhebash and Taskabychek rivers.

According to P. Polikevich (1923) the wolf does not live year-round in the taiga of the eastern part of the former Minusinsk County, where the snow is deep, but occurs only at the edge of the taiga, in summer when the young are nursed. The wolves migrate into the steppe at the beginning of winter. L. and I. Kozhanchikov (1924) do not record wolves from the part of the Minusinsk taiga drained by the Kazyr and Kizyr, and they probably do not occur there.

According to D. K. Solov'ev (1920), the wolf probably occurs in the Eastern Sayan at all altitudes and may be found on snow-covered mountains and in the steppe of the Minusinsk and Kansk areas. K. T. Yurlov, who visited the Eastern Sayan in winter 1952 and in summer 1956, does not confirm this wide distribution of the wolf in the mountains. Wolves are definitely rare and sporadically distributed in this area. According to K. I Gromov (1951), wolves are rare in the central part of the Eastern Sayans.

Wolves are common throughout Tuva, according to A. I. Yanushevich (1952), but particularly in the steppe, where they cause great losses to livestock.

Wolves are very rare northeast of Kansk, in the valley of the Taseev River (a left tributary of the lower Angara) (Troitskii, 1930.).

According to I. P. Kopylov, A. V. Dobrovol'skii and I. V. Shergin (1940), wolves are rare in the taiga of the Irkutsk Region; their numbers increase in the forest steppe and steppe in the Baikal area, where livestock breeding is developed; and they occur in large numbers in the Sayan area and in the Kuitun, Zima and Cheremkovo areas. Radde (1862) mentions that a wolf was killed on the main street of Irkutsk. There are no wolves near this city at present. F. F. Shilinger collected wolves in 1912—1913 in some localities in the northern, central and southern parts of the Irkutsk Region (coll. Moscow University).

There are few wolves in the upper reaches of the Lena, Kirenga, Tutura, Ul'kan and Ilga, according to B. E. Petri (1930). Wolves were abundant here in the past and attacked herds of domestic reindeer.

Wolves are rare in the forests of Siberia east of the Yenisei, between the Yenisei and the Lena, according to Krivoshapkin, 1865; Middendorf, 1869; Tret'yakov, 1869; Polyakov, 1873; Maak, 1886; S. P. Naumov, 1913; N. P. Naumov, 1934; and Tugarinov and others, 1934.

According to A. F. Middendorf (1869), wolves were very rare in 1840 from Yeniseisk to the Arctic Circle, but were more common further north. According to A. L. Chekanovskii (1873), wolves are generally rare on the Lower Tunguska but are more common on the upper reaches of this river. According to N. P. Naumov (1934), they occur in the valley of the Lower Tunguska and its tributaries but in much smaller numbers than in the forest tundra.

Wolves are very rare east of the Yenisei, in the valley of the Vilyui and on the Lena, according to R. Maak (1886). He writes that in 1850 "wolves were not rare on the Lena but occurred in much smaller numbers than at present. The appearance of the wolves there, between the Vitim and Olekma, has been attributed to the discovery of gold mines. Wolves began to appear first near the Station of Machi," where reindeer were used as pack animals and were left without supervision, becoming easy prey for wolves. Wolves are more common in the middle reaches of the Olenek River, particularly on the Arga-Sala River, and become abundant further north in the tundra. Numerous wolves also occur on the Muna, a left tributary of the Lena.

Wolves are probably not common on the Vilyui, according to A. I. Ivanov. However, according to K. E. Vorob'eva, the inhabitants of the Borisovo River Station complained that wolves were abundant there (Tugarinov and others, 1934).

Wolves were also abundant in the Verkhoyansk District, where S. A. Buturlin (1913) met "a family of new immigrants in the foothills of the Tas-Khayakh-Takh who were in a difficult position, as their riding reindeer had been driven into the mountains by the wolves. The Chukchi reindeer breeders complained of the abundance of wolves." I. D. Cherskii found wolves on the Suntara River near the Indigirka (Oimekon), and wolf tracks were found at the Nera River in the basin of the Zyryanka (Torabygyttakh) River. There were no wolves at the time in the area of Verkhnekolymsk.

Wolves are rare in the taiga of central Yakutia, according to A. Ivanov.

Wolves are distributed sporadically and are apparently rare in the southern parts of Yakutia, including the upper reaches of the Olekma, Aldan, and Maya Rivers and their tributaries (Tugarinov and others, 1934).

The above data on the distribution of the wolf in the forests of Yakutia are confirmed by recent data of V. I. Belyk (1953). According to this author the highest density of wolves in the forest zone has been observed in the cultivated areas of Yakutia.

A few wolves occur on the Kolyma, and also in the valley of the Berezovska River (Pfitzenmaier, 1928). According to N. G. Buxton, wolves are very rare in the valley of the Gizhiga River (J. A. Allen, 1903).

According to S. P. Krasheninnikova (1949), wolves were abundant in Kamchatka in 1730—1740, but were not hunted. Wolves were collected here by I. G. Voznesenskii in 1847—1848 (coll. Zool. Inst. Acad. Sciences USSR).

Yu. V. Averin (1948) writes that the wolf is widely distributed throughout Kamchatka from Lopatka Cape in the south to its northern limits. It is common in the middle and lower mountains in the Kronoki reserve in eastern Kamchatka. The number of wolves increases in winter through migration from neighboring areas. The highest winter concentration of wolves in the Kronoki reserve was reported from the Gamchen valcanoes, Schmidt Mountains, and the valleys of the Unana and Taunshits rivers, where the wolves are attracted by reindeer and bighorn sheep which pass the winter here.

Wolves occur in Transbaikalia, according to S. S. Turov (1924, 1925, 1936) mainly in the open taiga, e. g., near the mouth of large rivers, in the valleys of the Barguzin, Upper Angara, etc. The author observed wolves on the Svyatoi Nos Peninsula. According to G. G. Doppel'maier (1926), wolves are very rare on the shores of Lake Baikal, and only a few were observed in the Shangnanda district.

The number of wolves varies during the year on the Yablonovyi Range and depends on the migrations of roe deer, which are their staple food. They are numerous on the Unda Range (Kuznetsov, 1929).

According to E. Pavlov (1948), wolves are found in some years in the upper reaches of the Chita River and its tributaries, but their numbers decrease in years when there are fewer roe deer. There were many wolves in winter 1938/39 below the River Eramga where roe deer were grazing. In the spring roe deer pelts could be found everywhere near the Shargol'dzhin and Sakhaltui rivers for every kilometer traveled; they were the remains of the animals killed by wolves that winter.

Wolves are very rare and occur only sporadically in the area of the Uda River and the upper Selemdzha, according to N. T. Zolotarev (1934).

The wolf is common on the shores of the Sea of Okhotsk but is never abundant there. Thus, according to V. P. Sysoev (1952), "wolves are almost completely absent" in the lower Amur Region.

According to R. Maak (1859), wolves occur in the central and lower Amur country, but are very rare. They occur throughout the Ussuri valley, more rarely in the upper than in the lower reaches, are abundant on the Noru and Mureni Rivers, and occur on the Sungacha and near Lake Khanka (Maak, 1861). According to N. M. Przheval'skii (1870), wolves are distributed throughout the Ussuri Territory but are not very common.

Wolves are very common in the Jewish Autonomous Region's Bikin and Vyazemskoe areas, the Lazo and Nanai districts, and in the south of the Khabarovsk Territory, according to V. P. Sysoev. They are markedly less common in the Komsomol'sk District.

Wolves are relatively rare in the Maritime Territory. In the Iman River valley they occur mainly in the lower part of the valley, where only about 10 are killed per year (Zolotarev, 1936).

G. F. Bromlei (1951₁) states that wolves are locally rather abundant on the Sikhote-Alin, particularly near inhabited areas. G. L. Kaplanov (1948) reports that the wolf "increased markedly in numbers and extended its range on the slopes of the southern and central Sikhote-Alin and it is possible that this was caused by the high reproduction of the protected wapiti." Wolves have been found in considerable numbers in the upper reaches of the Bikin River, in the upper and middle reaches of the Iman, on the Armu and Kolumbe, in open burns near the upper Kema, and on the rivers Sitsa, Tun'sha, Sankhobe, and Iodzykhe.

The wolf occurs in the Sudzukhe Reserve on the shore coast of the south of Maritime Territory (between Sudzukhe and Vanchin bays). G. F. Bromlei collected wolves here in 1949, in the Tyapigou valley (coll. Zool. Moscow University).

In the Suputinka Reserve, situated about 50 km farther east on the upper reaches of the Suputinka River, wolves sometimes occur in large numbers, particularly in the winter, according to G. F. Bromlei; they are attracted there by the numerous ungulates in the reserve, and were collected in 1946 by G. O. Abramov (coll. Zool. Mus. Moscow University). They also occur near Suchan and Vladivostok (coll. Zool. Mus. Moscow University). M. I. Yankovskii collected wolves in the area of Sidemi Bay (coll. Zool. Inst. Acad. Sciences USSR).

In Sakhalin, according to L. Schrenck (1858), the wolf lives mainly in open country (in the northern part) or in areas covered with low larch. N. I. Suprunenko (1890) reported the distribution of the wolf in the tundra of the Tum' and Poronai river valleys as being rare near Notoro, near Manue, near Lake Raitsisk, and on the Sysun and Trautog rivers. Wolves collected by Suprunenko in Sakhalin are in the collection of the Zoological Institute of the Academy of Sciences of the USSR. Wolves are rare in the southern part of Sakhalin, according to N. M. Nikol'skii (1889).

Wolves occur in the Kuriles (in small numbers) only on Kunashir Island, though they have also been reported from Iturup Island (Kuznetsov, 1949).

Wolves are widely distributed and are locally very numerous in the forest steppe and steppe of Western Siberia and in the Transbaikalian steppe.

Wolves are common in the Kurgan, Omsk and Novosibirsk regions, and in the steppe and forest-steppe parts of the Altai Territory, except near towns. They were numerous in the past, according to P. Stepanov (1886), in the middle reaches of the Om River, particularly in winter when they even entered villages; wolves were less numerous in the valley of the Tartas River, which is more forested. These data correspond to the present distribution of the wolf. V. I. Telegin informed me that a pack of wolves was found in 1955 not far from Novosibirsk, near the village of Krokhalevka.

Wolves are common in the Baraba plain and in the Kulunda Steppe (Figure 11), in pine forests along the Irtysh. According to N. N. Egorov (1934), wolves are numerous in some years and cause serious damage to livestock.

In the Upper Ob forest near Barnaul, wolves are found on the outskirts of the forest and are numerous throughout the steppe near the forest, according to G. N. Likhachev (1930). They are also numerous in the steppe near the Altai, and in Troitsk, Biisk, Solton and adjacent areas of the Altai territory.

FIGURE 11. Baraba forest steppe. Biotope of the wolf. Photo by K. T. Yurlov

Wolves are very numerous in the forest steppe and steppe north of the Western Sayan (Achinsk forest steppe, Khakass and Minusinsk Steppe). According to D. K. Solov'ev (1920) they are abundant here and cause serious damage to cattle breeding. According to P. Polikevich (1923), wolves occur throughout the year in the steppe of the Minusinsk County and in the adjacent taiga in the western part of the county, where the snow is never deep. K. T. Yurlov found wolves in 1948 in the Shiza Uibta, and Beya steppes.

They also occur in considerable numbers in the Transbaikalia steppe and in the Barguzin steppe, according to G. G. Doppel'maier (1926), and cause considerable damage to the cattle breeding of the Buryats.

G. Radde (1862) recorded the wolf from the steppe between the Onon and Ingoda rivers and from the upper reaches of the Argun. B. A. Kuznetsov (1929) reported that wolves occur markedly more frequently in the steppe and forest steppe of Transbakalia than in the taiga and cause serious losses in winter by attacks on herds of cattle.

Review of subspecies. There are a number of subspecies of the wolf differing more or less in size, color and quality of the fur. Six subspecies have been described in the Soviet Union. Three subspecies occur in Siberia.

1a. **Canis lupus lupus** L. (1758). Common wolf

Described from Uppsala, Sweden. Color dark, with brownish gray or gray-reddish brown tone. Fur moderately long, very coarse and stiff;

length of the hairs of the winter fur on the back 85 — 120 mm. Size moderate: length of body 120 — 145 cm; condylobasal length of skull of males 250 — 262 mm, of females 230 — 247 mm. Distributed in the forest areas of Europe, in the tundra (except for its northeastern part), and in western Siberia.

1b. **Canis lupus albus** Kerr. (1792). Tundra wolf

Described from the lower reaches of the Yenisei River. Size large, fur long, fluffy (length of hairs of winter fur on the back 110 — 160 mm) and of whitish color, with almost complete absence of reddish brown tones and frequently with a dark stripe along the spine. Length of body to 160 cm. Condylobasal length of skull of males 245 — 257 mm, of females 227 — 233 mm. It is distributed in the tundra and adjacent forests in Siberia and on the Novosibirskie Islands.

1c. **Canis lupus altaicus** Noack (1910). Altai wolf

Described from the area of Lake Teletskoe. Characterized by rust yellow tone of the fur with ash gray underfur. Inhabits the Altai Mountains.

In addition to the above subspecies, others which are undescribed probably occur. The subspecific position of the wolves of middle and southern East Siberia and of the Far East is not known.

Biology. The wolf is a polytopic species, and inhabits the most varying climatic and landscape conditions: tundra, forest, steppe, desert and mountain, to the boundary of permanent snow. It avoids only the continuous taiga, where it is difficult to obtain food because of the deep and loose snow. It enters the taiga via river valleys where the forest is broken by open spaces and the snow conditions are more favorable. Its staple food is animals of large and medium size, including domestic animals. However, the wolf does not disregard small animals — rodents, frogs, lizards. It also catches birds nesting on the ground, and molting birds, and destroys their nests; in addition it feeds on fruits, berries and carrion. The type of food depends on the local fauna.

Rut takes place in the tundra in March—April and in other areas in February, in the central zone in mid-January, in the Caucasus at the end of December and in early January. The rut begins earlier in older individuals than in yearling-females. Gestation lasts 62 — 65 days. The females give birth in the forest in a lair, and in the tundra and steppe in burrows which they either dig themselves or take from other animals. The number of young in the litter is 5 — 8 on the average, more rarely 3, or as many as 12. The male participates in the rearing of the young. The eyes of the young open 10 — 12 days after birth. Lactation lasts 5 — 6 weeks. The female supplements the milk with regurgitated, semi-digested food at the end of the lactation period.

The family keeps together until the beginning of the next rut. The yearlings often join the family in winter and a pack of 10 — 15 wolves is thus formed. In cultivated areas and in the forest zone, wolves are more or less resident, but they make seasonal mass migrations in the tundra and in the mountains. They migrate in winter from the tundra south into the forest tundra, and in summer they move north into the tundra. Wolves hunt livestock and wild ungulates in the mountains, ascending in summer to the alpine zone and descending in winter into the valleys. Unusual mass migrations of wolves have been reported in different localities; they are probably caused by a sharp reduction of the numbers of animals which are the staple food of the wolves.

The wolf is crepuscular and nocturnal. Its hearing is well developed, its sight is not bad, but its sense of smell is markedly less developed.

The wolf causes considerable damage by killing livestock and valuable animals. The damage caused by wolves in the USA is estimated at about 25 million dollars. The wolf attacks humans very rarely. Rabid wolves are extremely dangerous. Control of wolves is a national duty.

2. Genus VULPES Oken (1818). Foxes

1816. Vulpes. Oken, L. Lehrbuch der Naturgeschichte. — Zoologie, 3, pp. 1033 — 1034. Miller, G. S. Catalogue of the Mammals of Western Europe, p. 352, London. 1912.

Ognev, S. I. Zveri Vostochnoi Evropy i Severnoi Azii (Animals of Eastern Europe and Northern Asia). 2, pp. 266 — 268. 1931; Ellerman, J. R. and T. C. S. Morrison-Scott. Checklist of Palaearctic and Indian Mammals, p. 223, London. 1951; Novikov, G. A. Khishchnye mlekopitayushchie fauny SSSR (Carnivorous Mammals of the USSR). pp. 56 — 57, Moskva-Leningrad. 1956.

Type of genus. Canis vulpes Linnaeus (1758).

Diagnosis. Foxes differ from wolves in their smaller size and low build. Body long, supported by relatively short legs. Head with narrow, long muzzle. Ears pointed, long, and when drawn forward reach eyes. Pupils elliptical. Tail bushy, longer than half body and head. Heel callus not developed on the soles, which are densely covered with hair; toe calluses small, oval and bare.

Yellow or reddish brown tones predominate in the color of the fur.

Interorbital space of skull slightly elevated above muzzle. Frontal area with a longitudinal groove from posterior part of orbits. Postorbital processes with well-marked fossae dorsally. Interorbital space wider than muzzle above the canines. Anterior palatine foramina about a third longer than the longitudinal diameter of the alveoli of the upper canines. Paroccipital processes lower than the tympanic bullae. Inner sides of tympanic bullae rounded, not forming projecting angles in the middle. Lower margin of external auditory meatus markedly extended and covering the meatus from below so that it is invisible. Lower jaw without a projection below the angular process.

Dental formula: $I\frac{3}{3}$; $C\frac{1}{1}$; $Pm\frac{4}{4}$; $M\frac{2}{3}$ = 42.

The lower canines may be short, so that they do not reach the alveoli of the upper canines if the jaws are closed (Vulpes corsac), or very long, extending beyond the alveoli of the upper canines. Upper carnassial tooth

(Pm⁴) with a well-marked external anterior projection. Lower carnassial tooth (Pm$_4$) with a well-developed entoconid. Lower posterior molar smaller than posterior half of the preceding molar (Figure 13).

Ventral ridge of os penis without a tubercle or projection at the base.

Geographical distribution. Europe, Asia, Africa (south to Cape Colony) and North America (to New Mexico and southern California).

Systematics. Foxes show very marked individual and geographical variation in skull structure, color and other characters. The range of variation has not been sufficiently studied. Numerous species and subspecies have been described but their systematic status remains problematical in many cases. The actual number of species of this genus therefore cannot be determined. The genus is represented in the USSR by four species, two in Siberia.

Key to Species of the Genus Vulpes in Siberia

1 (2). Size large: length of body and head of adults 60 cm or more, length of tail 40 cm. Length of skull 120 mm or more, zygomatic width 60 mm. Posterior side of ears black or brownish black. Tip of tail white. Legs anteriorly with a black or blackish tone. Reddish brown tones of various intensity predominate in the colors . . . . Vulpes (s. str.) vulpes L. (p. 32).

2 (1). Size smaller: length of body and head of adults to 60 cm, length of tail to 35 cm. Skull less than 120 mm long and zygomatic width 58 mm. Posterior side of ears grayish. Tip of tail black. Anterior side of legs black or black tone . Vulpes (s. str.) corsac L. (p. 47). .

2. **Vulpes vulpes** Linnaeus (1758) (Figure 12, Map II)

1758. Canis vulpes. Linnaeus, C.— Systema Naturae, X ed. p. 40, Pallas, S. P.— Zoographia Rosso-Asiatica, I, pp. 45—51. 1811; Eversmann, E. Estestvennaya istoriya Orenburgskogo kraya (Natural History of the Orenburg Territory), 2, Kazan; pp. 33—34. 1850; Simashko, Yu. Russkaya fauna (Russian Fauna). 2, pp. 505 -524, Sankt-Peterburg. 1851.

1758. Canis alopex. Linnaeus, C.— Systema Naturae, X ed. p. 40, Sweden.

1777. Canis caragan. Erxleben.— Systema Regni Animalis, p. 566. (Kirghiz Steppe).

1811. Canis melanotus. Pallas, P. S.— Zoographia Rosso-Asiatica, 1, pp. 44— 45 (Orenburg Steppes); Eversmann, E. Loc. cit., p. 35; Simashko, Yu. Loc. cit., p. 498.

1903. Vulpes anadyrensis. Allen, J. A. Report of the Mammals Collected in Northeastern Siberia by the Jesup. North Pacific Expedition with Itinerary and Field Notes by N. G. Buxton.— Bull. Amer. Mus. Nat. Hist., 19, pp. 167—171. (Vicinity of Markovo Village on the Anadyr).

1911. Vulpes kamschadensis. Brass, E. Aus dem Reiche der Pelze, p. 456.

1912. Vulpes vulpes. Miller, G. S. Catalogue of the Mammals of Western Europe, pp. 326—330, London; Adlerberg, G. P. Khishchnye zveri Arktiki (Carnivora Fissipedia of the Arctic).— In: Zveri Arktiki, pod redaktsiei prof. N. A. Smirnova, pp. 404—422, Leningrad, Izdátel'-stvo Glavsevmorputi. 1935; Ellerman, J. R. and T. C. Morrison-Scott. Checklist of Palaearctic and Indian Mammals, pp. 225—229, London. 1951; Bannikov, A. G. Mlekopitayushchie Mongol'skoi Narodnoi Respubliki (Mammals of the Mongolian People's Republic). pp. 112—127. Moskva, Izdatel'stvo AN SSSR. 1954; Novikov, G. A. Khishchnye mlekopitayushchie fauny SSSR (Carnivores of the Fauna of the USSR), pp. 58—67, Moskva-Leningrad. 1956.

1944. Vulpes (Vulpes) vulpes. Bobrinskii, N.A. Otryad Khishchnye. V knige: Opredelitel' mlekopitayushchikh SSSR pod redaktsiei N. A. Bobrinskogo (Order Carnivores. In: Key to Mammals of the USSR, edited by N A. Bobrinskii), pp. 144—145, Moskva.

Type and type locality. Type unknown. The species was described from the vicinity of Uppsala, Sweden.

FIGURE 12. Vulpes vulpes L. Specimen No. 4069, Zoological Museum of Moscow University. Painting by V A. Vatagin

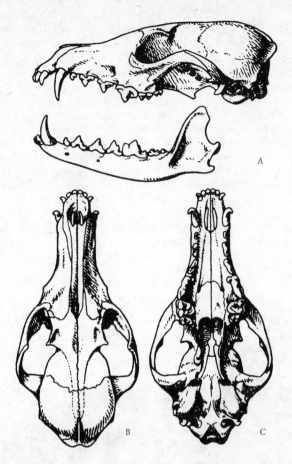

FIGURE 13. Skull of Vulpes vulpes L. (original):

A — lateral; B — dorsal; C — ventral.

Diagnosis. Size large. Length of body and head 60—90 cm, tail
40—60 cm. Weight: males 6—10 kg, females 5—8 kg. Condylobasal
length of skull of males 127—159 mm, females 115—165 mm; zygomatic
width: males 64—87 mm, females 64—80 mm. Posterior side of ears
black or brownish black. Tip of tail white. Anterior side of legs usually
with a black or blackish tone. Reddish brown tones of various intensity
predominate in the color.

Description. Body rather long and legs relatively short. Muzzle long,
pointed. Ears pointed, long; when drawn forward reach the eyes. Tail
bushy. Heel callus on soles not developed, soles densely covered with
hair; toe calluses small, oval, bare. Tail more than half as long as body
and head (Figure 12).

Fur with marked yellow or a reddish brown-yellow tone. The fur does
not become white in winter.

Summer fur markedly shorter and sparser than winter fur, underfur weakly developed. Color of summer fur dull. Cross-shaped pattern distinctly marked.

Fur of young fluffy, reddish brown-gray.

The geographical variation is most marked in the color and the quality of the fur. The color becomes lighter and the quality of the fur worsens towards the South. The color is more intense in mountain regions than in the steppe. Various types of individual variation of color predominate in a given locality.

Melanistic specimens are more common in northeastern Siberia and in mountains, but are rare in Western Siberia.

Skull (Figure 13) more slender than in the Arctic fox, the bones thinner and more delicate. Interorbital space little elevated above the rostrum. Postorbital processes usually with well-marked fossae on the dorsal side. Paroccipital processes small: their length from the point of junction with the posterior side of the tympanic bullae to their end is $1/4 - 1/5$ length of bulla. Canines long. The lower canines project markedly beyond alveoli of the upper canines, when the jaws are closed.

Os penis (Figure 14) smaller than that of Arctic fox: length $51.4 - 52.7$ mm (av. 51.8 mm). There is no projection or tubercle at the base of the ventral ridge.

Variations in fur color are both individual and geographical. The main types of color are caused by different degrees of melanism. The following types of color variation of the fox not connected with geographical variation are known in the fur trade:

FIGURE 14.
Os penis of
Vulpes
vulpes L.
(after
S. I. Ognev)

1. **Red fox.** Color reddish brown, often reddish all over the body. Underfur grayish with gray hair tips; the dark color of the underfur is usually not visible through the dark hair. A certain striation is caused by the light bands on the guard hairs of the back. The color is most intense on the back, upper neck and shoulders. Sides of body and neck more lightly colored. Chest and neck white. Venter usually white, rarely black. Some specimens lack light bands on the guard hairs and the color becomes brighter; such specimens are known by the name "Flame."

2. **Gray fox.** General color grayish brown, darker than in the red fox. Underfur gray without reddish-brown hair tips, sometimes almost black. T The dark cross pattern is distinct against the lighter background. Chest, neck and belly dark gray or black. Forehead and muzzle darker than in the red fox.

3. **Cross fox.** Muzzle darker than in the preceding variety. The black-brown cross pattern on the back is more distinct. Ventral side black.

4. **Black-brown fox.** Entire body blackish brown or black. Reddish brown and yellowish hairs absent. The tips of some guard hairs are sometimes white and a more or less marked whitish tone is present. Cross pattern less marked than in gray and cross foxes. The above color types are not always sharply marked and intermediate forms occur. Complete or partial albinos occur but are very rare.

Systematic notes. The fox shows very wide individual and geographical variation in skull structure, size, color and other characters.

The variation has not been sufficiently studied. Numerous subspecies have been described but their systematic position remains problematical in many cases.

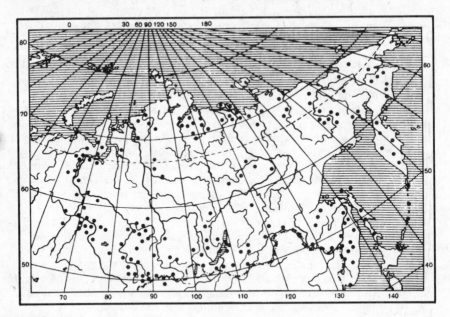

MAP II. Geographical distribution of Vulpes vulpes L. in Siberia

Geographical distribution. The area of distribution of the fox includes the whole of Europe, Asia (except the extreme south), and North Africa. North America is inhabited by a related species (Vulpes fulvus Desm.).

The fox occurs almost throughout the Soviet Union, except in high latitudes of the tundra and the greater part of the Arctic seas.

It is absent in Siberia only in the depth of the boreal tundra (which it occasionally enters). The fox cannot compete in the tundra with the Arctic fox, which is related to it ecologically but is better adapted to conditions in the tundra.

It is absent on Severnaya Zemlya, on the Novosibirskie Islands, on the Nordenskjöld Archipelago, on Vrangel Island, etc.

The vertical distribution of the fox in Siberia extends from the West Siberian plains to the alpine zone (Map II). It occurs up to 3,000 m in the Altai, according to A. M. Kolosov (1939); in Kamchatka it occurs from the shore to the forestless steppes in the high mountains, which it enters occasionally in summer (Averin, 1948). It was found on the peak of Krasheninnikov Volcano (1,860 m) and on Schmidt Volcano (about 2,000 m). Burrows and broods of foxes were found at altitudes of 1,000 to 1,300 m.

It is common in the northern taiga of the West Siberian plains, but its numbers here are markedly smaller than in the forest steppe and steppe.

The most northern records are as follows. Tracks of the fox were found on the Yamal Peninsula by B. M. Zhitkov (1913) in the Khadyta-Yakh valley (he reports it very rare further north, particularly in the northern half of the peninsula). According to A. N. Dubrovskii (1940), N. N. Spitsin reports the fox near Lake Yarro-To (68° N lat.). Foxes from the northern forestless desert near the sea and from the lower reaches of the Ob are mentioned by Vasilii Zuev of the Pallas expedition (Pallas, 1776). V. I. Telegin (personal communication) observed a young fox on the Taz Peninsula 50 km south of the Epoko trading post.

Schmidt (1872) records the fox from the tundra on the Gyda Peninsula; however, S. P. Naumov (1931) found no sign of the presence of the fox in the tundra on his visit and thinks that it occurs northwards to the boundary of the forest in the valley of the River Mudui-Yakha (68° N lat.). According to A. N. Dubrovskii (1940), in an opinion based on toponomical data and questionnaires, the fox is rather common here; thus, one of the rivers at about 71° N lat. is named Tene-Yakha (Fox River). Occurrence of foxes was reported by traders in 1935 in the Yantsa-Payuta-Yakha valley. According to the hunter N. V. Provorov, a fox was obtained at Cape Taran in January 1936 in the Khale-Yakha River valley (71° N lat.). Telegin found an inhabited burrow in the south of the Gyda Peninsula in the middle reaches of the river Bol'shaya Kheta and obtained a young fox (coll. S. U. Stroganov).

However, the above cases and many others refer to stragglers and do not define the natural northern boundary of the species which is more or less stable and generally coincides with the northern boundary of vegetation.

According to I. F. Brandt (1856), K. K. Flerov (1933), and others, the fox occurs rarely in the Northern Urals. It is very rare in the northern Transurals (S. A. Kuklin, 1937). The fox is very common in the lower and middle reaches of the Ob and Irtysh rivers and in the lower reaches of their large tributaries, but is very rare further away from these rivers in dense forests. It is almost absent in the upper and middle reaches of the rivers Northern Sos'va, Kazym, Tym, Agan, Trom-Yugan, Vakh, etc. I. S. Polyakov collected foxes in 1876—1877 near Obdorsk (now Salekhard), near Tobolsk and in the Irtysh valley (coll. Zool. Inst. Acad. Sciences USSR). Telegin obtained a fox in the middle reaches of the Demyanka River (coll. S. U. Stroganov). Foxes are rare in the taiga on the watershed between the Konda and Malaya Sos'va rivers, according to V. N. Skalon and V. V. Raevskii (in litt.), compared with the Ob valley, in which foxes are common, though less common than the wolf.

According to trade statistics, foxes are much rarer in the large Yamalo-Nenetsk National District than in the Khanty-Mansii District, which is smaller in area, but possesses open forests. The data of I. Ya. Slovtsov (1892) on the rarity of the fox in the southern taiga, e. g., in the former Tyumen, Ishimsk, and Yalutorovsk districts, do not correspond to the present density of the fox in this locality. According to recent trade data, the fox is very common in the southern part of the Tyumen area, in the Isetsk, Ishimsk, Omutinsk, Yalutorovsk, Oporovo, and adjacent districts. The fox is very rare north of the taiga in Siberia near the Yenisei. S. P. Naumov (1931) found traces of its activity near the Yanov-Stan and Sidorov River Station: the fox was found only once by the author further north, near the boundary of the forest zone (68° 20' N lat.).

Tomsk area. (Figure 15): The fox is common everywhere in the Narym Territory according to V. P. Anikin (1902), and also on the Chulym

River according to G. E. Ioganzen (1923). The fox is rare and occurs only
sporadically in forestless areas in the northern part of the region (including
the Vasyugan and Narym taiga), according to my data. In the southern
parts — Zyryanskoe, Asino, Tuganskoe, Pyshkino-Troitskoe, Tomsk,
Shegarka and Kozhevnikovo areas, where the forests are broken by
cultivated land, the fox is common. According to P. Stepanov (1886) it is
common between the middle reaches of the Tartas and Tara rivers and also
occurs along the Tara River; it is rare in the upper reaches of these rivers.
According to K. T. Yurlov (personal communication) it is not rare north of
the Tara River, and he observed foxes in 1957 near the village Ukrainka (on
the Bol'shaya Icha River) and obtained one specimen near the mouth of
the Uzas River and on the right bank of the Cheka River.

FIGURE 15. Flooded meadows in the Ob valley near the village Kozhevnikovo (Tomsk Region).
Biotope of *Vulpes vulpes* L. Photo by B. S. Yudin

The fox finds optimal conditions in the forest steppe of Western Siberia,
in the Kurgan and Omsk regions, and also in Kemerovo Region and in the
steppe near the Altai. The number of foxes is highest in Western Siberia.

In the Upper Ob forest near Barnaul the fox is distributed on the edge
of the forest and in the adjacent steppe (Figures 16, 17), according to
G. N. Likhachev (1930).

The fox is very common, according to my data, in Barnaul, Troitskoe,
Biisk, Salton and adjacent steppe areas. A number of skulls from the
Pavlov District were given to me by B. S. Yudin.

N. F. Kashchenko (1899) considered the fox to be common everywhere on
the Altai; according to A. P. Razorenova (1939) numerous foxes were
obtained in the western foothills and in the Ulagan, Ongudai, Chemal,
Uimoe, and Kosh-Agach areas. N. Hollister (1912) collected foxes in the

Chuiskie Belki near the Chagan-Burgazy Pass. According to K. T. Yurlov (personal communication) the fox is common throughout the Ukok Plateau, and particularly numerous near the Kalguta River.

It is widely distributed but not numerous in the Ust-Koksa area of the Gorno-Altai Region according to A. A. Nasimovich (1949), and markedly more numerous in the adjacent Ust-Kan area.

According to A. M. Kolosov (1939) the fox is numerous in the Chuisk steppe and on the slopes of the neighboring mountains. It occurs in large numbers near Lake Dzhulu-Kul. It was found near Kosh-Agach by B. S. Yudin, and by Yurlov on the slopes of the Sailyugem Range near the sources of the Ulandryk, Shibet, and Sardzhimat rivers.

According to P. B. Yurgenson (1938) it is rare near Teletskoe. It was found near the village of Kebezen, between Cape Kuporosnyi and Cape Idyp, in the upper reaches of the Klyk River between the rivers Chechenek and Okporok, in the middle and lower reaches of the Kamga River, and near the latter's mouth.

It is rare in the Gornaya Shoriya, according to Gol'tsmaier (1936), and is very common in the Khakas steppe and forest steppe, according to N. A. Kokhanovskii (personal communication). It is found frequently in the Kansk Steppe according to Yurlov.

It was found by Yanushevich and Yurlov (1949) in all landscapes in the Western Sayan except the alpine zone, and is most abundant in the steppe and forest steppe.

It occurs everywhere in the Tuva Autonomous Region (Figure 18), according to Yanushevich (1952), but is most abundant in the Upsa-Nur basin and in the Oversk, Tes-Kham, and Erzin districts. These three districts supply about 70% of the Region's fox catch. No more than 15 foxes are obtained per year on the eastern Tuva Plateau.

The fox is distributed everywhere in the Sayans, according to D. K. Solov'ev (1920), but is more numerous in the open steppe than in the taiga and in the mountains.

It is most common in the taiga of the Kazyr and Kizyr river valleys, according to L. and I. Kozhanchikov (1924).

It is rare in the central part of the Eastern Sayan, according to K. I. Gromov (1951). It is the most common species in the Stolby Reserve on the Eastern Sayan near Krasnoyarsk, according to A. B. Speranskaya. The fox was collected near Krasnoyarsk in 1892 by M. E. Kibort near the village of Nakhvalnoe (coll. Zool. Inst. Acad. Sciences USSR).

It occurs in the taiga between the northern slopes of the Sayans and the middle and lower reaches of the Angara River and its tributaries, but apparently in small numbers (Troitskii, 1930₂).

According to I. P. Kopylov (1948), V. V. Timofeev (1949), and others, it occurs throughout the Irkutsk Region; the highest density is observed in the forest steppe, but it is common in the northern parts of the Region (Lower Tunguska, and Angara-Lena areas) near the Sayans and near Lake Baikal (in high mountains, e. g., in Tofalariya).

It is not rare but varies in numbers in the forests of Trans-Yenisei Siberia, being commonest in river valleys in and localities with open forests. It occurs more rarely in the continuous taiga.

It occurs everywhere in the valley of the Lower Tunguska, according to N. P. Naumov (1934), but is numerous mainly in forests with a variegated landscape, usually along large rivers or at forest fringes in the wooded tundra. N. P. Naumov collected it near Chirinda, Nikongda, and Nyakshinda, and on the Imbukan River.

FIGURE 16. Forest steppe in the Baraba plain. Biotope of Vulpes vulpes L. Photo by K. T. Yurlov

It was found north of here by A. F. Middendorf (1875) in the eastern Taimyr, at the northern boundary of the krummholz forest in the valley of the Novaya River (Sanga-Yuryakh, around 72° N lat.). It enters the tundra on the Taimyr. E. O. Yakovlev (1930) records the fox in winter in the delta of the Yenisei (on the Brekhovskie Islands) and in the lower reaches of the Pyasina River (Khura River, 73° N lat.).

V. G. Heptner (1936) states that the fox is very rare in the northwestern Taimyr, enters only occasionally, and does not breed there. It was caught near Slobodskaya Inlet.

Detailed data on the distribution of the fox east of the Taimyr to the Kharaulakh Range are given by A. A. Romanov (1941). It inhabits forests near the tundra and occasionally occurs in the shrub tundra, particularly in the southern part, where forests in river valleys alternate with open spaces on the watersheds. The burrows are built only in forestless localities. It enters very rarely into the lichen and moss tundra, and only in years in which small rodents are abundant.

The fox occurs on the right bank of the Khatanga River (in the valleys of the rivers Bludnaya, Nizhnyaya, Zhdanikha and Kazachya), to the northern limit of the sparse forests (72° N lat.). It occurs in the valley of the Popigai River along the Anabyrka (72° N lat.), the Rassokha (71° N lat.) and near the mouth of the Fomich River (72° N lat.). It occasionally gets to the upper reaches of the Kharabyl River (72° N lat.) on the Syuryakh-Dzhyangy Range, and a fox was once obtained in the tundra near Lake Kieng-Kyuel (73° N lat.).

FIGURE 17. Edge of pine forest in Novosibirsk. Biotope of the fox. Photo by K. T. Yurlov

It is always present in the Anabar River valley and occasionally near other tributaries in the tundra and forests of the plain. It was found near the mouth of the Yakovlevka River (72° N lat.).

The fox builds burrows in the Olenek River valley, in the valleys of the Kelimyar and Pur rivers, and in their forested tributaries. According to A. Bunge (1883) it occasionally enters the Lena Delta, and tracks were found in the area of the left tributaries of this river by A. A. Romanov (1941), near the Tigil and Ayakit rivers and on the right bank, near the mouth of the Kengdei River and further south on terraces above the flood-plains to Kyusyur village. It has been found near the northern end of the Kharaulakh Range (72° N lat.) and in mountains near Neelov Bay and Tiksi Bay where, according to traders, broods of foxes were found.

The fox occurs everywhere south of the above localities between the Taimyr and Kharaulakh to the frontier.

According to R. Maak (1859), foxes are common in the valley of the Vilyui River and even more common in the middle reaches of the river near village Suntar. It occurs more rarely in the upper reaches of the Vilyui and on the Chona River. According to A. Ivanov, it is common in the valley of the Vilyui River and in central Yakutia (Tugarinov and others, 1934). According to V. I. Belyk (1953), it inhabits the entire forest tundra and taiga of Yakutia, and is occasionally caught in the southern Anabar districts and in the Allaikhov, Nizhne-Kolymsk, Bulun, and Ust-Yansk areas, where it sometimes occurs near 71° N lat.

S. I. Ognev (1931) described a subspecies of the fox coming from the south of Yakutsk. The fox is not rare in the Olekma-Vitim Mountains, according to I. S. Polyakov (1873).

The fox was found by N. M. Mikhel' (1939) on the lower Indigirka.
According to V. I Iokhel'son (1898) it occurs throughout the Kolyma
area and further north. F. Vrangel' (1841) found a fox on the ice about
100 km from the shore. S. A. Buturlin (1913) found burrows in the tundra on
Kamennyi Island, and saw pelts from various localities near the Kolyma
River and near Verkhoyansk and Abyi. It occurs along the Kolyma's
Yasachnaya, Popovka, and Korkodon tributaries and was also obtained
near Krestovskaya Station (coll. Zool. Inst. Acad. Sciences USSR).

FIGURE 18. Turan Steppe, Tuva. Fox biotope: Photo by K. T. Yurlov

Portenko (1941₂) writes that the fox is one of the characteristic and
common animals in the Anadyr territory and that the distributions of the fox
and the Arctic fox are separate. The fox is common in the western part of
the territory, except near villages. It is slightly less common in the lower
reaches of the Anadyr than in the middle and upper reaches. It is rare in
the maritime zone. According to L. O. Belopol'skii, it occurs more
frequently south of the Anadyr estuary than north of it, where it probably
occurs sporadically and may be found in winter. A fox was caught in March
on the shore near the village of Mainyny-tumy.

G. Maidel' (1894) wrote that "the fox and other carnivores (except the
wolf) are very rare in the Chukchi area," but he reported foxes from the
southern slopes of the Anadyr Range. Portenko (1941₂) thinks that the
fox is rare on the Anadyr Range. Telegin found a fox burrow near
the village of Anadyr in summer 1958 from which young were taken and an
adult was obtained in the middle reaches of the Anadyr River.

The fox is not rare in the land of the Olyutorka Koryaks, according to
A. V. Samorodov (1939). The author observed and collected it near the

rivers Apuka, Ilui, Achaivayam, etc. S. P. Krasheninnikov (1949) mentioned the abundance of animals in Kamchatka, including the fox. It was collected in Kamchatka in 1884 by Grebnitskii, and in 1909 by F. P. Rebushinskii (coll. Zool. Inst. Acad. Sciences USSR). According to Yu. V. Averin (1948) it is common throughout the peninsula.

According to N. V. Slyunin (1900) the fox occurs in the Gizhiga and Okhotsk districts but in smaller numbers than in Kamchatka. N. G. Buxton found foxes in the area of Gizhiga (J. A. Allen, 1903).

The fox is widely distributed in Transbaikalia. G. Radde (1872) recorded foxes from Lake Baikal, the Yablonovyi Range, the Bureya Mountains, the Onon river valley, and the upper reaches of the Amur.

According to G. G. Doppel'maier (1926) foxes are common on the northeastern shore of Lake Baikal, but their economic importance is small. According to S. S. Turov (1936), the fox is common in some areas on the shore as far as Svyatoi Nos and the Ushkan Islands. It also occurs on the Kudaldy River.

Foxes were collected in 1927 by P. S. Mikhno in the Kharangoi area, about 40 km west of Kyakhta (coll. Zool. Inst. Acad. Sciences USSR). Foxes are common everywhere in eastern Transbaikalia, both in the taiga and in the steppe, in the mountains and on the plains (Kuznetsov, 1929).

Foxes are common on the Stanovoi Range (Gassovskii, 1927), and occur in different biotopes in the taiga and in the alpine tundra above the timberline. According to E. Pavlov (1948) foxes are not common in the upper reaches of the Chita River and occur mainly in river valleys. In the valley of the Uda River, and in the upper reaches of the Selemdzha River, foxes are rare according to N. T. Zolotorev (1934), but they occur throughout the district.

Foxes are widely distributed in the Far East. According to L. Schrenck (1858), R. Maak (1859) and others, the fox is distributed throughout the Amur Basin and is common in the Ussuri valley.

According to N. M. Przheval'skii (1870) the fox occurs in large numbers throughout the Ussuri territory in the plains and mountain forests, but mainly near river valleys.

According to Zolotarev (1936) foxes are very rare on the Iman River and are found mainly in its lower reaches.

The fox occurs on the Sikhote-Alin (Bromlei, 1951). Foxes were collected in 1841 by M. I. Yankovskii in the area of the Sidemi Bay and in 1927 by M. Popov (coll. Zool. Inst. Acad. Sciences USSR).

Middendorf (1853) found foxes on the Shantar Islands, and foxes were collected by A. D. Baturin and G. D. Dul'keit (Ognev, 1929, 1931) on the Bol'shoi Shantar Island.

According to A. M. Nikol'skii (1889), Suprunenko (1890) and others, the fox is common on Sakhalin, particularly in the middle of the island: It has also been recorded from the Central Sakhalin and South Sakhalin reserves (Gerasimov, 1951). It occurs on all the Kurile Islands (Kuznetsov, 1949).

Survey of subspecies:

2a. **Vulpes vulpes tobolica** Ognev (1926). West Siberian fox

The subspecies was described on the basis of a specimen taken near Obdorsk. Color dirty reddish brown with a distinct cross pattern on back and shoulders. Gray foxes with completely black feet predominate.

Melanistic specimens are not rare. Fur extremely long, size very large. Condylobasal length of skull 151 — 159 mm, length of tooth row 70 — 75 mm. Distributed along the middle and lower reaches of the Ob.

2b. **Vulpes vulpes jakutensis** Ognev (1922). Yakutian fox

The subspecies was described from a specimen found in the taiga south of Yakutsk. It is darker than the preceding subspecies. Color more vivid, reddish brown with a cross pattern on back and shoulders. Fur short but luxurious and silky. Melanistic forms are rather common. Size large. Condylobasal length of skull 145.6 mm, length of upper tooth row 68 mm. Yakutia.

According to N. A. Bobrinskii (1944), the Yenisei Territory is inhabited by an as yet undescribed large fox with a luxurious, bright reddish brown fur. The forest steppes of Western Siberia are inhabited by a large fox with rough fur of light yellowish-reddish brown color. The Altai is inhabited by a related form which differs only in its more vivid color and luxurious fur.

2c. **Vulpes vulpes beringiana** Middendorf (1875). Tundra fox

The subspecies was described from the shore of the Bering Strait. It is characterized by a bright, intense reddish brown color on back and flanks with a distinct cross pattern. Melanistic forms are common. Fur luxurious. Size large. Condylobasal length of skull 142 — 156 mm, length of upper tooth row 69 — 72 mm. Chukchi, Anadyr Territory and Kamchatka.

2d. **Vulpes vulpes daurica** Ognev (1931). Daurian fox

The subspecies was described from the Kharangoi area. Color light yellowish-reddish brown with distinct whitish speckles and grayish stripes on the anterior side of the legs. Fur luxurious but coarse. Size large. Condylobasal length of skull 140 — 153 mm, length of upper tooth row 66 — 70 mm. Transbaikalia and on the Amur River.

Biology. Habitats of the fox are very variable and are found in many different landscapes, from the southern tundra to the lower desert areas, and it occurs in mountains up to the line of perennial snow. Like the wolf, it avoids only the great open taiga, with its poor fauna and deep and loose snow.

The fox feeds on animal and vegetable food, but mainly on rodents, birds, and insects (Figures 19, 20). The type of food depends on the local fauna. The fox makes seasonal migrations to different areas according to the distribution and availability of its food objects.

Rut takes place in February—March in the Turukhansk Territory and in April in the lower reaches of the Kolyma. Gestation lasts 52—56 days. A litter contains 4—6, rarely 10 young. The female gives birth in a burrow (Figure 21), and rarely in a den or the hollow part of a fallen tree. The burrow is usually situated on sandy ground and has several entrances; the nest chamber is situated at various depths.

The eyes of the young open after about 2 weeks. The male takes part in the rearing of the young. The young become independent in autumn and the litter disperses. Foxes reach sexual maturity in the second year.

FIGURE 19   Fox tracks in deep snow. Barnaul, Altai Territory. Photo by B. S. Yudin

More or less periodic fluctuations of the populations occur. These are connected with epizootics and with change in food conditions which influence reproduction and the mortality of the young.

45

FIGURE 20. Diggings and tracks of a fox catching rodents. Novosibirsk. Photo by B.S. Yudin

FIGURE 21. Terrace above the Poros River, Moshkovo Village, Novosibirsk Region. Marmot burrow occupied by a fox. Photo by B.S. Yudin

Foxes are subject to various infections and parasitic diseases. Molt takes place in April and May, varying according to the climatic conditions, and continues until autumn. The winter fur is complete in November. The fur becomes markedly worn during the winter and its quality decreases before the spring molt.

The fox is one of the most important fur animals. Black-brown foxes are bred on breeding farms.

3. **Vulpes corsac** Linnaeus (1768). Corsac fox
   (Figure 22, Map III)

1768. Canis corsac. Linnaeus, C. — Systema Naturae XII ed., 3, p. 223; Pallas, P.S. Naturgesch. des Korsaks, Neue Nordische Beiträge zur physik. und geograph. Erd-und Völkerbeschr., 1, pp. 29 — 38. 1781; Tilesius, W. Naturgesch. des Eisfuchses des Kaukasisch. Schakals und Korsakfuchses. — Nova Acta Academ. Leop. XI., Bonn. 1823; Eversmann, E. Estestvennaya istoriya mlekopitayushchikh zhivotnykh Orenburgskogo kraya (Natural History of Mammals of the Orenburg Territory), p. 36 — 37, Kazan. 1850; Simashko, Yu. Russkaya fauna (Russian Fauna). p. 495, Sankt- Petersburg. 1851. Table XXI, fig. 2.

1910. Vulpes corsac. Trouessart, E. L. Conspectus mammalium Europae. — Faune des Mammifères d'Europe, p. 95; Satunin, A. K. Opredelitel' mlekopitayushchikh Rossiiskoi imperii (Key to Mammals of the Russian Empire). p. 145, Tiflis. 1914; Ognev, S. I. A Systematical Review of the Mammals of Russia. — Ann. Mus. Nat. Hungarici, 23, pp. 234 — 238. 1926; Ellerman, J. R. and T. C. S. Morrison-Scott. Checklist of Palaearctic and Indian Mammals, pp. 229 — 230, London. 1951.

1931. Vulpes corsak. Ognev, S. I. Zveri Vostochnoi Evropy i Severnoi Azii (Animals of Eastern Europe and Northern Asia). 2, pp. 346—356, Moskva-Leningrad; Novikov, G. A. Khishchnye mlekopitayushchie fauny SSSR (Carnivores of the USSR). pp. 67—71, Moskva-Leningrad, Izdatel'stvo AN SSSR. 1956.

Type and type locality. The species was described after a specimen from the steppe between the Ural and Irtysh rivers.

Diagnosis. The corsac fox is markedly smaller than the common fox, but has longer legs. Length of body and head 50—60 cm, tail 25 — 35 cm. Condylobasal length of skull 106 — 120 mm, zygomatic width 59 — 68 mm.

Ears large and more widely separated than in the common fox. Whitish stiff hairs form a fringe on the ear margin. Posterior side of ears reddish brown-gray (not black as in the common fox). Tip of tail not white, as in the common fox, but black or dark brown. Lower lip and chin white. Legs without black or blackish tone on the anterior side. General color rather light, reddish brown or rust gray with a grayish tone (and with silvery tips on some guard hairs). Spine and shoulders more intensely colored than flanks. Venter white or yellowish, never black.

Description. The corsac fox is one of the smallest and most beautiful foxes of the Russian fauna. Only Vulpes cana from Baluchistan is smaller. The height of the corsac fox is $2/3$ that of the common fox. Tail relatively short (a good difference from Karagan fox); legs thinner and longer than those of the common fox (this is a biological adaptation to life in the open steppe). Muzzle very slender and pointed, with a small black snub nose. Eyes large and lively, more rounded than those of the common fox. Ears large with wide base. Vibrissae and the bristles above the upper eyelids very stiff and black (Figure 22).

Winter fur dense, pale straw yellow-whitish gray with brown speckling in the middle of back (intermediate between mikado brown and fawn color).

FIGURE 22. Vulpes corsac L. (original)

Flanks pale white with a yellowish tone. Chest and groin white. Forefeet whitish yellow anteriorly and rust-yellowish laterally. Coloration of hind feet similar but duller.

Anterior part of muzzle grayish-straw yellow-whitish with brown speckling, which is particularly distinct on forehead. Posterior side of ears gray-straw yellow; anterior margin of the ears white, ears whitish yellow inside.

Tail straw yellow-whitish with a brown pattern near the base and a blackish tone in the middle which forms a dorsal black patch in the basal half of the tail in some specimens. Underside of tail paler, whitish or yellowish.

Color of hairs on the back as follows: underfur ash gray with pale brown hair tips. Guard hairs gray at the base, with pale brownish subapical parts and white tips; some hairs have two black bands separated by a white band.

Intensity of the straw yellow tone of the flanks varies markedly in winter.

The fur is markedly shorter and coarser in summer specimens and the head is more grayish, as is the color of the posterior side of the ears. The back is more cinnamon brown because of the more intense reddish brown tips of the hairs of the underfur. Tail less bushy than in winter. Yellow color of the flanks less distinct.

The skull (Figure 23) differs markedly from that of other species and is smaller.

As noted by Satunin, the muzzle of the corsac fox is shorter. Thus, the ratio between the greatest length of the nasals and the length from the posterior margin of the nasals up to the highest point of the occipital crest is as follows:

Length of nasals	Length of the braincase according to the method of measurement described above
40.2	65.8:1.6
40.2	63.5:1.57
36	67.8:1.8
40.2	67.5:1.67
41.8	62.7:1.5
	1.5—1.8

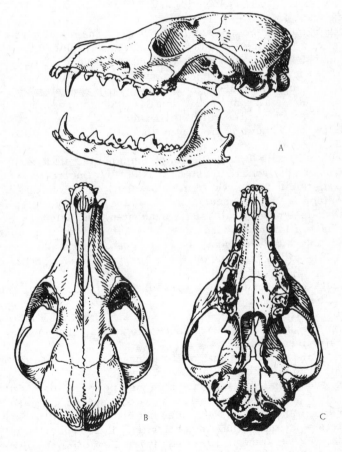

FIGURE 23. Skull of Vulpes corsac L. (original):

A — lateral; B — dorsal; C — ventral.

In the common fox these ratios are 1.2—1.5, i.e., the muzzle is markedly longer.

The muzzle tapers more gradually than in the common fox and is not as narrow at the level of the infraorbital foramina.

The facial part constitutes $\frac{2}{3}$—$\frac{3}{4}$ of the braincase, from the anterior margin of the orbit to the highest point of the occipital crest.

Facial length is $\frac{4}{5}$ to $\frac{5}{6}$ of the braincase in the common fox. The braincase of the corsac fox is relatively short but wider posteriorly than in the common fox. Sagittal crest little developed, semicircular lines extending from the inner parts of the postorbital processes and these joining at the anterior margin of the sagittal crest. Sagittal crest 10—15 mm long, weakly developed, and low. Tympanic bullae small and rather flat, differentiating the skull of the corsac fox from that of V. v. leucopus which, like the corsac fox, has a small skull. The tympanic bullae of V. v. leucopus are large and inflated and more closely approximated than those of the corsac fox. The external auditory meatus of V. v. leucopus is very characteristic and differs markedly from that of the corsac; it is 9 — 9.2 mm long in V. v. leucopus and only 5.5—6.5 mm long in the corsac fox.

The teeth of the corsac are small and weak. The small size of M^1 is characteristic. The outer edge of this transversely placed tooth is relatively broad in the common fox (including the small V. v. leucopus), markedly broader than the inner part of this tooth. This is different in the corsac fox: the outer part of M^1 is relatively narrow, slightly wider than its inner part; M^2 is also markedly smaller and narrower than in the small V. v. leucopus. The very small and weak lower M_2 is also characteristic; it is about $\frac{2}{3}$ the size of that of V. v. leucopus (Ognev, 1931).

Geographical distribution. The range includes the steppes of southeastern Europe from the eastern parts of the Dnepropetrovsk and Zaporozh'e districts in the west, and from the latitude of Sarepta in the north, the steppes of Ciscaucasia south of the Terek River, and the plains and steppes of Central Asia, Kazakhstan, and Western Siberian Transbaikalia. It probably also occurs in eastern Iran, Afghanistan, Dzhungaria, and in the Northeastern provinces of China and Mongolia.

We have the following data on the Siberian distribution of the corsac (Map III).

In Transuralia, according to S. A. Kuklin (1937), the corsac fox occurs — in small numbers — only in the southernmost districts of the Chelyabinsk Region, (south of the Ui River, i.e., below 54° N lat.) and in the southeastern districts of the Omsk Region (Pavlogradka, Shcherbakul, Cherlak, Omsk, and Krutinka areas).

It occurs in the extreme south of the Kurgan Region, and is common along the Irtysh to north of the latitude of Omsk.

It occurs occasionally in the Baraba Steppe in the Novosibirsk Region. A. A. Sludskii (1930) states that the corsac fox occurred in the Krupino and Tatar districts in the 1920s, but it does not occur there at present.

It sometimes occurs in the Tomsk Region. B. S. Yudin was informed that one specimen was obtained in 1943 near the village of Kozhevnikovo.

According to M. D. Zverev (1932), the corsac fox was common in the early 1920s in the former Rubtsov and Slavgorod districts and also in the

Kamen-on-Ob and Barnaul districts. It was "almost completely exterminated" in the 1930s. Only a few specimens are found in the former Rubtsovsk and Slavgorod districts at present, and in the Altai Territory it occurs only on the left bank of the Ob River according to V. N. Savinov (1953). The greatest number of pelts is obtained in the Kulunda, Slavgorod, Rubtsovsk, Mikhailovka, and Rodino areas. Numerous specimens were obtained near Pavlovsk in the past, according to N. F. Kashchenko (1900).

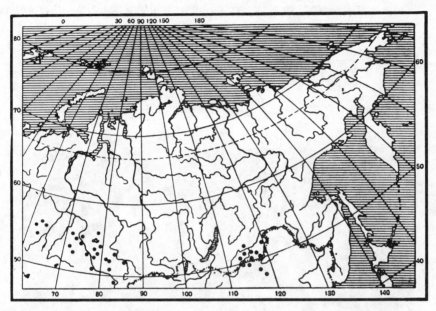

MAP III. Geographical distribution of Vulpes corsac L. in Siberia

According to Telegin the corsac fox is common in the Egor'ev and Uglovskoe areas. Yurlov (1952) observed them near burrows close to the village of Markovka in the Kluchi areas (Figure 24).

The corsac fox is distributed in the steppes of Transbaikalia. According to Maak (1859) it occurred in the steppe along the Argun and Onon rivers and local cossaks obtained it frequently. A. Cherkasov (1867) reported that it was numerous there, and Radde (1862) found it in the Onon and Aginsk steppe and in areas adjacent to Northeastern China (near the Dalai-Nor and Buir-Nor Lakes). It was collected on the northern shore of Lake Tarei-Nor (coll. Zool. Inst. Acad. Sciences USSR).

According to B. A. Kuznetsov (1929), the corsac fox is equally common in Eastern Transbaikalia's northern hilly part and in the plains in the south. He found the species in the steppe in the middle reaches of the Onon River near the villages Staryi Chindant and Ust-Borzya, near the lakes Bol'shoi and Malyi Tsaga-Nor, and near Kulusutai village. It was observed in the Borzya District of the Chita Region by A. A. Nasimovich (1951) southeast of the village Dauria. V. N. Skalon observed the corsac fox near the town of Borzya.

Subspecies.   There are 4 subspecies, 2 occurring in Siberia.

3a. **Vulpes corsac corsac** L. (1768).   Northern corsac fox

Described from the steppe south of Petropavlovsk. This is the largest
subspecies, distinguished by its rich winter fur and a very bushy tail.
Color very light straw gray. Length of body (from pelts) 56—65 cm, tail
23—27 cm. Distributed in Chkalov Region, northern Kazakhstan, and steppes
of the Altai.

FIGURE 24. Steppe in southern Kulunda. Biotope of the corsac fox. Photo by
K. T. Yurlov

3b. **Vulpes corsac** scorodumovi Dorogostajski (1935).
Transbaikal corsac fox

Described from Transbaikalia. Size very large. This subspecies needs
confirmation. Transbaikalia.

Biology. The corsac fox is a typical stenotopic species. Its habitats are
dry virgin land and semidesert, but it occurs in the steppe and mountains with
equal frequency. It avoids large forests, and thickets of shrubs and reeds, and
occurs in the forest steppe only in years in which food is scarce in its main biotopes. It avoids the vicinity of settlements and does not occur on cultivated land.
In the Baraba forest steppe, according to A. A. Sludskii (1930) the corsac
fox prefers "the bare level shores of salt lakes, shores with reed ditches
and low ridges. It occurs in smaller numbers on crests and virgin parts
of the steppe."
Yurlov informed me that he found corsac burrows in Kulunda in
fescue-Stina steppe with scattered dog rose bushes (Fighre 25).

52

The corsac fox is nocturnal. The day is passed in cover, usually in the burrow. It rarely digs its own burrow in Western Siberia and Transbaikalia, usually inhabiting abandoned burrows of marmots, foxes, badgers and other animals. In Siberia, burrows dug by the corsac fox itself are very primitive, usually consisting of a short passage ending in a small nest chamber. According to A. Eversmann (1850), the burrows in the Orenburg steppes are so short that hunters often pull the animal out with a stick split crosswise at the end, by screwing this end into the fur of the animal.

FIGURE 25. Burrow of the corsac fox. Kulunda, Klyuchi village in the Altai. Photo by K. T. Yurlov

There are two types of burrows of the corsac fox, the breeding burrow in which the female gives birth and nurses the young, and the temporary burrows. According to A. M. Kolosov (1935), in the steppe between the Ural and Emba rivers, temporary burrows constitute 70 % of all burrows. The corsac fox usually passes the day in a vacant burrow or lies under a bush, in a ravine, between stones, etc.

In the Transbaikalian steppe the corsac foxes usually inhabit burrows completely or temporarily abandoned by the Siberian marmot. There they hide in case of danger. I. P. Brom and others (1948) observed in the first half of August "a family of corsac foxes which roamed 300 m from the breeding burrow and passed the day in different burrows of the Siberian marmot. The young foxes were playing, and ran from one

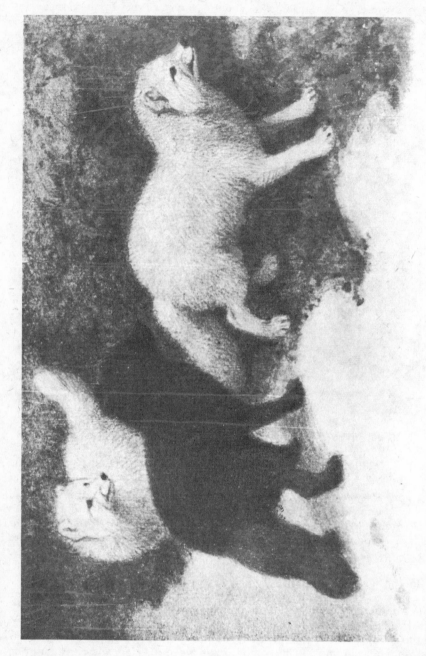

FIGURE 26. Alopex lagopus L. in the wild. Drawing by V. A. Vatagin

burrow to another, and often crawled into inhabited and uninhabited burrows." He also observed an adult marmot chase a fox which had entered its burrow. Corsac foxes are often caught in snares set for marmots. Similar observations were made by L. I. Galkina in the steppes of Western Siberia, Kazakhstan, and the Altai.

The corsac foxes form small packs in winter, and these roam more or less widely in search of food.

The senses of the corsac fox are well developed. It has excellent sight, hearing and smell. It runs with moderate speed and can be caught even by a slow dog. When it chases its prey, it sometimes gives a hoarse bark. The tracks of the corsac fox resemble those of the common fox, but are smaller.

The corsac fox feeds mainly on small rodents, birds, other vertebrates and insects. It also feeds on carrion.

The stomach contents of 18 animals examined in Transbaikalia by I. P. Brom and others (1948) contained the following: rodents, 85 %; carnivores (polecats and corsac foxes) 5.5 %; mammals (not determined) 16.5 %; birds, 5.5 %; insects, 22.0 %. The percentage of rodent species was as follows: Siberian marmot, 44 %; Daurian pika, 55 %; Daurian hamster, 16.5 %; narrow-skulled vole, 22 %.

Rut and mating takes place in February in the steppes of Western Siberia and Transbaikalia, and at the end of February and in March on the Altai's Chuya Steppe. Fights among males for the female are common during the rut. Gestation lasts 50—60 days. The litter consists of 2—11 young. Sixteen embryos were once found in Kazakhstan (Afanas'ev and others, 1953).

Migrations of the corsac fox are known. When deep snow makes catching of rodents difficult, the corsac fox migrates south, and when the ground is covered with ice mass migrations have been observed.

There are marked fluctuations in the populations of the corsac fox. The increase of its numbers in a certain area may be due to immigration from neighboring areas or to increased reproduction of the local population.

A decrease in the numbers of the corsac fox may be caused by migrations due to famine or by mass mortality from diseases.

Practical importance. The pelt of the corsac fox is strong and has a warm and beautiful fur. Four varieties are distinguished according to their quality: Petropavlovsk, Kazakhstan, Astrakhan, and Tashkent.

The corsac fox has been exterminated to a large extent, particularly in Western Siberia. Numerous animals are killed when the Siberian marmot is hunted, many corsac foxes being caught by snares placed in marmot burrows in the steppes of Transbaikalia, the south of Western Siberia, Kazakhstan, and on the Chuya Steppe in the Altai. The pelts of the corsac fox are in summer fur at this time, or molting, and cannot be used.

The corsac fox is caught in snares, by digging out burrows, with dogs (rarely with eagles), and is occasionally shot. Digging out burrows has a harmful influence on the numbers of the foxes by destroying their habitations.

The corsac fox is very useful in the control of harmful rodents, of which it kills large numbers. The damage caused by killing steppe game is much smaller than the benefit it brings through killing pests. The corsac fox is not known to attack domestic fowl.

3.   Genus ALOPEX Kaup (1829).   Arctic fox

   1829. A l o p e x. Kaup, J. I. Skizz. Entwicklungsgesch. und Natürl. Syst. der Europ.   Thierw., 1 p. 83; Miller, G. S. Catalogue of the Mammals of Western Europe, pp. 318—319, London. 1912; Ognev, S. I. Zveri Vostochnoi Evropy i Severnoi Azii (Animals of Eastern Europe and Northern Asia). 2, pp. 239—214. 1931; Ellermann, J. R. and T. C. S. Morrison-Scott. Checklist of Palaearctic and Indian Mammals, p. 223. 1951.
   1868. L e u c o c y o n. Gray, I. — Proc. Zool. Soc. London, p. 521 (type: C a n i s   l a g o p u s Linnaeus).

   Type species. C a n i s   l a g o p u s Linnaeus (1758).
   Diagnosis. The Arctic fox resembles the corsac fox in size and build, but appears lower. The body is relatively long and the legs are short. Muzzle shorter than in the common fox. Ears short and rounded: when drawn forward they do not reach the eyes. Pupils elliptical. Tail very furry, about half as long as body and head. The soles of the feet are densely covered with coarse fur. Winter fur white or smoke-brown. Yellow or reddish brown tones are absent in the color.
   The interorbital space of the skull is more steeply elevated above the rostrum than in the common fox. Postorbital processes either flat or with shallow dorsal fossae. Interorbital space wider by one quarter than the width of the muzzle above the canines. Anterior palatine foramina as long or slightly longer than longitudinal diameter of alveoli of upper canines. Paroccipital processes almost as high as the tympanic bullae or slightly lower. Inner sides of tympanic bullae rounded, without angles in the middle.
   Lower margin of external auditory meatus slightly extended and not covering the meatus, which is easily visible in ventral view. Lower jaw without rounded projection below the angular process.
   Dental formula: $I\frac{3}{3}$; $C\frac{1}{1}$; $Pm\frac{4}{4}$; $M\frac{2}{3}$ = 42.

   Canines relatively short. Lower canines only reach to or slightly beyond alveoli of upper canines when the jaws are closed. Upper carnassial tooth (Pm^4) with a poorly developed anterior-external projection (Figure 27). Lower carnassial tooth (M_1) with an entoconid. Lower posterior molar about as large as posterior half of preceding molar (Figure 27).
   Ventral ridge of os penis with a small projection or tubercle near the base.
   Geographical distribution.   Arctic zone of Eurasia and North America.
   Systematics.   Genus monotypic.

4.   **Alopex lagopus** Linnaeus (1758).   Arctic fox
(Figure 26, Map IV)

   1758. C a n i s   l a g o p u s. Linnaeus, C. Systema Naturae, I. X ed., p. 40; Pallas, P. S.   Zoographia Rosso-Asiatica, 1, pp. 51—57. 1811;

Simashko, Yu. Russkaya Fauna (Russian Fauna). 2, p. 499, Sankt-
Peterburg. 1851; Middendorf, A. Übersicht der Natur Nord- und Ost-
Sibiriens, 4, pt. 2, pp. 942 — 947. 1875.

1816. **Vulpes arctica.** Oken, L. Lehrbuch der Naturgeschichte, 3,
pt. 2, p. 1033.

1873. **Vulpes lagopus.** Bogdanov, M. N. Okhotnich'i i
promyslovye zveri i ptitsy Evropeiskoi Rossii (Commercial and Game
Animals and Birds of European Russia). — Zhurnal okhoty i
konnozavodstva, Nos. 13 — 14, p. 247; Trouessart, E. L. Conspectus
Mammalium Europae. — Faune des Mammifères d'Europe, p. 96. 1910.

1902. **Vulpes beringensis.** Merriam, H. — Proc. Biol. Soc.
Washington, p. 171. (Bering Island); Ognev, S. I. Zveri Vostochnoi
Evropy i Severnoi Azii (Animals of Eastern Europe and Northern Asia). 2,
pp. 260 — 266, Moskva-Leningrad. 1931.

1912. **Alopex lagopus.** Miller, G. S. Catalogue of the Mammals of
Western Europe, pp. 319 — 324; Satunin, K. A. Opredelitel'
mlekopitayushchikh Rossiiskoi imperii (Key to the Mammals of the Russian
Empire). p. 136, Tiflis. 1914; Ellerman, J. R. and T. C. S. Morrison-Scott.
Checklist of Palaearctic and Indian Mammals, pp. 222 — 223, London. 1951;
Novikov, G. A. Khishchnye mlekopitayushchie fauny SSSR (Wild Mammals of
the USSR). pp. 72 — 79, Moskva-Leningrad, Izdatel'stvo AN SSSR. 1956.

1912. **Alopex spitzbergensis.** Miller, G. S. Loc. cit.,
pp. 324 — 325.

1920. **Alopex beringianus.** Cherskii, A. I. Komandorskii pesets.
Materialy po izucheniyu rybolovstva i pushnogo promysla na Dal'nem
Vostoke (The Commander Arctic Fox. Data on Fishery and Fur-Bearing
Animal Commercial Hunting in the Far East), pp. 60 — 108.

1935. **Vulpes (Alopex) lagopus.** Adlerberg, G. P. Khishchnye
zveri (Carnivora Fissipedia) Arktiki (Carnivora Fissipedia of the Arctic). —
In: Zveri Arktiki pod redaktsiei prof. N. A. Smirnova, pp. 423 — 439,
Leningrad, Izdatel'stvo Glavsevmorputi; Bobrinskii, N. A. Otryad
khishchnye. V knige: Opredelitel' mlekopitayushchikh SSSR, pod redaktsiei
prof. N. A. Bobrinskogo (Order Carnivores. In: Key to Mammals of the USSR
edited by Prof N. A. Bobrinskii). pp. 146 — 147. 1944; Stroganov, S. U.
Opredelitel' mlekopitayushchikh Karelii (Key to the Mammals of Karelia),
pp. 66 — 67. — Karelo-Finskii Gosudarstvennyi Universitet, Petrozavodsk. 1949.

Type and type locality. Type not known. Described from Lapland.

Diagnosis. The diagnostic characters of the species are the same as those
of the genus.

Description. The Arctic fox resembles the corsac fox closely, and to a
lesser degree the common fox. It differs from the common fox in its shorter
body, shorter muzzle, and short ears. The ears are rounded and project little
from the fur. When drawn forward they do not reach the eyes. Tail very
bushy, about half as long as body and head. Legs shorter than in the
common fox. Soles of feet entirely covered with dense and coarse hair
(Figure 28).

Skull (Figure 27) shorter than that of the common fox, particularly the
facial region. Interorbital area more steeply elevated above the muzzle than
in the common fox. Postorbital processes either flat or with shallow dorsal
fossae. Paroccipital processes larger than in the common fox; their length
from the point of junction with the posterior margin of the tympanic bullae to
their ends is about one quarter the length of the bullae.

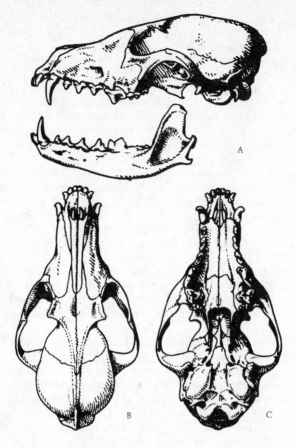

FIGURE 27. Skull of *Alopex lagopus* L. (original):

A — lateral; B — dorsal; C — ventral.

Canines relatively short and weak; the tip of the lower canines extends only slightly beyond the alveoli of the upper canines when the jaws are closed.

Os penis larger than that of the common fox; length of os penis 58.6 — 63.0 mm (av. 60.8 mm). A small projection or tubercle lies at the base of the ventral ridge.

There are two color forms: white and blue. The white form is characterized by marked seasonal dimorphism: summer fur on upper part of body and head is smoke gray, darker on the shoulders and the spine (so-called "cross") with flanks lighter and gradually changing into dirty white on the venter. Winter fur is solid white. The blue form has no marked seasonal change of color and never becomes completely white. The blue fox has a dark, smoky brown-gray color throughout the year.

Geographical distribution. The Arctic fox is distributed throughout the Arctic tundra, the shore and islands of the Arctic Ocean, and the Commander Islands. It migrates in winter far south via river valleys into the taiga, and appears regularly in the areas of Berezovo, Lower

Tunguska, Verkhoyansk and Sredne-Kolymsk. Single animals have been found as far south as 55° N lat.

The Arctic fox occurs in the Northern Urals down to about 65°N lat. in the south (I. F. Brandt, 1856). According to K. K. Flerov (1933), it is common in the Urals in the valleys of the Syn-Yakhi and Lyapin rivers; it may enter the Berezov area in winter.

The southern boundary of the Arctic fox's range in the northern part of Western Siberia extends, according to A. A. Dubrovskii (1940), along the rivers Baidarata (Pydarata), Shchuchya, Longot-Yugan, Byda, Khadyta, and Messo-Yakha, and coincides more or less with the northern limits of the forest, extending further south in interfluve areas. Burrows of the Arctic fox are found particularly far south on the watershed between the Nadym and Pur rivers (about 65° N lat.). In years in which Arctic foxes are abundant, the southern boundary of its burrows extends further into the forest tundra (Map IV).

A. N. Dubrovskii (1940) writes: "The following localities are recorded as places of high concentration for the Arctic fox: vicinity of Cape Trekhbugornyi, River Tanam, River Lobonkata, River Tambei, Cape Drovyanoi, Cape Napalkov, the northern end of the Gyda Peninsula (Mochui-Sale and Ivai-Sale peninsulas), the valley of the Poielovo-Yakha River (western half), the Malyi Yamal (on the watershed separating the drainages of Ob Bay and the Khaddutei River) and on the Pydarata-Enzor and Shchuchya-Iorkuta watersheds. It is found in large numbers in the valley of the Se-Yakha River, near Lake Nei-To, and in the valleys of the Tiutei-Yakh, Venui-Yakh, Kharasavaya, Morda, and other rivers.

The Arctic fox is common everywhere on the Yamal (Zhitkov, 1913). It occurs on Belyi Island (Tyulin, 1938). Arctic foxes were obtained in 1909 by D. Wardropper in the Salekhard district (coll. Zool. Inst. Acad. Sciences USSR).

According to S. P. Naumov (1931) it occurs on the Gyda Peninsula from the coast to the northern boundary of the forest or slightly further south (about 68°N lat.). According to A. F. Middendorf (1867), its southern boundary on the Yenisei is near Dudinka. According to N. P. Naumov (1934), it breeds in the Norilsk area (69°N lat.), near the upper Khantaika River, in the upper reaches of the Kureika and Kotui (Khatanga) rivers at 67° — 68° N lat. The boundary turns northeast of the source of Kotui, as the Arctic fox comes from the north near Lake Chirinda (67°45' N lat.) and in the area of Lake Yessei. Burrows are found again in the upper reaches of the Tukalan River (a tributary of the Kotui).

The Arctic fox is present throughout the year on the Taimyr Peninsula and on adjacent islands in the Kara and Laptev Sea (Shastin, 1939). Middendorf (1869) observed it in the north of the Taimyr Peninsula near 74°N lat. E. Toll (1909) recorded the Arctic fox on the Chelyuskin Peninsula. It has been recorded from the western part of the Taimyr by A. Byalynitskii-Birula (1907), and V. G. Heptner (1936) describes it as widely distributed in the northwestern part of the peninsula. It occurs on Dickson Island in autumn and winter. It is widely distributed on the southwestern shore of the Taimyr and on such adjacent islands as Sibiryakov and Rastorguev, etc. (Kirpichnikov, 1937; Kolyushev, 1935). It occurs in the area of Pronchishchevaya Bay (Popov, 1939).

It is one of the most common game animals in the tundra between Khatanga and the Kharaulakh Range (A. Bunge, 1887, A. A. Romanov, 1941, and others).   The most detailed description of the distribution of the Arctic fox in this area has been given by A. A. Romanov (ibid.), and we present his report below with only slight alterations.

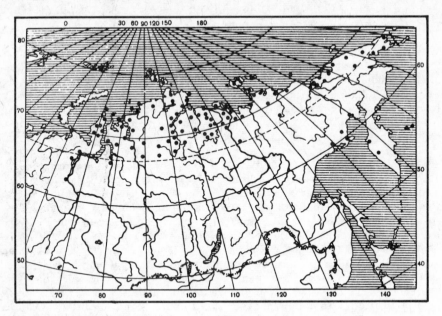

MAP IV. Geographical distribution of *Alopex lagopus* L. in Siberia

The most densely populated areas in the tundra west of Khatanga Bay and the Khatanga River are in the valley of the Greater Balakhna River and further north, and also in the system of small rivers flowing into Khatanga Bay north of 73° N lat.   The density decreases further south, and burrows of the Arctic fox are found only in small numbers at the northern boundary of the forest zone.

It is rare in the stony mountain tundra on the middle and upper reaches of the Popigai River, the left tributaries of the Anabar River, and the right tributaries of the Kotui River, and is found in this area only in years in which the animal is abundant.   In summer 1934, when the numbers of foxes were average, A. A. Romanov found only two Arctic foxes and three empty burrows in the mountains of Syuryakh Dzhangy and in the mountains on the lower reaches of the Rassokha and Fomich rivers, on a journey covering 400 km.   The upper reaches of the Anabar River (69° N lat.) are recorded as the southernmost localities where broods of Arctic foxes were found.

Between the Khatanga and Anabar rivers the coastal plain north of the Suolema River is very densely populated by the Arctic fox.   Burrows are numerous also in the tundra of the valleys of the Suolema and Sanga-Yurakh rivers, where there are many lakes; there all burrows were occupied in summer 1934 and the number of burrows and broods increased towards the north.   Thus, in the area of the Anna River and Lake Morkan, Romanov found 1—2 burrows per 10 km but in the Khopsokhtokh area further north he found 4 or 5 burrows per 10 km.

The Arctic fox digs burrows in smaller numbers in the tundra of the valleys of the Popigai and Bludnaya rivers, and in years in which its numbers are small, broods are very rare, particularly in the level tundra in the system of the left tributaries of the Popigai River and on the Bludnaya and Yakovlevka rivers.

The most densely populated area in the large territory between the Anabar and Olenek rivers is the plain north of the Pronchishchev Range, through which many rivers flow into the Laptev Sea. In years in which Arctic foxes are abundant there are not enough burrows, and many foxes give birth among tussocks on the surface and in fissures on the river banks. Broods were markedly less numerous on the Pronchishchev Range but their numbers varied less than in adjacent valleys. South of the Pronchishchev Range, numerous burrows were found in the lower lacustrine tundra on the lower reaches of the Yuelya River and near Lake Ulakhan-Kyuel'. This area is less populated by the Arctic fox than the coastal plain and in years in which Arctic foxes are abundant almost all burrows are occupied. The density is small south of the above lacustrine areas between the rivers Anabar, Buolkalakh and Olenek, and decreases from north to south. A large number of burrows remain unoccupied in the tundra near the northern limit of the forest (along the uninhabited right tributaries of the Udzha River and along the left tributaries of the Pur River), even in years in which Arctic foxes are abundant. In the forest near the tundra south of the Udzha and Pur rivers, in years with large numbers of Arctic foxes, broods are occasionally found in the stony mountain tundra of the Moi River (71° N lat.) and on the Chabyn-Tag (70° N lat.) and Mait-Dzhyangy (71°N. lat.) heights.

The most densely populated area between the Olenek and Lena rivers is the Chekanovskii Range north of the Mastak River. The valleys of the rivers flowing via the Olenek channel of the Lena and into Olenek Bay in the Laptev Sea are most densely populated. South of the Mastak River Arctic foxes dig burrows every year in the valleys of all tributaries of the Lena River to the Ayakit River and in the upper reaches of the right tributaries of the Kelimyar River. South of this area they dig burrows in small numbers and only in years when the population is large, when broods are occasionally found in the upper reaches of the Kyutyunga and Buor-Ayakit rivers (70° N lat.).

The largest population in the Lena delta is found on islands at the periphery of the archipelago, where Bunge collected it on Sagastyr Island (coll. Zool. Inst. Acad. Sciences USSR). In years in which Arctic foxes are abundant all burrows are occupied and some of the animals give birth on the open ground or among driftwood. The islands in the center of the archipelago are less populated than those on the periphery, and birth outside burrows has not been observed there. The southern islands of the delta near the Bykovskaya and Olenek channels are less populated, and even in years in which Arctic foxes are abundant some burrows remain unoccupied, while in years of low population most burrows remain empty.

The highest density of population is found on the Kharaulakh Mountains on the right bank of the Lena , in valleys of small rivers flowing into the

Buorkhaya Gulf, Tiksi Bay, Neelov Bay, and the Bykovskaya channel. Arctic foxes occur in smaller numbers on the right tributaries of the Kengdei River. The southernmost places where broods were found are the upper reaches of the Kharaulakh River (70° N lat.). Fox are distributed south along the Lena to Zhigansk, where they have been caught for many years (Khitrov, 1856).

The fox is very common in the Yana River delta, according to Bunge (1887), and is distributed throughout the tundra of Yakutia, according to V. I. Belyk (1953); it appears here in early winter in the forest tundra in large numbers. The commercial hunting boundary runs along 69° N lat., and in years of mass migration single Arctic foxes occur in the following districts: Novosibirsk, Vilyuisk, and Verkhne-Vilyuisk. The Arctic fox was collected by E. Toll in the area of Svyatoi Nos (coll. Zool. Inst. Acad. Sciences USSR). It is particularly abundant in the tundras on the lower reaches of the Indigirka (Mikhel', 1938).

It is found in large numbers in the lower reaches of the Kolyma. Further south, it breeds down to the northern limit of the forest — to about 69° N lat. (Iokhel'son, 1898). It was recorded as abundant by F. Vrangel' (1841) near Nizhne-Kolymsk and south of the mouth of the Kolyma, near Sukharnyi Island and Bol'shoi Baranov Cape, and in the area of the Chaun Gulf. According to S. A. Buturlin (1913), it is numerous further south of the estuary of the Omolon River. Buturlin collected the Arctic fox near the village of Sukharnoe (mouth of the Kolyma) and in the upper reaches of the Korelnikovaya River (Zhitkov, 1913). It may reach the Oimyakon area up to about 64−65° N lat. during mass migrations. "Commercial hunting boundary" in the valley of the Kolyma River is near Sredne-Kolymsk (Belyk, 1953).

The Arctic fox is widely distributed in the tundra of northeastern Siberia N. F. Kalinnikov (1912) found the Arctic fox on the Kolyma and Anadyr and on the coast of the Chukchi Peninsula. According to N. P. Sokol'nikov (1927), it occurs on the northern shore of the Anadyr territory (Figure 28), the shore of the Chukchi Peninsula, and more rarely in the Anadyr River valley. N. A. Gondatti collected an Arctic fox near Cape Dezhnev (coll. Zool. Inst. Acad. Sciences USSR).

According to L. Belopol'skii (1937), the Arctic fox is most abundant on the Chukchi Peninsula and in the eastern part of the Anadyr territory. According to L. A. Portenko (1941), it has a limited distribution in the Anadyr territory and digs burrows only in the coastal area and in some mountain regions. It appears in varying numbers during its winter migration and always in smaller numbers in the western part of the territory than in the eastern part.

According to A. V. Samorodov (1939), the numbers of Arctic foxes are small in the area of the Olyutorka Koryaks, and only 6 to 24 animals are caught every year. The Arctic fox occurs here mainly near the sea — in the tundra, on the seashore, and in river valleys.

The Arctic fox was found in Kamchatka by S. P. Krasheninnikov (1949), and is hunted by the local population. According to Steller, Arctic foxes were caught near Lopatka in winter, but these were probably stragglers. I. F. Brandt (1856), according to G. Voznesenskii, records that the Arctic fox occurs "throughout the western part of the Kamchatka to its southern tip and in the east usually only to Cape Ukinskii." Yu. V. Averin (1948), who studied the vertebrate fauna of eastern Kamchatka for five years, does not mention the Arctic fox. According to N. V. Slyunin (1900), the Arctic fox is occasionally found on the western shore of Kamchatka almost to the village of Golygino. Burrows have been found on the western shore of Kamchatka south to 55° N lat. (Ditmar, 1901), and on the eastern shore to 60° N lat.

FIGURE 28. Shore of the Anadyr estuary. Hilly tundra. Biotope of the Arctic fox. Photo by B. S. Yudin

The Arctic fox occurs on the Okhotsk shore of Siberia, but the southern boundary of its permanent range has not been determined.

According to N. V. Slyunin (ibid.) it occurs in the Gizhiga tundra in markedly greater numbers than in Kamchatka (see also Bogorodskii, 1853).

The Arctic fox inhabits all large islands in the Arctic Ocean and the Bering Sea. According to A. N. Dubrovskii (1940), burrows have been found on the Kara Sea islands of Belyi, Shokalskii, Olenii, and Sibiryakov, among others. According to G. L. Rutilevskii (1939), it occurs on Severnaya Zemlya only in the non-breeding period. It enters the island from the Chelyuskin Peninsula when large icefields appear in the Vil'kitskii Strait. Burrows have been found on Sverdrup Island. According to M. Konstantinov (1921), it is numerous on Novosibirskie and Lyakhov islands (see also Pallas, 1796). According to F. Vrangel' (1841), it occurs on Bear Island and particularly on Krestovoi Island. It occurs on Vrangel Island. It occurs on the Commander Islands in the Bering Sea, and is particularly abundant on Medny and Bering islands, where many skulls of the Arctic fox were collected in 1883 by N. A. Grebnitskii and in 1911 by A. I. Cherskii (coll. Zool. Inst. Acad. Sciences USSR).

The Arctic fox makes regular winter migrations and may travel thousands of kilometers beyond its normal area of distribution.

Straggling animals have been recorded from the following localities in Siberia. According to I.S. Polyakov (1877), K.K. Flerov (1933), and others, the Arctic fox sometimes appears in the area of Berezovo. V.N. Skalon and V.V. Raevskii (in litt.) report that the Arctic fox sometimes appears in the former Konda-Sosva Reserve. S. Shvetsov (1888) recorded stragglers in the Surgut Territory. S.M. Chugunov (1915) records 3 skulls obtained near the Surgut River and along the Yugan River; it is also found occasionally near the Vakh River. Skalon (1928) records an animal obtained near the huts of the Igotkiny on the Ob below Kolpashevo, and catches in the following localities: 30 km south of Narym, the village Alataevo, near the village Kargasok (near the mouth of the Vasyugan River), near the mouth of the Tym River, and on the Vasyugan River near the mouth of the Chezhapka River. Arctic foxes were obtained near the mouth of the Tol'ka River, in the upper reaches of the Sobun River (a right tributary of the Vakh River, and on the Ob River near the mouth of the Vakh.). I.P. Laptev (1953) records Arctic foxes in winter in the following localities in the Tomsk Region: Aleksandrovsk district, Aipolovo village (upper reaches of the Vasyugan River), near the village of Charymovo further north on the River Nyurolka, the village of Pudino on the Chuzik River, near Kolpashevo, and the valley of the Tym River.

P.E. Ostrovskikh obtained specimens in 1900 near the village of Dudinka on the Yenisei (coll. Zool. Inst. Acad. Sciences USSR). According to A.F. Middendorf (1867), the Arctic fox descends along the Yenisei to Igarka (68° N lat.), and specimens were caught near Turukhansk and Yeniseisk (near 58° N lat.). N.P. Naumov (1934) records catches in 1924 near Kuzmovka on the Stony Tunguska and in 1913 near the village of Bratsk on the Angara.

Maak (1859, 1886) recorded stragglers on the Muna and Chon, on the Vilyui and its tributaries, on the Tyung, Tyukyan and Khaingui, and near Suntar (62°N lat.). According to S.A. Buturlin (1913), the Arctic fox occurred in the area of Sredne-Kolymsk and at Malaya on the Alazeya, from which point it goes another 300 km further south along the river. According to Iokhel'son (1898), it occurs on the Kolyma 5—6° south of the northern boundary of forest vegetation; stragglers have been found 100 km or more to the south of Verkhne-Kolymsk.

The Arctic fox migrates in winter not only to the forest zone but also north. F. Nansen (1897) found Arctic foxes on the ice of the Arctic Ocean. When Nansen and his team abandoned the "Fram" and traveled with dogs on the ice, Arctic foxes attempted to steal their food at 85° N lat.

Thus, to summarize, the southern boundary of the "breeding range" on the continent coincides with that of the tundra, and the southern boundary of the autumn-winter zone of migration generally coincides with the northern boundary of the taiga; there is irregular straggling south and north of this area.

Biology. The Arctic fox is a typical inhabitant of the tundra and penetrates deep into the forest zone only during its winter migrations.

The food of the Arctic fox is very variable. It feeds on rodents, birds and eggs, fish, carrion, flotsam of the sea (dead animals, algae), insects, berries, etc.

The Arctic fox is monogamous, the male taking care of the brood together with the female. Rut in the tundra of Western Siberia takes place in April and early May, later in Eastern Siberia. Gestation lasts 52—53 days. The litter contains 3—12 young, occasionally as many as 18. Food conditions before and during gravidity have some influence on the size of the litter. When food is scarce the litter contains 5—6 young. The number of barren females and the mortality of the young also increase in years of little food. The brood disperses in autumn and the young become independent. They attain sexual maturity in the second year. The length of life is 8—10 years. Each family inhabits a definite area near the burrows. The burrows are usually dug at some elevated place. The same burrow is used for many years, by several generations.

Different ages and phases of molting have special names in the fur trade. The young are called "kopantsy" while blind, and then, up to the time they run out of the burrow, are called "nornik" ("burrow pups"). The young, on leaving the burrow at the age of about four months, are called "krestovatik" ("cross fox") and this name is also used for adults in summer fur. Young Arctic foxes in autumn, and adults beginning to become white toward winter, are called "sinyaki" ("blue animals"). Young Arctic foxes which have not attained full growth in winter and whose fur is short with a grayish tinge are called "nedopesk." Arctic foxes in winter fur are called "doshlye" or "roslye" ("old timers").

In winter, when food is scarce in the tundra, Arctic foxes migrate south to the taiga via river valleys, and north to the seashore were they feed on the flotsam of the sea.

The Arctic fox molts twice a year, in spring and in autumn, according to Boitsov. The spring molt in Siberia takes place from April to June and the autumn molt from September to November.

The numbers of Arctic foxes fluctuate markedly with a certain periodicity; large numbers coincide with mass outbreaks of the rodents — mainly lemmings — which are the Arctic fox's staple food. The influence of food on fertility and mortality has been mentioned above. Decrease in numbers is caused by epizootics, which occur periodically and occasion high mortality.

Practical importance. The Arctic fox is one of the most important fur animals of the USSR. The Arctic foxes of the Soviet Union are of first quality, the blue foxes being particularly highly valued. There are special farms on which blue foxes are bred.

4. Genus NYCTEREUTES Temminck (1839).
Raccoon dog

1839. N y c t e r e u t e s. Temminck, C. I. Van der Hoeven's Tijdschrift Nat. Geschied Physiol., 5, p. 285; Satunin, K. A. Opredelitel' mlekopitayushchikh Rossiiskoi imperii (Key to Mammals of the Russian Empire). pp. 1—145, Tiflis. 1914; Ognev, S. I. Zveri Vostochnoi Evropy i Severnoi Azii (Animals of Eastern Europe and Northern Asia). 2, pp. 359 — 361. 1931; Allen, G. M. The Mammals of China and Mongolia. pp. 345—346, New York. 1938; Ellerman, J. R. and T. C. S. Morrison-Scott. Checklist of Palaearctic and Indian Mammals, p. 232, London. 1951.

1850. N y c t e r e u t e s. Jäger. — Nova Acta Acad. Leopold. Carol., 22, pt. 2, p. 772.

Type species. Canis procyonoides Gray (1834).

Diagnosis. Size medium. Head relatively small, muzzle pointed. Ears short, projecting little from the fur. Hairs on cheeks long, forming whiskers. Soles bare. Fur dirty brownish gray. Cheeks black, with light hairs anteriorly and posteriorly. Skull little elevated in frontal area. Postorbital processes with shallow dorsal fossae. Inner sides of tympanic bullae rounded, without projecting angles in the middle. Paroccipital processes lower than tympanic bullae. Posterior margin of lower jaw with a characteristic rounded lobe below the angular process (Figure 5).

Dental formula. $I\frac{3}{3}$; $C\frac{1}{1}$; $Pm\frac{4}{4}$; $M\frac{2}{3}$ = 42.

Canines weak. The lower canines do not reach beyond the alveoli of the upper canines when the jaws are closed. Upper carnassial tooth (Pm^4) with a rudimentary inner lobe. Lower carnassial tooth (M_1) with an entoconid.

Geographical distribution. East Asia to the middle reaches of the Amur in the north, and to northern Indochina and Japan in the south.

Systematics. Genus monotypic.

5. **Nyctereutes procyonoides** Gray (1834).
Raccoon dog (Figure 29, Map V)

FIGURE 29. Nyctereutes procyonoides Gray (original)

1834. Canis procyonoides. Gray.— Illustr. Ind. Zool. 2. pl. 1; Schrenck, L. Reisen und Forschungen im Amur-Lande, pp. 53—87. 1858; Radde, G. Reisen im Süden von Ost-Siberien, pp. 75— 86. 1862.

1844. Nyctereutes viverrinus. Temminck, C. I. Siebolds Fauna Japonica.— Mammals, 40, pl. 8 (Japan).

1859. Canis (Nyctereutes) procyonoides. Maak, R. Puteshestvie na Amur (Voyage to the Amur). p.101, Sankt-Peterburg.

1907. Nyctereutes stegmanni. Matschie, P. Wiss. Ergebn. Filchners: Expedition nach China und Tibet.—Mammalia, p.175 (Southeastern China.)

1922. Nyctereutes koreensis. Mori, T.—Ann. Mag. Nat. Hist., 10, p.607. 1922 (environs of Seoul, Korea).

1951. Nyctereutes procyonoides. Ellerman, J R. and T. C. S. Morrison-Scott. Checklist of Palaearctic and Indian Mammals, pp.232—233, London.

Type and type locality. Type unknown. The species was described from Canton, China.

Diagnosis. The characters of the species are the same as those given above for the genus.

Measurements. Length of body and head: males, to 80 cm; females, to 60 cm; length of tail: males, to 26 cm, females, to 25 cm; length of ears: males, to 5.5 cm, females, to 5.0 cm.

Condylobasal length of skull: males, 111.0—127 mm; females, 104.0—123 mm; zygomatic width: males, 58.0 — 74.2 mm, females, 54.7—69.0 mm; length of the upper tooth row: males 41.3—50.2 mm, females 41.0—47.8 mm.

Description. Habitus distinctive, resembling that of large mustelid and the raccoon (Procyon lotor Desmarest) in color. Body moderately long, legs short. Head relatively small, short, narrow in the facial area, muzzle pointed. Ears short, broad, rounded, projecting only little from the fur. Hairs on cheeks long, forming whiskers. Tail very bushy, about one third as long as body. Soles bare. Winter fur dense and long but coarse. General color of winter fur dark brownish yellow with gray and straw yellow tinge. A cross-shaped pattern on the anterior part of the back. Ventral side yellowish brown. Chest black. Feet dark brown. Head and cheeks with dark stripes. A broad white stripe above the eyes to the ears. Tail covered with long hairs. Color of tail dark gray, brownish apically.

FIGURE 30. Os penis of Nyctereutes procyonoides Gray (after S. I. Ognev, 1931)

Summer fur sparser, shorter and coarser. Its color is more distinct, with a distinct cross pattern on the back.

Os penis narrower distally than that of the fox, with a better developed dorsal ridge and a shorter ventral groove, which does not reach the narrow end (Figure 30). Length 58—60 mm. maximum width 6 mm in the middle and about 2 mm at the base.

Skull (Figure 31) relatively small, conical. Dorsal outline in profile slightly convex in the frontoparietal area, descending slightly anteriorly to form a shallow saddle in the middle of the nasals. Height of muzzle above canines about one third height in area of tympanic bullae. Facial length slightly less than length of braincase. Frontal area with a median longitudinal groove. Postorbital processes with shallow dorsal fossae. Interorbital width greater by one quarter than width of muzzle above canines. Anterior palatine foramina about one third longer than longitudinal diameter of alveoli of upper canines. Bony palate continuing beyond posterior margin of the last molars by a distance about one third width of palate between molars. Paroccipital processes lower than tympanic bullae. Inner sides of tympanic bullae rounded but without projecting angles in the middle. Lower margin of external auditory meatus extended, covering meatus so that it is not visible in ventral view. Posterior lower margin of lower jaw separated from angular process by a deep concavity, forming a characteristic lobe (Figure 5).

Details of the dentition have been given in the diagnosis of the genus. The crowns of the inner upper incisors are trilobate.

Geographical distribution. Far East, northeastern provinces of China, Korea and Japan.

Nyctereutes has been acclimatized and distributed far beyond its original range in a number of regions in European Russia, the Caucasus, Kazakhstan and Siberia.

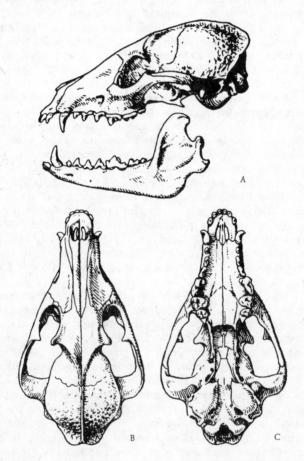

FIGURE 31. Skull of Nyctereutes procyonoides Gray (original):

A — lateral; B — dorsal; C — ventral.

It occurs in the Maritime Territory, and in the south of the Khabarovsk Territory and the Amur Region.

It occurs up to about 51° N lat. on the shore of the Tatar Strait, according to Schrenck (1858), and is found in the middle reaches of the Bureya and Zeya rivers. The northern boundary of the range extends from there to the Odzhal and Bureya mountains. It has been reported by G. G. Goodwin (1933) near Troitskoe on the Amur.

According to A. V. Afanas'ev (1935), the raccoon dog occurs along the Bureya no further than the Chekunda settlement. It was collected on the Bureya Mountains by G. I. Radde (coll. Zool. Inst. Acad. Sciences USSR), and its western boundary extends to the junction of the Shilka and Argun rivers (Radde, 1862). According to A. Cherkasov (1867), it occurs on the Onon River. R. Maak (1859 and 1861) records it as widely distributed in the valleys of the Ussuri and Sungari rivers; it is particularly numerous on meadow areas near the Muren and near Lake Khanka, where it was collected in 1914 by A. I. Cherskii. N. M. Przheval'skii (1870) states that it is distributed in the Ussuri Valley, also in the middle and mainly in the upper reaches of the Amur, but is most common in the south of the Ussuri territory. It was collected in the Maritime Territory, particularly near Chernigovka and Troitskoe (area of Lake Khanka), by A. Emel'yanov (coll. S. I. Ognev). According to G. D. Dul'keit, it occurs in a park on Cape Gamov, and in Vityaz' Bay in the Pos'et district (Ognev, 1931).

According to V. P. Sysoev (1952) the raccoon dog does not extend beyond the southern boundary of the Selemdzha, Upper-Bureya and Komsomolsk districts and is particularly abundant in the Leninskoe and other districts in the Jewish Autonomous Region and in the Arkhara district in the Amur Region. According to N. T. Zolotarev (1936), it is rare in the Iman River valley and occurs only in its lower reaches; some individuals enter the upper reaches of the river, where the author found tracks on the bank of the Kolumbe River, about 25 km from its mouth. The raccoon dog occurs on the eastern slope of the Sikhote-Alin Range and in the southern Maritime Territory, in the Sudzukhe reserve (Bromlei, 1951[1, 2]). It also occurs in the Suputinka reserve (Bromlei and Gutnikov, 1955).

The raccoon dog was collected in Sidemi in 1883 by M. I. Yankovskii (coll. Zool. Inst. Acad. Sciences USSR).

In Siberia it was introduced in some areas in the Altai Territory and in the Tomsk Region (Map V). However, attempts at acclimatization in Western Siberia were unsuccessful.

Subspecies. The raccoon dog forms several little differentiated subspecies. Ellerman and Morrison-Scott (1951) mention five subspecies. It is represented by one subspecies in the USSR.

5a. **Nyctereutes procyonoides ussuriensis** Matschie (1907).
Ussuri raccoon dog

1907. Nyctereutes ussuriensis. Matschie, P. Loc. cit., p. 178 (near mouth of the Ussuri); Satunin, K. A. Opredelitel' mlekopitayushchikh Rossiiskoi imperii (Key to Mammals of the Russian Empire), p. 146, Tiflis. 1914;

1907. **Nyctereutes amurensis.** Matschie, P. Loc. cit., p. 178. (Amur); Satunin, K. A. Abid., pp. 147—148. 1907.

1931. **Nyctereutes procyonoides ussurensis.** Ognev, S. I. Zveri Vostochnoi Europy i Severnoi Azii (Animals of Eastern Europe and Northern Asia), 3, pp. 361—371, Moskva- Leningrad; Ellerman, J. R. and T. C. S. Morrison- Scott. Checklist of Palaearctic and Indian Mammals, p. 233, London. 1951.

1944. **Nyctereutes procyonoides.** Bobrinskii, N A. Otryad khishchnykh. V knige: Opredelitel' mlekopitayushchikh SSSR, pod redaktsiei prof. N. A. Bobrinskogo (Order of Carnivores. In: Key to Mammals of the USSR edited by Prof. N. A. Bobrinskii), p. 148, Moskva; Novikov, G. A. Khishchnye mlekopitayushchie fauny SSSR (Carnivorous Mammals of the Fauna of the USSR), pp. 79 — 86, Moskva- Leningrad, Izdatel'stvo AN SSSR. 1956.

Type and type locality. Type unknown. The subspecies was described from the mouth of the Ussuri River.

Diagnosis. Relatively large. Condylobasal length of male skull 116—127 mm (108—117 mm in the nominate subspecies).

Measurements. Length of body with head: males 52—80 cm, females 47—60 cm; length of tail: males 20—26 cm, females 15—25 cm; length of ear: males 5.0—5.5 cm, females 4.0—5.0 cm. Weight in summer 4—6 kg, in winter 6—10 kg.

Skull measurements from 26 males and 18 females are as follows: Condylobasal length: males 116—127 mm (av. 122 mm), females 112—123 mm (av. 116.6 mm); zygomatic width: males 62.2—74.2 mm (av. 65.8 mm), females 54.7—69.0 mm (av. 63.7 mm); width of rostrum above canines: males 20.0—24.0 mm (av. 22.4 mm), females 19.7—22.6 mm (av. 21.8 mm); width between infraorbital foramina: males 26.0—29.5 mm (av. 28.4 mm), females 24.1—28.2 mm (av. 26.7 mm); interorbital width: males 20.2—24.9 mm (av. 22.8 mm), females 17.0—23.4 mm (av. 21.7 mm); postorbital width: males 19.3—23.0 mm (av. 21.7 mm), females 17.4—22.9 mm (av. 20.8 mm); maximum width of skull: males 42.5—46.7 mm (av. 45.2 mm), females 38.7—45.3 mm (av. 42.6 mm); height in area of the auditory bullae: males 44.2—49.2 mm (av. 46.4 mm), females 41.0—48.6 mm (av. 45.2 mm); length of braincase: males 52.8—55.6 mm (av. 53.7 mm), females 49.8—55.7 mm (av. 53.0 mm); length of the facial part: males 45.0—52 mm (av. 47.8 mm), females 44.5—49.3 mm (av. 47 mm); length of upper tooth row: males 44.8—50.2 mm (av. 46.7 mm), females 44.2—47.8 mm (av. 45.7 mm).

Geographical distribution. The range includes the Far East and perhaps adjacent areas of Northeast China and Korea. Details of distribution have been given in the description of the species.

Material examined. Far East, 44 specimens; European USSR, 15 specimens; total of 59 specimens examined, including 25 pelts.

Biology. Habitat of the raccoon dog is restricted to broadleaf forests and shrub thickets in plains and marshy areas with rivers, brooks, oxbows and small lakes. It occurs in open country, on meadows, hills, and among stones. It avoids conifer taiga. It lives in shallow burrows on low

mountains and on slopes of ravines. It often uses abandoned burrows of
badgers and foxes for breeding and shelter and sometimes lives among
stones, cracks in rocks, in hollow tree trunks, under roots of trees,
under overhanging trees, among shrubs, etc.

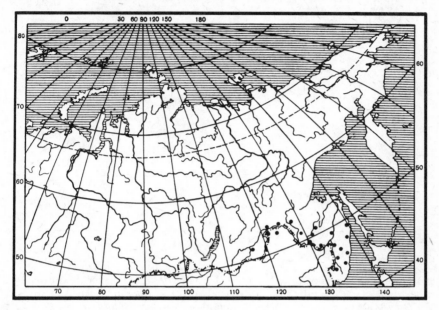

MAP V. Nyctereutes procyonoides Gray in Siberia

    The tracks of the raccoon dog are small; Formozov (1952) states: "The
footprints are not arranged in a straight line as in the fox, but in two rows in a
zigzag line.   The rounded footprints (4.5 — 5 cm wide) are very similar to
those of the cat but show marks of the short, blunt claws.   The step is
shorter than that of the fox (15 — 20 cm); the animal has a heavier gait; it
leaves drag trails when the snow is 10 cm deep, but when the snow is
deeper the groove is continuous." The animal moves slowly.
    Smell and hearing are its best developed senses, sight is less developed.
The animal is not very shy and is, in fact, rather trustful.   It defends
itself courageously when attacked.   The voice of the raccoon dog is a
characteristic whining and it growls when in danger.
    The raccoon dog is nocturnal.   When disturbed or hungry, it may be
active also during the day.
    The annual cycle is distinctly divided into two periods: hibernation, and
activity during the snowless period of the year.
    Hibernation in the Far East begins in November and continues until end
of March or early April.   The weight of the animal increases by the time of
hibernation by almost 50%.   The sleep is not deep and may be interrupted
during warm weather or thaw.   Some individuals do not hibernate in warm
winters.

The raccoon dog is very polyphagous. The composition of the food is very variable. The staple foods are small animals, fruits, berries, grain and roots of plants.

Examination of the feces, conducted by E. P. Spangenberg in the Iman River valley, showed the presence of the following food (Table 1).

TABLE 1. Occurrence (%) of various food items in the feces of the raccoon dog after S. P. Naumov and N. P. Lavrov (1941)

Type of food	May—June	October	End of November
Amphibia (frogs)	65	15	—
Mollusks	47	11	—
Insects	32	23	—
Fishes	19	23	24
Muridae	19	15	30
Reptilia	7	—	—
Birds	6	—	—
Fruits of trees	11	62	76
Grains of agricultural crops	4	19	12
Carrion (roe deer)	2	—	—

The table shows that the food is most variable in summer. The proportion of tree fruits and agricultural crops increases in autumn. The occurrence of a certain food is thus usually connected with its availability in the habitat and in the season. The raccoon dog feeds on flotsam of the sea and on fish in spawning places.

The raccoon dog is monogamous. Fights between males for the female are rarely observed in the mating period.

Rut occurs occasionally in February but usually in March. Gestation lasts 60—64 days. The litter may contain 19 young, but usually contains only 6—8. The young are born blind and are covered with almost black, soft fur. Their weight is 60—90 g. The eyes open on the 9th or 10th day. The teeth appear after 2—3 weeks. Lactation lasts 1.5—2 months. The male takes an active part in the care of the young. In the last days of gestation and the first days after birth the male brings food to the female, and later also to the young. The young become independent in the second half of summer, at the age of about 4—5 months, but live together with the parents. The entire family hibernates in the same burrow. Sexual maturity is reached at the age of 9—11 months.

Enemies of the raccoon dog are the wolf, glutton, lynx, yellow-throated marten, golden eagle, eagle owl and others. Competitive animals are almost all mammals and birds feeding on small vertebrates, roots of trees and bushes, and berries.

The diseases of the raccoon dog have been little studied. It has been found infected with piroplasmosis, rabies and some other diseases, and it is subject to helminthic infection.

Molt occurs only once a year as in other hibernating animals; it begins in the middle of spring and continues to the middle of autumn when the new coat is complete.

The raccoon dog has been released for acclimatization since 1934 in some regions of the RSFSR, Ukraine and Belorussia, Kazakhstan and Kirghizia. It has become acclimatized and is hunted in some localities.

The racoon dog was introduced in the Tomsk Region, Altai Territory, and the Buryat ASSR, but this attempt was unsuccessful, probably because of the harsh winter.

Practical importance. The fur is used for necklets, collars, and occasionally for fur coats. Its importance as game is not great as the animal occurs over a relatively small area. It has been successfully bred in captivity. It may cause damage to hunting by destroying young game animals.

5. Genus CUON Hodgson (1838). Red dogs, dholes

1838. C u o n. Hodgson. — Ann. Mag. Nat. Hist., 1, p. 152; Gray, J. Catalogue of Carnivorous Mammals etc., in the British Museum, p. 184. 1869; Blanford, W. T. The Fauna of British India. — Mammals, 1, p. 142, London. 1888 — 91; Allen, G. M. The Mammals of China and Mongolia, pt. 2, p. 358, New York. 1938; Pocock, R. I. The Fauna of British India. — Mammalia, 2, p. 146. 1941; Ellerman, J. R. and T. C. S. Morrison-Scott. Checklist of Palaearctic and Indian Mammals, p. 233, London. 1951.

1839. C h r y s a e u s. Smith, H. — Jardine's Nat. Libr. Mamm., 25, p. 167 (type: C a n i s d u k h u n e n s i s Sykes).

1842. C y o n. Agassiz, L. Nomenclator zoologicus, cont. nomina systematica generum animalium tam viventium quam fossilium, p. 113; Satunin, K. A. Opredelitel' mlekopitayushchikh Rossiiskoi imperii (Key to Mammals of the Russian Empire). p. 148, Tiflis. 1914; Ognev, S. I. Zveri Vostochnoi Evropy i Severnoi Azii (Animals of Eastern Europe and Northern Asia). 2, pp. 228 — 231. 1931.

1892. A n u r o c y o n. Heude, P. M. — Mém. Hist. Nat. Emp. Chin. p. 2, p. 102.

Type species. C a n i s p r i m a e v u s Hodgson 1883.

Diagnosis. Small canines of lean build, differing from wolves and foxes mainly in cranial characters and in dental structure and formula. Body moderately long, laterally compressed. Legs high and slender. Ears large and pointed, muzzle short and pointed. Tail very bushy, about half length of body and head. Fur light russet and dark rust red to black dorsally, white to reddish yellow ventrally. Frontal area of skull slightly elevated above muzzle. Postorbital processes with more or less marked dorsal fossae. Inner sides of tympanic bullae with projecting angles in middle. Paroccipital processes large, as high as tympanic bullae.

Dental formula: $I\frac{3}{3}$; $C\frac{1}{1}$; $Pm\frac{4}{4}$; $M\frac{2}{2}$ = 40.

Lower canines do not project usually beyond alveoli of upper canines when jaws are closed. Lower jaw without third molar (M_3). First upper molar (M^1) with only one tubercle at internal lobe (Figure 32). Lower carnassial tooth (M_1) with one small denticle at posterior edge.

Geographical distribution. Mountain areas of Eastern and Southern Asia from Turkestan (Dzhungarian Ala-Tau, Tien Shan, Eastern Pamirs) and South Siberia (Altai, Eastern Sayans, Yablonovyi and Stanovoi Range, mountains of the Amur area and Maritime Territory) to India, Indochina, Malaya and the Sunda Archipelago (Sumatra, Java and Borneo) in the South.

A   B

FIGURE 32. First upper molar dorsal:

A — Cuon alpinus Pallas; B — Cannis lupus L; 1 — internal tubercle (after G. A. Novikov, 1956).

Systematic notes. The genus C u o n is an aberrant branch of family Canidae. Zittel (1893) considered C u o n related to the African genus L y c a o n (Brooks, 1827) and the American genus I c t i c y o n (Lund, 1843) and included these with some extinct Canidae in the subfamily Simocyoninae. Simpson (1945) included in this family 12 other extinct genera from the Oligocene to the Pleistocene of Europe and North America.

From quarternary fossils in the Nizhneudinsk cave, I. D. Cherskii (1875) described the extinct species C u o n n i s h n e u d e n s i s, closely related to the contemporary C. a l p i n u s Pallas. Contemporary species of C u o n are first known from the Pleistocene of Asia.

The genus contains the following three species: the colthum, C. d u k h u n e n s i s (Sykes, 1831) in India; the buanzu, C. p r i m a e v u s (Hodgson, 1933) on the southern slopes of the eastern Himalayas; and the red dog, C. a l p i n u s (Pallas, 1811).

6. **Cuon alpinus** Pallas (1811). Red dog. (Figure 33, Map VI)

1811. C a n i s a l p i n u s. Pallas, P. S. — Zoographia Rosso-Asiatica, 1, pp. 34 — 35; Maak, R. Puteshestvie po doline reki Ussuri (Voyage in the Valley of the Ussuri River). p. 107, Sankt-Peterburg. 1861; Radde, G. Reisen im Süden von Ost-Siberien, pp. 60 — 62. 1862.

1869. C y o n a l p i n u s. Gray, J. Catalogue of Carnivorous Mammals etc., in the British Museum, p. 184; Greeve, C. Die geographische Verbreitung der Raubthiere, p. 141. 1894; Satunin, K. A. Opredelitel' mlekopitayushchikh Rossiiskoi imperii (Key to Mammals of the Russian Empire). p. 148, Tiflis. 1914; Sowerby, A. The Naturalist in Manchuria, 2 — 3, pp. 45 — 46. 1923; Ognev, S. I. Zveri Vostochnoi Evropy i Severnoi Azii (Animals of Eastern Europe and Northern Asia). 2, pp. 231 — 239. 1931. Figures 61 — 63; Novikov, G. A. Khishchnye mlekopitayushchie fauny SSSR (Carnivore Mammals of the Fauna of the USSR). pp. 86 — 89, Moskva-Leningrad. 1956.

1941. C u o n a l p i n u s. Pocock, R. I. The Fauna of British India. — Mammalia, 2, p. 149; Ellerman, J. R. and T. C. S. Morrison-Scott. Checklist of Palaearctic and Indian Mammals, pp. 233 — 234, London. 1951.

Type and type locality. Vicinity of Uda Ostrog (now Udskoe), lower Uda River.

Diagnosis. Cranial characters and dentition same as for genus. Dorsal side of body rust red, varying only in the tonal intensity.

Measurements. Length of body and head 100 — 113 cm, length of tail 45 — 50 cm, length of hind foot 20 — 23 cm, length of ear 8 — 9 cm.

FIGURE 33. Cuon alpinus Pallas (original)

Skull 171—200 mm long, condylobasal length 170—179 mm, zygomatic width 103.6—112 mm, interorbital width 36.6—40.2 mm, width of muzzle above canines 36.2—40.3 mm, mastoid width 67.2—72.3 mm, height near the tympanic bullae 67.0—71.1 mm, length of upper tooth row 74.0—80.9 mm.

Description. Build doglike, of a small gray wolf. Body moderately long, on relatively high legs. Head with broad, slightly raised forehead; muzzle pointed. Ears pointed, broadly separated. Tail very bushy, less than half length of body and head (Figure 33).

Winter fur very long, soft and dense; summer fur shorter, sparser and coarser.

Color of winter fur varies from pale grayish ocher to bright reddish rust. Throat, chest, flanks and venter reddish brown of varying shades. Outer side of ears colored like body. Tail dorsally more vividly colored. Legs slightly lighter than body.

Color of summer fur less vivid, relatively dull.

Young are dull gray or brownish, with less marked reddish brown tones.

Skull (Figure 34) resembles that of the wolf but is smaller and of slightly different proportions; it is shorter in facial part and braincase is higher. Facial part is about as long as braincase. Height of skull in area of tympanic bullae about half the condylobasal length. Upper outline of skull barely elevated near postorbital processes and descends gradually anteriorly, forming a distinct saddle in middle of the nasals. Longitudinal shallow groove in the middle of the frontals. Postorbital processes with poorly marked dorsal fossae. Braincase relatively broad. Sagittal and occipital crest moderately developed. Posterior margin of anterior palatine foramina lies behind the posterior margin of canines, in any case not

anteriorly.   Foramina are usually longer than longitudinal diameter of
alveoli of upper canines.   Hard palate shorter and broader than in the wolf,
almost half as long as wide behind Pm³ (from the choanal incisure to the
gnathion).   Praesphenoid with broad lateral pterygoid processes and with a
narrow process anteriorly.   Tympanic bullae moderately inflated, with well-
marked corners formed by the slanting posterior internal sides.
Paroccipital processes large, as high as the tympanic bullae.   Lower edge
of the external auditory meatus broad, covering the meatus so that it is not
visible ventrally.   Lower jaw without additional angle (subangulus) in its
posterior part below the angular process.

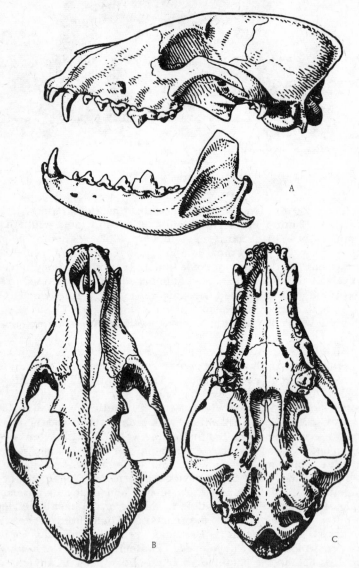

FIGURE 34. Skull of Cuon alpinus Pallas (original):

A — lateral; B — dorsal; C — ventral.

Dental formula and structure of the teeth were described in the diagnosis of the genus.

Systematic notes. The red dog is very rare and collections in Soviet museums possess only a few specimens. This species has therefore been only little studied systematically. Its relationships with the South Asian red dogs are not clear. This is not discussed here, but the red dog is certainly a polytypic species.

Geographical distribution. Mountains of Central and Eastern Asia and adjacent areas of Kazakhstan and South Siberia.

The following records are known from Siberia (Map VI).

It has been found repeatedly on the Altai. Bunge (1834) recorded it from the upper reaches of the Katun River and stated that it probably occurs along the Upper Uimon. The species does not occur here according to recent data, but occurs occasionally in the adjacent Kosh-Agach District (Nasimovich, 1949).

According to Gebler (1837) the red dog occurs near the sources of the Argut River and on the Chuya River, where V. V. Sapozhnikov found it in July 1897—1898 in the Yassatter valley in the Altai and in the valley of a tributary of the Belaya Berel, the River Proezdnaya (Koshchenko, 1899). The species is very rare on the Bukhtarma River, according to N. I. Yablonskii (1902). A. M. Kolosov (1939) states that it occurs rarely in the upper reaches of the Bashkaus and Chulyshman rivers and on the neighboring Mongolian ranges.

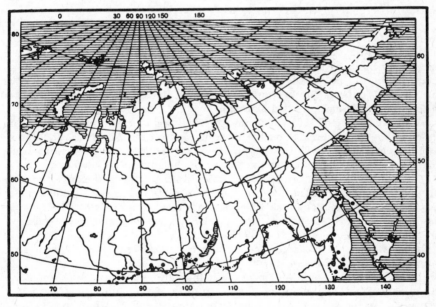

MAP VI. Geographical distribution of Cuon alpinus Pallas in Siberia

B. A. Kuznetsov (1948) found the red dog in neighboring areas of Kazakhstan, in the central part of the Tarbagatai and on the Saur Mountains. G. I. Polyakov (1941) recorded it from mountains near Lake Marka-Kul.

It does not occur in the northern Altai, according to Kashchenko, and is probably also absent in the central Altai. It does not occur in the former Altai Reserve, according to P. B. Yurgenson (1938).

It is rare in the mountain tundra on the Western Sayan, according to A. I Yanushevich and K. T. Yurlov (1949). A. I. Yanushevich (1952) thinks that the red dog occurs occasionally in the mountains of the Tannu-Ola Range.

It occurs in the alpine zone of the Eastern Sayan, according to D. K. Solov'ev (1920) and I. N. Shukhov (1925). K. I. Gromov (1951) records it in the central part of this area.

According to Pallas (1811) it occurs in the mountains near the sources of the Yenisei and Lena. According to Radde (1862) it inhabits the mountains along the eastern tributaries of the upper Yenisei; it rarely occurs in the Naku-Daban and Chernyi Irkut mountains, and on the right shore of the Irkut and on the Kharber elevation; it has been recorded from the Dzhida Mountains.

It occurs in the steppe near Soktuyi and Kulusutai in Transbaikalia, according to Radde (1862), but this has not been confirmed by later authors (Kuznetsov, 1929). It occurs on the southern end of the Yablonovyi Range and is numerous where the mountains reach the Amur River.

It is widely distributed and locally common in the Far East, but there are few records. Maak (1861) assumed that its northern boundary is the Stanovoi Range and that the red dog is common in mountains north of the Amur River. However, it is found occasionally in mountains on the Bureya River according to G. Radde (1862).

Pallas (1811) recorded it from Uda Ostrog (now Udskoe) in the lower reaches of the Uda River. R. Maak (1861) thought that it occurs but is never numerous in the Khekhtsyr Mountains near the mouth of the Ussuri River, in the mountains near Aua, and on the Tankhe Range. It occurs more frequently on Cape Kalang and in the mountains of Kech and is very rare in the Akuli Mountains further up the Ussuri. It is again rather common in the Situkhu Mountains and Daubikha.

A. M. Nikol'skii (1889) wrote that the red dog occurs in mountains on the shore of the Tatar Strait, on the Ussuri, and on the Amur. V. K. Arsen'ev (1950) found it on the Gorelaya River (a tributary of the Syao-Kem River), and it occurs occasionally in the valley of the Iman River according to N. T. Zolotarev (1936). K. Plyater-Plokhotskii (1936) records it from the Olginsk, Voroshilovsk, and Yakovlevsk districts in the Maritime Territory. It was found on the Yankovskii Peninsula, near Sidemi Bay and Slovyanskaya Bay (coll. Zool. Inst. Acad. Sciences USSR). It was also reported from this area by E. A. Bikhner in 1897.

It is common in Sakhalin, according to L. Schrenck (1858), and also inhabits the Kunashir and Iturup Islands and the southern Kuriles. Schrenck bases his opinion on the fact that the red dog is apparently known to the Sakhalin Gilyaks and on the similarity of the name for Cuon alpinus in the Gilyak and Japanese languages. A. M. Nikol'skii (1889) wrote that the animal is distributed to the southern tip of the island.

Recent studies in Sakhalin do not confirm its occurrence in this area.

Subspecies. Two subspecies are known in the Soviet Union.

6a.   **Cuon alpinus alpinus** Pallas (1811).   East Siberian red dog

Synonymy, bibliography and data on the type locality have been given in the description of the species.

Diagnosis.   Size large; length of skull 190.0 mm.   Frons projecting. Nasals relatively long, av. 66.0 mm.   Winter fur intensely rust red.

Measurements (two specimens).   Skull 191—200 mm long; maximum width of braincase 68.0—68.3 mm; facial length 76.3—80.9 mm; length of nasals 66.0—71.5 mm.

Geographical distribution.   Transbaikalia, Amur area and Maritime Territory.

Material examined. Two specimens.

6b.   **Cuon alpinus hesperius** Afanas'ev and Zolotarev (1935).   Central Asian red dog

1935.   Cyon alpinus hesperius.   Afanas'ev, A. V. and N. T. Zolotarev.   Novye dannye po sistematike i rasprostraneniyu krasnogo volka (New Data on the Systematics and Distribution of the Red Dog).— Izvestiya Akademii Nauk SSSR, Otdelenie Matematicheskich i Estestvenykh Nauk, Seriya VII, pp. 425—428.

Type and type locality.   Skull no. 15229, pelt no. 23894, in the collection of the Zoological Institute of the Academy of Sciences of the USSR, ♂, coll. Nezhivov.   Dzhety Su, Aksai.

Diagnosis.   Smaller than the preceding subspecies: length of skull 180 mm.   Forehead flat.   Nasals relatively short, about 57 mm.   Winter fur dull with little developed rust red tone.

Measurements (five specimens).   Maximum length of skull 171—194 mm; maximum width of braincase 61.0—67.5 mm; facial length 70.0—81.5 mm; length of nasals 53.2—62.0 mm.

Geographical distribution.   Altai, Tien Shan.

Material examined.   Eight specimens.

Biology.   Data on the biology very scanty.   Inhabits high mountains, where it occurs mainly in forests and locally in the alpine zone above the tundra.   It occurs in winter mainly on slopes with little snow or in localities with deeper snow.

Feeds on goats, sheep, deer, etc.   The red dog occurs in packs, probably families.

There are no data on its reproduction.

This is a very cautious and cunning animal.   It is rarely seen by man. Its voice is a loud howl.

Economic importance.   The red dog is caught only occasionally and in small numbers, as it occurs in uninhabited localities.   Red dogs have caused occasional damage to deer-breeding farms.

II.   Family   **URSIDAE**   Gray (1825) — Bears

1825.   Ursidae.   Gray.   Thomson's Annals of Philosophy, XXVI, p. 339.

Description. The family includes the largest representatives of the order. Body length 1.5 — 2.5 m; weight to 300 — 400 kg (brown bear) and 600 — 800 kg (polar bear). Build of body powerful, massive and heavy. Head large, broad; muzzle pointed. Eyes small. Ears small, rounded. Neck thick and short. Tail very short, not projecting from the fur. Legs of moderate length, plantigrade, with five toes; digits with large, non-retractile claws. Three pair of teats. Fur dense, long, of uniform color, varying from white (polar bear) to black (black bear).

Skull large, massive, with well-developed zygomatic arches. Tympanic bullae small, flattened dorsally, with their internal cavity not divided by a septum. Lower jaw with a small alveolar process below the angular process (Figure 35).

Dental formula: $I\frac{2-3}{3}$; $C\frac{1}{1}$; $Pm\frac{4}{3-4}$; $M\frac{2}{3}$ = 40 — 42.

Molars are strong, with broad and low crowns; masticatory surfaces flat, with blunt tubercles. Carnassial teeth little modified, small, and with little-marked, blunt tubercles. Upper carnassial tooth without additional internal lobe.

Systematics. The origin of bears and their relationship to other Carnivora is not clear. Arctocyon, a creodont of the Lower Eocene, is rather close to the bears in its omnivorous tuberculate teeth and the structure of its skull. Fossils of Ursidae are known from the Miocene of Europe and from the Pliocene of Asia. The genus most closely related to Ursus is Ursavus, with three molars characterized by flat crowns with low, blunt tubercles.

The contemporary family Ursidae is divided into 6 genera: 1. Ursus L., the brown bear (North Africa, Eurasia and North America); 2. Thalarctos Gray, the polar bear (islands and shore of the Arctic Ocean); 3. Selenarctos Heude, the black bear (Asia and North America); 4. Tremarctos Gervais, the South American bear (Andes, South America); 5. Melursus Mejer, the Indian bear (tropics of Southern Asia; 6. Helarctos Horsfield, the Malayan bear (tropics of Southern Asia).

Species of the first three genera occur in the Soviet Union, including Siberia.

Geographical distribution. Northern Hemisphere. In the Old World, to North Africa (Atlas Mountains) and Malayan Archipelago in the South. In the New World, to the Andes (South America).

Biology. Bears may be divided into two distinct ecological groups. The first group includes the most specialized species, — the polar bear (Thalarctos), typically stenotopic, associated with the shores of islands and of the continent and with floating ice in the Arctic Ocean, and thus a semi-aquatic form. The second group includes all the other species, these being eurytopic, inhabiting various types of forests, mountains with cliffs, etc., and terrestrial or semi-arboreal. Most bears are polyphagous. The structure of the teeth shows their adaptation to animal and vegetable food. Their large canines may kill large prey and the low molars, with their broad and flat masticatory surface and without sharp cutting cusps, are well adapted for masticating vegetable and animal food. The polar bear alone seldom eats vegetable food, its food consisting mainly of marine animals, fish, birds, eggs, etc.

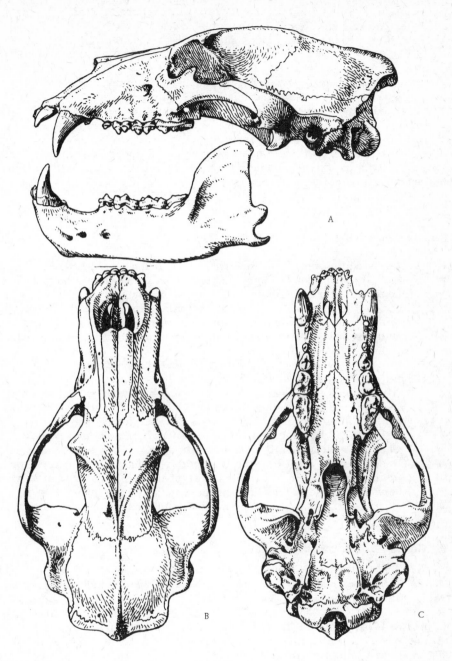

FIGURE 35. Skull of Ursus arctos L. (original):

A — lateral; B — dorsal; C — ventral.

Bears hibernate in cold localities but are easily awakened. Hibernation is connected with lack of food availability in winter. Bears do not hibernate in countries with little or no snow.

Birth of the young takes place usually in a den, in the middle of winter or in spring. The young are born blind. The litter usually contains 1—5 young.

Smell and hearing are well developed, sight is markedly weaker. The intelligence of bears is high and they are readily trained.

Practical importance. This differs according to local conditions. Bears are hunted commercially in some areas, and in others are hunted for sport. The pelts are used for clothing and carpets; fat and meat are used for food. The bones, tendons and intestines are used by the local population. Damage caused to livestock, bee keeping and crops is usually small and may be important only locally.

Key to Genera of Family Ursidae in Siberia

1 (2). Color white or white with a straw yellow tone. Soles covered with hair. Length of two upper molars less than width of bony palate between anterior molars. Biology semi-aquatic . . . . Genus **Thalarctos** — Polar bear (p. 141)

2 (1). Color dark. Soles bare. Length of two upper molars greater than width of bony palate between anterior molars. Biology terrestrial 3

3 (4). Fur glossy black. Chest with a transverse white spot. Ears large, projecting distinctly from the fur. Muzzle short: distance from anterior margin of orbit to anterior edge of alveolus of first incisor less than distance between ends of postorbital processes. Biology semi-arboreal. . . . Genus **Selenarctos**—Black bear (p. 133)

4 (3). Color of fur varying from dark brown or black to straw yellow. Chest of adults usually without white spot. Ears small and round. Nasal part of skull longer: distance from anterior margin of orbit to anterior margin of alveolus of first incisor greater than distance between ends of postorbital processes. Biology terrestrial . . . . Genus **Ursus**—Brown bear (p. 83)

6. Genus URSUS Linnaeus (1858). Brown bear

1858. U r s u s. Linnaeus, C. Syst. Nat., ed. 10, p. 47; Miller, G. S. Catal. Mamm. Western Europe, p. 285, London. 1912; Pocock, R. J.— Proc. Zool. Soc., p. 940, London. 1914; Idem., Journ. Bomb. Nat. Hist. Soc., 36, 2 p. 101. 1932; Idem., Fauna Brit. India, Mamm., 2, p. 169. 1914; Ognev, S. I. Zveri Vostochnoi Evropy i Severnoi Azii (Animals of Eastern Europe and Northern Asia). 2, p. 14. 1931; Allen, G. M. Mammals of China and Mongolia, p. 325, New York. 1938.

1864. E u a r c t o s. Gray, J.— Proc. Zool. Soc., p. 692, London (described as subgenus of U r s u s — U r s u s a m e r i c a n u s Pall); Merriam, H.— Proc. Biol. Soc. Washington, 10, p. 65. 1896 (as subgenus of

Ursus); Pocock, R. J.— Ann. Mag. Nat. Hist., Ser. 9, 1,. p. 384. 1918 (as genus); Allen, G. M. . Mammals of China and Mongolia, p. 330, New York. 1938 (as genus).

1864. Myrmarctos. Gray, J. Loc. cit., p. 694 (Myrmarctos eversmanni Gray = Ursus arctos Linnaeus).

1898. Ursarctos. Heude.— Mém. concernant l'histoire naturelle d'Empire Chinois, 4, 1, p. 17 (yesoenis).

1898. Melanarctos. Heude.— Loc. cit., p. 18 (Melanarctos cavifrons Heude = Ursus lasiotus Gray).

1914. Tremarctos. Pocock, R. J.— Proc. Zool. Soc. London, p. 932 (partim).

1917. Arcticonus. Pocock, R. J.— Ann. Mag. Nat. Hist., Ser. 8, 20, p. 129 (Ursus thibetanus G. Cuvier).

1923. Mylarctos. Lönnberg, E.— Proc. Zool. Soc. London, p. 91 (Ursus pruinosus Blyth).

FIGURE 36. Heads of bears (from N. A. Bobrinskii):

A — Ursus arctos L.; B — Selenarctos thibetanus Cuvier; C — Thalarctos maritimus Phipps.

Type species. Ursus arctos Linnaeus (1758).

Diagnosis. Size large. Weight of adults 100—480 kgs. Legs relatively high. Head larger than in polar and black bears, with a broader forehead and blunt muzzle (Figure 36); frontal area usually markedly elevated above muzzle. Ears small, round, densely covered with fur and not projecting laterally. Tail very short, covered by fur. Soles of feet bare. Fur dense, long, sometimes shaggy. Fur color varying from dark brown (almost black) to light clay yellow. Chest rarely with a white spot, which sometimes extends to the shoulders. Such spots are usually found in young bears, particularly in cubs. Muzzle relatively long: distance from anterior margin of orbit to anterior margin of median incisor alveolus greater than distance between ends of postorbital processes.

Dental formula: $I\frac{3}{3}$; $C\frac{1}{1}$; $Pm\frac{4}{4}$; $M\frac{2}{3}$ = 42.

Molars large, with broad and long crowns and with flatter and more bluntly tuberculate masticatory surface than in the polar bear.

Length of two upper molars ($M^1 + M^2$) not greater than width of bony palate between first molars (M^1). Last lower molar (M_3) narrow posteriorly, rounded triangular (Figure 37).

Biology. Terrestrial.

Geographical distribution. Northern Hemisphere from the krummholz zone south to North Africa, the Himalayas, North China, and Mexico.

Systematics. The species of genus Ursus are less specialized than those of Thalarctos in external characters and in dental structure,

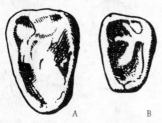

A   B

FIGURE 37. Posterior lower molar of bears (original):

A — Ursus arctos L.; B — Selenarctos thibetanus Cuvier.

particularly in the less marked carnivorous type of carnassials and the less developed tubercles on the molars. Fossils of Ursus are known from the Pliocene of Europe, Asia and North America.

The species composition of genus Ursus is difficult to determine. A revision of the family Ursidae is necessary.

Bears are characterized by a wide range of variation. Their systematics have not been thoroughly worked out and are a classical example of unrestrained creation of species. The number of the species described and of intraspecific forms is extremely large. Thus, according to Merriam (1918), North America is inhabited by 85 species of brown bears. According to S. I. Ognev (1931) the palearctic fauna contains 19 species and subspecies of brown bears, and he records the following 6 species from the Soviet Union: 1. Ursus arctos L., brown bear; 2. U. piscator Pucheran, Kamchatka bear; 3. U. mandschuricus Heude, Manchurian bear; 4. U. jesoensis Lydekker, Sakhalin bear; 5. U. pamirensis Ognev, Pamir bear; and 6. U. pruinosus Blyth, pika-eating bear.

Study of the literature and examination of material shows that most of the forms described are not valid. A radical revision of the whole family is necessary, but that is not the object of this book.

Study of new material and material owned by S. I. Ognev has proved that the above forms belong to the same species, though some of them may be regarded as subspecies.

The genus Ursus is thus represented in the Soviet fauna by the single species Ursus arctos L.

7. **Ursus arctos** Linnaeus (1758). Brown bear
(Figure 38, Map VII)

1758. Ursus arctos. Linnaeus, C. Systema Naturae, 10 ed., p. 47; Pallas, P. S. Zoographia Rosso-Asiatica, Vol. 1; pp. 64—69, Petropoli. 1811—1831; Middendorf, A. F.— In: Yu. Simashko. Russkaya fauna, p. 187 ff (Plates XI, XIA, XIB, XIC), St. Petersburg; Schrenck, L. Reisen im Amur-Lande, pp. 7—16, St. Petersburg. 1858; Kashchenko, N F. Opredelitel' mlekopitayushchikh zhivotnykh Tomskogo kraya (Key to Mammals of the Tomsk Territory). p. 13, Tomsk. 1900; Turkin, N V. and K. A. Satunin. Zveri Rossii (Animals of Russia). p. 56. 1910; Adlerberg, G. P. Khishchnye zveri (Carnivora, Fissipedia) Arktiki ((Carnivora, Fissipedia) of the Arctic). In: Zveri Arktiki pod redaktsiei prof. N A. Smirnova, pp. 279—296, Leningrad, Izd. Glavsevmorputi. figs. 1—3. 1935; Bannikov, A. G. Mlekopitayushchie Mongolskoi Narodnoi Respubliki (Mammals of Mongolian People's Republic). pp. 107—109, Moskva. Izdatel'stvo AN SSSR. 1954; Novikov, G. A. Khishchnye mlekopitayushchie fauny SSSR (Carnivore Mammals of the USSR). pp. 91—99. Moskva, Izdatel'stvo AN SSSR. figs. 8, 50—56 (partim). 1956.

1824. Ursus collaris. Cuvier et Geoffroy.— Hist. Nat. Mammifer., p. 42. pl. 212 (Siberia).

1840. Ursus longirostris. Eversmann, E.— Bull. Soc. Imp. nat. d'Moscou, p. 11; Eversmann, E. Estestvennaya istoriya mlekopitayushchikh Orenburgskogo kraya (Natural History of Mammals of the Orenburg Territory). p. 44, Kazan. 1850.

1844. Ursus ferox. Temminck. Fauna Japonica, p. 29. (nec Rafinesque, 1817).

1855. Ursus piscator. Pucheran.— Revue Mag. Zool., 7, p. 392. (near Petropavlovsk in Kamchatka); Ognev, S. I. Mlekopitayushchie severo-vostochnoi Sibiri (Mammals of Northeastern Siberia). pp. 30—34, Vladivostok. 1926; Ognev, S. I. Zveri Vostochnoi Evropy i Severnoi Azii (Animals of Eastern Europe and Northern Asia). 2, pp. 86—98. Figs. 23—26. 1931.

1867. Ursus lasiotus. Gray.— Ann. Mag. Nat. Hist., 3, 20, p. 301 (North China); Lönnberg, E.— Proc. Zool. Soc. London, p. 91. 1923.

1898. Ursus mandschuricus. Heude.— Mém. H. N. Emp. Chinois, Chang-Hai, 4, pp. 23—24. pl. 7, Figs. 1—1e (Maritime Territory); Sowerby.— Journ. Mammal., 1, 5, p. 225. 1920.

1901. Melanarctos cavifrons. Heude. Loc. cit., 5. pl. 1, figs. 6—8 (Tsitsihan, northwest of Harbin).

1920. Spelaeus piscator. Sowerby.— Journ. Mammal., 1, 5, p. 231.

1920. Spelaeus cavifrons. Sowerby. Loc. cit., p. 225; Sowerby. The Naturalist in Manchuria, 2—3, p. 56. 1923.

Type and type locality. Described from Sweden.

Diagnosis. The main characters of the species are the same as those given above for the genus.

Measurements. Length of body to 244 cm, height at the withers 135 cm, length of tail 21 cm, length of ears 15 cm, length of hind foot 28 cm. Weight to 400 kg.

Size of skull (74 male and 42 female specimens) as follows. Total length: males 311—455 mm, females 279— 379 mm; condylobasal length: males 300—419 mm, females 237—378 mm; zygomatic width: males 188—277 mm, females 147—242 mm; interorbital width: males 74—108 mm, females 57—92 mm; width of forehead: males 97—162 mm, females 81—127 mm; postorbital width: males 68—91 mm, females 63—81 mm; mastoid width: males 134—220 mm, females 103—195 mm; width of rostrum above canines: males 69—103 mm, females 57—93 mm; width between infraorbital foramina: males 72—95 mm, females 59—83 mm; length of upper tooth row: males 116—151 mm, females 107—142 mm; length of three lower molars: males 59—76 mm, females 59—74 mm.

Description. A large animal of heavy build. Head large with broad convex forehead and conical, blunt muzzle. Eyes small, short-sighted and widely separated. Ears small and round. Feet of moderate length. Callus on soles of forefeet not divided. Middle toes of hind feet not fused in basal third. Claws curved and long.

Fur relatively dense, particularly winter fur, shaggy, moderately long, consisting of stiff guard hairs and dense underfur. Hairs on muzzle short, gradually becoming longer posteriorly and on the body. Hair very long on withers and legs, particularly on thighs. Ears with dense, short hairs and projecting distinctly from the fur.

Winter fur denser than summer fur. Underfur well developed. Fur becomes coarser with age and is short in old bears.

Fur color very variable, from dark brown (almost black) to light brownish gray or straw-yellowish, with brown underfur visible through the fur.

Ears dark brown against light frontoparietal area. Legs darker than body, dark brown or black.

Young animals, particularly cubs, occasionally have a narrow white collar at base of neck. Collar usually disappears with age, persisting only rarely as a diffuse light patch.

Summer fur duller. Color becomes more reddish brown in old bears. Claws large, strong, curved, and brown or blackish with occasional pale yellow streaks. Length of claws to 100 mm.

Skull (Figure 35) large and massive, with widely separated zygomatic arches, relatively short facial part, moderately long frontal area, narrow but long and deep braincase. Upper outline of skull convex, higher in frontal area, usually gradually descending posteriorly and more steeply anteriorly so that there is a distinct saddle between interorbital and nasal part. Rostrum short and broad; distance from anterior margin of orbit to alveolus of median incisor almost one quarter of condylobasal length;

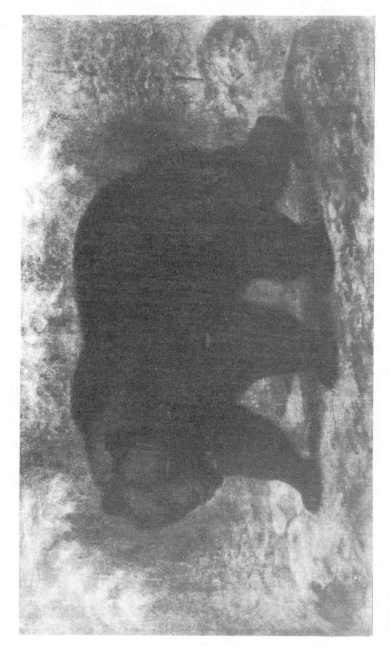

FIGURE 38. Ursus arctos L. (specimen of the Moscow Zoo). Painting by V.A. Vatagin

width of rostrum above canines usually greater than width between infraorbital foramina, rarely as long as this or slightly less. Nasal openings broad, markedly slanting posteriorly. Frontal area broad, more or less longitudinally concave, rarely flat or slightly convex. Postorbital processes short, massive, slightly curved backwards, directed laterally and ventrally. Postorbital area tapering markedly posteriorly. Braincase long, slightly inflated, and laterally compressed anteriorly. Sagittal and occipital crests varying with age and sex and individually. These crests are usually little marked in younger animals and in females but they may be strongly developed in males, particularly old males; sagittal crest divides into two branches in bregma area, extending to postorbital process and bordering frontal area posteriorly. Zygomatic processes of squamosae massive and fused with the upper margin of mastoid process. Zygomatic arches thick and laterally compressed; they are most widely separated in their posterior part, where zygomatic width is 60−65 % of condylobasal length. Orbits relatively small, rounded-oval, oblong in dorsoventral direction and at an obtuse angle to frontal plane of skull. Infraorbital foramina very small, slitlike, and vertically oblong, with their greatest diameter being barely $\frac{1}{3}$ the distance from their upper margins to orbit. Nasal very short and broad, tapering posteriorly, extending to frontal processes of supraorbital or slightly beyond them. Nasal processes of frontals and posterior ends of premaxillaries fused at about middle of nasals. Hard palate flat, rather narrow, uniformly wide and extending posteriorly beyond last molars for about $\frac{2}{3}$ of its width. Choanal incisure oval, concave anteriorly. Posterior choanal foramen very variable; height sometimes greater, sometimes smaller, and sometimes equal to width. Mesopterygoid fossa narrow, about $\frac{2}{3}$ as wide as long. Pterygoid processes slender but distinct. Mastoid processes very large and massive. Tympanic bullae flat, irregularly triangular, or trapezoidal. Auditory meati small and covered from above by zygomatic process of temporal. Basisphenoid distinctly concave. Paroccipital processes well developed and projecting markedly above surface of tympanic bullae. Foramen magnum relatively small. Occipital condyles large and massive. Lower jaw broad and massive, with a large and strong coronoid process.

Skulls of females not as large as in males, and zygomatic arches less widely separated; they are less angular, crests are less developed, and sagittal crest does not reach coronoid suture.

Teeth relatively small. Incisors of different types, with lateral incisors markedly larger than inner incisors; crowns of lower lateral incisors have additional tubercles. Canines thick and large, their longitudinal diameter at base about half width of palate between canines. Lower canines shorter than upper canines and more curved. First 3 premolars rudimentary; they usually fall out with age and their alveoli become closed. Upper carnassial tooth (Pm^4) $\frac{2}{3}$ size of first molar (M^1); its crown has 3 low blunt tubercles and it has two roots. Molars low, broad, and with blunt tubercles. First upper molar about $\frac{1}{3}$ shorter than last molar. Lower carnassial tooth (M$_1$) with long and narrow crown, almost as long as the second lower molar (M$_2$), and about a third less wide. Third lower molar (M$_3$) roundedly oval with truncate posterior outer part, about $\frac{2}{3}$ as wide as long.

Os penis massive, straight or slightly curved, gradually tapering anteriorly, and with blunt rounded ends and triangular transverse section; 138 — 145 mm long, and 11 — 12 mm wide at base.

Systematic notes. We accept the view that the brown bear in Europe, Siberia, and adjacent parts of Asia belongs to a single species Ursus arctos L., which may be divided into local forms. The brown bear is very polymorphous, the large number of synonyms in the list proving its great variation. In addition to age, sex and geographical variation, there is a wide range of individual variations. The entire organism of the bear is subject to these variations, from its general habitus to structural details of the skull.

Individual variations. There are several types of habitus of the brown bear, the extreme variants of which are the leptosome and the eurysome types. The first type is characterized by a narrow, long and lean body. The second type has a loose constitution, a broader and shorter body, and shorter legs.

Size and weight vary similarly. There are giant specimens, and dwarfs.

Variations of habitus among bears in the same locality were recorded by A. F. Middendorf and others. These variations were made the basis for the creation of species, all of which have proved to be invalid. Even recently some authors (Dinnik, 1914; Satunin, 1915; Smirnov, 1916; Ognev, 1931) have seen two forms of the brown bear in the Caucasus as subspecies: a large form (U. a. caucasicus Smirnov), and a small form (U.a. meridionalis Middendorf) in the same area and biotope. G. P. Adlerberg (1935) showed that these forms are only extreme variants of the subspecies called U.a.caucasicus Smirnov (1916). E. Eversmann (1840, 1850) considered the large and small forms known as "scavenger" and "anteater" as different species. According to Eversmann the "scavenger" is very tall, weighs 324 — 486 kg, and has a short muzzle and projecting forehead, while the "anteater" is half as large and has a long muzzle and flat forehead. The first form was named by E. Eversmann Ursus arctos, the second form being named Ursus longirostris. However, the characters used by Eversmann have no systematic value.

A. F. Middendorf (Yu. Simashko, 1951), who studied a large amount of material in detail, concluded that the length of the muzzle and the form of the forehead cannot be used to distinguish specimens from the same area, though cranial characters do distinguish bears from distant geographical areas, e. g., bears from the Baltic area as against bears from the shores of Bering Strait.

N.A. Mel'nitskii (1915) states that the form of the head, the size, and the fur color of bears of the same age vary markedly in the same locality. Mel'nitskii observed during 30 years in the Novgorod Province that "adult bears differ markedly in head form, fur color, weight, and build. Long- and short-muzzled, light and dark brown, and even almost black specimens were found, and weight ranged from 40 to 225 kg. There were bears with short and disproportionately wide bodies and the reverse. One of the particularly large-boned bears had a forehead 35.6 cm wide between the ears, and very broad feet so wide apart, that it appeared to be a very large animal, while in fact it was only 177.8 cm long from the nose to the root of the tail and weighed only 147.4 kg."

There are frequently bears with a very long or short muzzle and with a very narrow or wide forehead. "Among the latter there were specimens

in which the forehead was out of proportion because of its width"
(Mel'nitskii, 1915).

The above data are confirmed by numerous observations in nature and in
zoological gardens in the European USSR, Siberia and Central Asia.

The skull of the brown bear also shows wide individual variation.
However, the cranial characters vary less than the external characters.

Both external characters and individual variations of the skull have been
used to create taxons of various rank, from the little different "natio" to the
species. Even at present, species and intraspecific forms have been
described from a few skulls. Reexamination of the material has proved that
the features on which authors based their descriptions were of no
systematic value.

The skull of the bear varies more than in other animals in sculpture,
proportions of the parts, and size (Figures 39 — 42). Skulls of bears
of different ages from the same locality may have weakly developed
crests and other juvenile traits, short and long muzzles, widely or narrowly
separated zygomatic arches, flat, concave or even convex foreheads,
occipital and sagittal crests of different development and so-called
"breaks," and markedly varying cranial measurements. It has been
observed repeatedly that a skull with the characters of one form may be
found in the area of distribution of another form. A. F. Middendorf recorded
a bear from the Peterburg region with the characters of
U. a. meridionalis Middendorf, which inhabits the Caucasus, and our
collection contains a skull of U. a. jeniseensis Ognev which closely
resembles that of U. a. beringianus Middendorf.

The individual variation of the bear develops in the direction of
geographical variation and masks it in the same manner that age variation at
some stages of ontogenesis masks sexual dimorphism. The cranial
variations of U. arctos are interconnected.

The size and shape of the skull of the bear reach their final development
and systematic significance in adult animals, when the sutures between the
bones disappear. The elements of the skull (frontal area, sagittal, occipital
and other crests, processes and zygomatic arches) cease to grow and the
proportions between the parts of the skull and its sculpture become definitely
established. Only at this stage are sexual dimorphism and systematic
characters fully developed, with the skull assuming the specific form
characteristic of the species and the intraspecific forms. Systematic
conclusions made without consideration of these facts are of no validity.

The study of a large number of skulls has proved that only size can be used
for systematic purposes. This character, together with characters of the
fur (structure and color) and their predominance in the population
determine the subspecies of Russian bears.

The determination of U. arctos subspecies according to the above
principles is difficult because of material shortage. There are not enough
skulls in the collections for the selection of series from different localities
comparable by age and sex, which are large enough to be treated
statistically. Some questions therefore remain open (e.g., the systematic
status of the Kolyma bear), or have to be decided provisionally (e.g., the status
of the Sakhalin bear).

The geographical variation of the brown bear shows that, towards the
East, its body and skull tend to become larger and the fur tends to become
longer and deeper in color.

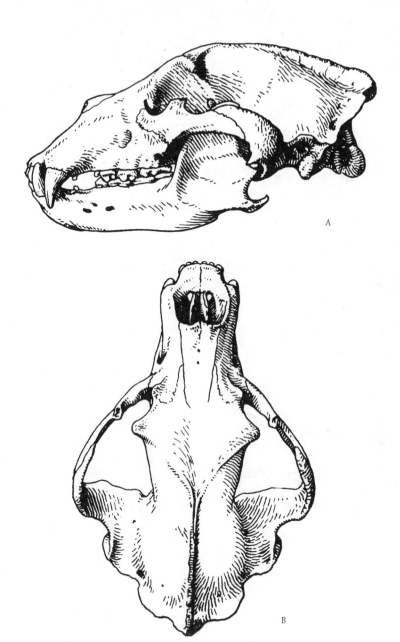

FIGURE 39. Skull of Ursus arctos L.:

A — lateral; B — dorsal. Specimen No. 3239, coll. S. U. Stroganov, Vakh River, V. N. Nadeev (original).

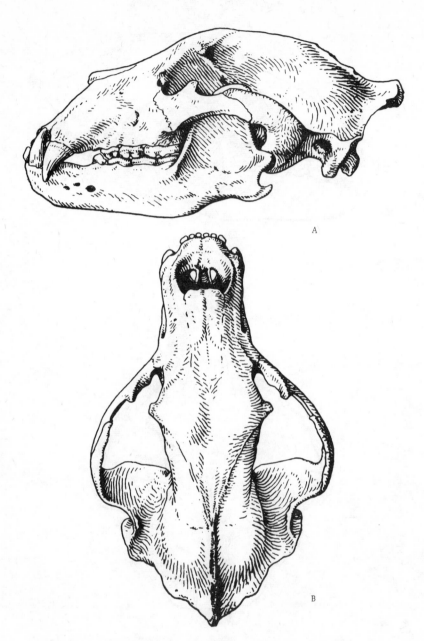

A

B

FIGURE 40. Skull of Ursus arctos L.:

A — lateral; B — dorsal. Specimen No. 3248, coll. S.U. Stroganov, Turukhansk (original).

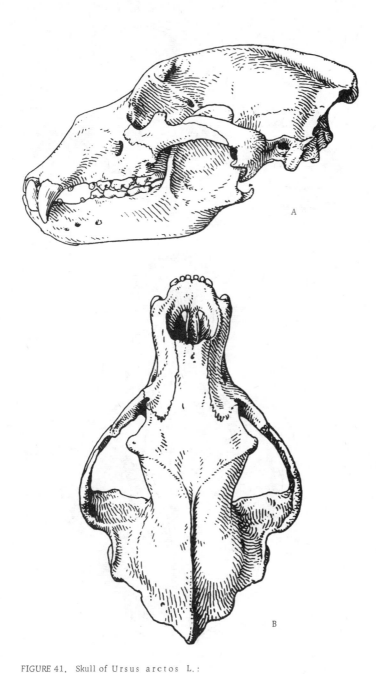

FIGURE 41. Skull of Ursus arctos L.:

A — lateral; B — dorsal. Specimen No. 4151, coll. S. U. Stroganov, western slope of the Dzhugdyr. G. A. Fedoseev (original).

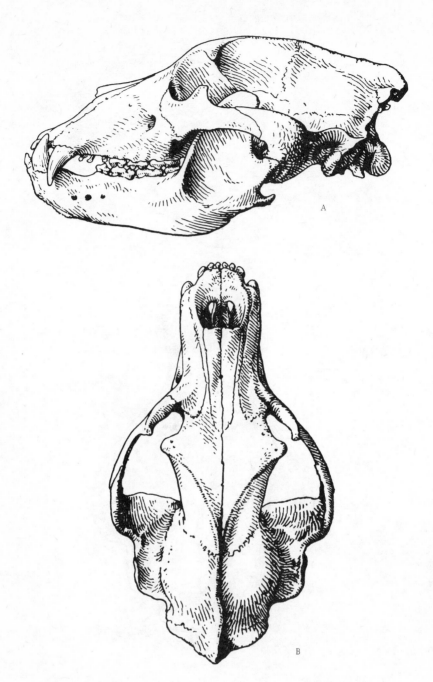

FIGURE 42. Skull of Ursus arctos L.:

A — lateral; B — dorsal. Specimen No. 2552, coll. S. U. Stroganov. Okhotsk coast. G. A. Fedoseev (original).

Geographical distribution. Forest areas of Europe, North Africa (Atlas Mountains), and Central, Southwest, and North Asia (including the Far East).

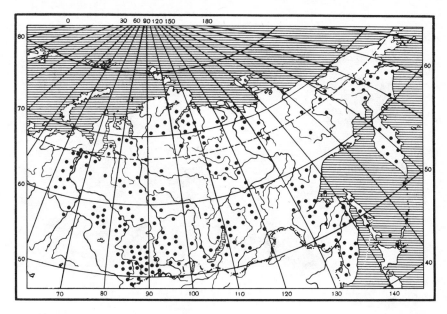

MAP VII. Geographical distribution of Ursus arctos L. in Siberia

In Siberia the bear inhabits the entire forest zone from the Urals to the Pacific, including Sakhalin, Karagin Island, the Shantar Islands, and part of the Kurile chain.

The altitudinal range of the bear in Siberia, according to G. I. Radde (1862), reaches 2,400 m in the Eastern Sayan and 1,700 m in the Yablonovyi Range. G. A. Fedoseev found bears at an altitude of 2,000 m in the Stanovoi Range. The bear is found in Kamchatka, according to Yu. V. Averin (1948), from the shore to altitudes of about 2,000 m. It is not rare at 1,200 m in the mountains on the northeastern shore of Lake Baikal, according to Turov (1936).

Records of the distribution of the brown bear in Siberia are given in Map VII.

The bear was recorded by E. Hofman near 67° N lat. in the northern Urals, according to Brandt (1856). According to Flerov (1929) it is widely distributed in the Northern Urals northwards to the last larch forests on the Lesser or wooded Urals in the area of the Soba River, from which area it enters the tundra in summer. It occurs in the valleys of the Voikar and Syn rivers and is common in the valley of the Bol'shaya Kharuta, but is particularly numerous in the upper reaches of the Lyapin River and of its right tributary the Man'ya.

According to V. M. Sdobnikov (1937) it does not occur on the Yamal but does occur on the Ob-Taz Peninsula, penetrating the tundra there far beyond the

tree line (Figure 43). Bears have for example been found in the valley
of the Epoko River (in summer and autumn 1935). A recently dug den
of a bear was found in a small valley in the same year.

FIGURE 43. Valley of the River Malaya Kheta, Gyda Peninsula. Bear biotope.
Photo by V. I. Telegin

According to V. N. Skalon (1931), the bear is occasionally found in the
West Siberian forest tundra on the right bank of the Ob, and enters the
tundra during its summer migrations, occasionally reaching the Ob and Taz
bays.

According to S. P. Naumov (1931) it is common in the forests of the
watershed between the Taz and the Yenisei rivers to Sidorovskaya Pristan'
(66° N lat.), where it is hunted by the local population. The bear is rare
further north in the southern forest tundra and is not found there every year.
The northernmost recorded occurrence of a bear is on the middle reaches of
the Poelovo River (near 68° N lat.).

Bears are common throughout the taiga of the West Siberian plains,
except at the southern periphery of the taiga (at the boundary of the forest
steppe), where they are absent or very rare.

The bear is common in the valley of the Lower Ob. It has been found on
the left shore near the village of Muzhi (between Beregovoi and Salekhard,
(coll. Zool. Mus. Moscow Univ.). V. V. Raevskii (1947) recorded the bear
as common in the former Konda-Sosva Reserve.

L. G. Kaplanov (1935) found bears on the Demyanka River. Bears were
common throughout the taiga in the Ob-Yenisei watershed and were
locally numerous in thinly populated areas.

Bears are very common on the upper reaches of the Polui, Nadym, Pur,
and Taz rivers, and our collection contains material from the valleys
of the Vakh and the Taz rivers.

FIGURE 44. Siberian stone pine taiga in the valley of the Irtysh River. Bear biotope.
Photo by K. T. Yurlov

S. M. Chugunov (1915) and I. D. Kiris (1934) report bears numerous in the
Surgut taiga.

According to Plotnikov (1901) and Anikin (1902), our own recent observations,
and information from A. P. Zhdanov, bears occur in large numbers throughout
the Narym taiga, even near settlements. Bears are distributed throughout
the Aleksandrovskoe area in the Tomsk Region, according to I. P. Laptev
(1953). Yurlov obtained a bear in June 1959 on the River Vartovskaya,
about 50 km from its mouth, and often found tracks all along the river.
It occurs further south in the Parabel', Kolpashevo, and Verkhne-Ketskii
areas. Numerous tracks were found in the valley of the Ket' River and of
its tributary the Lisitsa. Burrows of varying age, made by marmots and
dug out by bears, are found everywhere — particularly in the Kolpashevo
and Verkhne-Ketskii districts. Bears are common also in the Bakchar'
and Shegarka areas of the Tomsk Region.

According to Laptev, there are dense bear populations along the lower
reaches of the Chulym, Ket', Tym, and Vakh, [along] the middle and upper
reaches of left tributaries of the Ob emptying into the Ob between the mouth
of the Chulym and the mouth of the Vasyugan, along the right tributaries of
this river [the Vasyugan?], [and] on the upper reaches of rivers in the Ob-
Irtysh interfluve (Figure 44). Laptev observed tracks in 1952 in the valley
of the Nyurolka River, and along the Lar'-Egan River south of the village of
Aleksandrovskoe on the Ob. Yudin (1956) reported the bear from the
Kozhevnikovo area in the Tomsk Region.

The southern boundary of the distribution of the bear in Western Siberia usually coincides with the southern boundary of the taiga, and with the northern part of the forest steppe in some localities.

FIGURE 45. Taiga in the valley of the Tara River. Bear biotope. Photo by K.T. Yurlov

According to S.A. Kuklin (1937), the bear occurs in the Kargapolsk district of the Kurgan Region and in the Omutinskii area of the Tyumen Region. Further east, it is distributed in the Tara River valley and the upper reaches of the Tartas and Om', where it was common according to P. Stepanov (1886) (Figure 45). It still occurs in these localities, and our collection has two skulls collected there by Yurlov (upper reaches of the Uzas and of the Bol'shaya Icha, a right tributary of the Tara River).

The bear occurs in the Severnoe, Karagat, and Kolyvan areas of Novosibirsk Region, but is rare. According to Yurlov, bear dens have been found in the last ten years and animals obtained in the following localities: northwest of the village of Surguty, north of the village of Novoplotnikovo, west of Paramonovo village, and in the Chugraevska Bog at the southwestern end of the Uzakla Marshes.

The bear disappeared relatively recently from the Novosibirsk region. The last bear was killed here in 1935 in a forest on the Bibikha River, about 60 km north of Novosibirsk, and tracks of another bear were found in the same year about 40 km from the city (Zverev, 1937).

The southern boundary of distribution lies along the right bank of the Ob in the valley of the Iksa River, where a bear was killed in 1946 near Ust'-Tula village.

Bear were living on the right side of the Koltyrak River in 1951 (northeastern part of the Maslyanino area), according to Yurlov.

G. M. Krivoshchekov found tracks of bears on the right shore of the Inya River in June 1958, near the Otgonka Station, 87 km east of Novosibirsk.

The bear occurs in the forest steppe in Western Siberia only in the upper Ob forest near Barnaul, where it inhabits the thinly settled forests between Petrovka and Bol'shaya Rechka (G. N. Likhachev, 1930).

Bear are widespread in the Altai Territory, occurring almost throughout the taiga of the Gorno-Altaisk Region and locally in the taiga of the neighboring Charyshskoe, Soloneshnoe, Altaiskoe, Solton, and Staraya Barda areas. They also occur in the taiga of the Salair Mountains and in the taiga of the Sorokino, Zalesovskii, Togul, and Eltsovsk districts (Savinov, 1953).

Bear have been recorded from the Altai by all zoologists who have visited there (Nikol'skii, 1883; Kashchenko, 1899, 1902; Yurgenson, 1938; Turov, 1939, etc.).

Detailed data on the distribution of the bear in the Ust' Koksa area have been given by A. A. Nasimovich (1949), who finds bears common in the forests of the area and particularly abundant on the upper reaches of the Katun, e.g. [the?] upper Zaichikha, and this river's tributaries Multa, lower Kuragan, Kogupla, and Ak Kem. Bears are also numerous near Tyungur. The bear is common on the upper reaches of the Koksa River and its tributaries, the Karagai and Krasnoyarka. Bears are less common on the Terektinskii Range, which is less wooded and contains fewer secure hiding places. Bears occur occasionally along the rivers Tyugurka, Gromatukha (a tributary of the Koksa), Chernaya, Bol'shoi Terekhtam, Komandinki, etc.

A. P. Razorenova (1939) observed bears in the foothills of the Altyn-tu and at the timberline in Orochengansk pass on the left, forested shore of the Belaya Borel River. Tracks are often found in alpine meadows at the timberline atop the Terektinskii Range, on the peak of Mt. Saptan, and at the foot of Belaya Borel Glacier. Bears have been found around Kuragan village and near Kobezen, Ongudai, and Kotanda.

A bear was obtained in 1938 by V. N. Nadeev in the valley of the Nyrna River, a tributary of the Uimen. Yurlov found bear tracks in 1952 on the Seminsk and Kuraiskii ranges.

Two skulls were collected on the eastern shore of Lake Teletskoe by P. G. Ignatov (Kashchenko, 1902). According to P. B. Yurgenson (1938), the bear occurs throughout the former Altai reserve, but is more common from the mouth of the Oior River and Mt. Cheptu to the Korbulu and Korbu ranges. It is very common on the Azhi Range, in the valley of the Kamga River and of Kamga Bay, and along the rivers Bol'shoi and Malyi Mionok, Turochak and Atkichu. P. B. Yurgenson writes, "It is still common, though less so, on the Korbu Range along spurs and western slopes of the Abakan; in the basin of the Kygi River it is again more common, but becomes rare in the valley of the Chulcha River (a right tributary of the Chulyshman). Only single specimens occur in the valley of the Shavla River and the upper reaches of the Chulyshman River. Bears are less common on the upper reaches of the rivers Bol'shoi and Malyi Abakan than near Lake Teletskoe.

"The area of maximum population density coincides with the area of dark forests of Siberian stone pine and stone pine—fir forests. The attraction of the brown bear to dark conifer taiga has been observed throughout the valley of the Yenisei River."

According to B. A. Kuznetsov (1948), the bear occurs throughout the mountain taiga in the southern Altai, and though rare in the northern and western Altai is numerous in the eastern Altai, particularly on the upper reaches of the Bukhtarma River. G. I. Polyakov (1914) found the bear in the area of Lake Marka-Kul.

According to K. T. Yurlov, the bear occurs in the Kozhurla area (between the Kok-Su and Ak-Alakhi rivers), and on the lower and middle reaches of the Dzhazator River, appearing in spring in the bare mountains near its sources and on the upper reaches of the Chagan-Burgazy River.

FIGURE 46. Taiga on the Kulumys Range, Western Sayan. Bear biotope. Photo by K. T. Yurlov

Yurlov saw bear tracks in the valley of the lower Ters (a right tributary of the Tomi River), in the Kuznetsk Ala-Tau, and on the upper reaches of the Andreevka and Kuchumanda rivers (tributaries of the Taidon River).

The bear inhabits the entire Gornaya Shoriya taiga, being very common here according to G. Gol'tsmaier (1936). Yurlov observed signs of bear in the Tomi basin at the following places: near the mouth of the Mras-su River, near Syrkash village, on the rivers Usa and Nazas, on the upper reaches of the Soltadka River, in the valley of the

Bel-su River, and on Mt. Salon (between the rivers Teba and Luzhba). It is also common on the right bank of the Kondoma River along the rivers Migash and Tesh, etc.

Yurlov observed it further southeast in taiga and old burns between the Chulym and Yenisei rivers from the upper reaches of the Syr River and the Byuza River to the village of Bakhta.

According to Yanushevich and Yurlov (1949) the bear is distributed throughout the forest zone in the Western Sayan and also enters the subalpine and high mountain tundra. These authors collected bears in 1948 on the Kolupaevka River (a right tributary of the Tanzybai), in the valley of the Gremyachaya River, at the sources of the Buiba River, and also observed them in the valley of the Kebezh River below the mouth of the Chernaya Rechka River, on the Kulumys Range, on the Oya Range, on the Irgaki, and on the Tikhaya River near Aradan (Figure 46).

In the taiga in the western part of the former Minusinsk County, the bear is found occasionally as a visitor from other areas, according to P. Polikevich (1923). It is common in the taiga on the right bank of the Yenisei.

The bear occurs in the Minusinsk taiga in the area of the Kazyr and Kizir rivers, according to L. and I. Kozhanchikov (1924), both on mountains and plains. It occurs in the mountains only in summer, and descends to the plains in spring.

The bear is not rare in Khakassiya, and we have skulls from near Abakan.

We examined skulls from Krasnoyarsk obtained by M. E. Kobort in 1892 — 1894 on the Kolba, Ungut and Zherzhul rivers, tributaries of the Mana River, and from the valleys of the Roevaya and Sliznevaya rivers. Bears are common in the "Stolby" reserve (south of Krasnoyarsk) on the watershed between the lower reaches of the Bazanikha and Mana rivers, according to V. A. Gorokhov (1951). The Zoological Museum of Moscow University possesses skulls of bears collected by A. Ya. Tugarinov on the Mana River and in the former Krasnoyarsk and Achinsk counties.

According to D. K. Solov'ev (1920) the bear is widely distributed in the Eastern Sayan and occurs in large numbers throughout the forest zone; in summer it is also found above the timberline, on alpine meadows and near snow patches. It occurs in large numbers in summer in the upper reaches of the rivers Kana and Agula near Lake Medvezhye (Figure 47).

Bears were obtained in the taiga along the Biryusa River in 1889 by P. S. Proskuryakov (coll. Zool. Inst. Acad. Sciences USSR). G. A. Fedoseev hunted bears in 1938 near the Mozharskie lakes, on Mt. Kubar, on the right shore of the Kizir River (between the Nichka and Shinda rivers), on the Penza and Kansk White Mountains (upper reaches of the Kal'ta River and on the shore of Lake Medvezhye), in the valley of the Belaya Vala River, and in the Agulsk Gorge. In 1939 Fedoseev got bears in the Tunkinskie Belki [Alps] on Mt. Bazaltovye Bratya and on the upper reaches of the Kitoi River.

Yurlov obtained bears in 1956 in the alpine tundra above the timberline near the sources of the Chistaya River (a tributary of the Agul River), near Lake Medvezhye, in the valley of the Orzogoi River, and on the upper reaches of the Kinzelyuk River (coll. S. U. Stroganov). He also found bears in the taiga along the Kingash and Kuzho rivers, and in the taiga and the alpine zone above the timberline on the road from the northern foothills to the central part of the Eastern Sayan.

Bears are found in Tuva, according to P. Polikevich (1923), mainly on the upper reaches of the Bol'shoi and Malyi Yenisei. According to Yanushevich (1952) bears are common in the eastern Tuva uplands and in Tannu-Ola, where 100—150 bears are obtained per year.

According to V. N. Troitskii (1930_2) the bear occurs in the taiga of the valleys of the Chuna and Angara rivers. G. A. Fedoseev obtained bears in 1943—1946 in the Angara River valley below the village of Kezhma, on the banks of the Kada and Fitli rivers, and found them in the valley of the stony Tunguska at Ugoyan above the village of Chemdalsk and near the Chula lakes on the upper reaches of Chula Creek.

Bears inhabit the whole taiga in the Irkutsk region, according to I. P. Kopylov (1948) and V. V. Timofeev (1949). According to Kopylov, A. V. Dobrovol'skii and I. A. Shergin (1940), bears occur in large numbers on the upper reaches of the Lower Tunguska, in the Sayans, in the Lena valley, and throughout all taiga biotopes of Cisbaikalia. Fedoseev hunted bears in the Tunguska area in the following localities: the Nepo River (above Tomka village), near the village of Karelin, and on the upper reaches of the Nerunda River.

A. I. Cherepanov (in litt.) observed bears on the upper reaches of the Lena, and there and on the upper reaches of the Tutura, Kirenga, and Ulkan rivers "bears are particularly abundant in the valley of the Nazima River, where their tracks are found almost everywhere in summer" (B. E. Petri, 1930).

Bears occur throughout the taiga north of the above localities; according to S. I. Ognev (1931), the bear is abundant in the Yenisei taiga. Bears are common in the taiga near the mouth of the stony Tunguska, and I have hunted them there.

FIGURE 47. Lake Medvezhye, Eastern Sayan. Subalpine meadow and stone pine—fir forest. Biotope of the bear. Photo by K. T. Yurlov

Valuable data on the distribution of the bear in the valley of the Yenisei have been given by N. P. Naumov (1934), who writes that in the Tunguska area the bear is unevenly distributed, being common along the Lower and Stony Tunguska but less so in the northern part of the territory. The bear numbers decrease considerably in areas of sparse northern larch forests mixed with forest tundra, and in forestless areas. Bears occur in greater numbers in taiga with stone pine—fir forests. According to Naumov, the bear is common along the Yenisei up to about Potapovskii or Luzin. It is rare further north. Bears are occasionally caught on the rivers Bol'shaya and Malaya Kheta, and on the upper reaches of the Gyda River near 70. N lat. V. I. Telegin obtained a bear in 1958 in the valley of the Bol'shaya Kheta, where bears are common (coll. S. U. Stroganov).

The above data agree with those of E. O. Yakovlev (1930), who recorded bears on the left bank of the Yenisei and on the upper reaches of the rivers Pelyatka, Yar and Tanam (68° N lat.).

The boundary of the bears range reaches higher latitudes on the right side of the Yenisei. N. P. Naumov (1934) writes that bear has been caught near its northern limit of distribution in the following localities: near the mouth of the Novaya River, where it joins the Khatanga near 72° N lat.; on the rivers Medvesh'e and Romanikha near 70° N lat. (often); on the Kheta River near Polovinka Station, on the Ikan River (a tributary of the Pyasina) near 70° N lat., and on the Dudypta River at the mouth of the Kamennaya River near 70° N lat.

A. F. Middendorf (1867—1869) recorded bears as rare on the Yenisei near 71° N lat., but as penetrating as far north as 72° N lat. on the Taimyr Peninsula.

According to E. O. Yakovlev (1930), the bear occurs on the right bank of the Yenisei near Lake Pyasino, on the Kamennaya River (a left tributary of the Kheta River), and on the Volosyanka, Podkhrebetnaya, and Malaya Rossomashya. It has been recorded from the Khatanga area (about 72° N lat.). The northernmost point of occurrence of the bear in winter is the middle reaches of the Novaya River (72° N lat.), according to Yakovlev. The brown bear has been recorded at 74° N lat., where it may occur alongside the polar bear.

A bear was obtained by I. Berdnikov in 1912 on the Khatanga River 17 km from the Anovar winter camp (coll. Zool. Inst. Acad. Sciences USSR).

Between the Khatanga and the Lena, according to Romanov (1941), the bear occurs — but very thinly — in the forests edging the tundra. The northern boundary of its distribution generally coincides with the limit of the forest, though in the mountains it is occasionally found above the timberline. The author gives the following localities where bears were found.

The Khatanga basin, where the bear reaches the northern limit of the forest, and occurs regularly in the system of the Kazachya, Nizhnyaya and Bludnaya rivers.

The Popigai basin, from which hunters report bear in mountain valleys north to the Khara-Tes elevation, where they occur on the upper reaches of the Sopochnaya and Poperechnaya rivers.

The valleys of the rivers Fomicha and Rassokha and the upper reaches of the Popigai, where bears are numerous. They have been killed in the alpine tundra, on the upper reaches of the Yakovlevka River, near the northern end of Yakovlevka Mountain (72° N lat.).

Bears have been found regularly in the valleys of the Olenek and Anabar rivers along the tributaries of the Khorgukhuonka, Kelimyar, Pur and Udzh. They have been found near the mouth of the Oiyun-Yuryagya on the Anabar River (72° N lat.).

Bears are found every year in the valley of the Ayatka River, and the author saw tracks in August 1926 some 10 km from the mouth of the river.

Near the Lena, Romanov (1941) reports bears near the mouth of the Egelyakh River (71° N lat.). On the right bank of the Lena, bears have been recorded along the Kengdei River in the Karaulakh Range right to the river's mouth (71° N lat.).

According to I. I. Kolyushev (1936), dens of the bear have been found on the lower Lena 30 km south of the village of Kumakh-Sura (about 71°N lat.).

The bear is common in the taiga of northern Yakutia between the lower reaches of the Lena and Yana rivers and in the mountains on the watershed between the Indigirka and Kolyma. The bear sometimes enters the tundra in search of food (Tugarinov, Smirnov and Ivanov, 1934).

Bunge (1887) considered the bear common in the valley of the Yana River, and particularly numerous between the Yana and Adycha rivers.

The bear is common in the valley of the Vilyui River but is not uniformly distributed. Maak (1859, 1886) found bears more frequently and saw tracks on the lower Vilyui, where bears occurred even on islands on the river. On the central Vilyui, which is more densely settled, bears occurred more rarely, particularly near the village of Suntara. Bears are usually common further up the river to and above the mouth of the Chona, but decrease further toward the source. Bears become rarer the further north one goes between the Vilyui and Olenek rivers. They were found in large numbers on the watershed between the Olekma and Vitim rivers by I. S. Polyakov (1873).

According to A. I. Ivanov, the bear is common in the western, less inhabited part of central Yakutia but is considerably rarer near Yakutsk and on the Lena-Amga Plateau (Tugarinov, Smirnov and Ivanov, 1934). According to V. I. Belyk (1953), the bear is distributed throughout the wooded part of Yakutia. It is rare in central and southern Yakutia, since it has been intensively hunted. North of the valley of the Vilyui, bears are rare in the Markha basin above the mouth of the Markoko River, and in the Olenek area. The conditions of existence are unfavorable, as berries are scarce (reindeer moss predominates).

Bears were obtained on the upper reaches of the Kolyma River in 1936 by A. Shokhin near the mouth of the Chubakalakh River (coll. Zool. Mus. Moscow University). According to V. I. Iokhel'son (1898), S. A. Buturlin (1913), and others, the bear is not rare throughout the Kolyma area. There are collections by S. A. Buturlin (1905) from the villages Ambolikha, Zabortsevo, Timkino and Krestovsk.

The bear is widely distributed on the Chukchi and Kamchatka peninsulas and on the Okhotsk coast.

N. Buxton recorded the bear as common along the Kolyma and Anadyr rivers and on the western shore of the Sea of Okhotsk (J. Allen, 1903).

Recent data on the distribution of the bear in the Anadyr territory are given by L. A. Portenko (1941), who states that the bear is common but not numerous here. It is irregularly distributed, mainly in the western and southeastern part of the territory, and the author gives the following data.

The bear is common in the upper reaches of the Anadyr River. Although Portenko did not find bears near the village Markovo, they occasionally visit summer stores of fish and have been killed there. Further away from Markovo, bears are common near the fortress. The author saw tracks near the mouth of the Shchuchya River between the Modinskaya Povarnya (an inn), and the Poperechnaya River and further south. Bears are common near the village of Penzhino and, according to S. D. Pereleshin are numerous in the Penzhina area. Numerous tracks were found on the banks of the River Penzhina to 100 km above Penzhino village.

The bear is also common in the valleys of the rivers Main, Tanyurer and Algan. V. F. Ovsyannikov (1929) and A. I. Karaev (1926) also record the bear from this area. It also occurs near Lake Krasnoe.

N. P. Sokol'nikov (1927) thinks that bears are more numerous in the valley of the Anadyr than in other parts of Chukotka, but according to the Chukchis the bear occurs in greater numbers on the seashore south of the Anadyr Gulf near Cape Barykov than along the river.

L. O. Belopol'skii found the bear near the village of Anadyr; I have a collection of skulls made by B. S. Yudin from the locality. According to the Chukchis, the bear occurs in the valleys of the rivers Tovaima and Volchya. Yudin found tracks on the shore between Cape Meininytumy and Russkaya Koshka, and near the Kolba River (Portenko, 1941).

Portenko thinks that bears occur on the northern slopes of the Anadyr Range (recorded by V. Ya. Isaev, who wintered at Cape Schmidt) and that bears are "a normal occurrence everywhere on the Anadyr Range." Bears have also been found on the southern slopes of the range east of the Belaya River and on the Kanchalan River.

According to A. V. Samorodov (1939), the bear is very common in the Olyutor district in Kamchatka. Thirty to eighty bears are shot every year in the valley of the Apuka River on a territory of 1.5 million hectares. Bear occurs on Karagin Island in the Bering Sea.

According to A. A. Silant'ev (1898), the greatest number of bear pelts in Russia was obtained in the Uda and Okhotsk districts and in Kamchatka.

The bear is common throughout the valley of the Uda River and on the upper reaches of the Selemdzha River, according to N. T. Zolotarev (1936).

Bears are abundant in Kamchatka. All who have visited this country have noted the large numbers of them. I. G. Voznesenskii, who traveled in Kamchatka in 1840, saw more than 100 bears in one day and reports that the inhabitants of one single village [penal colony] killed more than 200 bears per year (Middendorf, 1869).

The large numbers of bears in Kamchatka were noted by K. Ditmar and members of the F. P. Ryabushinskii Expedition (1901).

Ditmar stressed the abundance of bears on the whole peninsula, and according to P. Yu. Schmidt (1916), who took part in Ryabushinskii's expedition, the abundance of bears often hindered the progress of the expedition near Lake Kronotskoe. The bears frightened the horses and had to be killed and the expedition had to stop to prepare the bodies.

Averin (1948) and Sysoev (1952) confirm the abundance of bears in Kamchatka. Averin writes that the number of bears in the Kronoki reserve is enormous. He gives the following example: the famous hunter

A. F. Cherepanov (Voronov), observed 40 bears in August 1921 along a 30 km route in the tundra. A. P. Krupenin of the staff of the reserve observed 18 bears (including 2 females with cubs) on 18 October 1939, during a march of 12 km in the tundra. Averin observed 15 bears while covering 16 km along the shore.

Averin records collections of bears on the eastern shore of the peninsula in the Kronoki reserve in the following localities: Olga Bay, the valley of the Olga River, the mouth of the Trukhinka River, the crater of the Uzon Volcano, the middle reaches of the Kronotskaya River, the mouths of the Tatyana and Medvezhka rivers, and the middle reaches of the Bogachevka River.

Bears are so numerous on the Okhotsk shore and on the Shantar Islands that Middendorf in 1867 named these places "Land of the bears." However, there are few exact data on the distribution of bears on the Okhotsk shore.

Bears were hunted repeatedly on the Dzhugdzhur and Pribrezhnyi Range and on the Stanovoi Range by G. A. Fedoseev during his geodesic work in 1937 and in 1948 — 1953. According to Fedoseev, bears were found in the following localities on the Stanovoi Range: the upper reaches of the Gonam (Guonam) and Algami rivers in the valley of the Zeya River along its tributaries Matyuka, Lyuchna, and Etna, on the upper reaches of the Maya Polovinnaya (a left tributary of the Uda River), on the upper reaches of the Chulikan River (a left tributary of the middle Maimakan), in the southwestern part of the Yudoma-Maya Plateau along the Net River, on the Dzhugdzhur Range along the upper reaches of the right tributaries of the Severnyi Ui, on the southern slopes of the Pribrezhnyi Range, and on the shore of the Sea of Okhotsk in the area of Nasikan Island.

G. N. Gassovskii (1927) recorded bears on the southern slopes of the Stanovoi Range. N. T. Zolotarev (1936) observed bears in the valley of the Uda River and its tributaries Shevli and Gervikan.

G. A. Fedoseev, hunter, engineer and outstanding writer, shot bears along the shore of the Tugur Peninsula, on the right bank of the Nemelen River about 100 km from its junction with the Amgun, near the mouth of the Omal River, on Mt. Sanakh (south of the village of Duki on the Amgun), on the bare Dierskii mountains, on the Dusse-Alin Range, and on the upper reaches of the Kerbi River at the southern end of the Yam-Alin Range.

In Transbaikalia, the bear inhabits the Khamar-Daban, Ulan-Burgasy and Barguzin ranges in large numbers (Lavov, 1955). Fedoseev hunted bears in 1934 and 1937 in the alpine zone of the Ika Range, in the valley of the Golonda River, on the Ulan-Burgasy Range, in the valley of the Turku River, and near the sources of this river on the Khurkhak Range, as well as on the Svyatoi Nos Peninsula.

Material is available from Transbaikalia from the mouth of the Kudalda River, Lake Kudalda, the upper reaches of the Kabanya River and the valley of the Bol'shoi Chivyrkui River. Z. F. Svatosh obtained a bear in 1925 in the Barguzin reserve in the valley of the Sosnovka River, and Turov (1922) collected a bear near Zmeinaya Bay on the Svyatoi Nos.

According to Turov (1936), bears are numerous on the northeastern shore of Lake Baikal, and can be observed in the evening near the shore of the Lake. Tracks were also seen by this author near Lake Frolikha. He mentions an encounter with a bear in the alpine zone at an altitude of 1,200 m near the Urbikan River.

Bears were observed by Radde in 1862 on the Yablonovyi Range. According to B. A. Kuznetsov (1929) they are still common in the taiga on this range and in the foothills, and are occasionally found in forests on the Unda Chain. Bears were nearly exterminated in the 1850s on the Nerchinsk Range, and survive only in the most secluded areas (e. g., near the sources of the Gazimur River).

E. Pavlov (1948) mentions an area in the Chita Region where the bear is relatively common: the upper reaches of the Chita River, above the River Eramga, where the author found tracks, excrements and other signs of the presence of bears on the river bank in 1938 and 1939.

The bear occurs everywhere in the uninhabited taiga on the Stanovoi plateau. G. A. Fedoseev (1948—1953) hunted bears in the following localities: in the alpine zone of the northern Muiya Range near the sources of the upper Angara and the Ulan-Makita (a left tributary of the Muiya), below the alpine zone on the southern Muiya Range near the mouth of the Muiya River, near Lake Leperunda, on the western and eastern end of the Udokan Range (Kuanda River, upper reaches of the Tas River, Lake Kolar, and upper reaches of the Khan River), on the Olekminsk Stanovik and in the upper reaches of the Tungir River (a right tributary of the Olekma River), and on the southern end of the Borshchovskii Range in the upper reaches of the Ingoda River.

In the Far East the brown bear occurs in the Amur and lower Amur regions, in the Maritime Territory, and on the Shantar Islands, Sakhalin, and some of the Kuriles.

L. I. Schrenck (1858) recorded the brown bear as common in the Amur valley but less common than on Sakhalin. The Zoological Institute of the Academy of Sciences has specimens of bears collected by Schrenck on the lower reaches of the Amur.

R. Maak (1859) often observed bears in traversing the Amur valley and the islands, and saw bear tracks near the mouth of the Ussuri and near large lakes connected with the Amur.

Maak (1861) observed bears along the whole Ussuri River, near the Syngachi River and in the valleys of the Daubikhe and Sandukhu rivers. The Zoological Institute of the Academy of Sciences has skulls collected by Maak from near Lake Khanka.

N. M. Przheval'skii (1870) recorded the bear throughout the Ussuri territory. He hunted bears repeatedly. The largest animal was obtained on the Suchan River. According to D. K Solov'ev (1925), 1,000 bears were killed yearly in the Maritime Territory before the revolution.

According to A. N. Formozov (1952), bears occur in large numbers on the lower Amur, and he observed numerous tracks of bears on the shore of the Tatar Strait.

Bears have been obtained in the valley of the Samarga River in the Ussuri taiga by V. K. Arsen'ev (1950). Goodwin (1933) found the skull of a bear in the valley of the Nelta River, 60 km north of Khabarovsk.

According to N. T. Zolotarev (1936), the bear occurs everywhere in the forests in the Iman River valley but is most common in the upper reaches of the Iman River and along its tributaries the Kolumbe and Armu. Bears are particularly numerous on Mt. Khousu in the valley of the Kolumbe River.

According to L. G. Kaplanov (1948), bears are very numerous in the Sikhote-Alin reserve; in the Suputinka reserve (Voroshilov District of the Maritime Territory), according to G. F. Bromlei and Z. I. Gutnikova (1955), the bear does not live permanently but enters in autumn and migrates into the northern taiga in winter.

The skull of a bear was found on Malyi Shantar Island by A. F. Middendorf in 1852 (coll. Zool. Inst. Acad. Sciences USSR). Fourteen skulls were collected by A. D. Baturin and G. D. Dul'keit on Bol'shoi Shantar Island (Ognev, 1929). Bears still occur on the Shantar Island.

There are a number of references in the literature which mention the occurrence of the bear in Sakhalin, beginning with I. F. Krusenstern (1811). There is general agreement that the number of bears on Sakhalin is enormous.

According to Schrenck (1858), bears were more numerous on Sakhalin than on the continent in the Amur valley. I. S. Polyakov (1884) observed tracks of bears in the valley of the Tokoi, a tributary of the Onenaya River. On the lower reaches of this river, and in the Susui-Onenai plain, numerous tracks were seen by P. P. Glen (1868), and near Taraika by Brylkin (1864). F. Schmidt (1868) never found as many tracks as on the shores of Lake Tauro. According to A. M. Nikol'skii (1889), bears occur throughout Sakhalin, and this author observed tracks near Aleksandrovka on the upper Tym, particularly on the lower reaches of the river.

There are fewer bears in Sakhalin at present, but they still occur in considerable numbers. The bear is common in the taiga of the Sredne-Sakhalinskii reserve (Poronaisk district) according to M. V. Gerasimov (1951); bears are particularly abundant in the southern Sakhalin reserve (Nevel'sk and Anovsk districts). The zoologist G. O. Krivolutskaya, who worked for several years on Sakhalin, kindly provided the following data on the distribution of bears on the island. The bear occurs in varying numbers throughout the island. It is common on Schmidt Island. The bear occurs sporadically in little-inhabited localities in the so-called tundra in northern Sakhalin. It is numerous in the Tym-Poronai plain. Bears are particularly numerous in the following mountain districts: on the Kamyshevskii Range, in the east Sakhalin mountains, and on the Kril'on Peninsula, mainly on its eastern shore.

The bear occurs on Paramushir, Simushir, Iturup and Kunashir islands in the Kurile chain according to B. A. Kuznetsov (1949).

Description of subspecies. The bear forms a large number of subspecies and local forms. Several dozens of these forms have been described. Ellerman and Morrison-Scott (1951) record seven subspecies from Eurasia. According to my data the following subspecies may be considered to occur in the USSR: 1. U. a. arctos L. (European USSR and West Siberian plains); 2. U. a. jeniseensis Ognev (Altai, Sayans, Baikal area and Transbaikalia); 3. U. a. beringianus Middendorf (Kamchatka, Okhotsk coast, Amur area and Maritime Territory, Shantar Islands and Sakhalin); 4. U. a. meridionalis Middendorf (Caucasus and Transcaucasia, except in its southwestern part); 5. U. a. syriacus Hemprich and Ehrenberg (southwestern Transcaucasia); 6. U. a. leuconyx Severtsov (mountains of Central Asia, except the Pamir and Gissar); 7. U. a. pamirensis Ognev (Pamir, Gissar Range and neighboring mountains of northern Tadzhikistan).

Three subspecies are considered provisionally to occur in Siberia.

7a. **Ursus arctos arctos** Linnaeus (1758). Common
brown bear

1758. U r s u s   a r c t o s.   Linnaeus, C. Systema Naturae, ed. 10,
p. 47.
1824. U r s u s   c o l l a r i s.   Cuvier, F. Histoire Naturelle des
Mammifères, pt. 42, pl. 212 (Siberia, without details);
Trouessart, E. L., following Pallas, gives the Urals as terra typica for
U r s u s   c o l l a r i s.
1931. U r s u s   a r c t o s   a r c t o s.   Ognev, S. I. Zveri Vostochnoi
Evropy i Severnoi Azii (Animals of Eastern Europe and Northern Asia).
Vol. 2, pp. 20—33, Moskva-Leningrad; Adlerberg, G. P. Khishchnye
zveri (Carnivora, Fissipedia) Arktiki (Carnivora, Fissipedia of the
Arctic). In: "Zveri Arktiki," pod redaktsiei prof. N. A. Smirnova,
pp. 296—299, Leningrad, Izdatel'stvo Glavsevmorputi. 1935. (partim);
Ellerman, J. R. and T. C. S. Morrison-Scott. Checklist of Palaearctic and
Indian Mammals, pp. 236—237, London. 1951 (partim).

Type and type locality. See description of the species.
Diagnosis. Height and quality of fur average. Condylobasal length of
male skull av. 332 mm. Hairs moderately long, relatively sparse and
stiff. Color of fur varying from dull, light brownish straw-yellow to dark,
almost blackish brown. Individuals with various brown colorings
predominate. Bears of black color constitute 10 % of population. Tips of
the guard hairs often light, creating grayish tone of the fur. Legs darker
than body, dark brown or dull black. Claws blackish brown, strongly
curved, length of claw belonging to middle toe of foreleg 55 — 65 mm.
Measurements. Weight and measurements of the common bear vary
markedly. The literature gives the following data on the weight of the
nominate subspecies.
According to A. Brehm (Life of Animals, 2nd Russian edition), the
weight of bears in Western Europe attains 250 kg (350 kg in very large and
fat specimens). According to A. F. Middendorf (Simashko, 1850), animals
were obtained in the middle of the 18th century in southwestern Europe
which weighed 200 kg. A bear was killed in Brandenburg in 1601 which
weighed 412 kg.
There are numerous data on bear weights in the European USSR.
Very large animals were found in the former Orenburg Province.
F. K Larents (1885) wrote that a bear sent to him from Karachev
County weighed 360 kg (without viscera), and with the viscera would
probably have weighed 416 — 448 kg. S. A. Buturlin considered this weight
as maximum for Central European bears, but such a great weight is reached
extremely rarely. Those weighing markedly less are more frequently
encountered.
A. A. Shirinskii-Shikmatov (1900) killed a bear weighing 335 kg in 1899
near Vesegonsk.
Large bears used to inhabit the forests near Moscow; P. N. Belousov
killed an enormous bear weighing 288 kg without viscera in 1890 between
the villages of Khotkovo and Zagorsk (S. I. Ognev, 1931).

I killed a bear in the Kalinin Region in 1929 which weighed 246 kg. A bear weighing 230 kg was obtained in 1931 near the village of Lukovnikovo.

N. A. Mel'nitskii (1915) gives the following data for the former provinces of Tver, Novgorod, and Olonets, after information from M. V. Andreevskii (who hunted bears from 1871 till 1897). The following weights have been reported: 82 bears of below 80 kg, 34 bears of 80—112 kg, 23 of 112—160 kg, 2 of up to 192 kg, and a single bear of 208 kg.

According to the bear hunter L. F. Vinnitskii, who took part in numerous winter hunts in Olonets and Novgorod provinces (on which about 800 bears were killed), the largest animal weighed 290 kg. The largest female bear weighed 176 kg.

S. V. Lobachev (1951) states that three males killed in the Kirov Region weighed 73, 126 and 160 kg, and a female weighed 110 kg.

According to L. P. Sabaneev (1878), very large bears are found in the northern Urals, with pelts 178 cm long; they become smaller further south, to the extent that bear pelts are no longer than 134 cm in Sverdlovsk at present.

There are no exact data for the bear in Siberia, but to judge from the size of the skulls, the weight of the bears is the same as that of animals from the forests of Europe. A female bear obtained by K. T. Yurlov on 11 June 1959 in the Tomsk Region weighed 98 kg.

The decrease in bear weights seen (in particular) in settled areas is probably due to the more intensive hunting, as the majority of the bears are killed before they reach maximum size and weight.

Skull measurements (14 males and 6 females) were as follows: condylobasal length: males 302—363 mm (av. 332 mm), females 260—318 mm (av. 288 mm); zygomatic width: males 203—232 mm (av. 217 mm), females 147—196 mm (av. 176 mm); maximum width of skull: males 160—181 mm (av. 168 mm), females 121—153 mm (av. 150 mm); interorbital width: males 75—88 mm (av. 83 mm), females 58—73 mm (av. 68 mm); width between the ends of supraorbital processes: males 97—130 mm (av. 116 mm), females 81—98 mm (av. 90 mm); postorbital width: males 67—79 mm (av. 74 mm); females 57—73 mm (av. 68 mm); width of rostrum above canines: males 75—81 mm (av. 78 mm), females 57—72 mm (av. 63 mm); width between infraorbital foramina: males 79—90 mm (av. 74 mm) [sic], females 62—70 mm (av. 64 mm); width of the nasal opening: males 49—55 mm (av. 50 mm), females 31—46 mm (av. 42 mm); height of the nasal aperture: males 44—56 mm (av. 48 mm), females 38—49 mm (av. 43 mm); length of nasals: males 96—101 mm (av. 98 mm), females 68—88 mm (av. 78 mm); length of upper tooth row: males 116—136 mm (av. 124 mm), females 106—120 mm (av. 117 mm).

Systematic notes. The nominate subspecies of the common brown bear is well characterized.

It differs markedly from the Caucasian bear (U. a. m e r i d i o n a l i s Middendorf, 1851; U. a. c a u c a s i c u s, Smirnov, 1916) in its generally more reddish tone of brown and in the markedly darker-colored fur on the legs.

It differs from the South Siberian bear (U. a. j e n i s e e n s i s Ognev, 1924) in its smaller size (condylobasal length of skull averages 332 mm as against

340 mm in U. a. j e n i s e e n s i s) and in quality of fur. The hairs, in contrast to U. a. j e n i s e e n s i s, are shorter, sparser and stiffer, and lighter.

Geographical distribution. European USSR, West Siberian plains, and Central Siberian Plateau eastwards to the middle and lower reaches of the Lena.

Material examined. European USSR, 36 skulls and 23 pelts; Western Siberia, 15 skulls and 10 pelts; Nenets National District, 10 skulls; western and central Yakutia, 7 skulls. Total 68 skulls and 33 pelts.

7b. Ursus arctos jeniseensis Ognev (1924). South Siberian bear

1924. U r s u s a r c t o s j e n i s e e n s i s. Ognev, O medvedyakh, vodyashchikhsya v Rossii (Bears in Russia). — Priroda i Okhota na Ukraine, Nos. 1 — 2, pp. 110; Yurgenson, P. B. Materialy k poznaniyu mlekopitayushchikh priteletskogo uchastka Altaiskogo gosudarstvennogo zapovednika (Data on Mammals of the Teletskoe Section of the Altai State Reserve). — Trudy Altaiskogo Gosudarstvennogo Zapovednika, No. 1, pp. 103 — 110, Moskva, 1938.

1924. U r s u s a r c t o s b a i c a l e n s i s. Ognev, S. I. Loc. cit., p. 112 (Irkutsk Province, Transbaikalia); Doppel'maier, G. G. Sobolinyi promysel na severo-vostochnom poberezh'e Baikala (The Sable Trade on the Northeastern Shore of Lake Baikal), Verkhne-Udinsk. Moskva. 1926; Ognev, S. I. Zveri Vostochnoi Evropy i Severnoi Azii (Animals of Eastern Europe and Northern Asia). Vol. 2, pp. 81 — 85, Moskva-Leningrad. 1931 (Kudaldy-Transbaikalia); Bannikov, A. G. Mlekopitayushchie Mongol'skoi Narodnoi Respubliki (Mammals of Mongolia). p. 110. Moskva, Izdatel'stvo AN SSSR. 1954.

1931. U r s u s a r c t o s j e n i s e e n s i s. Ognev, S. I. Zveri Vostochnoi Evropy i Severnoi Azii (Animals of Eastern Europe and Northern Asia). Vol. 2, pp. 78 — 81, Moskva-Leningrad.

1935. U r s u s a r c t o s a r c t o s. Adlerberg, G. P. Khishchnye zveri (Carnivora, Fissipedia) Arktiki (Carnivora, Fissipedia of the Arctic). In: Zveri Arktiki pod red. prof. N. A. Smirnova, pp. 296 — 299, Leningrad, Izdatel'stvo Glavsevmorputi (partim).

1951. U r s u s a r c t o s c o l l a r i s. Ellerman, J. R. and T. C. S. Morrison-Scott. Checklist of Palaearctic and Indian Mammals, p. 237, London (partim).

Type and type locality. No. 6170, coll. Zool. Inst. Acad. Sciences USSR, male, sen., 27. IX. 1884, coll. M. E. Kibort. Ungut River (a tributary of the Mana) near Krasnoyarsk.

Diagnosis. Differs from the nominate subspecies in its larger size and in features of the coat. Condylobasal length of skull 340 mm in males (332 mm in U. a. a r c t o s). Fur longer and denser, softer and more luxurious than in the nominate subspecies. Color of fur varying from light pale brown (with a stray yellow tinge of varying intensity) to dark brown with more or less marked stray yellow and cinnamon brown black tones. Dark brown individuals predominate. Legs are markedly darker than back and flanks.   Claws blackish brown or brown, and strongly curved; claw length on middle toe of forefoot is 70—85 mm.

Skull measurements (18 males and 4 females): condylobasal length: males 322 — 385 mm (av. 340 mm), females 309 — 372 mm (av. 320 mm); zygomatic width: males 193 — 252 mm (av. 221 mm), females 170 — 237 mm; (av. 215 mm); maximum width of skull: males 164 — 209 mm (av. 168 mm), females 148 — 199 mm (av. 160); interorbital width: males 72 — 103 mm (av. 84 mm), females 67 — 100 mm (av. 79 mm); width between ends of supraorbital processes: males 99 — 141 mm (av. 118 mm), females 87 — 138 mm (av. 108 mm); postorbital width: males 70 — 82 mm (av. 76 mm), females 67 — 80 mm (av. 72 mm); width of rostrum above canines: males 75 — 91 mm (av. 78 mm), females 60 — 70 mm (av. 64 mm); width between infraorbital foramina: males 70 — 88 mm (av. 76 mm), females 58 — 71 mm (av. 64 mm); width of the nasal openings: males 46 — 56 mm (av. 52 mm), females 37 — 48 mm (av. 43 mm); height of the nasal opening: males 47 — 61 mm (av. 51 mm), females 40 — 52 mm (av. 46 mm); length of nasals: males 79 — 104 mm (av. 93 mm), females 62 — 89 mm (av. 74 mm); length of upper tooth row: males 122 — 143 mm (av. 132 mm), females 112 — 136 mm (av. 128 mm).

Systematic notes. U. a. j e n i s e e n s i s is intermediate in some characters between U. a. a r c t o s and U. a. b e r i n g i a n u s. It is closer to U. a. a r c t o s in skull measurements, but differs in that its bones are more massive and the crests and processes of the skull more strongly developed.   The skull as a whole is more strongly built but not as strongly as in U. a. b e r i n g i a n u s, being smaller and lighter.

The quality of the fur in U. a. j e n i s e e n s i s differs from that of other Siberian bears. Its fur is denser, silky, and luxuriant, and usually dark brown.   The hairs are less long than those of U. a. b e r i n g i a n u s but the fur is denser and softer.

Geographical distribution.   Altai, Sayans and mountains of Cis- and Transbaikalia.

Material examined.   Altai, 22 skulls and 8 pelts; Sayans, 35 skulls and 16 pelts; Irkutsk Region, 7 skulls and 2 pelts; Transbaikalia, 10 skulls and 8 pelts.   Total 74 skulls and 34 pelts.

7c. Ursus arctos beringianus Middendorf (1851). Far Eastern or Kamchatka bear

1851. U r s u s   a r c t o s var. b e r i n g i a n a. Middendorf, A. Untersuchungen an Schädeln des gemeinen Landbären. — Verhandl. d. Mineralogisch. Gesellsch., p. 74.

1855. U r s u s   p i s c a t o r. Pucheran. Notes mammalogiques. — Rev. et Magaz. de Zool. pure et appl., 7, p. 392, Paris. (Petropavlovsk Kamchatskii).

1898. U r s u s   m a n d s c h u r i c u s. Heude. Memoires concernant l'histoire naturelle de l'Empire Chinois par des pères de la compagnie de Jésus, 4, pp. 23 — 24, Chang-Hai. (Ussuri River in the Maritime Territory); Ognev, S. I. Zveri Vostochnoi Evropy i Severnoi Azii (Animals of Eastern Europe and Northern Asia). Vol. 2, pp. 98 — 104, Moskva-Leningrad. 1931.

1914. U r s u s a r c t o s b e r i n g i a n u s. Satunin, K. A. Opredelitel'
mlekopitayushchikh Rossiiskoi imperii (Key to Mammals of the Russian
Empire). p. 94, Tiflis; Adlerberg, G. P. Khishchnye zveri (Carnivora,
Fissipedia) Arktiki (Carnivora, Fissepedia of the Arctic). In: Zveri
Arktiki pod redaktsiei prof. N A. Smirnova, pp. 299 — 305, Leningrad,
Izdatel'stvo Glavsevmorputi. 1935; Ellerman, J. R. and
T. C. S. Morrison-Scott. Checklist of Palaearctic and Indian Mammals,
p. 238, London. 1951.
    1924. U r s u s a r c t o s k o l y m e n s i s. Ognev, S. I. O medvedyakh,
vodyashchikhsya v Rossii (Bears in Russia). — Priroda i Okhota na
Ukraine, Nos. 1—2, p. 112. (Zabortsevo, the Kolyma River);
Ognev, S. I. Zveri Vostochnoi Evropy i Severnoi Azii (Animals of Eastern
Europe and Northern Asia). Vol. 2, pp. 85 — 86, Moskva-Leningrad. 1931.
    1931. U r s u s j e s s o e n s i s subsp. nov. Ognev, S. I. Ibid., Vol. 2,
pp. 104 — 106 (southern Sakhalin).
    1936. U r s u s a r c t o s l a s i o t u s. Zolotarev, N. T. Mlekopitayushchie
basseina reki Imana (Mammals of the Basin of the Iman River). pp. 84 — 86.
Moskva-Leningrad, Izdatel'stvo AN SSSR. 1936.

Type and type locality. Not given by Middendorf. The description is based
on a number of skulls from Kamchatka, the Okhotsk coast, the coast of
Siberia, and the Shantar Islands. S. I. Ognev (1931) designates as type specimen
No. 1226 of the Zoological Institute of the Academy of Sciences of the USSR, coll.
by A. F. Middendorf from Malyi Shantar Island.
    Diagnosis. This subspecies differs from the preceding subspecies in its
very large size and in features of the fur. Condylobasal length in male
skulls reaches 380 mm (332 mm in the nominate subspecies and 340 mm
in U. A. j e n i s e e n s i s).
    Fur very long, dense and soft, its color varying from pale straw yellow
to blackish brown and dull coal black. Dark individuals predominate. Legs
are usually of same color as the body. Claws dark brown, sometimes
with light yellowish streaks in the distal half; claw length on middle toe
of forepaw to 100 mm.
    Measurements. Weight and measurements are very variable. The
following data on the weight of this subspecies are available. S. I. Ognev
(1932) states that, according to A. D. Baturin (who killed numerous bears in
Kamchatka) "the weight of the largest specimens probably reaches 640 kg."
    Ognev quotes local hunters saying that bears in the Ussuri territory may
weigh 480 kg.
    The data on weights of 640 and 480 kg have not been confirmed and are
probably "hunter's tales." All bears examined weighed much less.
    A male bear from Kamchatka measured by Baturin weighed
288 — 320 kg. A bear of similar weight, killed at Suchan in the Ussuri
territory, is mentioned by N. M. Przheval'skii (1870).
    Such giant animals are very rare and smaller animals are usually found.
    According to Yu. V. Averin (1948), the weight of five males from
Kamchatka was 144 — 285 kg; two females weighed 127.6 and 176.6 kg.
    According to G. F. Bromlei (in litt.), three males in the Sikhote-Alin
reserve weighed 219 — 307 kg and two females 198 — 199 kg. Bears in the
Maritime Territory usually weigh 160 — 180 kg.

Body measurements (15 males and 8 females): length of body and head: males 108—244 cm (av. 186 cm), females 100—182 cm (av. 160 cm); height at withers: males 118—135 cm (av. 129 cm), females 94—99 cm (av. 96 cm); length of tail: males 10—21 cm (av. 17 cm), females 15—18 cm (av. 16 cm); length of ears: males 14—17 cm (av. 16 cm), females 10—15 cm (av. 14 cm).

Skull measurements (22 males and 9 females): condylobasal length: males 333—419 mm (av. 380 mm), females 304—378 mm (av. 345 mm); zygomatic width: males 207—277 mm (av. 253 mm), females 201—242 cm (av. 223 cm); mastoid width: males 156—220 mm (av. 195 mm), females 150—195 mm (av. 174 mm); interorbital width: males 80—108 mm (av. 96 mm), females 71—92 mm (av. 83 mm); width between ends of suborbital processes: males 115—162 mm (av. 139 mm), females 103—127 mm (av. 120 mm); postorbital width: males 75—91 mm (av. 81 mm), females 70—81 mm (av. 76 mm); width of rostrum above canines: males 75—103 mm (av. 83 mm), females 70—93 mm (av. 75 mm); width between infraorbital foramina: males 77—95 mm (av. 82 mm), females 65—83 mm (av. 72 mm); width of nasal opening: males 48—69 mm (av. 52 mm), females 46—54 mm (av. 50 mm); height of nasal opening: males 48—65 mm (av. 58 mm), females 42—59 mm (av. 51 mm); length of the nasals: males 93—131 mm (av. 105 mm), females 89— 96 mm (av. 93 mm); length of upper tooth row: males 130—151 mm (av. 143 mm), females 119—142 mm (av. 132 mm).

Systematic notes. The systematic status of U. a. b e r i n g i a n u s is clear to anyone who has seen them in nature and studied the material. These are very large, dark animals. The skull is large and massive with strongly developed crests and processes.

Study of a large amount of material, including age, individual and seasonal variations of external and cranial characters, shows that the Kamchatka bear does not differ taxonomically from the bears of the Amur area and the Maritime Territory. U. a. m a n d s c h u r i c u s Heude (1898) is the latest synonym of U. a. b e r i n g i a n u s.

We also find no significant differences in bears from Sakhalin.

With regard to U. a. k o l y m e n s i s Ognev (1941), the author of this subspecies later doubted its validity, and came to the conclusion that its status should be checked and studied more thoroughly on good material. Such material is not available, so the systematic position of U. a. k o l y m e n s i s should be left open for the time being.

The subspecific status of the Anadyr bear is also not clear. According to Ognev (1941), the Anadyr area is inhabited by small animals of the type of U. a. k o l y m e n s i s and by large animals of the type of U. a. b e r i n g i a n u s. L. A. Portenko (1941) examined about 20 pelts of bears from Markov and Anadyr and all were small animals. A skull brought from Anadyr by B. S. Yudin is also small. However, the collection of the Zoological Institute of the Academy of Sciences contains a skull of the Anadyr bear (No. 8731, ♂ 5. V. 1907, coll. of N. P. Sokol'nikov) which is no smaller than that of the Kamchatka bear. New collections are necessary to solve this question.

Geographical distribution. Kamchatka, Okhotsk coast, Dzhugdzhur and Stanovoi ranges, Amur area and Maritime Territory, Shantar Islands and Sakhalin.

Material examined. Anadyr, 3 skulls; Kolyma, 6 skulls; Kamchatka, 63 skulls and 18 pelts; Okhotsk coast, 2 skulls; Dzhugdzhur and Stanovoi ranges, 4 skulls and 2 pelts; Amur area and Maritime Territory, 30 skulls and 6 pelts; Shantar Islands, 4 skulls; Sakhalin, 3 skulls and 2 pelts. Total: 115 skulls and 28 pelts.

Biology. The bear is a typical inhabitant of large forests, and occurs in forestless mountains only in a few localities in the south, e. g. in the Pamirs. It migrates from the taiga to the tundra in spring and summer, and in the mountains into the zone of alpine meadows.

The habitat of the bear in Siberia includes biotopes associated with plain and mountain taiga. The bear prefers large forest tracts with berries, cedar, stone pine, nuts and other fruits and broken by mossy marshes, overgrown burns, windbreak areas, areas crossed by rivers, and canyons in the mountains. The population density is higher in the taiga in dark conifer forests of Siberian stone pine and stone pine—fir forests. Monotypic sparse forests and small groves are avoided by the bear.

The bear finds optimal conditions in the Narym taiga in old stone pine and mixed forests with rich food, numerous fallen trees, etc., and with dry secluded places suitable for dens.

The bear inhabits similar biotopes further east, on the middle and lower reaches of the Yenisei. According to N. P. Naumov (1934), in the Turukhansk area the bear prefers places with smooth relief covered by dense and dark forests of Siberian stone pine and firs. The numbers of bears decrease further north where larch forests mixed with forest tundra predominate.

FIGURE 48. Thicket of Japanese stone pine on the shore of Gizhiga Bay. Biotope of the brown bear. Photo by B.S. Yudin

Further south, in the area near the Altai, the animal occurs sparsely in the upper Ob forests near Barnaul. According to G. N. Likhachev (1930), the bear is common between the Petrovka and Bol'shaya Rechka rivers. He writes: "This is a very wild and inaccessible place, with many marshes. Tracts of old forest, between marshes overgrown with dense thickets of bramble and fallen trees and anthills, provide plenty of food and protection."

According to P. B. Yurgenson (1938), the bear prefers dark conifer taiga on the Altai. This is also the case on the Kuznetsk Ala-Tau and on the Sayans.

In the Irkutsk Region, according to I. P. Kopylov and others (1940), the bear inhabits forests of stone pine and larch, and pine—larch forests. In the high mountains of the southern and northeastern Baikal area, and in the Sayans, the summer habitats of the bear are alpine meadows and bare mountains. On the northeastern shore of the Baikal, G. G. Doppel'maier (1926) records that the bear occurs everywhere in summer; along the lake shore, in pine forests, in stone pine — fir forests, and on the bare mountains.

In the mountains between the Olekma and Vitim rivers, according to I. S. Polyakov (1873), the bear keeps to dense forests consisting of larch, willow and poplar with undergrowth of whortleberries and bilberries. "Tracks and places where bears have wallowed, rested, and torn the bark off trees to obtain insects, ants, etc. are everywhere..."

On the upper reaches of the Chita River bears occur mainly in mountain larch taiga with numerous ravines overgrown with bilberries, whortleberries, black currants, and others. At the end of summer the bears visit the bare mountains, where they feed on nuts of the Japanese stone pine (Pavlov, 1948).

FIGURE 49. Kamchatka. Biotope of the brown bear. Photo by N. A. Violovich

On the Kolyma the bear inhabits forests, including the krummholz zone (Buturlin, 1913).

According to A. V. Samorodov (1939), the preferred habitat of the bears in summer in the Olyutorka area of Kamchatka is river valleys with alder thickets and with Japanese stone pine on the slopes. The bears are attracted by spawning fish (Figure 48).

In Kamchatka the bear mainly occupies the lower and middle zone of mountains (Averin, 1948). In the Maritime Territory it mainly inhabits remote areas of the Ussuri taiga in riverain mixed forests and broad-leaf forests (Figure 49). According to N. M. Przheval'skii (1879), "the bears (in the Ussuri territory) usually keep to river valleys with coppices, where they find plenty of food (roots, berries and grapes and sometimes kill young including roe deer."

According to G. F. Bromlei (in litt.) the brown bear in the Maritime Territory keeps mainly to dark conifer taiga of the Okhotsk type. It enters broadleaf forests of the Manchurian type only occasionally.

The size of the bear population in various biotopes varies, because of migrations due to changes in food supply on the biotope and to the intensity of attacks by bloodsucking insects.

However, the bear generally stays in a given area, making the above migrations only in a few localities.

According to L. P. Sabaneev (1878), bears on the Urals make yearly migrations in autumn from the western to the eastern slopes, for distances of 200—300 km. Bears which pass the winter on the eastern slopes return in spring and summer to the western side. These migrations are probably due to snow being earlier, and being longer lasting on the western slopes than on the eastern slopes, which prolongs the period of hibernation by about a month.

Local migrations of bears have been observed everywhere. To escape bloodsucking flies and mosquitoes the bears often move into the tundra on the Northern Urals, and to mountain slopes where the wind reduces the numbers of bloodsucking flies (Flerov, 1929). In northern Siberia bears enter the krummholz zone and tundra in summer when searching for food or trying to escape from bloodsucking flies, sometimes going as far as the seashore. In mountains the bears may ascend to the alpine zone to escape bloodsucking flies. The same happens in the Ussuri territory.

According to N. P. Sokol'nikov (1927) and L. A. Portenko (1941), bears in the Anadyr valley move to rivers in spring, when they come out of hibernation, even before the ice breaks. The rising water drives them to high localities where they hunt fish in small rivers. The bears again descend into the Anadyr valley after the floods.

The bears concentrate in autumn in the taiga, where there are berries and stone pine, and in settled areas near oat fields. N. T. Zolotarev (1934) states that in summer the bears in the Uda and Verkhnaya Selemdzha valleys stay near water bodies, where they find some protection from bloodsucking flies and sufficient food (they feed on the last year's berries and on fresh vegetation in spring, in summer hunting elk and in August feeding on spawning chum salmon). The bears migrate back into the mountains in autumn, the berries there ripening at this time. In Kamchatka, on the coast of the Sea of Okhotsk, and in the Maritime Territory the bears concentrate on the seashore and near rivers where fish are spawning.

According to A. A. Nasimovich (1949), bears in the Central Altai migrate in autumns when snow is early and heavy (e.g., 3 and 4 October 1942), from the upper zone of the mountains to the lower zone, closer to the so-called "den areas" for which the Gromatukha canyon, Lake Talmen, and the forests on the Krasnoyarka are famous.

According to D. K. Solov'ev (1920), the bears in the Eastern Sayan move to the mountains in summer and may be found above the timberline near patches of snow and on alpine meadows. When there is much snow in autumn the bears leave the high mountains and move to the forests, where they hibernate.

Migrations of bears to den areas have been recorded by G. D. Dul'keit (1959) from the Mana River valley. The bears move from areas with much snow to areas with less snow, descend to the valleys and cross rivers.

According to M. A. Lavov (1955) many bears in Transbaikalia descend in summer from the mountains into the valleys of taiga rivers and to the shore of Lake Baikal. When the nuts of stone pine and Japanese stone pine ripen, the bears concentrate in stone pine forests and in forests with plenty of berries (whortleberries, bilberries, bramble, currants, etc.). After the snow falls, the bears, now quite fat, leave the feeding places and search for places suitable for dens, traveling sometimes 20 — 30 km. Some bears on the Khamar-Daban move to the upper belt of mountains.

According to G. F. Bromlei (in litt.), the bears in the Ussuri territory wander over large areas (5,000 — 10,000 hectares) from one locality to another according to the seasonal feeding conditions. The bears migrate in autumn from localities with little food, going hundreds of kilometers to areas with plenty of nuts, acorns and berries. The main food plants which cause movements of bears are the Korean pine, Mongolian oak, the cherry tree, bilberry, and to a lesser degree hazelnut, Manchurian walnut and whortleberry.

The connection between bear density and a biotope's food resources may be judged from the following data. G. F. Bromlei (in litt.) found only 2 — 3 bears on the Sitsa River (Terenei area) in early May along 100 — 120 km of route. In September, in a year of good crops of stone-pine nuts, bears were found on each day's march of 10 — 12 km. Bears were observed every day during the spawning of the chum salmon in the Sitsa and the masu salmon in the Tatibe (a tributary of the Iman River). Yu. A. Salmin (1939) observed 9 bears catching fish for three hours on the bank of the Sitsa River. He saw three adult bears feeding on whortleberries in marshes.

The number of bears in the Siberian taiga is proportional to the area of berries, the presence of Sorbus, and the crops of stone pine nuts.

The den in which the bear hibernates is built in extremely remote places in the taiga with many fallen trees, in inaccessible marshes, and more rarely in open areas like forest glades with sparse trees and shrubs. In the mountains bear dens are usually situated on slopes, among rocks or in ravines.

One of the main conditions for den building is that the locality be dry and that an opening at the leeward side can be made.

The den of the bear is often situated near human settlements. A. A. Romanov (1941) reported that a bear in the Rossokha River valley went to sleep, after an unsuccessful pig-hunt, near a camp of nomads, building its den with branches under a rock. "The bear lay near the camp throughout the winter and the deer breeders could not make up their minds to kill it."

In some areas, e. g., on the Altai, the dens are situated in localities where the bears concentrate before hibernation. Thus, according to P. B. Yurgenson (1938), local hunters knew of 26 dens which were occupied for many years along Lake Teletskoe on the 10 km from Cape Karatash to Cape Azhi. According to N. P. Sokol'nikov (1927) and L. A. Portenko (1941), bears build dens in the Anadyr valley mainly on mountains and on high, dry places.

The den is a cavity under a fallen tree, or among roots, under overhanging branches or rocks, or a small natural cave.

It is lined with moss, grass or dry leaves, branches and bark of trees. There are also dens without lining.

The bear may sometimes dig a cavity on an open place and cover it with branches. All dens found by F. F. Shillinger in the former Yeniseisk province were deeper than those in the European USSR (Ognev, 1931).

According to D. K. Solov'ev (1920), "the dens in the Eastern Sayan are very deep in the soil or in a deep cave or cleft in a rock." The bear in the Sayans does not hibernate on the surface of the ground, under the branches of a tree, as in the European USSR. "Dens which we examined made an angle of 45° to the surface and were about 2 meters deep. The narrow entrance widened into a round chamber in which a man could stand comfortably; the bottom was lined with moss. Dens in rock clefts and caves are of varying depth (6 — 8 m) and usually among rocks so that they are not easily accessible."

P. B. Yurgenson (1938) states that one of the dens near Lake Teletskoe was situated on the top of a steep cliff above the river. "This den was only a widening in a rather long, narrow cave that man could only enter on all fours."

According to M. A. Lavov (1955), dens in Transbaikalia are mainly built on steep mountain slopes in inaccessible places. They are usually built under the roots of old trees or under large rocks. Some dens are dug in the soil in dense thickets of fir (Abies sibirica Ledeb.). The den is a pit with a slight down-gradient. It is wider inside the chamber. The lining consists of branches of firs which have been cut near the den and it is by these broken branches that local hunters find dens.

According to A. Cherkasov (1867), dens of all the types described are found in southwestern Transbaikalia. According to A. F. Middendorf (1867), bears in Eastern Siberia occasionally lie on pine branches, and the den is usually lined with moss, pine needles and bark of trees, leaves or plants.

According to Yu. V. Averin (1948), the dens of bears in Kamchatka are situated, "under the roots of fallen birches, among stones, in natural caves, etc. Branches, dry leaves, and plants are usually dragged into the den." G. A. Fedoseev (1956) mentions a den on the Dzhugdyr Mountains in a steep ravine under the roots of a fallen spruce.

According to N T. Zolotarev (1934), the dens in the Uda and Verkhne-Selemdzha area are built on the southern slopes of mountains, in spruce—fir forest or in thickets of Japanese stone pine.

In the Iman River valley bears often build their dens in foothills or in narrow and deep valleys of brooks (Zolotarev, 1936).

V. I. Iokhel'son (1898) gives a description of the den of a bear on the Kolyma. "The bear closes the entrance from within so well that it is visible only when there are fresh traces of its work; but all traces are soon covered with snow and only a small hole is kept open by the respiration of the sleeping bear. If there are branches of larch above the den, the warm air from the draft hole forms a curly wide beard of snow on the branches."

The exit of the den is usually at the side opposite the prevailing winds. This is usually, but not always, the southern side. N. P. Sokol'nikov (1927) is of the opinion that on the Anadyr the entrance to the den is directed north because females with cubs have to remain for a long time in the den; if the entry were directed south water would enter in spring when the snow thaws.

Bears which begin hibernation early (in particular, pregnant females) build their dens more carefully than bears which wait until the snow falls. Males and pregnant females hibernate singly and only very rarely are two bears found in one den. A female which did not gather fat in the summer often hibernates with its cubs in their first year.

The hibernation of the bear usually continues without interruption for 6 — 7 months. Hibernation enables the bear to pass the period without food, which is scarce because of the deep snow. The bear is not in the state of torpor characteristic of other hibernating animals; its sleep is not deep and may be defined as drowsiness. The animal is easily awakened and immediately active. When alarmed, the bear rapidly escapes from the den. Hibernation is deeper in mid-winter, particularly during strong frost. Hibernation is not very deep in autumn and spring. Females with cubs sleep more deeply.

The bear does not feed, and its intestine is empty throughout hibernation. The animal subsists on the subcutaneous fat accumulated before hibernation, which is also a good thermo-insulator.

Respiration and heartbeat of the hibernating bear are slowed down and the body temperature falls to 29 — 34°C. There is a marked reduction in oxygen consumption and in production of carbon dioxide, so that the intervals between breaths increase and are sometime irregular: there may be a pause of 2 — 4 minutes after 5 — 10 breaths, during which breathing ceases completely (Lobachev, 1951).

Bears change their behavior when going into hibernation. An old and experienced bear does not go directly to its den but attempts to cover its tracks: it makes deviations through dense thickets, marshes, obstructions and almost inaccessible parts of the forest. Some bears, particularly young ones, go directly to the den or at a right angle from their course.

D. K. Solov'ev writes: "I sometimes passed near the den making a circle along the trail of the bear without seeing the den. The bear came out of the den during the night, walked about for some time and lay down again; he was found the next day emerging unwillingly from his den. Another bear who lay down without making any deviations did not permit us to approach riding on reindeer nearer than 60 paces. He came out and escaped before our eyes." The locale was the Eastern Sayan.

The bear begins hibernation in autumn, with the beginning of cold weather and snow; it comes out in spring with the first thaw.

The dates of beginning and end of hibernation depend on the climate, the weather and the fatness of the bears. In the severe climate of the North and of the mountains of Siberia, bears begin hibernation earlier and come out later than in southern areas. In years with early cold and snow, bears hibernate earlier than in years with a long and warm autumn. In years with a rich crop of stone-pine nuts, the fat bears hibernate earlier than in years with poor crops. Thus, according to P. B. Yurgenson (1938), in years with a poor crop of stone-pine nuts the bears on the Altai begin hibernation very late. There was a poor crop of stone-pine nuts in 1934 and tracks of bears were observed until 10 December, or even 20 December.

According to K. K Flerov (1929), bears begin hibernation at the end of October. According to A. N. Dubrovskii (1940), the bears in the Yamal-Nenets National District begin hibernation in September. According to V. N. Skalon and V. V. Raevskii (in litt.), the earliest date at which bears begin hibernation in the Konda-Sosva reserve is mid-September, but some bears are still awake in October (a bear was observed on 20 October 1940).

According to G. D. Dul'keit (1959), the bears begin hibernation in the Mana River valley and in the northeastern Altai before the snow is permanent. Females with cubs begin hibernation earlier, before winter; their tracks cease to be found by October, the beginning of the hibernation of the chipmunk. According to A. A. Nasimovich (1949), the bears on the Central Altai begin hibernation between October 10—25, but when alarmed they may even be awake in December.

In the Narym taiga and further north on the Ob, the bear begins hibernation when the snow falls, in the first half of October or in the first third of November. According to A. A. Romanov (1941), in the Rossokha valley (lower Khatanga River) bears may be active in early November. For example, in 1933 a bear was found near a winter camp of reindeer breeders and attempted to attack domestic reindeer. Afterwards he lay down in his den under a rock near the camp.

According to I. I. Kolyushev (1936), the bear begins hibernation in the lower Lena area in late September or early October. According to N. P. Sokol'nikov (1927) the bear begins hibernation on the Anadyr in early October, but comes out of the den for some time at first and begins hibernation permanently at the end of October.

According to Yu. V. Averin (1948), "bears begin hibernation in late October in the Kronoki reserve in Kamchatka, but females with young of the same year begin earlier than single animals. The dates are very variable and fluctuate annually. In years with a good food crop — berries, fish or nuts — the bears begin hibernation earlier but in years with a poor food crop the animals remain active for a long time and begin hibernation irregularly."

The last bear tracks [in the Kronoki reserve] have been observed on the snow occasionally in late November and early December.

According to M. O. Krivoshapkin (1865), bears begin hibernation in the former Yeniseisk district after 15 October but a few bears may be active until 10 November. According to V. V. Timofeev (1949), the bears begin hibernation in the Irkutsk Region in the second half of October. According to D. K. Solov'ev (1921), the bears begin hibernation in the Eastern Sayan at different dates, according to locality and weather, in late October or in early November. According to I. S. Polyakov (1873), the bears begin hibernation in the mountains between the Olekma and the Vitim rivers in mid-October.

According to Z. F. Svatosh, a bear began hibernation in Transbaikalia in the Gramotukha River valley on 20—27 October 1914 (Ognev, 1931). According to M. A. Lavov (1955), the bear begins hibernation in Transbaikalia in October and tracks usually disappear by the second half of this month. According to A. A. Cherkasov (1867), bears begin hibernation in southern and southwestern Transbaikalia in late September. E. Pavlov (1948) reports that bears on the upper Chita River begin hibernation in the first half of October. Bears in the Selemdzha and Uda valleys begin hibernation at the end of October or in early November, according to N. T. Zolotarev (1934).

According to Radde (1862), bears in the Amur area begin hibernation in late October. N. M. Przheval'skii (1870) states that bears in the Ussuri territory begin hibernation in mid-October; in the Iman valley this starts in December according to N. T. Zolotarev (1936), and in southern Sakhalin in late October, according to Dobrotvorskii (1870), though there some bears do not hibernate at all.

The different dates for the beginning of hibernation in adjacent areas with a similar climate are due to meteorological conditions in the given autumn.

Some individual bears may delay hibernation because food is plentiful (carrion, oats in forest glades, etc.); they do not begin hibernation at the normal time but remain active for a long time. According to Yu. V. Averin (1948), "a stranded whale, or a spawning place of coho salmon in autumn, or similar food, may delay hibernation of the hungry and lean bears until autumn. The bears may remain until the food is finished and lie down to sleep on the snow." Such bears are called "wanderers." They begin hibernation very late, when the snow is so deep that it is difficult to obtain food and movement becomes impossible. It seems that bears which have not accumulated sufficient fat in summer and autumn become "wanderers."

Bears sometimes come out of the den during warm spells for some time and then go back to sleep. According to P. B. Yurgenson (1938), the bears in the Altai know the location of most dens and "a disturbed animal may move from one den to another. If a den is occupied by a strong and large animal, he moves on, but if the den is empty or occupied by a weak animal he drives it out and the other animal has to search for a den."

The bear lies curled up in the den, feet pressed to the body, the nose covered with the forelegs. Animals sometimes change position. The movements of the bear in the den may be judged by the dust accumulating near the entrance.

The dates of awakening and emergence from the den depend on the locality and the meteorological conditions in the spring of a given year. This date usually coincides with the first thaw on mountain slopes with southern exposure.

However, the date of mass awakening for bears also depends on the type of the autumn in which the animals began to hibernate, and this is characterized by the following rule. If food is scarce that autumn the bears begin hibernation late and are insufficiently nourished, and so awaken earlier in spring. But if food is plentiful in autumn, the bears become fat, begin hibernation early, and awake later in spring.

The time of awakening in spring can be predicted if the date of beginning of hibernation is known.

According to L. G. Kaplanov (1935), the bears come out of hibernation in the Demyanka River valley in Western Siberia in late April. According to V. V. Raevskii and V. N. Skalon (in litt.) they come out in April in the Konda-Sosva reserve (the extreme dates were 3 April 1945 and 29 April 1939).

However, according to our data (from the Tomsk Region), the emergence of the bears cannot be fixed at a certain date. If the spring is early, the bears leave the den in mid-March or early April, and when the spring is long they come out by mid-April.

According to A. M. Nasimovich (1949), the bears come out of hibernation in the Central Altai in early April — at about the same time as the badger.

In North Siberia bears awaken and leave the den later. According to K. K. Flerov (1929), bears in the Northern Urals and in the lower Ob area awaken in late March or early April. According to A. N. Dubrovskii (1940), they come out in the Yamal-Nenets National District when the snow thaws, usually in May. According to A. F. Middendorf (1876), the bears awaken in the middle of May on the Taimyr, in the upper reaches of the Pyasina River. According to I. I. Kolyushev (1936), the bears come out of the den in early May near Bulun, on the lower reaches of the Lena. According to S. A. Buturlin (1913), the bears awaken in early May on the lower Kolyma. According to N. P. Sokol'nikov (1927) and L. A. Portenko (1941), the bears awaken in the second half of April or in early May in the Anadyr area.

According to I. I. Kolyushev (1936), bears are still in their dens in early May near Bulun, on the lower Lena. "The bears probably come out of their dens in the second half of May... "

N. V. Slyunin (1900) states in his description of the Okhotsk-Kamchatka area that "bears come out of the den in the first days of spring, earlier in southern Kamchatka than in the Gizhiga area." According to N. Buxton, the bears leave the dens in the Gizhiga area in early April and two weeks later near the village of Markovo (Anadyr).

According to Yu. V. Averin (1948), the bears leave their dens about 10 April in Kamchatka. "Most bear leave the dens in the second half of April or in early May. The first to come out are lean and single animals who did not accumulate sufficient fat before hibernation, and bears whose dens were warmed by the sun or flooded." The bears leave the dens earlier near the coast than deep in the peninsula. Females with newborn cubs come out earlier, in the middle of May. According to N. T. Zolotarev (1934), the bears leave the dens in late April or early May on the upper reaches of the Ud and Selemdzha rivers.

The dates of awakening vary in the Amur and Ussuri valleys, according to the weather, from 20 March to the middle of April. Females with cubs emerge later.

The bears leave the den in early April on the upper reaches of the Chita River (Pavlov, 1948).

According to D. K. Solov'ev (1921), the bears in the Eastern Sayan leave the den in early April when the snow thaws, particularly when the dens are flooded. But if there are frosts, the animals probably go to sleep again.

Bears in the Irkutsk Region leave their dens in late March or early April, according to I. P. Kopylov (1948).

According to P. B. Yurgenson (1938), the bears begin to leave their dens on the Altai usually in mid-April, and most animals are already out of their dens at the end of the month.

Females with cubs leave the den later than males and barren females.

The claws grow during the winter sometimes to a length of 10 cm. In the mountains and on stony ground, the claws are usually worn, but they are little worn in the plains and on soft soil, and make walking difficult. The bears then go to a large tree, stand on their hind legs, and scratch the bark, leaving deep grooves and hanging strips of bark. Resin drips from these scratches. Bears may scratch the same tree the next year. A. N. Formozov (1952) saw "old larch trees (on the lower Amur) seriously damaged by the bears, the resin containing fur of varying age and color. The bears probably worked here for dozens of years" (Figure 50).

FIGURE 50. Claw marks of the bear on a tree (after N. N. Formozov, 1952)

The presence of bears in a certain biotope is easily recognizable by various signs of activity: excrement, excavated anthills, turned logs, broken tree stumps, traces on berry plants, on paths and on the banks of water bodies where the bears come to drink, and by "bear markings" on the bark of trees, broken branches, excavated chipmunk burrows, etc. (Figure 51).

The tracks of the bear (Figure 52) differ from the tracks of other animals by their large size and by the distinct marking of the claws.

The length of the print of the hind foot is 20—30 cm from the posterior margin of the sole to the end of the claws.

The bears make paths in thickets and these paths are used for many years. Such paths were observed by A. F. Middendorf (1869) on the Shanta Islands and on the shore of the continent .

"You will find well-trodden paths everywhere in the middle of the forest or on bare mountains, signs of intensive activity. You will look for settlements but you are in a large area uninhabited by man, there is no human settlement and not a human soul anywhere. These paths are the track of wild animals... They are the trails of the bear.

"As the prints of the forelegs and hind legs of the same side are superimposed, they form longitudinal pits one after the other. On the mainland these become transformed into furrows, and are also used by

deer. It would be impossible to pass through thickets in this territory
without encountering the activity of the bear.   The bears appear here as
pioneers of civilization making roads for humans" (Middendorf).

FIGURE 51. "Spring marking" of the bear on a fir
tree. Photo by F. D. Shaposhnikov

A similar path, used by the bears along the seashore in search of food
washed ashore, was found by A. N. Formozov (1952) in the taiga on the shore
of the Tatar Strait. "A trail extended for many kilometers through a dense fir
forest, trampled in the deep moss down to the rock. It gave the impression
that somebody in large felt boots had marched along on this trail, placing his
legs one after the other, and made a furrow 10 — 20 cm deep."
    K. Ditmar (1901) described such trails in Kamchatka.   "These remarkable
roads lead to a suitable mountain pass, avoiding steep cliffs and
impassable thickets of stone pine and alder; the trails lead to rivers and

lakes with abundant fish and to places with plenty of berries. Kamchatka
is riddled from north to south and from east to west with such well-trampled

trails.   Trails are often found which from time
immemorial have served as roads for the bears; they are well
trodden, about half a meter wide and free of plants.
Anyone without experience would think this a footpath
leading to a village......"

The famous botanist V. L. Komarov (1940) drew
attention to the trails of bears in Kamchatka. According to

him, "alder groves are one of the main obstacles for
travelers in Kamchatka who do not use the highways. The
main stem of this shrub lies almost on the ground, and its
branches are vertical. The bears make their paths through
the alder thicket; the paths are low tunnels and a man is
able to pass, but a horse cannot pass there and to make this
possible the forest would have to be felled, requiring much
time and labor."

The senses of the bear are well developed; hearing and

smell are very acute, sight being weaker. Taste is well
developed. The intelligence of the bear is high. It is
easily tamed and trained for circus performances.

The bear is usually silent. It may sometimes utter a
subdued grumble, but it may also howl.

The movements of the bear are usually slow and appear

awkward, but when it is alarmed or in danger the bear
moves rapidly. It is rapid in attack. It may cross broad
rivers if necessary, and stalks its prey quietly. Young
bears can climb trees but heavy adult animals are unable to
do so.

FIGURE 52. Foot-
prints of Ursus
arctos L. (after
A. N. Formozov, 1952)

Bears usually avoid humans. When alarmed they often
panic and escape. In many localities bears never attack
humans, but they may be aggressive against humans
in others.

Rare cases of unprovoked attacks have been recorded in
the Narym territory and in Transbaikalia. S. S. Turov writes that a large
bear attacked him and his companion on Svyatoi Nos, 2 km from
Zmeinaya Bay. "Despite our shouting and shooting (of hazel grouse), the bear
attacked us from a distance of 20 paces at a rapid gallop and was killed only at
5 paces." A. Cherkasov (1867) mentions a bear stalking humans and,
"there were cases when bears approached hunters so quietly that the
hunters did not notice them until they felt the heavy paws of the animal."

The bears in the Ussuri territory and in Kamchatka are usually very peace-
ful, and attack humans only when wounded and not always even then.

The bear is mainly nocturnal but it may be found browsing or during
migrations in the late morning and sometimes at other hours of the day.

The bear is omnivorous; its food is very variable and consists of both
vegetables and animals. It feeds on succulent herbs, young shoots
and leaves, roots and bulbs, berries, nuts, acorns, etc. It also feeds on
insects and insect larvae and is particularly fond of ants, bumblebees,
wasps, worms, mollusks, amphibians, birds and eggs, and small animals.
It occasionally attacks ungulates, mainly young cattle. It feeds occasionally
on carrion.

The food of the bear varies according to season and locality and sometimes according to individual taste.

When the bear comes out of the den it wanders through the taiga, digging roots and pine cones from under the snow; it feeds on the last year's berries on thawed places, excavates burrows of chipmunks and mice, turns tree trunks in search of insects and other invertebrates, excavates anthills, etc. When the floods recede it searches pools and backwaters, catching fish and frogs and feeding on their spawn. D. V. Ternovskii (in litt.) informed me that the stomach of a bear killed on the Altai on 28 May 1950 contained the following: green plants, pine nut shells and five young moles. According to K. T. Yurlov, the bear in the southeastern Altai enters the steppe, digging marmots from their burrows.

The bear may occasionally feed on carrion or kill an elk or a deer. As the vegetation grows, the food of the bear contains more herbs and other plants. In late summer and autumn it feeds on forest berries and fruits. The bear is very fond of brambles, whortleberries, bilberries and cranberries. It feeds on birdcherry, Sorbus and currants. The bear feeds in late summer on oats from fields near the forest. It prefers grains in the stage of milky ripeness. It may also feed on ripe grain. A bear was killed during the day feeding on a field of oats in September 1956 near Pikhtovka village in the Kolyvan area of the Novosibirsk Region. K. T. Yurlov found, in the stomach of a bear and a cub killed on 11 June 1959 on the Vartovskaya River, leaves of aspen and pine nuts. The pine nuts become an important food in autumn. The bear breaks branches when it collects nuts and fruits and may break the stems of Sorbus and pines, causing damage to shrubs. It feeds on food stores of chipmunks and other rodents.

V. I. Telegin (in litt.) found the following in the stomach of a bear killed on 7 September 1956 on the Bol'shaya Kheta River (left bank of the lower Yenisei): crowberries, bilberries, roots from stores of rodents, and a water vole.

Examination of feces (several dozen) by Telegin showed that the bear had fed in late August and early September on crowberries, ptarmigan berries, blueberries, red currants, horsetail, reindeer moss, voles and other small animals.

In northeastern Siberia, Kamchatka and the Maritime Territory, the bear feeds in the summer on fish ascending rivers for spawning (chum salmon, pink salmon and other migratory fishes).

The bears in Kamchatka concentrate on the banks of rivers when the fish are spawning. The famous zoologist I. G. Voznesenskii observed more than 100 bears on one day in the middle of the last century during the spawning of salmon.

According to Yu. V. Averin (1948) the appearance of spawning fishes in summer in Kamchatka's rivers (pink salmon, sea trout, Arctic char, coho salmon and chum) causes concentrations of bears near rivers.

Averin writes: "The valleys of rivers with fish show signs of the activity of generations of fishing bears; their trails run along the banks of the rivers and cross them, emerging from valleys and low mountains. When the vegetation is high in summer (2 — 2.5 m) the trails of the bears are the only means of movement in the valley."

According to Yu. V. Averin (1948), the bears in the Kronoki reserve catch fish "in small backwaters where the fish collect or on shoals where the fins of the fish are visible while they move against the current. The bears either enter the water attempting to drive the fish into the shallows, or stand in the water, lowering the head to the surface while waiting for the fish and catching it rapidly with the paws. The bear may use only one 'hand' to throw the fish to the bank. The catching of fish is easier in spawning places with calm water, where the fish are less cautious and strong. When the fish are numerous the bear eats mainly the head and part of the back; when fish are scarce, they are eaten completely. The stomach of a large bear may contain 20 kg of fish. However, plants and berries are always found together with fish."

The seasonal changes in the bear's diet are as follows according to Averin:

"The first crowberries and blueberries ripen in late July. The bear feeds on them in large quantities. Fish remain the staple food of most bears but berries become more important.

Bears are often found in August in the open berry-covered tundra, feeding on berries for days. They prefer crowberries to blueberries. The spawning of pink salmon ends in the second half of August and the summer fish, sea trout and Arctic char also decrease, leaving the autumn fish: chum, red salmon, coho salmon and Arctic char; the last two are found on the spawning places until December. These fish enter numerous small brooks and become available to the bear on a large territory. The most important foods, blueberries and crowberries, are important until mid-September. Blueberries become less available at this time and crowberries are replaced by the berries of Sorbus and pine nuts."

According to A. M. Nikol'skii (1889) the main food in autumn in Sakhalin is fish; when fish are abundant the bear eats only the head, leaving the body The roe is eaten after it has been deposited.

The composition and seasonal changes in the food in the Ussuri area are shown in Table 2, compiled by G. F. Bromlei (in litt.).

TABLE 2. Diet composition of the brown bear in the Ussuri area at different seasons (% of the food items in 76 feces and 2 stomachs)

Type of food	Spring (20 March — 15 May)	Summer (16 May — 31 August)	Autumn (1 September — 3 December)	Throughout the year
I. Vegetable food	61.1	68.8	73.2	68.9
1. Various plants	22.3	28.4	1.0	13.3
2. Berries	17.0	29.4	36.8	33.9
3. Nuts	9.5	4.3	27.3	10.1
II. Animal food	35.1	31.4	26.8	31.1
1. Mammals	23.5	0.6	2.9—90.0	4.0
2. Fish	—	8.7	17.2	10.1
3. Insects	31.1	21.4	3.6	16.8

Similar data on the composition of the food for bears in the Ussuri area are given in Table 3 (by G. F. Bromlei; based on food remnants and activity connected with food gathering.

TABLE 3. Proportions of food items of the brown bear (% of the 147 food remnants examined and traces of activity)

Type of the food remnants and activity of the animal	Spring	Summer	Autumn	Throughout the year
Excavated chipmunk burrows	20.5	—	27.8	6.2
Hollows in the turf.	12.1	12.0	14.4	5.5
Turned logs	35.5	12.1	30.5	17.8
Broken tree stumps.	19.2	13.7	22.6	14.4
Carrion (elk and roe deer).	40.0	—	20.5	5.4
Traces of catching wild boar	30.0	—	—	4.1 / 13.5
Remnants of fish	—	14.7	39.9	1.2
Destroyed bee hives	6.3	—	4.5	8.2
Remnants of Petasites. .	12.6	23.3	—	7.1
Remnants of cow parsnip . .	—	22.6	—	13.9
Remnants of blueberries . .	—	63.9	—	

When the bears come out of their dens in spring in the Ussuri area they concentrate on bilberry stands at the boundary of the forestless vegetation, and remain here until early June. If bilberries become scarce the bears descend into the foothills, into the zone of Manchurian forest, collecting nuts, acorns and insects. The bears move to valleys of brooks and rivers in early summer feeding on Angelica, cow parsnip and Petasites. In river valleys they feed on migratory fish, Oncorhynchus masu and O. keta. In autumn they remain in different zones according to the available food. When bilberries are abundant they climb to the zone of forestless vegetation, feeding on berries until hibernation. When bilberries are scarce, the bears concentrate in the upper levels of the Manchurian forest, feeding on nuts and berries. The bears descend regularly to the rivers to catch chum salmon. When food conditions in the Manchurian forest are poor, the bears concentrate near the spawning places of chum salmon, and after having caught all the fish available become "carnivorous," attacking ungulates.

The seasonal changes in food composition in the Altai have been recorded by P. B. Yurgenson (1948). Feces of the bear contained remnants of Umbelliferae (50—90 %), thistles and other plants from May 20 to late June. In summer, the bears fed mainly on berries. Stone-pine nuts appeared in the food in the first half of August.

The voracity of the bear is greatest in autumn. The bear accumulates a large quantity of fat before hibernation. The fattest bear in Kamchatka had a layer of fat 15 cm thick on the ribs in late autumn (Averin, 1948), and 30—50 kg of fat can be obtained from a bear at this time.

The following data on the reproduction of the bear are available. The bear reproduces slowly. It becomes sexually mature at the age of 3—4.5

years. The female has its first young in the 5th year, rarely in the 4th. The female goes into heat only once in every two years. This is due to the fact that a female who gives birth in winter is occupied throughout the next summer with feeding and educating the young. When the young are lost, the female mates again and may bear young in two successive years. Opinions in the literature about the times of heat vary.

According to L. P. Sabaneev (1878), the rut of the bear in the area near the Urals occurs in the first half of July. Rut in the middle of July has been recorded in the Urals (Naumov, Lavrov, 1941).

In Western Siberia rut takes place in September in the Demyanka valley, according to I. I. Barabash-Nikiforov (1947), in the north of the Omsk area, according to I. N. Shukhov (1928), and in the former Tomsk Province, according to L. N. Lyalin (1903). These dates contradict dates of other authors in neighboring areas and are probably due to inaccurate observation.

The above data may be based on cases of delayed rut or of rut delayed in certain years. The dates of rut for the bear vary not only in different localities but also in different years in the same area. They also vary individually.

Rut in the Narym taiga takes place mainly in July according to my data, but some individuals may mate later, in the first half of August. Rut begins in the Altai, near Lake Teletskoe, in the middle of May according to P. B. Yurgenson (1938).

According to I. P. Kopylov (1948) and V. V. Timofeev (1949), rut in the Irkutsk Region begins in late May and continues until early July, but may be prolonged until August in some females.

Rut in the Olekma-Vitim Mountains, according to I. S. Polyakov (1873), occurs about 12 July and at the same time in Transbaikalia (Cherkasov, 1867). According to E. Pavlov (1948), rut coincides with the blossoming of Lilium tenuifolium Fisch. in the second half of July in the Chita Region.

According to N. P. Sokol'nikov (1927), rut on the Anadyr in Chukotka usually occurs in mid-June, and mating of bears in Kamchatka was observed by A. D. Baturin in late May (Ognev, 1931). According to Yu. V. Averin (1948), rut occurs in Kronoki (eastern Kamchatka) from the middle of May until late June, to judge from indirect data (trampled vegetation and tracks of bears, fresh wounds in males, and observations of local hunters). Rut occurs in July in Manchuria, according to N. D. Baikov (1915).

The bear is polygamous. Several males chase a female and there are often fights between males. A. Cherkasov (1867) writes that the rut of the bears in Transbaikalia is accompanied by noise and "usually occurs in secluded places but mainly near forest streams and mountain rivers in a cool place... The animal is very ferocious during the rut; its eyes are dull, its sight is poor, it runs with the tongue hanging out, does not feed and foams at the mouth."

According to P. B. Yurgenson (1938) the bears in the Altai descend at the beginning of the rut from the mountains and howl loudly. The author heard from eye witnesses that a female with cubs avoids the males as they usually attack the cubs. P. B. Yurgenson thinks that this is the reason that females with cubs are not found "on mountain slopes warmed by the sun where numerous bears concentrate." Females with cubs "stay in dark conifer forests, although there is little food."

According to Yu. V. Averin (1948), during the rut males fight fiercely for the females. Thus, a hunter found a female on 4 June 1939 — in a birch forest on the upper Kozelskaya River — which was being courted by two males: a large male near the female and a small male at some distance. "When the large male attempted to mate, the small bear attacked it howling. The two males were shot and the female escaped. The males probably had a fight, since both, particularly the large male, had numerous wounds."

The litter usually contains 1 — 3, rarely 4 young. The hunters F. Chudinov and I. Rukavishnikov found 5 cubs in a den with their mother in 1958 in the Kirenski District of the Irkutsk Region (Khodorin, 1959). An exceptional case was reported by A. Shirinskii-Shikhmatov (1900). He killed a gravid female in late December in the former Valda county in Novgorod Province and six completely developed embryos were found. The young would have been born in January, according to their development.

Gestation lasts 7 months on the average. The young are born in the den, during hibernation, from January to March (rarely later, according to the mating data).

According to L. P. Sabaneev (1878), the birth of the young in the Northern Urals takes place in March or even in April and in the Southern Urals in February, but K. K Flerov (1929) thinks that the young are born in February or March in the Northern Urals, as blind young are found at this time.

The birth of the young takes place from the second half of January to late February in Western and Central Siberia, and in some cases even in March.

According to local hunters, the young are born in the Chita area in late February and early March (Pavlov, 1948). According to A. Cherkasov (1867), the young are born in southwestern Transbaikalia in March and rarely in April.

According to Yu. V. Averin (1948), the time of birth in Kamchatka is January to the first half of February. According to N. P. Sokol'nikov (1927), the young are born in late March.

The young are born blind, very small and with short fur, usually with a white collar. The eyes open after one month. The weight of a newborn cub is about 1.5 kg. The size and the weight of newborn cubs in the Moscow Zoo was as follows, according to T. A. Adolph (1949): Length of body 230 — 280 mm, weight 501 — 502 g. The milk teeth are fully developed after three months. The first molar appears at five months. The replacement of the milk teeth takes place at the age of six months. The replacement of the premolars ends at 7 — 8 months, the third and fourth incisors are replaced at 8 — 10 months and the canines at the age of one year. The last molar (M_3) appears at the age of 10 — 12 months.

The small size of the cubs may be regarded as an adaptation to the severe winter. If the young were large, it would be difficult for the mother to nurse them during hibernation.

Like hibernating males, females which give birth during hibernation do not feed. The fat reserves accumulated before hibernation are sufficient not only to sustain the life of the mother, but also to produce milk.

A female which has given birth lies curled up, holding her young near the teats and covering them with her paws. If alarmed or in danger, she leaves the young. When the female comes out of the den in spring, the maternal instinct developes and she defends her young against real or imaginary attack.

The young are able to follow the mother at the age of 3 — 4 months, when she comes out of the den to search for food. The lactation period lasts about 4 months, but the female stays together with the young throughout the summer and also hibernates with them in the following winter. When the young are 15 — 16 months old, the females drive them away and they begin their independent life.

The young grow slowly and those coming out of the dens in spring weigh 2 — 4 kg. By winter, i.e., at the age of about 9 — 10 months, they weigh only 15 — 25 kg. Differences in the rate of growth and in weight between cubs of the same litter may be several kilograms, this being for several reasons. The young may be of different sizes and weights at birth, and may be fed differently during lactation (the stronger cubs driving the weaker ones away and thus impeding their growth); diseases may also influence the growth of the young.

Cubs hibernating for the first time, i.e., at the age of 9 — 10 months to about two years, are called "lonchaki" (yearlings). The weight of these cubs is 20 — 50 kg. The young in the third year are usually called "tret'yaki" or "pestun" ("nurse"). Their weight is 50 — 80 kg and they reach sexual maturity at this age. The females bear young in the fourth year.

The weight of the "lonchaki" and "tret'yaki" varies sometimes by a factor of three in litters of different mothers. Sole cubs and cubs of earlier birth are always larger than twins born later or than cubs emaciated because of disease.

Cubs whose growth was retarded for the above reasons continue to be small when fully grown, and may be called "starvelings." This is the reason for the widely held opinion among hunters, which has also found its way into the literature (Pallas, 1811 — 1831; Eversmann, 1850; Cherkasov, 1867) that some regions have two types of bears, which differ in size: the small "anteaters" which feed mainly on ants and berries, and larger "scavengers" which feed mainly on carrion or on large animals they themselves kill.

When a female remains barren, the last year's cubs lie together with her, particularly if they are the underdeveloped "starvelings" mentioned above. Hunters think that the so-called "pestun," i.e., a cub in the third year hibernates together with the mother. This opinion is certainly an anthropomorphism. The "pestun" is said to act as nurse to its younger brothers and sisters. This has been repeatedly reported in the hunting literature (Shirinskii-Shikhmatov, 1900; Cherkasov, 1867).

The differences in size of the cubs and particularly the marked differences between males and females are probably the origin of the notion about the "pestun" or nurse. However, its existence has not been proved. Specialists on the biology of the brown bear like A. F. Middendorf (1867, 1874), N. A. Mel'nitskii (1915) and others think that the stories about the "pestun" are hunters' tales.

The length of life of the bear is 30 — 40 years according to Krumbigel (1930). It may live to 50 years in captivity. P. A. Manteifel' (1934) mentions a bear which lived 34 years in a zoo but was very weak in its last years. A. Cherkasov (1867) reports a story about a very old bear found in 1855 in the Nerchinsk mountains near Shilkinskii Zavod. It was so old that it had no resistance, and was "killed like a calf." The teeth and claws of this animal

FIGURE 53. Selenarctos thibetanus. From a specimen in the Moscow Zoo. Painting by V. A. Vatagin

133

were completely worn, and it was very thin. Cherkasov writes: "This bear was unable to build a den, and went into hibernation between two stones on a cliff, where it was killed in autumn. Its skin was very scruffy; the fur was reddish brown, hanging in strands."

The bear has few enemies. It is occasionally attacked by wolves, and in the Far East tigers have been known to attack it. The bear is sometimes infected with helminths, but rids itself of these before hibernation.

Molt occurs once a year, in spring, taking place at various dates from April to June according to the local conditions. The fur is shed gradually during the molt, beginning from the groin. The new coat is not fully grown in until autumn.

Practical importance. The damage caused by the bear is important only locally, and only in densely settled areas. It may harm stands of oats and corn, occasionally attack livestock, and cause damage to beehives. In thinly settled areas the damage caused by the bear is small. The bear attacks humans only when wounded or when surprised near its prey, but even then not always.

The fur is warm and strong but of little value. The pelts are used as carpets. The meat and fat have a good taste and nutritive qualities and are used as food. The fat of the bear could be used for technical purposes and has been used for popular remedies.

7.   Genus SELENARCTOS Heude (1901). Black bears

1901. Selenarctos. Heude, P. M. — Mém. Hist. Nat. Emp. Chinois, 5, p. 2; Ognev, S. I. Zveri Vostochnoi Evropy i Severnoi Azii (Animals of Eastern Europe and Northern Asia). Vol. 2, pp. 118—119. Moskva-Leningrad. 1931; Ellerman, J. R. and T. C. S. Morrison-Scott. Checklist of Palaearctic and Indian Mammals, p. 239, London. 1951.

1917. Arcticonus. Pocock, R. J.   A New Genus of Ursidae. — Ann. Mag. Nat. Hist., 20, p. 129. (for Ursus thibetanus Cuvier, 1823).

1938. Euarctos. Allen, G. M. The Mammals of China and Mongolia, pt. 1, p. 330, New York (nec Gray, 1864; partim).

Type species. Ursus thibetanus G. Cuvier (1823).

Diagnosis. The black bear is smaller than the brown bear. Length of body to 180 cm and weight to 150 kg. Muzzle short and pointed, fronto-parietal area flat. Ears large, rounded, projecting markedly from fur. Soles of feet bare. Fur relatively short, glossy, black. Chest with white or orange-yellow patch of crescent shape. Muzzle short: distance from anterior margin of orbit to anterior margin of middle incisor alveolus less than distance between ends of postorbital processes. Ratio of length of upper molars to width of bony palate as in the brown bear. Last lower molar (M_3) not narrowing posteriorly, rounded-rectangular.

Biology Semi-arboreal.

Geographical distribution. Baluchistan and Afghanistan to Formosa, Hainan, Japan and the southern part of the Soviet Far East.

Systematics. Genus monotypic. Selenarctos closely resembles American bears of the genus Euarctos Gray (1864) in external and cranial characters. More detailed study may prove a close relationship between these genera, and they may eventually have to be united in a single genus.

8. **Selenarctos thibetanus** G. Cuvier (1823). Black or Himalayan bear (Figure 53, Map VIII)

1823. Ursus thibetanus. Cuvier, G. Ossements Fossil., 4, p. 325; Satunin, K. A. Opredelitel' mlekopitayushchikh Rossiiskoi imperii (Key to the Mammals of the Russian Empire). p. 95, Tiflis. 1914.

1841. Ursus torquatus. Wagner, J. A. Supplementband zu Schreber "Die Säugethiere," 2, p. 144.

1857. Ursus japonicus. Schlegel. — Handb. d. Tierkunde, 1, p. 42 (Japan).

1862. Ursus tibetanus. Radde, G. Reisen im Süden von Ost-Sibirien in den Jahren 1855 — 1859, pp. 12 — 14, St. - Petersburg. 1862; Przheval'skii, N. M. Puteshestvie v Ussuriiskoi oblasti (Voyage in the Ussuri Region). pp. 245 — 246, Sankt-Peterburg. 1870; Grum-Grzhimailo, G. E. Opisanie Amurskoi oblasti (Description of the Amur Region). p. 330. 1894; Satunin, K. A. — In: Turkin, N. V. and K. A. Satunin. Zveri Rossii, pp. 173 — 176, Moskva. 1910.

1864. Ursus formosanus. Swinchoe, R. — Proc. Zool. Soc. London. p. 380. (Formosa-Taiwan).

1877. Ursus gedrosianus. Blanford, W. T. — Proc. Asiat. Soc. Bengal., p. 204. 1877 (Baluchistan).

1897. Ursus rexi. Matschie, P. Sitzungsber. Gesellsch. Naturforsch. Freunde Berlin, p. 72. (Japan).

1901. Selenarctos mupinensis. Heude, P. M. — Mém. Hist. Nat. Emp. Chinois, 5, p. 2. pl. 2, figs. 1, 2, 9 (Muping, Szechwan, China).

1901. Selenarctos ussuricus. Heude, P. M. Loc. cit., fig. 10. (Ussuri); Sowerby, A. C. — Journ. Mamm., Vol. 1, No. 5, p. 226. 1920.

1901. Selenarctos leuconyx. Heude, P. M. Loc. cit., figs. 3, 4, 8 (nec Ursus leuconyx Severtzov, 1872). (Shensi, China).

1920. Ursus clarki. Sowerby, A. C. — Journ. Mamm., Vol. 1, No. 5, p. 226 (new name for S. leuconyx Heude, 1901).

1951. Selenarctos thibetanus. Ellerman, J. R. and T. C. S. Morrison-Scott. Checklist of Palaearctic and Indian Mammals, p. 239, London.

Type and type locality. The species has been described on the basis of a specimen from Sylhet, Assam.

Diagnosis. The main diagnostic characters of the species are the same as those of the genus and have been given in the diagnosis of the latter.

Measurements. There are no exact data. We give the measurements of the Ussuri black bear, the largest subspecies.

Description. In addition to the characters given in the diagnosis of the genus, the following characters should be noted. Body of black bear is more compact and slender. Muzzle pointed and long, frontal area very flat. Ears large, rounded, projecting markedly from fur and directed laterally. Feet smaller than in brown bear, with bare soles; claws short, strongly curved.

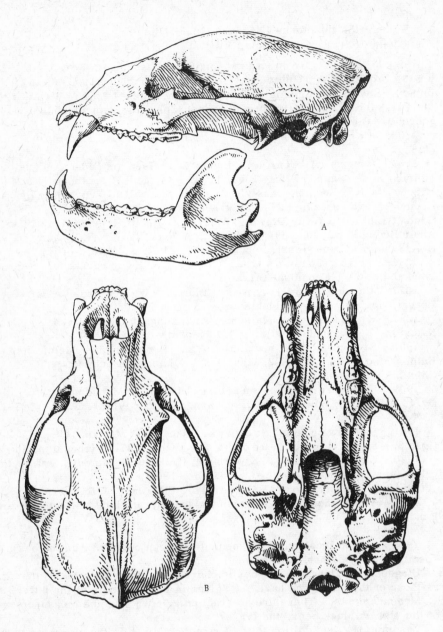

FIGURE 54. Skull of Selenarctos thibetanus Cuvier (original):

A — lateral; B — dorsal; C — ventral.

Fur of moderate length. Hairs on muzzle and forehead short, adpressed. Fur longer on occiput, withers, neck, and cheeks. Fur glossy black. Well defined white or orange-yellow spot on the anterior part of chest, usually of crescent shape and sometimes covering base of neck (Figure 53).

Skull (Figure 54) oval-oblong, and dorsoventrally flattened. Upper outline of skull regularly convex in profile. Sagittal crest weakly developed and not extending anteriorly beyond a third of parietals even in old males. Lambdoidal crest and mastoid processes distinct, making occipital part relatively high and broad. Frontal area convex longitudinally, with at most a very shallow median groove; transverse profile of the upper outline of the frontal area is convex, sometimes slightly concave dorsally. Posterior part of the skull from the posterior margin to the orbits longer, and rostrum shorter, than in brown bear. Distance from the posterior end of occipital crest to line joining ends of postorbital processes markedly longer than distance from this line to anterior margin of premaxillaries. Zygomatic arches weakly developed and not widely separated. Lower jaw short. Last lower molar situated behind anterior margin of orbit. Canines large. Molars small. Anterior premolars sometimes persist throughout life. Last lower molar (M_3) almost rounded-rectangular with weak posterior construction.

Systematic notes. The black bear forms a number of subspecies differing in size and fur quality. A well-marked subspecies occurs in Siberia.

Geographical distribution. The black bear is distributed throughout most of the southern half of Asia, from Baluchistan and Kashmir to Indo-China, Thailand and the [Soviet] Far East, including adjacent islands (Taiwan, Hainan and Japan), north to the Ussuri valley and the middle and lower reaches of the Amur.

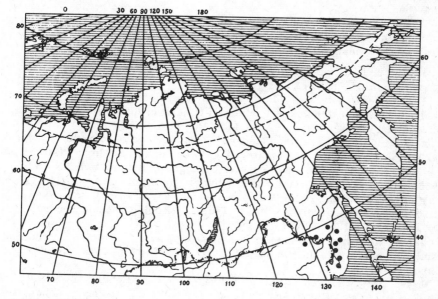

MAP VIII. Geographical distribution of Selenarctos thibetanus Cuvier in Siberia

137

There are the following data on the distribution of the black bear in the Soviet Union (Map VIII).

According to Maak (1861), it occurs in the Ussuri River valley. The Ussurian subspecies has been described from this area (Heude, 1901). N. M. Przheval'skii (1870) reported it as distributed throughout the Ussuri territory.

The black bear was collected in the Iman River valley in 1911 by N.I. Shingarev (coll. Zool. Inst. Acad. Sciences USSR). According to N. T. Zolotarev, it occurs in the Iman valley only to a point 30 km from the mouth of the Kolumbe River.

According to G. F. Bromlei (1953), the northern boundary of its range runs from Innokentiya Bay on the Sea of Japan southwest to the Sikhote-Alin Mountains, crossing the sources of the Samarga River. It then runs via the middle reaches of the rivers Khor, Anui and Khungari to the Amur River above Komsomolsk. Occasionally found near Lake Bolon, the bear is rare on the lower reaches of the Kur and Urmi. Further west it occurs throughout the Jewish Autonomous Region and is common on the southern slopes of the Dur and Shuki-Poktoi ranges. The boundary then crosses the southern slopes of the Bureya, Vanda, and Aagar-Aul mountains, and extends into Manchuria along the southern slopes of the Lesser Khingan Range.

The black bear is common in the central and southern part of the Sikhote-Alin reserve and occurs in the Sudzukhe reserve. G. F. Bromlei collected the black bear on the northern slopes of Tumannaya Mountain, on the rivers Ta-Chingouza, Sandagou and Taukhe (coll. Zool. Mus. Moscow University), and in the Suputinka reserve (coll. S. U. Stroganov).

Subspecies. Eight subspecies are known, but their systematic position has not been sufficiently studied. Only one subspecies occurs in the Far East of the USSR.

8a.   **Selenarctos thibetanus ussuricus**   Heude (1901).
Ussuri black bear

1901. Selenarctos ussuricus. Heude, P. M.— Mém. Hist. Nat. Emp. Chinois, 5, p. 2. pl. 2, fig. 10.

1924. Selenarctos thibetanus ussuricus. Ognev, S. I. O medvedyakh, vodyashchikhsya v Rossii (Bears in Russia).— Priroda i Okhota na Ukraine, Nos. 1—2, p. 113; Buturlin, S. A.— In: A. A. Shirinskii-Shikhmatov. Medved' i medvezh'ya okhota, p. 10, Moskva, 1927; Zolotarev, N. T. Mlekopitayushchie basseina reki Imana (Mammals of the Iman River). pp. 86—89. Moskva-Leningrad, Izdatel'stvo AN SSSR. 1936; Bromlei, G. F. Gimalaiskii medved' (Selenarctos thibetanus ussuricus Heude, 1901) (The Himalayan Bear (Selenarctos thibetanus ussuricus Heude, 1901)).— Zoologicheskii Zhurnal, Vol. 34 No. 1, pp. 111—129. 1939 (biology).

1928. Selenarctos thibetanus wulsini. Howell.— Proc. Biol. Soc., 41, p. 115, Washington. 1928. (Eastern Tombs, Chili, North-Eastern China).

1944. Ursus (Selenarctos) thibetanus. Bobrinskii, N. A. Otryad Khishchnye. Ordo Carnivora. V knige: Opredelitel' mlekopitayushchikh

SSSR, pod redaktsiei prof. N. A. Bobrinskogo (Order Carnivores. In: Key to the Mammals of the USSR, edited by Prof. N. A. Bobrinskii). p. 137; Novikov, G. A. Khishchnye mlekopitayushchie fauny SSSR (Carnivores of the Fauna of the USSR). pp. 99 — 102, 281 — 282, Moskva-Leningrad, Izdatel'stvo AN SSSR. 1956.

1951. Selenarctos thibetanus ussuricus. Ellerman, J. R. and T. C. S. Morrison-Scott. Checklist of Palaearctic and Indian Mammals, p. 239, London.

Type and type locality. The subspecies has been described from the Ussuri River valley.

Diagnosis. Size large, fur longer and shaggier than in the nominate subspecies.

Measurements. Length of body and head: males 153 — 180 cm (av. 165 cm), females 128 — 145 cm (av. 139 cm); length of tail: males 9 — 11 cm (av. 10 cm), females 7 — 10 cm (av. 9 cm); length of ears: males 12 — 15 cm (av. 14 cm), females 12 — 15 cm (av. 13 cm); weight of males: 110 — 150 kg, females 65 — 90 kg.

Condylobasal length of skull: males 270 — 315 mm (av. 295 mm), females 260 — 274 mm (av. 269 mm); zygomatic width: males 185 — 228 mm (av. 206 mm), females 162 — 174 mm (av. 168 mm); length of the upper tooth row: males 110 — 113 mm (av. 112 mm), females 97 — 102 mm (av. 100 mm).

Systematic notes. This is a well-characterized form, whose main difference from the nominate subspecies is the size of the skull (the condylobasal length of the skull is 265 mm in S. th. thibetanus and 285 mm in the Ussuri subspecies).[*]

Geographical distribution. Data are given in the description of the species.

Material examined. Maritime Territory, 11 specimens; Szechwan, 3 specimens: total, 14 specimens.

Biology. The biotopes of the black bear are broadleaf and, to some extent, mixed Manchurian forests. It occurs occasionally in forests on the Okhotsk taiga, from which it is being displaced by the brown bear.

According to G. F. Bromlei (1956), it inhabits oak forests on the Sikhote-Alin Range, and mixed forests with a large variety of trees (the fruits of which are eaten by the bear) and with large linden and poplar trees (in whose hollows it hibernates). These forests are usually easily accessible, and contain few fallen trees. Such areas are found mainly in river valleys, due to the dense undergrowth of birdcherry, honeysuckle, maple, hazelnut and vines, in which the bears will remain for a long time if there is plenty of food. The black bear is less inclined to migrate than the brown bear, provided food conditions are favorable, and is mainly resident. The individual range of the bear is 500 — 600 hectares, i. e., a third or quarter that of the brown bear. The bear avoids conifer taiga. When nuts, acorns, berries and other foods are scarce, the bear migrates to places with more food, this causing a fluctuation in its numbers in a given area and time. Thus, according to G. F. Bromlei (1956), 1 — 43 bears are killed per year in the Vladivostok area. This is confirmed by a den-by-den bear census made by this author on the Ta-Chindzhan Range. Data are given in Table 4.

---

[*] According to R. Pocock, 1941, and G. Allen, 1938.

TABLE 4. Number of bears found in dens on the Ta-Chindzhan Range in 1945—1947 (according to G. F. Bromlei)

Years	Number of dens checked	Occupied	Empty
1945—1946	42	6	36
1946—1947	38	22	16

The winter dens are usually situated in localities with plenty of food, and there is thus no spring migration. The black bear hibernates in winter.

The bears begin to hibernate even before the snow falls, in the first half of November. Females with young begin hibernation first; they are followed by young and barren females, then by older animals, and finally by old males. When there is little food in autumn the bears begin hibernation on about 18—22 November, and in southern areas of the Maritime Territory as late as November 28. When there are plenty of nuts and acorns they begin hibernation before November 15. Hibernation lasts 4—5 months.

The dens are usually in tree holes, and more rarely on the ground under roots and branches of a fallen tree or in rock clefts. The bear prefers old poplars with hollows, and linden trees whose soft wood enables it to widen the hole with claws and teeth and to smoothen the walls. The den is occasionally situated in a hollow oak, stone pine, birch, or elm. The bear does not occupy hollows with holes at different heights, as it must avoid drafts. The height of the entrance to the den varies. Tree holes with an entrance above are often occupied by barren females or by females with young. Old bears may hibernate in hollows with an entrance directed downwards, closing it with pieces of wood from the inside. There is no lining in the hollow other than rotten wood.

In cliffs the bear hibernates under overhangs or in caves, lining the den with dry leaves, grass, and other plant debris. The bear may hibernate under tree roots, where it digs a hollow which may accommodate only half its body. The dens on the ground are usually built on northern slopes, on which snow remains until late March. Black bears have been known in rare cases to hibernate without any cover.

The bears in the hollows are easily awakened in the first month of hibernation by a slight noise or a knock on the tree, but will refuse to come out until night, when the hunters have left. Thus, to force a bear, particularly a female with young, to come out during the day, one has to drive it out—by cutting a hole in the tree or by smoking it out. The bear sometimes remains in the hollow even if smoke is used, and the hunters then have to fell the tree. Bears are generally shot in the hollow throught a small hole made in the tree and then dragged out through a specially-cut "window." The poplars and linden trees suitable for bear dens are gradually being destroyed by this method of hunting.

The black bear sleeps more deeply from December to February, being then even more difficult to drive out of the hollow. The bears sleep less soundly in dens on the ground, and when awakened leave them readily, except for females with newborn cubs (G. F. Bromlei).

The senses are as well developed in the black bear as in the brown bear, but it is less easily trained. Its voice resembles that of the brown bear but has a higher pitch. Its movements are rapid and agile. It climbs well on trees, pulls down and breaks off branches, etc.

It feeds on vegetable and animal food. The plant content of the food is markedly higher than in the brown bear. The food of the black bear in different seasons is given in Table 5, compiled by G. F. Bromlei (1956).

TABLE 5. Proportions of food items of the black bear (percentage of total remains in feces and stomachs)

Type of food	Season and number of samples examined			
	spring 29 feces	summer 21 feces	autumn 38 feces	throughout the year 7 stomachs and 88 feces
I. Vegetable foods	88.0	81.0	98.0	89.1
1. Herbs	29.4	24.3	—	11.2
2. Buds, bark and leaves	6.3	9.2	6.1	9.9
3. Bark, lichen and moss	29.8	16.2	16.4	17.2
4. Berries	1.5	22.1	27.2	26.9
5. Nuts and acorns	21.0	9.2	48.3	23.9
II. Animal foods	12.0	19.0	2.0	10.9
1. Ungulates	—	1.0	—	0.3
2. Mice and voles	1.2	—	—	0.3
3. Fish	—	0.4	0.5	0.4
4. Insects	10.8	16.8	1.5	9.7
5. Mollusks	—	0.8	—	0.2

Similar results have been obtained by examination of food remnants and traces of the black bear's activity. These are presented in Table 6 (next page; after G. F. Bromlei, with some abbreviations).

Tables 5 and 6 show that vegetative parts of plants predominate in the spring food of the black bear, being found in 65.5% of the feces and stomachs examined. Generative parts of plants constitute 22.5%, and animal food 12.0%. The relationship between the types of food changes in summer in favor of berries and insects. Berries, nuts and acorns predominate in autumn. The most frequently found animal foods are insects in spring and summer, i.e., when their numbers are highest. Thus, the following may be concluded: 1) vegetable foods predominate in the food of the black bear; 2) animal food is mainly represented by invertebrates, mainly insects common in the biotopes of the bear; 3) there are changes in the food objects; 4) seasonal changes are due to the predominance of some food objects and depend on the composition of the biocenosis in a given habitat.

Autumn is the most favorable season as regards food. There are plenty of ripening stone-pine nuts and acorn, and later grapes, hazelnuts, walnuts and others. The black bear does not attack large mammals and rarely feeds on carrion. When the crop of nuts is poor, it searches for larvae and pupae of insects (in rotten tree trunks, in the turf, etc.). When acorns and stone-pine nuts are plentiful, the bear feeds on them for a long time in the same locality.

TABLE 6. Relationship between various foods of the black bear (in percentages of total food remains examined and of traces of the animal's activity)

Type of food remains and traces of activity	Season and number of samples examined			
	spring 62	summer 37	autumn 65	throughout the year 164
"Nest" on birch.	0.1	—	—	0.6
"Nest" on Mongolian oak.	—	15.2	—	12.5
"Nest" on birdcherry	—	24.6	6.8	14.6
"Nest" on Actinidia . .	—	1.1	18.3	3.7
Broken branches of Siberian stone pine	41.9	—	48.1	11.2
Birch bark	1.9	—	—	0.6
Remnants of Petasites .	12.6	19.0	—	16.1
Remnants of cowparsnip and Angelica	—	17.5	—	10.1
Remnants of bog whortle-berry in marshes	—	7.5	—	13.9
Damage to oats and corn. .	—	2.8	—	2.0
Chipmunk burrows excavated	1.9	—	—	0.6
Hollows in turf	9.7	—	19.3	5.1
Overturned logs.	12.0	5.7	5.8	8.2
Broken stumps	18.0	6.1	—	8.5
Damaged beehives.	1.0	1.0	1.7	1.8

G. F. Bromlei, who observed the black bear in nature, writes: "When the bear feeds on trees, it leaves broken branches in the form of 'nests.' Such 'nests' are not made on purpose, but are the result of its method of obtaining food. The bears cannot always reach the fruit, and may bend down the branches to break twigs. After the fruit from a broken branch has been eaten they throw away the branch and pull the next one down. In this way heaps of branches accumulate on birdcherry trees, Actinidia, stone pines or oaks. No 'nests' are found on large stone pines or oaks after a visit from the bear, because it has to throw the heavy branches to the ground to collect the fruit."

The mating of the black bear occurs from early June to late July, according to Bromlei (1956). The earliest birth recorded was on December 29, and the latest in late March. Most births occur in mid-February. There are usually 2 cubs, more rarely one or three. The newborn cubs are small. Two cubs, a few days old, were 265 mm long, and weighed 710 g. The cubs reach a length of 70 cm and weight of 14 kg in autumn. Lactation lasts 3—3.5 months and ends 1—1.5 months after the bears come out of the den. The female does not leave the young after the end of lactation, and they remain with her until the end of the second summer and sometimes hibernate with her. The young bears become independent in the third year.

The enemies of the black bear are the tiger, and apparently also the wolf. Packs of wolves may attack young cubs which have become separated from their mothers.

Two species of ticks are found on the black bear: Ixodes persulcatus and Dermacentor silvarum. The following endoparasites have been recorded: Dicrocoelium lanceatum and various species of nematodes.

Molt begins about one month after the bear leaves the den; it is very prolonged and continues throughout the summer. The autumn molt lasts from late August to mid-October. According to G. F. Bromlei (1956), the epidermis on the soles is shed in January, during hibernation. The old, hardened skin is discarded in a complete sheet and replaced by new epidermis.

Practical importance. The economic importance of the black bear is small. It is killed only in small numbers. It may damage beehives.

8.   Genus THALARCTOS Gray (1825). Polar bear

1825. Thalarctos. Gray, I. — Ann . Philosophy, N. S., q0, p. 62. July 1825; Ellerman, J. R. and T. C. S. Morrison-Scott. Checklist of Palaearctic and Indian Mammals, p. 240, London. 1951.

1825. Thalassarctos. Gray, J. — Ann. Philosophy, N. S., 10, p. 339, November. 1825; Ognev, S. I. Zveri Vostochnoi Evropy i Severnoi Azii (Animals of Eastern Europe and Northern Asia). 2, pp. 124 — 126, Moskva. 1931.

1896. Thalassiarchus. Kobelt, W. Berichte Senckenberg. naturforsch. Gesellschaft.Frankfurt am Main, p. 93; (instead of Thalarctos).

Type species. Ursus maritimus Phipps (1774).

Diagnosis. Very large. Body length to 220 cm, rarely even 300 cm, weight 600 — 800 kg. Females are smaller and lighter than males. Body longer and more laterally compressed than in brown bear. Neck longer. Head relatively small, with a less broad frontal area and slightly elevated frontoparietal area, making upper outline of skull convex. Ears short and round, projecting little from the fur. Tail short, almost covered by fur. Paws broad and soles covered with dense fur. Fur dense, thick, very long and shaggy. Color of fur varies from pure white to white with straw yellow tone. Rostrum long: distance from anterior margin of orbit to anterior margin of middle incisor alveolus as long as distance between ends of postorbital processes or less. Molars relatively small, with narrow crowns and with better developed tubercles on the masticatory surface than in brown bear. Length of two upper molars ($M^1 + M^2$) less than width of bony palate between anterior molars (M^1).

Biology. Semiaquatic.

Geographical distribution. Islands and ice of the Arctic Ocean, and Arctic shores of the continent [i. e., Asia], of North America (and adjacent islands), and of Greenland.

143

Systematics.   Genus monotypic.

9. **Thalarctos maritimus** Phipps (1774). Polar bear
(Figure 55, Map IX)

1774. U r s u s   m a r i t i m u s .   Phipps. Voyage toward the North Pole,
p. 185.
1776. U r s u s   m a r i n u s .   Pallas, P. S. Reise durch verschiedene
Provinzen des Russischen Reichs, 3, p. 691; Desmarest.—
Mammalogie, p. 165. 1820; Simashko, Yu. Russkaya fauna (Russian Fauna).
2, Sankt-Peterburg. 1851.
1792. U r s u s   p o l a r i s .   Shaw.— Mus. Leverianum, 1, p. 7
(instead of m a r i n u s).
1908. T h a l a s s a r c t o s   j e n a e n s i s .   Knottnerus-Meyer, Th. Über
den Eisbären und seine geographische Formen.— Sitzungsb. Gesellsch.
Naturforsch. Freunde Berlin, p. 184. (Jena Island, Spitzbergen).
1908. T h a l a s s a r c t o s   s p i t z b e r g e n s i s .   Knottnerus-Meyer, Th.
Loc. cit., p. 184. 1908 (Svenskoya Island, Spitzbergen).
1910. T h a l a s s a r c t o s   m a r i t i m u s .   Satunin, K. A.— In:
Turkin, N. V. and K. A. Satunin. Zveri Rossii, 3, p. 36, Moskva;
Satunin, K. A. Opredelitel' mlekopitayushchikh Rossiiskoi imperii (Key to
Mammals of the Russian Empire). p. 92, Tiflis. 1914; Ognev, S. I. O
medvedyakh, vodyashchikhsya v Rossii (Bears in Russia).— Priroda i
Okhota na Ukraine, Nos. 1—2, p. 114. 1924.
1912. T h a l a r c t o s   m a r i t i m u s .   Miller, G. S. Catalogue of the
Mammals of Western Europe, p. 298, London; Ellerman, J. R. and
T. C. S. Morrison-Scott. Checklist of Palaearctic and Indian Mammals,
p. 240, London. 1951.
1932. T h a l a s s a r c t o s   m a r i t i m u s .   Birulya, A. A. K voprosu
o geograficheskikh formakh belogo medvedya, etc. (The Geographical Forms
of the Polar Bear, etc.).— Trudy Zoologicheskogo Instituta AN SSSR, 1,
pp. 99 — 134.
1935. U r s u s   (T h a l a s s a r c t o s)   m a r i t i m u s .   Adlerberg, G. P.
Khishchnye zveri (Carnivora, Fissipedia) Arktiki (Carnivora, Fissipedia of
the Arctic). In: Zveri Arktiki, pod redaktsiei prof. N A. Smirnova,
pp. 305 — 316, Leningrad, Izdatel'stvo Glavsevmorputi;
Bobrinskii, N. A. Otryad khishchnye. Ordo Carnivora. V knige: Opredelitel'
mlekopitayushchikh SSSR (Order Carnivora, In: Key to Mammals of the
USSR). p. 138, Moskva. 1944; Novikov, G. A. Khishchnye mlekopitayushchie
fauny SSSR (Carnivores of the Fauna of the USSR). pp. 102 — 107. Moskva-
Leningrad, Izdatel'stvo AN SSSR. 1956.

Type and type locality. The species has been described from
Spitzbergen.
Diagnosis. The characters of the species are like those of the genus.
Measurements. Length of body and head: males 197 — 222 cm, females
135 — 185 cm; length of tail: males 20 — 33 cm, females 8 — 16 cm; length of
ears: males 9 — 11 cm, females 8 — 10 cm.
Skull: (12 males and 13 females) condylobasal length: males
361.0 — 388.2 mm, females 318.0 — 335.0 mm; zygomatic width: males

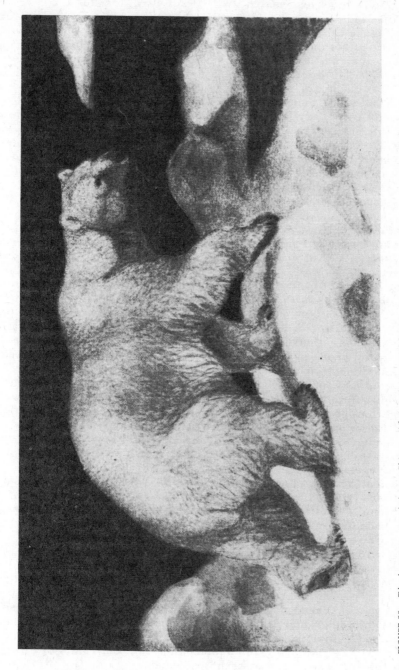

FIGURE 55. Thalarctos maritimus Phipps. After a specimen in the Moscow Zoo. Painting by V. A. Vatagin

188.6—253.0 mm, females 170—198.2 mm; interorbital width: males
87.0 — 106.2 mm, females 75.0—90.0 mm; width between ends of
supraorbital processes: males 108.1—145.0 mm, females 112.0—107 mm;
postorbital width: males 66.0—78.8 mm, females 63.8—71.9 mm; width of
rostrum above canines: males 87.0 — 113.0 mm, females 80.3—86.2 mm;
width of nasal opening: males 53.7—60.3 mm; width between infraorbital
foramina: males 81.2—90.3 mm, females 79.8 — 70.0 mm; mastoid width:
males 142.7—178.1 mm, females 135.0— 158.5 mm; width of bony palate:
males 58.7—68.2 mm, females 53.7—61.6 mm; length of upper tooth row:
males 123.3—140.2 mm, females 118.6—125.0 mm.

Description. Very large, of heavy build. Body longer than in brown
bear. Anterior part of body more compressed than posterior part. Neck
thinner and longer than in brown bear. Head appears disproportionately
small for enormous body; head long, with long muzzle, low forehead and
slightly convex nose in profile. Ears very small, projecting little from
fur. Forelegs shorter than hind legs. Paws massive and broad, soles
densely covered with long hairs which cover small calluses. Claws thick,
slightly curved; claws 3.5 —6.5 cm long, almost completely hidden in fur at
sides of claws. Fur long, dense, thick and stiff. Fur on back relatively
short, fur longer and shaggy on the flanks, on venter and on hind legs.
Fur white (silvery in young bears), with straw-yellow and yellowish tones in
old bears (Figure 55).

Skull (Figure 56) with a less elevated forehead, and a longer braincase,
than in the genus U r s u s , markedly shorter fronto-nasal area and broader
muzzle. Upper outline of skull in profile less convex than in brown bear
and not descending steeply anteriorly; saddle in interorbital and nasal areas
slightly marked. Distance from anterior margin of premaxillaries to level
of postorbital processes usually smaller, in some subadults occasionally
as long as distance from this level to most posterior point of supraoccipital
crest. Width of rostrum above canines is greater than width between
infraorbital foramina. Molars narrower with better developed tubercles
than in brown bear (a character of highly developed carnivorous life).
Length of two upper molars (M^1 + M^2) less than width of bony palate
between anterior molars (M^1). Width of occipital condyles markedly
greater than length of upper tooth row from fourth premolar (Pm^4) to
posterior molar (M^2).

Systematic notes. Knottnerus-Meyer (1903) recorded six species of
polar bears (sic!). However, as A. A. Birulya (1932) has shown, the
conclusions of Knottnerus-Meyer were based on insufficient skull material.
Birula made four of these species synonyms, but left open the status
of T. e o g r o e n l a n d i c u s Kn.-Meyer (East Greenland) and of
T. l a b r a d o r e n s i s Kn.-Meyer (Labrador), for which no material was
available to the author. Knottnerus-Meyer based his "species" of polar
bears on characters due to age or on secondary sexual characters of the
skull.

Birulya (1932) recognizes three subspecies of polar bear, and these
differ slightly in cranial characters. He considers the following subspecies
as valid: T. m. m a r i t i m u s Phipps, 1774 (western Spitzbergen),
T. m. m a r i n u s Pallas, 1776 (Western Siberia), and T. M. g r o e n -
l a n d i c u s Birulya, 1932 (western Greenland).

Reexamination of Birulya's material confirms his taxonomic conclusions. No new material has been received since then. We need much material from the whole area of distribution before we can establish a sound system of intraspecific forms for Thalarctos maritimus, and there is no such material at present.

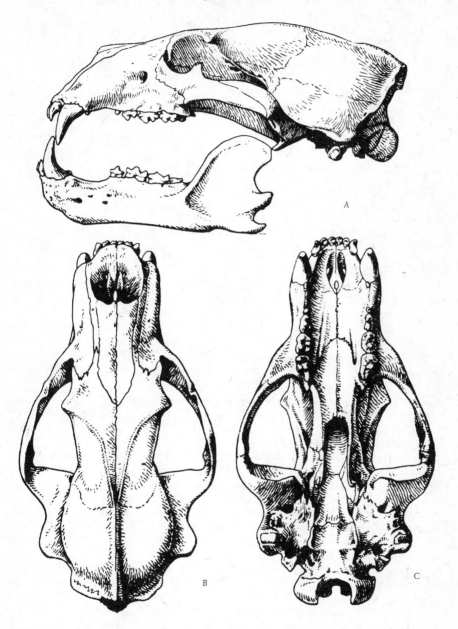

FIGURE 56. Skull of Thalarctos maritimus Phipps (original):

A — lateral; B — dorsal; C — ventral.

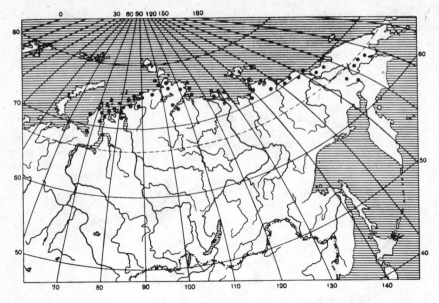

MAP IX. Geographical distribution of Thalarctos maritimus Phipps in Siberia

Geographical distribution (Map IX). The polar bear inhabits a vast area of floating ice fields and islands in the Arctic Ocean, and a narrow coastal zone of Arctic Eurasia, North America, and Greenland.

According to B. M. Zhitkov (1913), it is not rare near the mouth of Ob Gulf (in the Malygin Strait) and on the shores of the Kara Sea south of the Sharapo sandbars (71°— 70° N lat.); in winter the bear may move south to Baidarata Bay (68° N.lat.) or deep into the Ob Gulf (cf. A. N. Dubrovskii, 1940). It occurs on Belyi Island, where winter campers kill several bears every year (Tyulin, 1938).

According to S. P. Naumov, the polar bear is rare on the Gyda Peninsula, but occurs at the northern tip of Cape Evai-Sale. The polar bear probably occurs in larger numbers on the eastern shore, in the Yenisei Bay.

The bear frequents these localities, according to Dubrovskii, mainly in the period of complete freeze, until the ice breaks in the Gulf of Ob and in Baidarata, Gyda, and Yenisei bays. The bear occurs here in summer only when ice fields are driven to the shore. In rare cases the bears summer on the Vil'kitskii Islands and on the northern shores of Belyi, Olenii, Sibiryakov, and Shokal'skii islands. K. K. Chapskii observed a bear swimming in the sea on 7 September 1934 off the Gyda Peninsula near Cape Taran.

The polar bear rarely goes deep into the Taimyr, but occurs all along the shore and is at times common in some localities and on adjacent island. According to V. G. Heptner (1936), it is common near Dickson Island and also occurs on neighboring parts of the mainland.

The polar bear has been observed in the northwestern Taimyr by L. P. Shastin (1939), and on the Nordenskjöld Archipelago, particularly on

Taimyr, Pet, Nansen, Russkii, and Bianki islands. The bears occur on the Chelyuskin Peninsula and in the Vil'kitskii Strait, according to G. L. Rutilevskii (1939), throughout the year, and are very common there. L. M. Starokodomskii obtained a polar bear in 1913 at about 76° N lat. and 111° E long., and also near Cape Chelyuskin. The bear has been collected by the Russian Arctic Expedition in the Taimyr Strait and in Middendorf Bay (coll. Zool. Inst. Acad. Sciences USSR).

The polar bear is common in Pronchishchev Bay, particularly near Morzhovaya Spit, and was collected there by L. N. Popov (1939).

Polar bears are known to straggle further south. Thus, according to Middendorf (1867), the bear is occasionally found near Tolstyi Nos (70° N lat.) and in the mouth of the Khatanga River. According to E. O. Yakovlev (1930), a polar bear was killed in winter 1929 on the Samoedskaya River, a left tributary of the Dudyita, at about 70° N lat.

It is widely distributed on the Novo-Sibirskie Islands, and was observed by F. Nansen during the voyage of the "Fram" in 1893 — 1896 (Nansen, 1897). The bears have been hunted for a long time by the Pomors on these islands (Mel'nitskii, 1915). M. Brusnev (1904) found large numbers of polar bears in autumn 1903 on Novaya Sibir Island, mainly on the northern, eastern and southeastern shores of the island. The Russian Arctic Expedition collected it on Kotelnyi Island (coll. Zool. Inst. Acad. Sciences USSR). It has been found on Novo-Sibirskie ice floes far from shore in high northern latitudes, e.g., north of Franz Josef Land at 82° N lat. and approx. 83° N lat, and northwest of the Novo-Sibirskie Islands and Severnaya Zemlya at 77° — 83° N lat. (Birulya, 1939); but these are not the northern limits of its distribution. It may occur even further north on the ice: the crew of the first floating station "Severnyi Polyus" ("North Pole") observed a bear with cubs on 4 August 1937 near 88° N lat.

According to A. A. Romanov (1941) the range of the polar bear includes the Laptev Sea, with its islands and shore. A few individuals may occur further south, in the valleys of large rivers. The author records the following localities. In winter 1934 a hunter found one bear near the mouth of the Bol'shaya Balakhna (73° N lat.) and another near Lake Kieng-Kyuel in the Khatanga-Anabar tundra (73° N lat.), the southernmost point of occasional occurrence given by local hunters being the mouth of the Suolima River (Anabar River area, 73° N lat.). A. A. Romanov observed a bear in 1933 on the Olenek River near the Kyangkil area (72° N. lat.). The author found tracks in May 1937 on the right shore of the Bykovskii outlet of the Lena, near Lake Ebelyakh (72° N lat.). The bear has been found on Begichev, Vstrechnyi, Erkeger, Dunai and Kuba islands in the Laptev Sea.

According to Bunge (1883, 1887), polar bears are found every year in the mouth of the Lena; they occur (rarely) in the mouth of the Yana River and further east on the shore, and are found occasionally at Kazach'e on the Yana. Dr. Bunge obtained a polar bear on Sagastyr' Island near the Lena delta (coll. Zool. Inst. Acad. Sciences USSR). It occurs regularly in the Lena delta according to A. I. Ivanov (Tugarinov et al., 1934).

Along the Kolyma coast of Eastern Siberia, according to Buturlin (1913), polar bears sometimes hibernate in dens. A female with a cub was killed on March 1905 near the Medvezhya River, between Capes Sukharnyi and Enraukun. It occurs on the Bear Islands and on Krestovskii Island (cf. Iokhel'son, 1898). Local inhabitants told the author that bears may enter the taiga, and old-timers recalled sightings not only at the mouth of the Omolon, but also 10 versts further up the Kolyma.

On the Anadyr, according to Sokol'nikov (1927), polar bears keep to the north shore in winter, occurring on the pack ice in summer.

According to L. A. Portenko (1941), bears occur here more frequently near the sea and in the western half of the area. The author observed a swimming bear from a ship on 11 July 1931 between Tumanskaya and the Anadyr, a few kilometers from the shore. The passengers of the ship saw a second bear swimming towards the shore. S. V. Kertselli (1921) reports the catch of a female bear with two cubs in 1920 on the Pokul'nei Range; the tracks were found of one bear in Utesiki and of another in the Penzhino area. According to L. Belopol'skii (1937), bears are common on the ice in the Chukchi Sea, and Portenko (ibid.) reports the following data collected by Belopol'skii on bears in the Anadyr: "On 25 February 1931 the author observed tracks near Nikolai Bay, 5—7 km from the shore of the Anadyr Estuary. Tracks of 2 bears were found on 27 February east of Russkaya Koshka, along with several further east, 10—15 km from the shore, on 28 February, and a track was found further west on 21 April. The polar bear was observed in winter 1929/1930 on the shore near the mouth of the Khatyrka River, and in winter 1930/1931 bears were killed in Shlyupochnaya Bay (one) and on Cape Olyutorskii (two)." The polar bear was found deep in the territory in winter 1929/1930, near the village of Il'muv'e, 100 km below the village of Ust-Belaya; one bear was killed in 1931 between the upper reaches of the Kanchalan and Tavaima rivers, 180—200 km from the seashore. It occurs on Wrangel Islands, and Prof. Portenko (1941) thinks that this island may be the richest focus of reproduction for the polar bear in the Soviet Arctic. According to traders, at least 100 females give birth on this island, each to two, three and rarely even four cubs. Thus more than 200 young are born every year on the island, and these spread out throughout the Arctic.

The polar bear is absent from the area of the Olyutorka koryaks. according to A. V. Samorodov (1939). Local inhabitants say that two bears arrived in 1931, via floating ice, on the shore of Olyutorskii Bay (cf. L. A. Portenko, 1941 p. 12).

The polar bear occasionally enters the Bering Sea on drifting ice. Yu. V. Averin (1948) reports that a polar bear was killed in June 1919 on the shore of the Kronotskii Peninsula (Kamchatka), having arrived there with the northern ice. A second bear was killed in February 1931, 5 km from the seashore on the Berezovaya River, 80 km to the south of the Kronoki reserve G. D. Dul'keit found a polar bear in 1928 in the Sea of Okhotsk near 59° N lat., and a bear was killed in Tavi Gulf on Ol'skii Island (Ognev, 1931).

The above survey of the distribution of the polar bear shows that a large part of its range consists of islands and shores in Siberian waters.

Subspecies. The polar bear is represented by a single subspecies in Siberia.

9a. **Thalarctos maritimus marinus** Pallas (1776).
Siberian polar bear

1776. Ursus marinus. Pallas, P. S. Reise durch verschiedene Provinzen des Russischen Reichs, 3, p. 691.

1931. Thalassarctos maritimus marinus. Ognev, S. I.
Zveri Vostochnoi Europy i Severnoi Azii (Animals of Eastern Europe
and Northern Asia). 3, pp. 128 — 131, Moskva-Leningrad;
Birulya, A. A. K voprosu o geograficheskikh formakh belogo medvedya, etc.
(The Geographical Forms of the Polar Bear, etc.). — Trudy Zoologicheskogo
Instituta AN SSSR, 1, p. 111. 1932.
1935. Ursus (Thalassarctos) maritimus marinus.
Adlerberg, G. P. Khishchnye zveri (Carnivora, Fissipedia) Arktiki
(Carnivora, Fissipedia of the Arctic), ed. prof. N. A. Smirnov, p. 316,
Leningrad, Izdatel'stvo Glavsevmorputi.
1951. Thalarctos maritimus maritimus. Ellerman J. R. and
T. C. S. Morrison-Scott. Checklist of Palaearctic and Indian Mammals,
p. 240, London (partim).

Type and type locality. Western Siberia, mouth of the Ob River.

Diagnosis. The subspecies is distinguished from the one subspecies by
a smaller zygomatic width, a skull index of 0.62 (0.67 in T. m. maritimus),
a flatter skull, and a broader depression on the frontal area.

Measurements. Same as those given above for the species.

Systematic notes. The characters given in the diagnosis are distinct
only in old specimens. The Siberian polar bear will probably prove
identical with the nominate subspecies from Spitzbergen if more material
becomes available.

Geographical distribution. Arctic shore of Siberia and neighboring
islands.

Material examined. Greenland, 1 specimen; Spitzbergen, 6 specimens;
Novaya Zemlya, 3 specimens; Franz Josef Land, 2 specimens; Novo-Sibirskie
Islands, 3 specimens; Yamal, 8 specimens; Taimyr, 17 specimens; Laptev
Sea, 22 specimens; Wrangel Island, 2 specimens. Total, 64 specimens.

Biology. A typical inhabitant of the ice floes of the Arctic Ocean. It occurs
mainly on drifting ice, but also on the shores of islands and of the mainland.
The bear usually does not move further from the sea than a few
kilometers; it is rarely found in the tundra. However, it may occur 200 km
from the seashore on migrations.

The bears spend most of their time drifting through Arctic waters, on ice
floes, sometimes arriving in areas far from their native locality.

In addition to these passive migrations there are also regular migrations
connected with changes in ice conditions and with migrations of marine
animals, mainly seals.

Polar bears migrate south in autumn over the ice-covered sea, and are
transported north in summer on floating ice. In this way, according to
A. A. Birulya (1932), the bears move south in the Atlantic part of the
Arctic, reaching Iceland, the southern tip of Greenland, Bear Island
and the northern shore of Europe. There are recorded migrations
of polar bears between Novaya Zemlya and Franz Josef Land. Seasonal
migrations of the bears in the Siberian part of the Arctic have been observed
on the Yamal (Zhitkov, 1913), the Gyda (Dubrovskii, 1940), and the Taimyr
(Middendorf, 1867; Rutilevskii, 1939), and on the watershed between the
lower Khatanga and the Lena (Ramonov, 1941), on the lower reaches of the
Yana (Bunge, 1883, 1887), on the shore of the Kolyma (Buturlin, 1913), and
in the Anadyr area (Sokol'nikov, 1927; Portenko, 1941).

The polar bear is perfectly adapted to life under severe Arctic conditions its fur is dense and long, and saturated with fat so as not to become wet or frozen. Together with a well-developed layer of subcutaneous fat 3—4 cm thick, this reduces heat loss and protects the animal against the cold.

The bear swims well and rapidly, about 6.5 km per hour. Bears have been found in the open sea, 10—20 km from the shore, or on floating ice. dives well and can stay under water as long as 2 minutes, swimming a long distance in this time. Its movements on shore are agile, particularly on hummocky ice; it moves rapidly and surely, clambers easily on large ice floes, and jumps over heights of 2 m without effort. G. L. Rutilevskii (1938 observed bears jumping from a height of 4 m, and into water from a height of 6 meters. The bear does not walk very rapidly, and dogs overtake it easily on level terrain. The usual movement is a slow amble. If hunting or escaping from danger, it gallops. According to G. L. Rutilevskii (1939) an adult male walking slowly will move 4—5 km per hour, one in search of food 5.5 km per hour, one trotting 8—12 km per hour, and one galloping 15 km per hour. The greatest speed is developed for short distances, but the bear is completely exhausted after a rapid run. A hunter can overtake a fat bear on level terrain in 15 km. Females with young may move 2.5—4 km per hour.

The senses of the polar bear are well developed, particularly hearing and smell.

There are contradictory data in the literature on hibernation of the polar bear. Some authors think that only gravid females hibernate, and that males are active throughout the year. According to other authors, males also take to a den in winter. Rutilevskii (1939) thinks that all bears hibernate but that dates vary according to sex and age of the animal. The time passed in the den is 160—170 days for gravid females, 115—125 days for barren females, 106 days for females with one-year-old cubs, and 50—60 days for adult males.

Active males are encountered throughout the winter, but L. N. Popov (1939) reported that a male was killed in a den on the eastern shore of the Taimyr on 9 December 1934.

Hibernation begins from early November to mid-December. The bears come out of the den in March—April.

Dens are apparently built only on land. No dens have been found on floating ice. The den is situated in hollows under rock or stones, under overhanging bank, or in snowdrifts. The den is without any lining; it is gradually covered with snow and only a hole for respiration remains.

The polar bear feeds only on animals, mainly marine animals—ring seal, bearded seal and others. It also catches fish and marine invertebrates and will catch birds and feed on eggs in summer.

The polar bear occasionally attacks terrestrial animals—reindeer, Arctic fox and rodents. It will also feed occasionally on moss and algae. Information on the diet of the polar bear has been given by V. I. Tsalkin (1936), who examined stomachs of bears killed in Franz Josef Land. Sixty four (44 %) of 145 stomachs examined proved to be empty. The other 81 stomachs contained the following food remains: ringed seal—in 55 stomachs (68 %), walrus in 18 (22 %), bearded seal in 4 (5 %), birds in 1, and a vegetable mass in 3 (4 %). Thus, the ringed seal is the main food animal of the polar bears in this locality. The staple food of the polar bear in the area of Cape Chelyuskin is bearded and ringed seal, according to Rutilevskii (1939). On the Taimyr and on Franz Josef Land the stomach of the bear usually contains remains of walruses, the reason being that the bears feed on walrus carcasses left by hunters. The polar bear probably does not attack adult walruses.

The large number of empty stomachs indicates starvation, which occurs rather frequently in the Arctic. However, the polar bear is capable of eating a very large quantity of food when it is available. V. I. Tsalkin (1936) found 71 kg of walrus meat in one stomach (a normal meal is 6—8 kg).

Seals are hunted on the ice; the bear stalks them adroitly when the seals lie on the ice, or watches for them near holes, cracks and "polynyas." The bear approaches its prey carefully, hiding behind hummocks and blocks of ice; on open ice the bear attempts to approach against the wind and under cover of irregularities on the ice, then rapidly jumps on the seal and kills it with a stroke of the paw. It sometimes also lies near a breathing hole of the seals and patiently awaits their appearance. When the head of a seal appears, the bear breaks its skull with its paw and drags it onto the ice.

The bear eats the skin and the fat of the seal, burying the rest of the body in the snow. The bear usually does not return to its prey, but will sometimes lie down near the kill and, after a rest, devour it completely or partly.

Rut occurs during a prolonged period beginning in spring and ending in August. Gestation lasts about 8 months. Corresponding to the prolonged period of rut, the period of birth is also longer, from late January to May. The litter consists of 1—2, rarely 3 young. L. N. Popov (1939) reported the bagging of a female bear with 4 cubs on 10 April 1936 in Pronchishchevaya Bay on the eastern shore of the Taimyr.

The young are born in the den. The newborn are very small, blind and have weakly developed fur. Their weight is 650—840 g on the third day (Novikov, 1956). The eyes open after one month. When the cubs become stronger, the family leaves the den and the cubs' diet is supplemented by meat. A cub is capable of eating 2.5 kg of fat at the age of six months. Lactation continues apparently to the age of 15 months, according to Rutilevskii (1939).

The teeth appear at the age of 1.5—2 months. Replacement of the milk teeth takes place at the age of 5.5 to 10 or 11 months. The female remains with her cubs for two seasons. Sexual maturity begins at the age of 3—4 years. The female gives birth every two years.

Molt occurs once a year, from late May to August; it begins on the muzzle and forelegs. The dates of the molt vary according to age, sex, and probably the state of the animal's health. The cubs' first molt takes place in the June after birth, i.e., in their second year. It ends in July in the young and in August in adults. The underfur grows in September. The growth of the fur continues until the next molt.

Practical importance. The skins are used mainly as carpets. The meat is of nutritive value and tasty. Liver and kidneys are poisonous. The importance of the polar bear in the maritime trade has always been small, because only small numbers of bears were obtained. The polar bear is now protected. Hunting is permitted only by licence.

The polar bear usually does not attack humans, but when very hungry may visit settlements, occasionally attacking dogs and destroying the stores of winter campers.

III.   Family MUSTELIDAE Swainson (1835) — Mustelids

1835. Mustelidae. Swainson, W. Nat.Hist. and Classif. of Quadrupeds, p. VII, 361, London; Miller, G. S. Catalogue of the Mammals of Western Europe, p. 340, London. 1912; Satunin, K. A. Opredelitel' mlekopitayushchikh Rossiiskoi imperii (Key to the Mammals of the Russian Empire). p. 95, Tiflis. 1914; Ognev, S. I. Zveri Vostochnoi Evropy i Severnoi Azii (Animals of Eastern Europe and Northern Asia). 2, pp. 426 — 430. 1931; Simpson, G. G. The Principles of Classification and a Classification of Mammals. — Bull. Amer. Mus. Nat. Hist., 85, p. 112, New York. 1945; Ellerman, J. R. and T. C. S. Morrison-Scott. Checklist of Palaearctic and Indian Mammals, p. 243, London. 1951.

Description. Family includes medium- to small-sized members of order, varying in physical structure and mode of life. Body elongated, legs short, build typically slender and lithe; aberrant species (badgers, ratels, gluttons) massive and awkward. Head oval, elongated, relatively flattened with more or less blunted muzzle. Neck short, but extremely mobile in most species. Length and furriness of tail vary. Limbs pentadactyl digitoplantigrade or plantigrade. Claws blunt or sharp, not retractile. In most species, anal glands at base of tail, producing secretion with pungent odor. Fur mostly long and luxurious, and varies from almost monotonous monocolored in some species to bright spotty and striped in others. Bony palate continues far back beyond edge of last molars. Tympanic bullae moderately or strongly flattened; internal cavity of each bulla without septa.

Dentition extremely variable and adapted to various foods. Number of teeth 28 — 38. Molars $\frac{1}{2}$, occasionally $\frac{1}{1}$. Canines well developed.

Number of premolars varies. Last upper premolar and first lower molar are conspicuous as carnassial teeth. Internal lobe of upper carnassial varies in size but is usually well developed. Molars in most members of family are pointed and tuberculated, bluntly tuberculate in a few.

Systematics. The origin of family Mustelidae is unclear. Forms with features of the family are known from the Oligocene of Europe and North America. These were small carnivores with sharp teeth. Most of them still had two upper molars. These ancient animals are usually aligned with the primitive dogs of the extinct subfamily Cynodictinae, or even with the Oligocene representatives of the viverrids.

Mustelinae, Lutrinae and Melinae had already been differentiated by the Miocene. The last two subfamilies are the most primitive ones.

In the modern fauna the Mustelidae are represented by 125 species belonging to 22 genera. The USSR is inhabited by 19 species of 9 genera, included in 5 subfamilies.

Siberia contains 18 species, belonging to 8 genera and 4 subfamilies.

Geographical distribution. Distributed in all countries of the world except Australia and Madagascar.

Biology. Mustelids inhabit all kinds of landscapes, living in most variable biotopes. They include highly specialized climbing, semi-arboreal, terrestrial and amphibious forms. Most mustelids have well-developed hearing, sight, and smell. Many are monogamous. They feed mainly on small mammals, birds and other vertebrates, and invertebrates. Some are polyphagous and in addition to animal food eat some vegetable food: fruits, berries, roots, etc.

Practical importance. Of the highest economic significance. Most species have valuable fur and are objects of hunting and the fur trade. Some species (sable and American mink) are bred on state animal farms. Many species (Siberian polecat, ermine, weasel, etc.) benefit agriculture by exterminating obnoxious rodents. The damage to the economy caused by some species consists in attacks on useful animals, but is generally small and of local importance only.

Key to Subfamilies, Genera and Subgenera of Family
Mustelidae Occurring in Siberia

1 (6). Upper carnassial tooth with large talon, occupying more than half of lingual side of crown . . . . 2.

2 (5). Digits are either fused together or divided, but connected throughout their extent by swimming webs. Claws extremely short and weak. Tail dorsoventrally flattened, tapering markedly from expanded root towards end. Head is highly flattened and broad. Fur is dense and soft. Fur color uniform, or somewhat darker dorsally than ventrally. Semi-aquatic. Upper molar (M^1) frontally extended; longitudinal axis of crown smaller than transverse axis by one third or even one half; size of tooth is approximately equal to that of upper carnassial, or somewhat larger. Mastoid processes are in form of flattened projections representing a continuation of occipital crest. Nasal section of skull short, in length equal to or slightly longer than width above canines. Premolar formula $\frac{4}{4}$ or $\frac{3}{3}$, total

32 or 36 teeth. . . . . Subfamily **Lutrinae** - Otters (p. 185).

3 (4). Digits both on front and on hind legs divided (separate) but joined by swimming web reaching ends of toes. Hind limbs not similar to flippers; middle hind toes (II and III) longest, outer ones (I and V) are shortest. Soles of feet bare. Length of body less than 100 cm, of tail over 40 cm. First upper premolar (Pm^1) situated outside tooth row, to inside of canine. Carnassials and molars with sharp tubercles and cutting crests. Lower jaw contains 3 incisors on each side. Dental formula: $I\frac{3}{3}$; $C\frac{1}{1}$; $Pm\frac{4}{3}$; $M\frac{1}{2} = 36$.

. . . . Genus **Lutra** - Otters (p. 187).

4 (3).   Toes of forepaw fused together. Hind limbs are shaped like flippers and completely covered with hair; their external toe (V) is longest, and others become gradually shorter. Length of body over 100 cm, of tail over 40 cm. First upper premolar (Pm^1) situated between canine and second premolar (Pm^2). Carnassials and molars with flat masticatory surfaces, no cutting cusps with rounded blunted tubercles. Lower jaw contains only two incisors on each side. Dentition: I$\frac{3}{2}$; C$\frac{1}{2}$; Pm$\frac{3}{3}$; M$\frac{1}{2}$; = 32. . . . .
. . . . Genus **Enhydra** - Sea otters   (p. 201).

5 (2).   Toes not fused together and not connected by swimming webs. Claws extremely large and powerful. Tail not flattened and only slightly tapered distally. Body broad and short. Head narrow and not flattened. Fur sparse and coarse. Fur color contrasting: ventrally black-brown and dorsally grayish. Terrestrial plantigrade animals. Upper molar (M^1) not frontally extended, and longitudinal axis of crown larger than its transverse axis; this tooth 3 — 4 times larger than upper carnassial (Pm^4). Mastoid processes project in form of anteriorly oblique digitate protrusions behind auditory apertures (meati). Nasal section of skull elongated, its length being almost twice width of rostrum above canines. Premolar formula: $\frac{4}{4}$; total number of teeth 38 . . . .
. . . . Subfamily **Melinae** - Badgers (p. 158).

6 (1).   Upper carnassial tooth with small talon occupying less than half of lingual site of crown. . . . .
. . . . Subfamily **Mustelinae** - Polecats and martens

7 (8).   Semiplantigrade. Soles only partially covered with hair in winter. Tail shaggy. Longitudinal axis of upper carnassial tooth (Pm^4) parallel to longitudinal skull axis. Sagittal crest of skull overhangs back of head as large and powerful protrusion. Condylobasal length of adult skull not less than 130 mm, length of upper tooth row not less than 49 mm. Tympanic bullae small and flattened . . . .
. . . . Genus **Gulo** - Gluttons   (p. 244).

8 (7).   Digitigrade. Soles completely covered with hair in winter, while in summer pads become naked. Tail not shaggy. Longitudinal axis of upper carnassial tooth extends at angle to longitudinal skull axis. Sagittal crest not overhung by large protrusion above occiput. Condylobasal length of skull less than 130 mm, length of the maxillary [upper] tooth row less than 49 mm. Tympanic bullae relatively large and inflated. . . . . 9.

9 (14). Lower carnassial tooth bears additional denticle on inner sides at base of middle tubercle . . . . 10.

10 (11). Fur color spotty. Processes of pterygoid bones (hamulary processes) joined by bony bridges with inner anterior corners of tympanic bullae (Figure 57, A). Auditory tubules absent. External auditory meatus covered above by edge of temporal bone, open below. Last lower premolar lacks additional denticle behind principal cusp. Talon of upper carnassial tooth flat, without denticle. Infraorbital foramina barely one third size of upper canine alveolus. Premolar formula: $\frac{3}{3}$; total number of teeth 34 . . . .
. . . . Genus **Vormela** - Mottled polecats (p. 412)

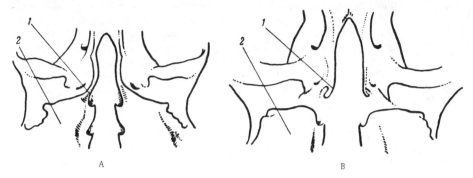

FIGURE 57. Mutual displacement of auditory bullae and process of pterygold bone (hamulary):

A — Mottled polecat, V o r m e l a p e r e g u s n a Güld; B — Siberian polecat, M u s t e l a e v e r s m a n n i Lesson; 1 — pterygoid (hamulary) process; 2 — auditory chamber.

11 (10). Fur color not spotty. Processes of pterygoid bones (hamulary) not joined with tympanic bullae by bony ridges (Figure 57 B). Auditory tubules present. External auditory meatus more or less dorsally open, covered from below by projection of auditory tubule. Last lower premolar with additional denticle behind main cusp (Figure 58 A). Talon of upper carnassial provided with large denticle. Infraorbital foramina almost equal in size to upper canine alveoli. Premolar formula: $\frac{4}{4}$; total number of teeth 38 . . . . Genus **Martes** - Sables (p. 209).

12 (13). Tail furry, length about one half length of body with head. Color more or less uniform, lacking vivid spottiness. Os penis with bifurcation or small ring distally . . . . Subgenus **Martes** s. str. - True martens (p. 213).

13 (12). Tail not furry, length about two thirds length of body with head. Color very vivid and rather spotted: upper part of head, posterior part, tail, and legs black, body yellow. Anterior end of os penis has four blunt processes . . . . Subgenus **Lamprogale** - Spotted martens

14 (9). Lower carnassial tooth lacks additional denticle on inner side at base of middle cusp . . . . 16 .

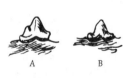

FIGURE 58. Structure of posterior lower premolar (Pm₄):

A — pine marten, M a r t e s m a r t e s L.; B — European polecat, P u t o r i u s p u t o r i u s L. (after S. U. Stroganov, 1949).

15 (18). Color of limbs and chest, or of entire body, dark brown. Toes joined basally by swimming membrane (web). Tympanic bullae triangular, close anteriorly and markedly separated posteriorly. Distance between jugular foramina greater than half length of auditory bullae. Mastoid processes highly developed and project markedly laterally . . . . Genus **Putorius** - Polecats (p. 351).

16 (17). Color not uniform: lighter color of underfur seen through dark tips of guard hair. Edge of ears fringed with white. Swimming webs on hind paws do not reach bases of third

phalanges of toes. Distance from choanal incisure to lower edge
of foramen magnum markedly less than mastoid width of skull.
Mastoid width greater than half condylobasal length of skull.
Width between external edges of occipital condyles as large or
almost as large as width of rostrum above canines. Os penis
uncinate at tip. Subgenus **Putorius** s. str. -True polecats (p. 355)

17 (16). Color uniformly dark brown (except for pure white on lips and
occasional white spots on chest or neck). Underfur dark. Edges
of ears not fringed with white. Natatory (swimming) webs on
hind paws reach bases of third phalanges of toes. Distance
from choanal incisure to lower edge of foramen magnum as
large as mastoid width (in extreme cases just a bit less).
Mastoid width approximately one half condylobasal length of skull.
Width between external edges of occipital condyles markedly larger
than width of rostrum above canines. Os penis spoonlike, bent
downward in terminal third. . . Subgenus **Lutreola** - Minks (p. 394)

18 (15). Limb and chest color different from general body color. Swimming
web rudimentary. Tympanic bullae long and oval, lying parallel to
each other, in extreme cases only insignificantly displaced
posteriorly. Distance between jugular foramina from nearly
equal to down to half length of tympanic bullae. Mastoid
processes weakly developed, project only slightly to either side.
. . . . Genus **Mustela** - Weasels (p. 261)

19 (20). Distinctly bicolored: cinnamon brownish upper side sharply
contrasting with white underpart. Winter fur white in some
northern forms. Length of tail markedly less than one half length
of body with head. Infraorbital foramina larger than alveoli of
upper canines. . **Subgenus Mustela** s. str. True weasels (p. 264)

20 (19). Color uniformly russet throughout body except for lips and small
white spot on chest and neck. Fur does not become white for
winter. Tail length greater than one half length of body with head.
Infraorbital foramina smaller than alveoli of upper canines. . . .
. . . . Subgenus **Kolonocus** - Siberian weasel (p. 309)

1. Subfamily M E L I N A E Baird (1857) — Badgers

1857. Melinae. Baird. Mamm. North. Amer., p. 148.

Description. Low, stocky and awkward general build, sizes rather
large for mustelids, adapted to fossorial activity. Body thick, relatively
short, with broad back. Neck short, not well marked, and not very mobile.
Head elongated, with long pointed muzzle. Ears short and round, not closed
by a valve. Limbs short, plantigrade, with naked soles and large blunt
claws. No swimming webs between toes. Tail not compressed dorsoventrally, and short, being shorter than head. Fur extremely coarse.
Color more or less contrasting.

Skull long and round. Mastoid processes sharply projecting, in form of
massive, anteriorly oblique blunt protrusions behind auditory
apertures (meati). Tympanic bullae relatively high and convex. Nasal
aperture elongated, length almost twice width of rostrum above canines.

Infraorbital foramina more than twice size of upper canine alveoli. Auditory meati smaller than alveoli of upper canines.

Dental formula: $I\frac{3}{3}$; $C\frac{1}{1}$; $Pm\frac{4}{4}$; $M\frac{1}{2}$=38.

Upper carnassial tooth (Pm^1) extremely small and triangular in transverse section; talon extremely large, occupying all or two thirds of lingual part of crown. Upper molar sagittally elongated; several times larger than upper carnassial.

Geographical distribution. The range of the subfamily examined includes the temperate and tropical zones of both hemispheres. In Eurasia, it occupies all of Europe (except for north Scandinavia, the Kola Peninsula, and the basin of the Pechora River), a vast territory in Asia, and Siberia north approximately to a line from 65° N lat. on the Ob to 52° N lat. on the shore of the Sea of Okhotsk, extending further to Japan; it reaches south to Asia Minor, Palestine, Iran, northern India, Burma, Indochina and Sumatra.

Systematics. Fossil members of this subfamily are known from the Miocene. The extinct genus P r o m e l e s Weith has been described from the Lower Miocene of Pikermi; in tooth structure it is close to modern species of the genus M e l e s Brisson. A characteristic feature is the elongated crown of Pm^4 and the quadrate crown with tuberculate masticatory surface of M^1.

The size of the subfamily is not yet established. Several authors include in it as many as 12 genera and subgenera. S. I. Ognev (1931) includes only two genera: the South Asian A r c t o n y x Cuvier, and the true badgers, M e l e s Brisson.

Simpson (1945) includes in the subfamily the following genera: 1) M e l e s Brisson (Eurasia), 2) A r c t o m y x Cuvier (southern Asia), 3) M y d a u s Cuvier (east India), 4) T a x i d e a Waterhouse (North America), 5) H e l i c t i s Gray (South Asia), and 6) M e l o g a l e Geoffroy (southern Asia).

The subfamily is represented in the fauna of the Soviet Union by the single genus M e l e s Brisson.

9. Genus MELES Brisson (1762). Badgers

1762. M e l e s. Brisson, M. J. — Regn. Animal. in Classis, 2nd ed., 9, p. 13; Satunin, K. A. Opredelitel' mlekopitayushchikh Rossiiskoi imperii (Key to Mammals of the Russian Empire). p. 98, Tiflis. 1914; Ognev, S. I. Zveri Vostochnoi Evropy i Severnoi Azii (Animals of Eastern Europe and Northern Asia). 3, pp. 431—432, Moskva-Leningrad. 1931; Ellerman, J. R. and T. C. S. Morrison-Scott. Checklist of Palaearctic and Indian Mammals, p. 271, London. 1951.

1795. T a x u s. Cuvier et Geoffroy. — Magazin Encyclopédique, 2, p. 184. (U r s u s m e l e s Linnaeus).

1815. M e l e s i u m. Rafinesque. Analyse de la Nature etc., p. 59, Palermo. (new name for T a x u s).

1925. M e l e d e s. Kastschenko, N. M e l e d e s subg. nov. Mammalia Carnivora. — Zapysky Fizychno-Matematychnoho Viddilu Ukrayins'koi Akademii Nauk, 1, p. 4.

Type species. Ursus meles Linnaeus (1758).

Diagnosis. The features of the genus coincide with those of the subfamily. In addition, the following characteristic traits may be mentioned. Arctomyx Cuvier (1825) is differentiated from the genus by having a black neck, shorter tail, and dark claws, and by structural features of the skull and dentition.

Geographical distribution. Temperate zone of Eurasia.

Systematics. Members of genus Meles have been discovered in the Lower Miocene strata of Iran and China, and in the Pleistocene of Europe. The genus is apparently a monotypical one.

10. Meles meles Linnaeus (1758). Badger (Figure 59, Map X)

1758. Ursus meles. Linnaeus, C. — Systema Naturae, 10 ed., p. 48.

1785. Meles taxus. Boddaert, P. — Elench. Anim., 1, p. 80. (Europe); Pallas, P. S. — Zoographia Rosso-Asiatica, pp. 70 — 73. 1811; Blasius. Säugethiere Deutschlands, p. 204. 1867.

1808. Ursus vulgaris. Tiedemann, F. Zoologie zu seinen Vorlesungen, entworf., 1, p. 376 (instead of Ursus meles).

1816. Meles europaeus. Desmarest, A. — Nouv. Dict. Hist. Nat., 3, p. 465 (instead of meles).

1827. Meles communis. Billberg. — Synop. Faun. Scandinaviae, p. 16 (instead of meles).

1867. Meles leptorhynchus. Milne-Edwards, A. — Ann. Nat., Zool., Ser. 5, Vol. 8, p. 374 (vicinity of Peking, China).

1868 — 74. Meles leptorhynchus. Milne-Edwards, A. Recherches pour servir à l'hist. — Nat. des Mammifères, p. 190. pl. 25; pl. 26; figs. 3, 4; pl. 27, figs. 3, 4; pl. 28, figs. 3, 4.

1868. Meles chinensis. Gray, J. — Proc. Zool. Soc., London. p. 207, (Amoy, China).

1875. Meles canescens. Blanford. — Ann. Mag. Nat. Hist., 16, p. 310 (between Shiraz and Isfahan in Iran).

1891. Meles schrenkii. Nehring. — S. B. Ges. Nat. Fr. Berlin, p. 103 (new name for Meles taxus Schrenck, 1858).

1907. Meles hanensis. Matschie. — Wiss. Ergebn. Exped. Filchner China, 10, p. 138 (Hinganfu [Angkang], Shensi, China).

1907. Meles tsingtauensis. Matschie. — Loc. cit., p. 138 (Siningfu, Tsinghai, China).

1907. Meles tsingtauensis. Matschie. — Loc. cit., p. 142 (Tsingtao, Shantung, China).

1907. Meles blanfordi. Matschie. — Loc. cit., p. 143 (Kashgar).

1910. Meles tianschanensis. Hoyningen-Huene. — Zur. Biol. Estländisch. Dachses, p. 63 (Tien Shan Mountains).

1913. Meles melanogenys. Allen, J. — Bull. Mus. Nat. Hist. 32, p. 433 (Musan, Northern Korea).

Type and type locality. The species has been described from material from Sweden. The vicinity of Uppsala can be taken as terra typica.

Diagnosis. The diagnostic features of the species are identical with those of the genus.

Measurements. Length of body with head 60—90 cm, length of tail 16—22 cm, length of the hind paw 11.5—13.0 cm, height of ear 5—7 cm. Weight up to 24 kg; old males are known to weigh some 30—34 kg.

Skull measurements (48 males and 40 females) are as follows: condylobasal length: males 113.0—140.0 mm, females 100.0—133.6 mm; zygomatic width: males 68.0 — 89.5 mm, females 62.2—85.5 mm; width of rostrum: males 28.2—34.5 mm, females 24.0—33.0 mm; infraorbital width: males 25.2—34.5 mm, females 22.0—33.0 mm; width between ends of postorbital processes: males 25.2—40.8 mm, females 24.7 — 38.5 mm; postorbital width: males 19.9—27.2 mm, females 18.1—26.2 mm; mastoid width: males 55.9—71.9 mm, females 52.3—67.0 mm; length of braincase: males 59.9 — 71.9 mm, females 56.3—66.5 mm; length of facial section: males 39.9—53.2 mm, females 36.5 — 49.9 mm; height in area of osseous bullae: males 46.1—62.2 mm, females 44.1—57.2 mm; length of upper tooth row: males 38.2—46.9 mm, females 35.2—46.0 mm

FIGURE 59. The badger Meles meles L. (original)

Description. Fur coarse and sparse, with slightly developed underfur. Guard hairs on body and tail bristly and long (on back reaching length of 70 — 80 mm), and markedly shorter on head and limbs. Color of fur variable. On back, fur generally gray-brown, strewn with speckles changing in intensivity and hue in various forms usually darker along spine and becoming lighter on flanks. Dark band on either side of head, extending from nose through eyes and including ears (or touching their upper edges). Forehead and cheeks white, yellowish, or brown. East Asian badger sometimes has dark forehead and cheeks, with lateral bands poorly visible.

Summer fur shorter and sparser than winter fur. Underfur almost absent. Color darker, blacker, and thinner in summer fur than in winter fur. Fur of young individuals shorter, softer and paler.

Claws long and sharp, slightly recurved, a light or dark rusty color. Claw length of middle digit on forepaws reaches 30 — 35 mm along curvature and 22 — 26 mm along chord.

Os penis more or less archedly recurved, and oval in transverse section. Bone highly expanded distally in form of spoon furrowed by small longitudinal groove. Length of bone 72 — 76 mm.

Skull (Figure 60) very bulky and thick-boned. Skull configuration ovally long without sharply projecting angles and facets, save that occipital and sagittal crest extremely conspicuous in adults. Upper contour of skull convex, higher in region between bregma and postorbital processes, descending gently anteriorly and more or less abruptly towards back of head. In distal part of nasals, profile line slightly concave and extending in oblique angle to anterior part of interparietal bones. Facial section broad and long; rostrum almost as wide above canines as between infraorbital foramina; facial length reaches 65 — 75 % of length of braincase.
Zygomatic arches massive, particularly in anterior part, and moderately approximated; zygomatic width usually less than 60 % of condylobasal length. Postorbital processes extend to sides and down in form of massive and low tubercles. Frontal area convex and not delineated anteriorly. Postorbitals narrow, with occasional sharply marked constriction, particularly in old animals. Braincase elongate, roundly oval, and markedly convex laterally and dorsally. Sagittal crest extremely thin but very high, approximately as high as half the infraorbital width in very old individuals; on back, crest forms conspicuous projection overhanging back of head and fusing with supraoccipital crest. Occipital crests powerful, sharply projecting upwards and backwards. Nasals distinguished by extreme variation of form and size, being narrow or wide, more or less compressed laterally, and extending backwards to level of back ends of supramaxillary bone's frontal processes but often going beyond this level.

Nasal aperture extends backwards at acute angle to longitudinal axis of skull's lower side; longitudinal axis diameter longer than transverse one. Infraorbital foramina extremely large, more than twice size of upper canine alveoli, and ovally elongated horizontally or vertically. Orbits relatively small, anteriorly round, ovally elongated. Hard palate relatively narrow and long, extending backwards behind molars for distance approximately equal to palate width between anterior parts of molar crowns. Choanal incisure broad and anteriorly bluntly rounded, without projections extending into middle part. Anterior foramina of palate irregularly pyriform, and smaller than alveoli of lateral upper incisors. Pterygoid fossae rather deep and large. Mesopterygoid fossa broad and short, its width being usually less than distance between carotid foramina. Hamular processes of pterygoid bones relatively long and pointed. Mastoid processes massive, projecting in blunt processes into both sides and obliquely anteriorly behind auditory apertures (meati). Tympanic bullae ovally angular, rather high and inflated on inner side from which they slant steeply in direction of auditory tubes and mastoid processes. Distance between tympanic bullae markedly greater than width of pterygoid fossa.

Auditory tubes well developed. Paroccipital processes well developed, projecting above surface of posterior part of tympanic bullae. In lower jaw coronoid process very broad and blunted. Angular process relatively small. A well-developed crest in posterior part of lower jaw, from anterior side of coronary process base almost to angular process, and below masseteric fossa.

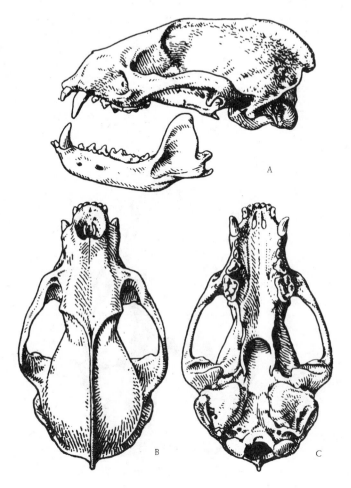

FIGURE 60. Skull of the badger Meles meles L. (original):
A — lateral view; B — dorsal view; C — ventral view.

Female skulls characterized by relatively smaller size, with crests not so conspicuously developed, giving general skull sculpture juvenile as well as feminine traits.

Teeth, excepting upper molar, relatively small. Incisors slightly divided on tips into three more or less conspicuous lobes. Upper lateral incisors markedly larger than middle incisors. Canines oval in basal cross section, extremely long and sharp. First premolars (Pm[1]) often disappear with aging of animal, particularly in upper jaws where even alveoli of these teeth may disappear; individuals are encountered in which anterior premolars occur only in lower jaws. Second upper premolar (Pm[2]) markedly smaller than third (Pm[3]). Upper carnassial tooth extremely small, only fraction of size of molar (M[1]); talon of this tooth extremely large and broad, occupying two thirds of lingual part of crown; talon triangular in transverse section (Figure 61). Upper molar extremely characteristic; very low and large, several times (by a factor of 3−4) larger than carnassial, somewhat longer than broad. Masticatory surface of M[1] bears three longitudinal crests with sharp tubercles: two on edges and one in middle; these are worn down as animal ages, and masticatory surface of tooth becomes flat. Lower canines bending markedly backwards. Premolars increase in size towards back of jaw. Second (Pm$_2$) in European subspecies possessing two roots, in Asiatic subspecies usually one.

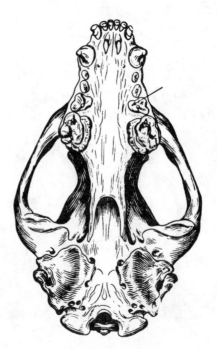

FIGURE 61. Skull of the badger M e l e s
m e l e s L. (original). Arrow shows upper
carnassial tooth

Lower carnassial tooth (M$_1$) elongated, three times as long as Pm$_4$, with crown markedly expanded anteriorly: masticatory surface of anterior half of crown bearing three large cusps, posterior half bearing two rows of blunt tubercles. Last molar (M$_2$) markedly smaller than preceding one, round in cross section, and with more or less conspicuous tubercles lying along sides.

Systematic notes. The badger is an extremely polymorphic species. Over the vast extent of its range, which includes Europe and almost all of Asia, it is divided into numerous local forms differing in color and in osteological and other features. These features are subject to wide variations, extreme variants having been taken by some taxonomists for individual species. For instance, the common so-called sand badger and a number of other fictitious species are present in the list of synonyms given at the beginning of this chapter.

A characteristic of the intraspecific forms of the badger is that they make up two groups of geographically representative subspecies: a European (of the type Meles meles L.) and an Asiatic (of the type M. leptorhynchus Milne-Edwards).

The European badgers of type M. meles have black bands on the head which extend back to envelop the ear from above and below. Infraorbital foramina are usually elongated vertically. The first premolars (Pm^1 and Pm_1) are mostly present; the second lower premolar (Pm_2) has two readily conspicuous roots.

Asiatic badgers of the type M. leptorhynchus are characterized by black bands on the head which rarely extend back, but which do extend upward over the ear without enveloping it from below. Infraorbital foramina are usually horizontally elongated. The first premolars (Pm^1 and Pm_1) usually disappear at an early age. The second lower premolar (Pm_2) has one root.

Numerous transitions, however, occur between these groups, showing the animal's very great variability. The intermediate individuals are encountered not just in border zones, but also well within the ranges.

The color features are extremely variable. The zone over which Siberian badgers range contains specimens indistinguishable in color from M. meles. Badgers from the Chatkal Range, which belong to the subspecies M. m. severzovi Heptner [also known as Geptner] 1940, include specimens in which the black bands on the side of the head are not narrow and in which these even widen to the back. In some individuals the black bands envelop the ear and are almost joined on the occiput along their inner sides. Ognev (1940) states that Chatkal badgers are similar in their headdress to M. meles but similar in skull structure to M. leptorhynchus. Heptner (1940) has justly included them in a distinct subspecies of M. meles. The presence of transitions between sharply differentiable neighboring populations has also been noted by Ognev (1913).

The craniological features of the badger are subject to broad individual variation. Changes in the form of the anteorbital foramina are none other than variations of an individual order. The same locality may contain individuals in whom the anteorbital foramina are simply rounded or ovally elongated vertically or horizontally.

In general, there are no craniological differences, except perhaps for skull dimensions, by which local populations can (and should) be characterized. The variability of skull features in general has been noted by Ognev (1931). According to this author, between the badgers of groups M. meles and M. leptorhynchus are subspecies with transitional craniological features, for example, M. m. m i n o r Satunin (Transcaucasia, Kopet-Dagh) and M. m. c a n e s c e n s Blanford (Iran).

FIGURE 62. The badger M e l e s m e l e s L.   Southwestern Altai. Photo by B. S. Yudin

Odontological features (presence or absence of the first upper and lower premolars, the structure of the second premolar) do not provide a solid basis for the establishment of species. Badgers are indeed divided by coloration and tooth structure into the two above-mentioned groups of forms, but in the individuals of the two groups variations in the number of premolars and in the structure of the second lower premolar are not a rarity, since of the 18 skulls collected in neighboring areas of Kazakhstan six have the first premolar either present or closed over with skin but with the alveoli nevertheless still visible. Two skulls of the same series show that the first premolars have been preserved on one side only, and similar variations also occur in badgers of Transbaikalia and in the Far East (Figure 62).

Geographical distribution. Includes Eurasia except for northern areas of Siberia.

In Siberia the badger ranges throughout the southern part of the country from the Urals up to and including the Maritime Territory (Map X).

The altitudinal distribution extends from the plains of the Western Siberian lowland to the subalpine zones of South Siberia. The animal is known to occur in the following Siberian locations.

In the northern Transurals and in the basin of the Lyapin River, according to K. K. Flerov (1933), it occurs occasionally along riverbanks and is known to only a few hunters. The author failed to collect the animal.   V. N. Skalon (in litt.) writes that Lapin told him he had obtained a badger from a burrow near the city of Salekhard in 1940.

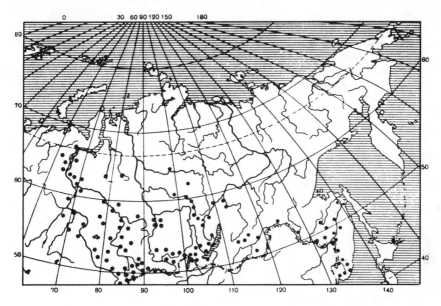

MAP X.   Geographical distribution of the badger Meles meles L. in Siberia

Further south, in the Konda-Sosva taiga, the badger is extremely rare and occurs sporadically.   Its burrow have been discovered near the yurts [tents] of Tunzinkurt, north of the former Konda-Sosva reserve (V. N. Skalon and V. V. Raevskii, in litt.).   It has been recorded in the territory of the above-mentioned reserve by V. V. Vasil'ev and others (1941).   In 1939 it was found in the lower reaches of the Malaya Sosva River, and in autumn of 1939 one was found drowned in this river (beyond 63° N lat.).   The store in the village of Skarkaly on the Ob occasionally receives a few badger pelts.

I. Telishchev (1931) communicates that in the fall of 1930, on the right shore of the Ob River between the Nizyamsk and Aleshkinskie yurty (about 62° 50' N lat.), an animal trail was encountered by him which "immediately seemed to me to be that of the badger." One of the local inhabitants owned a hat made of badger fur; the owner of the hat had bagged the badger near the Aleshkinskie yurty.

I. P. Laptev (1955), basing his information on questionnaires, reports the badger's presence at the mouth of the Kazym River, some 5 km from the village of Polnovat, and along the Sorum-Yugan River (a left tributary of the Kazym).   The same author includes the badger in a list of mammals in the Aleksandrovskoe area of the Tomsk Region.   S. M. Chugunov (1915) mentions the badger on the Vakh River.

The northern boundary of the badger's range in Western Siberia, according to A. I. Yanushevich (1952), coincides with the boundary of the permafrost, which extends below Berezov on the Ob and along the upper reaches of the Pur and the Taz.

While the above communications regarding the habitat and northern boundary of the badger are not impossible zoogeographically, they nevertheless need corroboration through actual collection of the animal.

According to I. Ya. Slovtsov (1892), badger occurs in the Surgut, as well as in the (former) districts of Turinsk, Yalutorovsk, Ishim, Kurgan, Tyukalinsk and Tara (now southern areas of the Tyumen Region and northern part of the Kurgan Region) where it is, however, rather rare.

Fur trade statistics show abundant badger populations in the Tyumen Region only in the Abatskoe area, the population being of moderate size in the areas of Vikulovo, Ishim, Tobolsk, and the Khanty-Mansi National District. The lowest catch is provided by the following areas: Baikalovo, Golyshmanovo, Berdyuzh'e, Vagai, Dubrovnoe, Isetskoe, Maslyanskoe, Novo-Zaimka, Omutinskoe, Tyumen, Uvat, Uporovo, Yurginskoe, Yalutorovsk and Yarkovo.

In the Narym taiga, according to V. P. Anikin (1902), the badger occurs infrequently. According to our data, it is found in the Kolpashevo and Verkhneketskii areas of the Tomsk Region. According to G. E. Io' hansen (1923), it is rather common in the area of the middle reaches of the Chulym River.

According to materials available to me, it is not rare in the Asino, Tomsk, Shegarka and Kozhevnikovo areas of the Tomsk Regions, in the forest and forest steppe areas of the Omsk and Novosibirsk regions, and in the Altai and Krasnoyarsk territories. It is widely distributed in the neighboring Kazakhstan areas. According to B. A. Kuznetsov (1949), it is occasionally encountered in pine forests on the right bank of the Irtysh River north of Semipalatinsk, and is not rare in the Altai foothills near the city of Rubtsovsk. It is even more common in the southern Altai proper, where it has been recorded near the villages of Sekisovka, Pikhtovka, and Katon-Karagai in the Narym River valley.

It is common in the valleys of the Tara and Tartas rivers, according to P. Stepanov (1886). We have collections of materal from the Karakanskii pine forest, Novosibirsk woodland, and the Kashlamskii pine forest.

In the upper Ob pine forest near Barnaul, according to G. N. Likhachev (1930), it ranges in large numbers throughout the forest and its burrows are encountered both on the fringes and deep in the forest. According to my data, it ranges in the Troitskoe, Biisk, Solton and neighboring areas of the steppes around the Altai, occurring sporadically along overgrown ravines.

In the Altai it is one of the most widely distributed species. According to N. F. Kashchenko (1899), it is common everywhere here, having been collected by the author in Ongudai. According to A. M. Nikol'skii (1833), it is encountered near Uimon and the Cossack village of Altaiskoe.

In the Ust-Koksa area, according to A. A. Nasimovich (1949), it is common; traces of permanent occupancy by the animal have been observed by the author in the Lebed' River area between Ak Kaba and Kotanda. A. P. Razorenova (1939) collected the badger in the Kuragan River valley and on the Chulyshman.

The badger was reported near Lake Teletskoe by N. F. Kashchenko (1901, 1902) and P. B. Yurgenson (1938), and was obtained there by the 1933 Turov—Heptner Expedition (coll. Zool. Mus. Moscow University). N. F. Kashchenko (1901) described an Altai subspecies of the badger from materials collected near the southern shore of Lake Teletskoe (from the Kyrsai ravine area at the point where the Chulyshman River empties into the lake, and from the Bele area on the eastern shore of the lake's main pool). Yurgenson (1938) collected the badger in the Ydyi area on the western shore of the lake, opposite the village of Yailyu. In addition, this author recorded the badger in the following localities: 1) along slopes of southern exposure and on crests of the Azhi and Akai ranges; 2) around points Kobukhtu and Chechenek; 3) on slopes of southern exposure on Mt. Tumazein above the Chulysh area; and 4) on slopes in the Chiri village area merging with the steppe, and on Kygyiskii Bay. V. G. Heptner observed traces of the badger (1934) in the valley of the Oroktoi River (a tributary of the Erinag River).

In the Western Sayan, according to A. I. Yanushevich and K. T. Yurlov (1949), badgers inhabit the steppe and forest steppe zones. In the Tuva Region, according to Yanushevich (1952), badger is encountered everywhere and is caught in all districts of the region. As reported by the Kazhanchikov brothers (1924), it occurs in the taiga along the Yenisei from the Bol'shoi rapids to the mouth of the Usa, and along the Kazyr from its upper reaches to its mouth. It occurs in the Chuna-Angara area of the former Kansk District and is caught by traders in small numbers (Troitskii, 1930_2).

The animal has been collected in the area of Krasnoyarsk as follows: in 1946 by V. Torgashev near the villages of Solontsy, Drokino, and Tvorogovo, on the Sobakino River (some 15 km above town along the Yenisei), and in 1923 by S. S. Turov near the village of Khlopkunovo, some 90 km from Krasnoyarsk. It is common in the "Stolby" reserve (A. B. Speranskaya, in litt.) and has been collected in the Achinsk District by F. F. Shillinger (coll. Zool. Mus. Moscow University). According to N. A. Kokhanovskii (in litt.), the badger is among the commonest animal species there.

In the Irkutsk Region, according to V. V. Timofeev (1949) and other sources, it occurs in small numbers everywhere except for the Katanga area. In the foothills around the Baikal and the Sayans the animals are encountered more often, and they also inhabit Tofalyariya [Karagas tribal lands along the rivers Bizyusa, Uda, Iya, etc.].

R. Maak (1859) wrote that badgers were often encountered around Irkutsk, and that he saw their burrows near the village of Malaya Elanka and in the sandy hills on the banks of the Ida near Bokhonsk village. From the upper Oka and Irkutsk, and to the south of the Tunkinskie Gol'tsy Mountains, the badger has been reported by Radde (1862). According to I. S. Polyakov (1873), it is encountered on the plains between the Irkutsk and the upper reaches of the Lena. According to A. A. Pogudin (1930), it ranges sporadically in the former Kirensk District.

It occurs in small numbers in the alpine zones above the timberline along the Chanchur River and on the territory of the Tutur Tungus people (Petri, 1930). According to N. P. Naumov (1934), it is common on the right shore of the Yenisei along the Angara — Stony Tunguska watershed

and along the Angara River. It inhabits, in small numbers, the upper
reaches of Stony Tunguska and was obtained here in the Verkhnyaya
Kontora factory area, in Vana-Vara, Oskoba, Taimba, and Bachinskaya;
in the middle reaches of the river (the Kuyumba and Baikit factories) it is
only occasionally encountered, and it is not found down the river. The
northernmost point of occurrence is reported by N. P. Naumov to be near
the mouth of the Taimura River (about 64° N lat.), a tributary of the
Nizhnyaya Tunguska.

V. B. Podarevskii (1936) reports the northernmost occurrence of the
animal as the mouth of the Vivi River (a right tributary of the Nizhnyaya
Tunguska); it also inhabits the Mutorai River in the Chunya River valley.

According to a survey carried out by R. Maak (1886), it occurs rather
often along the Lena from the upper reaches to the mouth of the Vitim
River, but does not occur further down the river according to local
inhabitants.

As reported by Podarevskii (1936), according to trade statistics few
specimens of badger pelts enter from the Badaibo area. It inhabits the
Vitim-Olekma area only sparsely. The Tungus report that badger burrows
are present along the Nerchugan River. An average of eight pelts per year
are taken throughout the district.

It is widely distributed in Transbaikalia, according to Radde (1862),
particularly toward the Kentei Mountains, occurring more rarely to the
east — the Khingan direction. In southwest Baikalia, according to
I. P. Kopylov (1948), it inhabits the Khamar-Daban foothills. In eastern
Transbaikalia, according B. A. Kuznetsov (1929), it occurs in the Yablonovyi
and Undinsk ranges. It is rarely encountered in the upper Chita River
(Pavlov, 1948), but this author collected the animal near the mouth of the
Shargoldzhin River. It was collected in the Transbaikalian steppes by
G. Radde, and Kashchenko (1901) described the Transbaikalian badger from
a specimen in this collection. A pelt was brought by B. A. Kuznetsov (1929)
from the area of Nerchinsk. In the Borzya area of the Chita Region the
badger was collected (1945) by P. B. Yurgenson and D. Bibikov (coll. Zool.
Mus. Moscow University).

According to Schrenk (1858), the badger is encountered throughout the
Amur, and along the Ussuri from its mouth to the confluence with the Nora
River; according to this author the northern boundary extends from the
Bureiya Range to the area of Nikolaevsk, i. e., to about 52° 50' N lat.
According to R. Maak (1859) it is encountered in the upper Amur some
50 miles below Albazin. On the stretches beginning at the Khingan's eastern
slope and terminating below the mouth of the Ussuri River, the badger has
often been encountered. Maak (1861) observed badger and badger burrows
throughout the Ussuri valley — right up to Lake Khanka. According to
local inhabitants it also occurs on the Daubikhe and Sandukhe, and to the
south of these rivers.

These data correspond with Przheval'skii's observations (1870) that the
badger is present in large numbers throughout the Ussuri territory.

In the area of Lake Khanka, near the village of Evseevka, the badger
has been collected by N. F. Ikonnikov and N. I. Shingarev (Ognev, 1911). The
latter also collected the animal on the Iman River (coll. Zool. Inst. Acad.
Sciences USSR). According to N. T. Zolotarev (1936), it is common in the middle

part of the Iman valley, becoming less common upriver.   G. F. Bromlei reported the badger in the Suputinka reserve.

It is not present on Sakhalin or on the Shantar or Kurile islands.

Survey of subspecies. As mentioned above, Meles meles is divided into a large number of subspecies. Ellerman and Morrison-Scott (1951) report 24 subspecies for the Palaearctic and India. Thirteen subspecies have been described for the USSR. The validity of the numerous subspecies described should be checked on freshly collected material.

According to our data, Siberia is inhabited by 4 subspecies.

10a.   **Meles meles sibiricus** Kashchenko (1900).
Siberian badger

1900. M e l e s   t a x u s   s i b i r i c u s. Kashchenko, N. F. Opredelitel' mlekopitayushchikh zhivotnykh Tomskogo kraya (Key to Mammals of the Tomsk Territory), Tomsk. pl. 15.

1901. M e l e s   a r e n a r i u s   s i b i r i c u s. Kashchenko, N. F. O peschanom barsuke (M e l e s   a r e n a r i u s Satunin) i o sibirskikh rasakh barsuka (The Sand Badger (M e l e s   a r e n a r i u s Satunin) and the Siberian Races of the Badger).— Ezhegodnik Zoologicheskogo Muzeya Akademii Nauk, Vol. 6, p. 111; Satunin, K. A.   Opredelitel' mlekopitayushchikh Rossiiskoi imperii (Key to Mammals of the Russian Empire). p. 101, Tiflis. 1914.

1901. M e l e s   a m u r e n s i s   r a d d e i. Kashchenko, N. F. O peschanom barsuke (M e l e s   a r e n a r i u s Satunin) i o sibirskikh rasakh barsuka (The Sand Badger). — M e l e s   a r e n a r i u s Satunin) and the Siberian Races of the Badger). — Ezhegodnik Zoologicheskogo Muzeya Akademii Nauk, Vol. 6, p. 613 (Eastern Siberia and the Transbaikalian Steppes) ; Satunin, K. A. Opredelitel' mlekopitayushchikh Rossiiskoi imperii (Key to Mammals of the Russian Empire). p. 102, Tiflis. 1914.

1931. M e l e s   l e p t o r h y n c h u s   r a d d e i. Ognev, S. T. Zveri Vostochnoi Evropy i Severnoi Azii (Animals of Eastern Europe and Northern Asia). Vol. 2, pp. 481 — 482, Moskva-Leningrad.

1951. M e l e s   m e l e s   s i b i r i c u s. Ellerman, J. R. and T. C. S. Morrison-Scott. Checklist of Palaearctic and Indian Mammals , p. 272, London.

1951. M e l e s   m e l e s   r a d d e i. Ellerman, J. R. and T. C. S. Morrison-Scott. Loc. cit., p. 272.

1954. M e l e s   m e l e s   l e p t o r h y n c h u s. Bannikov, A. G. Mlekopitayushchie Mongol'skoi Narodnoi Respubliki (Mammals of the Mongolian People's Republic). pp. 105 — 107.   Moskva, Izdatel'stvo AN SSSR (partim).

Type and type locality. Described from a specimen taken in the flat-lying central part of the Tomsk Province (according to the present administrative division, this corresponds to the area of Kolyvan city in the Novosibirsk Region).

Diagnosis. Characterized by moderate skull size (condylobasal length being 126 mm against 134 mm in nominate subspecies), and by rather high,

relatively soft, and light-colored coat. General tone of back is
yellowish gray,with occasional straw yellow and sandy straw yellow tinges,
and more or less strewn with silvery striation. Dark bands on either side
of head narrow, extend above ear, and do not envelop it below; color varies
from light brownish gray to darker brown-grayish black.

Measurements. Length of body with head (6 males and 4 females):
males 67.5 — 75.0 cm (av. 72.0 cm), females 62.0 — 69.2 cm (av. 66.8 cm);
length of tail: males 18.5 — 23.5 cm (av. 21.4 cm), females 17.4 — 22. 2 cm
(av. 19.6 cm); length of the hind paw: males 10.0 — 12.7 cm (av. 11.6 cm),
females 8.2 — 8.6 cm (av. 8.4 cm); height of ear: males 3.8 — 4.1 cm
(av. 3.9 cm), females 3.7 — 4.0 cm (av. 3.8 cm). Weight of adult males
10 — 13.6 kg.

Dimensions of skull (7 males and 5 females): condylobasal length:
males 123.0 — 128.7 mm (av. 125.8 mm), females 116.0 — 118.7 mm (av.
117.4 mm); zygomatic width: males 75.6 — 80.5 mm (av. 78.0 mm), females
68.4 — 70.2 mm (av. 69.2 mm); mastoid width: males 64.0 — 75.4 mm (av.
68.7 mm), females 58.6 — 62.0 mm (av. 60.2 mm); width between anteorbital
foramina: males 28.6 — 31.2 mm (av. 30.4 mm), females 26.5 — 28.0 mm
(av. 27.4 mm); width of rostrum above canines: males 28.8 — 29.6 mm,
females 26.5 — 28.8 mm (av. 27.0 mm); interorbital width: males
27.3 — 28.3 mm (av. 27.8 mm), females 26.2 — 27.0 mm (av. 26.6 mm);
postorbital width: males 22.0 — 24.6 mm (av. 23.8 mm); females
20.0 — 24.0 mm (av. 23.2 mm); height in area of tympanic bullae; males
53.0 — 56.6 mm (av. 54.2 mm), females 48.5 — 52.3 mm (av. 50.4 mm);
length of upper tooth row: males 40.2 — 42.7 mm (av. 41.8 mm), females
36.5 — 38.0 mm (av. 37.0 mm).

Systematic notes. N. F. Kashchenko (1900, 1902) has differentiated two
subspecies of the badger within the West Siberian Lowland and the
Transbaikalian steppes: the West Siberian M. m. s i b i r i c u s and the
East Siberian M. m. r a d d e i. These subspecies he has based on features
of fur color, claws, and overall dimensions.

According to this author, the West Siberian badger is characterized by
the head color pattern (configuration and disposition of the black lateral
band), the general dark hair color, dark rusty claws, and rather long
dimensions (length of body 70 — 75 cm). The Transbaikalian badger,
according to Kashchenko, differs from the preceding in having a darker
general fur color tone, light colored claws, and large size (length of body
more than 100 cm).

According to Ognev (1931), of all the badgers inhabiting the stretches
from China to the Orenburg steppes and Astrakhan semideserts,
M. m. s i b i r i c u s engenders the greatest doubts. The study of two
specimens (from the vicinity of Novosibirsk and from the former Achinsk
County) did not confirm Kashchenko's data about the large sizes of
M. m. s i b i r i c u s or about this form showing some variation in color
from the sand badger (M. m. a r e n a r i u s Satunin). As a result, Ognev
does not recognize the validity of M. m. s i b i r i c u s and does not even
present it in any list of synonyms.

The study of Ognev's original paper and of newly collected material lead
to a different treatment of the taxonomic position of the badger of the
Siberian Plain.

Color dimorphism is characteristic of the badger. Animals of light and dark color occur in populations of any subspecies. However, the color type characteristic for a given subspecies usually predominates numerically. Individuals of a different color type occur much more rarely in the composition of a given population and represent one of the individual color variations.

Study of the material has shown that two types of color characterize the badgers of Western Siberia, North Kazakhstan, the Far East and other areas.

According to Radde (1862), Eastern Siberia is populated by two forms of badger: a large pale form, inhabiting the mountains of the Transbaikal steppes, and a smaller dark form in the wooded mountains. A.G. Bannikov (1954) reports similar color forms in Mongolia as well.

However, these color forms, judging by observations in the field, are not localized biotopically but occur throughout the same biotopes. The information given by Radde and other authors about the biotopical differentation between badger color forms is probably based, in this case, on insufficiently precise observation. As we had the occasion to say before, color dimorphism is in the badger a phenomenon of individual variation and no taxonomic significance can be attached to it.

As to M. m. sibiricus, study of the material shows that it differs in its predominating color type from M. m. arenarius, which is characterized by a less vivid color. The Siberian badger also has a higher and softer coat, with relatively dense underfur. Its dimensions, as presented in the diagnosis, are on the average smaller than those of the nominate subspecies. Conclusions about dimensions of individual badger forms can at present only be conjectural. The phenomenon, mentioned by Bannikov (1954), of a gradual decrease in size from west to east is not confirmed by the material studied, as the badger forms display a variegated picture. In order to elucidate real somatic and craniological metric differences between badger forms, statistical investigation of as yet unavailable material is necessary. There are thus no grounds for abolishing M. m. sibiricus.

M. m. sibiricus and M. m. raddei are taxonomically indistinguishable on the basis of features used for interspecific differentiation of the badger, the features on which the descriptions of these "subspecies" are based being similar in all details. In conclusion, the West Siberian and Transbaikalian badgers should be recognized as identical.

Geographical distribution. The lower part of Western Siberia, and southern areas of Central Siberia and Transbaikalia.

Material studied. The basin of the lower Irtysh — 20 pelts and 2 skulls; Omsk, Novosibirsk and Tomsk regions — 60 pelts and 14 skulls; area of Barnaul — 2 pelts and 2 skulls: total, 82 pelts and 18 skulls.

10b. **Meles meles aberrans** subsp. n. North Kazakhstan badger

Type and type locality. No. 4180 (skull and pelt) in collection of S. U. Stroganov, ♂ adult, 4 September 1957, coll. of L. I. Galkina. Bogembai village in Akmolinsk Region of Kazakhstan.

Diagnosis. Distinguished from M. m. s i b i r i c u s by somewhat shorter and coarser fur and dark color. Back and flanks gray brown, in general tone near to sepia, and densely flecked with silvery streaks. Dark bands on side of head broad (27 — 30 mm), and extend above ear, encompassing it anteriorly and above; color black or intense black-gray-brown.

Measurements. Length of body with head (7 males and 4 females): males 68.0 — 76.0 cm (av. 74.0 cm), females 62.0 — 68.0 cm (av. 65.0 cm); length of tail: males 16.5 — 23.0 cm (av. 22.4 cm), females 16.0 — 22.4 cm (av. 19.2 cm); length of hind foot: males 11.0 — 12.6 cm (av. 11.8 cm), females 9.0 — 11.4 cm (av. 10.3 cm); height of ear: males 5.5 — 7.3 cm (av. 6.2 cm), females 5.0 — 7.2 cm (av. 6.0 cm). Weight of adult males 12 — 14 kg.

Skull measurements (7 males and 5 females): condylobasal length: males 127.0 — 132.2 mm (av. 130.5 mm), females 122.2 — 125.0 mm (av. 124.0 mm) zygomatic width: males 75.0 — 84.0 mm (av. 79.9 mm), females 70.0 — 74.6 mm (av. 73.5 mm); mastoid width: males 66.5 — 67.4 mm (av. 67.0 mm), females 63.8 — 65.4 mm (av. 64.3 mm); width between anteorbital foramina: males 28.2 — 30.0 mm (av. 29.2 mm), females 26.0 — 27.8 mm (av. 27.0 mm); width of rostrum above canines: males 29.6 — 32.5 mm (av. 31.4 mm), females 26.8 — 28.2 mm (av. 27.6 mm); interorbital width: males 26.3 — 28.4 mm (av. 27.5 mm), females 24.4 — 26.8 mm (av. 25.0 mm); postorbital width: males 20.8 — 24.6 mm (av. 22.4 mm), females 18.8 — 21.2 mm (av. 20.2 mm); height in area of tympanic bullae: males 53.6 — 58.0 mm (av. 55.2 mm), females 50.0 — 52.8 mm (av. 51.5 mm); length of upper tooth row: males 40.0 — 43.2 mm (av. 41.6 mm), females 35.6 — 39.2 mm (av. 37.2 mm).

Systematic notes. The arrangement of the dark lateral bands on the head, and the structure of the dentition (absence of the first upper small molars) relate M. m. a b e r r a n s subsp. n. to the so-called sand badgers of the type of M. m. a r e n a r i u s. It differs from the latter, and from M. m. s i b i r i c u s — to which it is nearest taxonomically — mainly in the more saturated dark hair color so characteristic of this subspecies.

Ognev (1931) reports some peculiar traits for two badgers obtained by A. S. Khokhlov near Lake Zaisan and by V. I. Plotnikov on the Tarbagatai and preserved in the collections of the Zoological Institute of the Academy of Sciences of the USSR. Study has shown that these are really dark colored animals and that, by the peculiar head-color pattern (notably the great width of the black lateral band), the general saturation of the dark color on the dorsal side of the body, and other features, these Zaisan and Tarbagatai badgers are subspecifically identical with the Akmolinsk specimens.

Geographical distribution. Occupies the northern areas of eastern Kazakhstan. Found in the Akmolinsk, Kokchetav, and Pavlodar areas, near Lake Zaisan, and on the Central Tarbagatai.

The pine forests of the upper Ob (e.g., the Karakan pine forest) are inhabited by M. m. s i b i r i c u s, while the Altai in the area of Lake Teletskoe is inhabited by M. m. a l t a i c u s.

Material studied. Akmolinsk Region — 6 specimens; vicinity of Kokchetav — 4 specimens; near Pavlodar — 3 specimens; Lake Zaisan — 1 specimen — and Tarbagatai — 1 specimen: total — 15 specimens.

10c. **Meles meles altaicus** Kashchenko (1911). Altai
badger

1911. M e l e s   a m u r e n s i s   a l t a i c u s. Kashchenko, N. F. O
peschanom barsuke (M e l e s   a r e n a r i u s   Satunin) i o sibirskikh rasakh
barsuka (The Sand Badger (M e l e s   a r e n a r i u s   Satunin) and the Siberian
Races of the Badger).— Ezhegodnik Zoologicheskogo Muzeya Akademii Nauk,
Vol. 6, p. 613; Kashchenko, N. F. Mlekopitayushchie, sobrannye
Altaiskoi ekspeditsiei P.G. Ignatova v 1901 g. (Mammals Collected by the Altai
Expedition of P.G. Ignatov in 1901).— Ezhegodnik Zoologicheskogo Muzeya
Akademii Nauk, Vol. 7, pp. 3—4. 1902; Satunin, K. A. Opredelitel'
mlekopitayushchikh Rossiiskoi imperii (Key to Mammals of the Russian
Empire). p. 102, Tiflis. 1914.

1931. M e l e s   l e p t o r h y n c h u s   a l t a i c u s. Ognev, S. I. Zveri
Vostochnoi Evropy i Severnoi Azii (Animals of Eastern Europe and Northern
Asia). Vol. 2, pp. 409—481, Moskva-Leningrad.

1951. M e l e s   m e l e s   a l t a i c u s. Ellerman, J. R. and
T. C. S. Morrison-Scott. Checklist of Palaearctic and Indian Mammals.
p. 273, London.

Type and type locality. No. 9972 coll. Zool. Inst. Acad. Sciences USSR,
♂, 7 September 1910, from the collections of P. G. Ignatov's expedition.
Altai, eastern shore of Lake Teletskoe, the Bele Site area.

Diagnosis. Differentiated from M. m. s i b i r i c u s by smaller skull
(condylobasal length is about 118 mm against 126 mm in M. m. s i b i r i c u s),
relatively broader black bands extending on either side of head above the
ear, dark brown grayish to gray color at top of head, and darker back.

Measurements. Dimensions of male skulls (4 specimens): condylobasal length 115.0—120 mm (av. 117.5 mm); zygomatic width 71.3— 79.9 mm
(av. 74.3 mm); mastoid width 61.2—63.8 mm (av. 62.2 mm); width between
anteorbital foramina: 26.3—28.0 mm (av. 27.6 mm); width of rostrum
above canines: 24.6 —26.8 mm (av. 25.3 mm); interorbital width
24.2—25.3 mm (av. 24.8 mm); postorbital width 18.2—21.1 mm (av.
20.3 mm); height in area of tympanic bullae: 54.9—56.3 mm (av. 55.7 mm);
length of upper tooth row 36.7—40.8 mm (av. 39.2 mm).

Systematic notes. The validity of the Altai badger as a distinct
subspecies needs additional material for verification. M. m. a l t a i c u s,
according to N. F. Kashchenko (1901), is similar to M. m. s i b i r i c u s
in head pattern, but the black lateral bands are relatively broader, the
color of the fur darker, and the dimensions smaller (length of body
65 —70 cm). The number of Altai specimens in our collection is
extremely small, and I have only four specimens from the vicinity of
Lake Teletskoe. Though they indeed have the features reported above
in the diagnosis of M. m. a l t a i c u s, it cannot be ruled out that this
may be an extreme case of that individual variation so characteristic
of M. m e l e s. The material studied shows the Altai badger to agree in
fur color with the north Kazakhstan M. m. a b e r r a n s, but it has a
markedly smaller skull.

Geographical distribution. Widely distributed on the Altai. Obtained
in area of Lake Teletskoe. Probably the badgers collected on the Ongudai

(Kashchenko, 1898) and in the valleys of the Kuragan and Chulyshman rivers (Razorenov, 1939) are systematically identical with this form.

Materials studied. Total of 4 specimens from area of Lake Teletskoe.

10d. **Meles meles amurensis** Schrenck (1858).
Amur badger

1858. Meles taxus amurensis. Schrenck, L. Reisen und Forschungen im Amur Lande, 1, pp. 17—24. tab. 1.

1891. Meles schrenckii. Nehring, A. Über Mogera robusta n. sp. und über Meles sp. von Wladiwostock in Ost-Sibirien.— Sitzungsb. der Gesellsch. Naturforsch. Freunde Z. Berlin, pp. 103—113.

1911. Meles amurensis. Kashchenko, N. F. O peschanom barsuke (Meles arenarius Satunin) i o sibirskikh rasakh barsuka (The Sand Badger (Meles arenarius Satunin) and Siberian Races of the Badger).— Ezhegodnik Zoologicheskogo Muzeya Akademii Nauk, Vol. 6, p. 612; Ognev, S. I. O kollektsii mlekopitayushchikh iz Ussuriiskogo kraya (The Collection of Mammals from the Ussuri Territory).— Ezhegodni Zoologicheskogo Muzeya Akademii Nauk, Vol. 16, pp. 491—496. 1911—1912.

1914. Meles amurensis amurensis. Satunin, K. A. Opredelitel' mlekopitayushchikh Rossiiskoi imperii (Key to Mammals of the Russian Empire). p. 102, Tiflis.

1931. Meles leptorhynchus amurensis. Ognev, S. I. Zveri Vostochnoi Evropy i Severnoi Azii (Animals of Eastern Europe and Northern Asia). Vol. 2, pp. 482—483, 494—495.

1936. Meles meles leptorhynchus natio amurensis. Zolotarev, N. T. Mlekopitayushchie basseina reki Imana (Mammals of the Iman River Basin). pp. 91—93. Moskva-Leningrad, Izdatel'stvo AN SSSR.

1944. Meles meles amurensis. Bobrinskii, N. A. Otryad khishchnye. Ordo Carnivora. V knige: Opredelitel' mlekopitayushchikh SSSR pod redaktsiei prof. N. A. Bobrinskogo (Order of Carnivores (Order Carnivora). In: Key to Mammals of the USSR, edited by Prof. N. A. Bobrinskii). pp. 131—133, Moskva; Novikov, G. A. Khishchnye mlekopitayushchie fauny SSSR (Carnivorous Mammals of the Fauna of the USSR). p. 218. Moskva-Leningrad, Izdatel'stvo AN SSSR. 1956.

1951. Meles meles amurensis. Ellerman, J. R. and T. C. S. Morrison-Scott. Checklist of Palaearctic and Indian Mammals, p. 272, London.

Type and type locality. The type has not been preserved. The area near the mouth of the Ussuri River is taken as terra typica.

Diagnosis. Distinguished from Siberian form by extremely dark fur color and small skull (condylobasal length of skull is on the average 116 mm against 126 mm in M. m. sibiricus). Back is dark, saturated grayish to brown-gray with more or less developed brown or russet brown-gray tinges and has streaks due to silvery tips of guard hairs. Dark bands on either side of head extend above ears; color of these varies from brownish gray-brown to black-gray-brown and coal black. Medial frontoparietal band dark brown (the intensity varying), only slightly lighter than lateral hair.

Measurements. Skull dimensions (4 males and 4 females) as follows: condylobasal length: males 113.0 — 117.8 mm (av. 116.0 mm), females 109.0 — 112.2 mm (av. 110.2 mm); zygomatic width: males 71.6 — 75.4 mm (av. 72.6 mm), females 64.8 — 73.2 mm (av. 67.2 mm); mastoid width: males 60.0 — 63.5 mm, females 55.3 — 58.2 mm (av. 56.8 mm); width between anteorbital foramina: males 24.0 — 26.2 mm (av. 25.3 mm), females 22.2 — 25.6 mm (av. 24.0 mm); width of rostrum above canines: males 28.2 — 29.2 mm (av. 28.8 mm), females 26.2 — 28.2 mm (av. 27.3 mm); interorbital width: males 26.1 — 27.3 mm (av. 26.8 mm), females 22.1 — 24.6 mm (av. 23.2 mm); postorbital width: males 20.0 — 22.4 mm (av. 21.3 mm), females 18.2 — 21.9 mm (av. 20.2 mm); height in area of tympanic bullae: males 47.0 — 52.0 mm (av. 48.5 mm); females 46.2 — 51.9 mm (av. 47.0 mm); length of upper tooth row: males 38.4 — 39.3 mm (av. 38.7 mm), females 35.2 — 37.0 mm (av. 36.8 mm).

Systematics. The Amur badger is the darkest badger form known today, and is immediately recognized even without comparative material. Dark head color particularly characterizes this distinctive subspecies.

On the basis of systematic features (head pattern as well as odontological features) the Amur badger is undoubtedly related to the group of forms termed sand badgers (type a r e n a r i u s or l e p t o r h y n c h u s).

Geographical distribution. Maritime Territory and the Amur area, and north apparently as far as 52.5° N lat. The badger occurring in the adjacent areas of Korea and Northeast China probably belongs to the same form.

Material studied. Twenty-four pelts and 17 skull specimens from various areas in the Maritime Territory, the southern parts of Khabarovsk Territory, and the Amur Region.

Biology. Inhabits variegated biotopes. The natural situation on the ground is not as important for the animal as are ground conditions, making it possible to build burrows on dry unflooded sites. As a result, the distribution of the badger is sporadic, and it may be locally absent for considerable distances.

In the taiga zone of Western Siberia it prefers areas of sparse taiga with dissected topography and low groundwater level. In the Demyanka River basin, according to I. N. Barabash-Nikiforov (1937), it lives in dry pine woods, stone-pine woods and riverain deciduous forests. In the northern part of the Omsk Region (Znamenskoe and Tevriz districts), according to I. N. Shukhov (1928), the badger inhabits hilly areas and ravines. In the Surgut area, according to I. P. Laptev (1958), it occupies wooded ridges.

In the Narym taiga the badger lives in various types of taiga. It finds optimal conditions in Siberian stone-pine forests broken by pine and leafy vegetation and having areas with debris and elevations with good ground conditions for burrow construction.

In the pine forests along the Ob in the southern part of the Tomsk and Novosibirsk regions and in the mountain ranges of the Altai territory it inhabits a variety of covers, provided hills, wooded crests, or river bluffs suitable for burrowing are available (Figure 63).

In the southern part of the Tomsk Region (Kozhevnikovo area) Yudin (in litt.) observed badger burrows in the high slopes of steppelike ravine areas among fields and small insular groves of aspen or birch, as well as on steep mountain slopes in the riverine pine forests and in fir—Siberian stone-pine forests.

FIGURE 63. A mixed forest on mountain slopes in the vicinity of the city of Novosibirsk. Badger biotope. Photo by V. I. Telegin

In the northern Kemerovo Region, according to the same author, badgers made their burrows not only in wooded parts of high ravine slopes, but sometimes also in open stretches on them.

In the forest steppe of Western Siberia badgers live in birch copses on the slopes of various ravines, on high river- and lake-banks, and in areas overgrown with shrubs and reeds.

In the Kulunda Steppe, according to Yudin (in litt.), the badger inhabits small islands of birch with admixtures of birch and aspen, these alternating with meadows, marshes and solonchaks [salt marshes]. The burrows are most often situated on elevations near thickets of reeds in marshes. Burrows may also be encountered on elevations in the open steppe.

In neighboring areas of northern Kazakhstan the badger inhabits river valleys, ravine slopes, high crests near lakes, insular pine forests, etc. (Sludskii, 1953).

In the Irkutsk Region, according to I. P. Kopylov (1948), it lives in forest massifs with dry soils and in pine and pine—larch vegetation with dense under-growth and regrowth. In the forest steppe biotopes it inhabits hills, ravines and glades.

In the Altai, according to P. B. Yurgenson (1938), the badger has been observed to inhabit various biotopes: steppelike slopes of southern exposure with some curtains of spirea and with small copses of birch; southern slopes with glades of tall herbs and mixed stands consisting of pine, larch, birch and other varieties: similar stands on lacustrine terraces; and pine copses of stream mouths and shrub-covered rock streams on the shores of Lake Teletskoe (Figure 64). Traces of the badger's activity have occasionally been encountered in Siberian stone-pine forests in the upper parts of mountain regions. In the area of Lake Teletskoe traces of the badger's presence are encountered at heights up to 1,100—1,200 m. Here, its burrows are mainly found in lakeside bluffs and in fissues and crevasses of cliffs. The badger may also use small caves. In south-

FIGURE 64.   Environs of Zmeinogorsk, Altai. Biotope of the badger. Photo by V.I. Telegin

west Transbaikalia, according to A. Cherkasov (1867), the badger is ubiquitous both in steppe and in forest areas. In the steppe it inhabits ravines and shrubs, and in forest localities it inhabits insular groves on sun-baked northern mountain slopes (Figure 65).

In the eastern part of Transbaikalia, according to B. A. Kuznetsov (1929), the badger digs burrows along ravines and canyons. In the mountains of the Yablonovyi and Undinkii ranges it inhabits secluded gulleys and ravines.

In neighboring Mongolia, according to A. G. Bannikov (1954), the badger "prefers copses, river valleys, and dry stretches of steppe in which it inhabits the shrubbery. In the taiga, the alpine steppe and the alpine taiga above the timberline the animal does not occur, but it may ascend along the brush in river valleys to more than 2,500 m. More rarely it inhabits dry depressions bare of trees or brush, in which case it lives among the stony stretches.

In the mountains of the Bureya Range, according to Radde, it keeps to the naked rocks.

In the Amur area and the Maritime Territory, according to K. Plyater-Plokhotskii (1936), "it is found only in the forest areas," and in the Suputinka reserve, "it inhabits Siberian stone-pine and broadleaf forests on the southern slopes of mountains" (Bromlei and Gutinkova, 1955).

The badger digs its own burrows; these are complicated structures, all the more so when they are used over a number of years and by several generations. They are repaired and expanded each year.

The burrows consist of sinuous subterannean galleries, lying at various depths and sometimes in several stories with numerous ramifications, blind alleys, extensions, and a rather large nesting chamber. The chamber is usually reached by several passages, serving both for entry and exit and for ventilation. There may be 2 — 8 such passages, or even (in extreme cases) as many as 20. The nesting chamber lies at depths ranging from 70 — 80 cm to 4 — 6 m, depending on such factors as ground texture and ground water level.

FIGURE 65.   Forest steppe near the city of Novosibirsk.   A badger trail.   Photo by B. S. Yudin

The nesting chamber may curve considerably.   The diameter is about 50 — 100 cm and the height about 65 cm.   The entry passages are roundedly oval, about 20 — 34 cm high and 37 — 54 cm wide.   They are markedly smaller at their openings on the top of the mound, and are barely seen since the soil and vegetation around them are not trampled down.   The overall area occupied by a badger burrow may reach 10,000 m². Well trampled trails usually lead out from the burrows leading to watering and browsing places, and these trails can be from a few dozen meters to 2 — 3 km long.

The burrows of young badgers, and those designed only for temporary use, are less complex and not so vast.   They are usually not deep and have only one, very rarely two, entry holes.

The badger almost constantly refurbishes, widens and deepens its subterranean construction, making it more complex.   With time the passages lengthen, and may reach several hundred meters arranged in several storeys, made more complicated by numerous ramifications, passages, forks, and additional chambers and passages lying in blind alleys.

The nesting chamber is usually lined with dry grass, leaves and moss. This lining is renewed in spring and autumn.   The degree to which the burrow is inhabited can be determined from fresh trails and other traces of the animal near the exit passages.   In addition, an accumulation of freshly dug-up earth can be seen near inhabited burrows, particularly in spring, when the badger's digging activity is particularly vigorous. According to G. N. Likhachev (1956), the earth expelled from the burrow is not left near the entrance, the badger throwing the earth backward some distance with a forepaw action. This creates a narrow longitudinal "trench" some 20—22 cm on the accumulation of the expelled earth. Such a "trench" is a characteristic feature of a badger burrow (whereas in the fox this earth surrounds the entrance to the burrow in a fanlike pattern).

Cases are known of foxes living together with badgers in the same burrow. This is observed occasionally in vast badger burrows in the parts not currently used by the badger. Most often the fox occupies burrows discarded by the badger. It can live there only so long as it does not disturb the badger, since on being disturbed the badger, being the stronger animal, may throw out its uninvited roommate. G. N. Likhachev (1956), who studied the badger's mode of life for several successive years in the broadleaf forest of Tul'skie Zaseki, reported observing two fox broods which had been destroyed by the badger in its own burrow.

A badger burrow occupied by foxes can be recognized from the food remnants, excrement, etc. strewn about near the entrance. Burrows occupied by the badger itself never contain such signs of activity, since the badger is an extremely clean animal and maintains the cleanliness of its burrows.

The badger usually lives alone in its burrow; however, in 1956 and 1958 V. I. Telegin discovered adult males and females living together when he dug out two badger-covered areas near the city of Novosibirsk. Though they were in the same burrow, the animals had separate nests.

The badger probably feels completely safe in its subterranean abode, and will not leave the burrow even when unsuccessful hunters try to force it out with measures intended to destroy the burrow (digging, building fires at the entrance, etc.). Badger prints are similar in general traits to those of the otter but differ in having sharper claw prints and less widely separated toes. The length of the badger's hind paw is about 8 cm and the pace length is usually 20—25 cm. The animal usually moves at a slow pace or with a waddling gait; when frightened it may run. The animal swims fairly well.

Smell and hearing are well developed, while sight is markedly weaker. It often puffs loudly while searching for food. The voice resembles grunting, and when excited the badger may give vent to a short and intermittant growl. In fights, and when under attack by dogs, it screeches loudly.

The badger is a crepuscular and nocturnal animal and during the day is encountered only rarely outside its burrow. It claims for itself a territory with a radius of up to 3—4 km around its burrow, and only in rare cases will it venture further away. I did, however, once — near the city of Tomsk — encounter a badger some 6 km from the nearest burrow. In areas with a severe climate the badger goes to sleep for the winter. This winter sleep does not involve numbness of the body as, for instance, in jerboas or ground squirrels, being only accompanied by some drop in body temperature, but never below 34.5°C.

In autumn the badger fattens up in preparation for its hibernation, its weight more than doubling. During the winter sleep the animal loses some 50—60% of this autumn weight.

The badger's sleep is not deep and can be interrupted. During warm weather it may sometimes awaken and even emerge from the burrow. D. V. Ternovskii, a member of the staff of the Siberian Branch of the Academy of Sciences of the USSR, caught a badger in the Kudryashovo pine forest in a trap set at the exit of a burrow in November, when the winter snow cover was already in place. On the Altai (in the valley of the Baigol River), according to Yudin (in litt.), a local hunter found three badgers sleeping in the hollow of a fallen tree in late March 1952. It turned out that the burrows were flooded by meltwater and the badgers who left had found a hollow and lain down to sleep in it. The badgers were revealed by their tracks on the snow. In the Ussuri territory, according to N. M. Przheval'skii (1870), badgers will often leave their burrows in the middle of the winter on warm days and roam around a bit in the vicinity.

The length of the badger's hibernation depends on local climatic factors. In Western Siberia the animal lies down in October and awakens in late March or in April. Depending on the meteorological conditions of the year these times may vary by two weeks. In the northern Omsk Region and the Demyanka River valley, the badgers go to sleep in late October (Shukhov, 1928; Barabash-Nikiforov, 1937). In the Tomsk, Novosibirsk and Kemerovo regions, according to my data, they lie down during October and early November. In the Altai (the Ust-Koksa area) the badger goes to sleep earlier than the bear, before 10 October (Nasimovich, 1949).

The animal awakens in early spring, and as large snow-free areas appear it begins to emerge from its burrows. In the localities mentioned above, this usually occurs in April. In the Kulunda Steppe the presence of the badger has been observed in late March (Egorov, 1934).

The various times for awakening from hibernation depend not only on the weather but also on the microclimate of the given biotope. On the Central Altai, A. A. Nasimovich (1949) reports, quoting local inhabitants, that on slopes well warmed by the sun badgers awaken in the last third of March, while on those without sun they sleep to early April.

In Transbaikalia the badgers emerge from their burrows in March (Cherkasov, 1867; Radde, 1862). In the Khabarovsk Territory, according to V. P. Sysoev (1952), hibernation lasts from November to March. In the Ussuri territory, according to N. M. Przheval'skii (1870), badgers awaken rather early from winter sleep. In the Suputinka reserve the badger goes to sleep in mid-November and awakes in mid-April — when the snow thaws on the southern slopes.

The diet of the badger in Siberia has not been completely studied. However, what is known at present shows that it, like the brown bear, is an omnivorous carnivore with a varied diet. The badger eats both animal and vegetable food, but its staple diet consists of animal food. The animals eaten are various invertebrates (primarily worms), insects, frogs, reptiles, birds (with their eggs and young), small mammals, etc. As for plants, it eats various roots, grasses, berries and mushrooms.

Unfortunately, almost no concrete data are available on the composition of the Siberian badger's diet. In the contents of three badger stomachs obtained in the first half of May in the Novosibirsk forest D. V. Ternovskii discovered the following: cockchafers — 31 specimens, Caprinae — 33 specimens, Carabidae — 3 specimens, undiagnosed beetles — 1 specimen, remnants of frogs — 3 specimens, of lizards — 1 specimen, and vegetable remnants — an insignificant amount.

A general idea of the badger's feeding habits can be gained from the results of a study made of its diet in the Tatar Autonomous Republic and in Kazakhstan. In analyzing 474 examples (stomachs and excrements), I. V. Zharkov and V. P. Teplov found (1932) insects 77% of the time and vertebrates 60.8% of the time. Plant material occurred in only 28.3% of the specimens. Of the vertebrates, 54.2% were mammals (86% of these Muridae), 8.6% were amphibians, 2.3% were birds, 1.5% were bird eggs, and 0.6% were reptiles.

In studying 221 items from the Buzuluk pine forest (a large forest massif in the steppes between the Volga and the Urals), S. A. Shilova-Krassova (1951) found remains of vertebrates 44.5% of the time and remains of invertebrates 96.8% of the time. The vertebrates were: mammals (Murinae) — 17.1%, birds — 4.1%, and reptiles — 22.5%; insects predominated among the invertebrates, forming 95.4% and including cockchafers — 68.9%, Coprinae — 26.2%, etc.

In Kazakhstan, according to A. A. Sludskii (1953), 144 items collected over a long period of years on the lower Ili River showed the following: mammals — 23.6% of occurrences; birds — 8.3%; bird eggs — 12.5%; reptiles — 31.9%; insects — 94.4% (including the mole cricket — 74.3%; the Asiatic locust — 16.9%; and beetles — 31.9%); and plants — 15.0%.

As for Tadzhikistan, 318 items I examined from the Vakhsh Valley turned out to consist of 67.8% of remnants of various animals and 32.2% of plant remnants. The animals included mammals — 18.2% [of the time]; birds — 7.2%; reptiles — 8.3%; amphibians — 1.2%; fish (mosquito fish) — 3.2%; and insects (beetles and insect larvae) — 87.2%. The plant material included the following: roots and stems of grasses — 9.3%; oleaster berries — 6.8%; watermelons and melons — 2.0%; and undiagnosed vegetable remnants — 8.6%.

There are only a few reports indicating that badgers devour crops. G. P. Adlerberg (1935) reported damage to oats. I myself have seen damage done to oat fields — near the village of Kislovka in the Omsk area; and on the banks of the Ushaika River near Tomsk Yudin (in 1950) killed a badger in oat fields about 2 km away from the nearest badger burrows.

In the Far East, according to K. Plyater-Plokhotskii (1936), the badger eats corn, gnawing the stem of the plant at the height of 25—30 cm, pulling it on the ground, tearing away the leaves around the cob and eating out the grains. In a single night a badger may damage 8—10 cornstalks. Once accustomed to visiting a cornfield, the badger visits it assiduously, making trails leading to the field from the forest.

As can be seen by comparing the data presented above, the makeup of the badger's diet markedly reflects the composition of the local fauna and flora. The primary place in the diet is held everywhere by insects, among these by beetles and beetle larvae. The beetles (cockchafers, Coprinae, mole crickets, and locusts) are especially important in wooded areas lying on the steppes and on the desert (e. g. the Buzuluk pine forest, and the tugai* forests on the lower reaches of the Ili and Vakhsh rivers), where they occur in 87.2 — 96.8% of the data examined. Reptiles also become noticeable here (18.3%), a result of the large numbers and considerable array of species locally present.

Of the vertebrates, the most important ones for the badger are other mammals, particularly in Tataria and to some extent in Kazakhstan as well (54.2 and 17.1%). Muridae predominate, larger rodents (hares and ground squirrels) being recorded only in a few individual cases. Birds occur markedly more rarely.

The biology of badger reproduction has been studied only slightly. The process is complicated in the badger, as in other animals, by a latent stage in the development of the fertilized egg. Following their fertilization in the spring, the eggs remain in a stage of rest and inhibited development till the middle of September. Fairly reliable data on badger reproduction have been obtained from observations in the Moscow Zoo. However, here as well, the data given by various authors for the times of mating and gestation are contradictory. Thus, V. I. Osmolovskaya (1948) reports that badgers mate some 3 — 6 days after parturition, that mating has been observed from late March but usually in April only, and that gestation lasts 339 — 343 days. According to P. A. Manteifel (1948 the badgers in the Moscow Zoo mate most often in mid-March, and the gestation time is 343 — 371 days, "though more often, as later confirmed by staff members of other zoological gardens, the female badger is pregnant about 357 days." Mating, however, is known to take place in July, and in one case the length of gestation was determined to be 271 — 284 days. Rut may occur in summer, in young females or in those which for some reason were not fertilized in the spring. Males remain sexually active throughout the spring and summer. In nature (along the lower Ili River) an increase in testes size and in the number of mature spermatozoa in them has been noted on March 16 and 24. An adult male observed on 25 May had small spermless testes, and there were no sperm in the epididymis (Sludskii, 1953).

The time of birth has not been established for Siberia, but is probably in March—April. Around Tomsk I encountered nursing females in mid-April. In the Kashlamskii pine forest near Novosibirsk, nursing females have been observed on 27 April and 8 May. Yudin caught a nursing female on 24 May in the Novosibirsk forest, and V. P. Anikin (1902 encountered a nursing female around Narym on 29 July.

Litter size is 1 — 6, generally 3 — 4. The young are born blind, with the auditory meatus closed, and are covered with whitish fur. The length of the body of the newborn is up to 130 mm, the tail length being 30 mm and the weight about 15 g. At the age of one month the teeth begin to appea the upper canines first, followed by the lateral incisors and then, eventually by the last two premolars of the two jaws. The eyes open on the 33rd — 38th day

---

* [Tugai — bottomland complex with forests, shrubs and meadows in rich valleys.]

The hair cover darkens gradually, and by one month after birth has become gray. By the age of two months the fur color of the young is similar to that of the adults. At the age of 2.5—3 months, the young switch to independent feeding. By fall, some families disperse, with the young beginning to dig individual burrows. Some of the broods do not disperse, the young lying for the winter in the same burrow as the mother. A case of finding an adult female and four young in the same burrow on the lower Ili is reported by A. A. Sludskii (1953). Sexual maturity sets in during the second year of life. According to Sludskii, the females reach sexual maturity at the age of 2—3 years.

Badger populations exhibit certain fluctuations, engendered mainly by local causes (flooding of burrows during high water, unrestrained hunting, etc.) but by more general factors as well (e. g., poor feeding conditions, which hinder reproduction). However, concrete data for determining the population dynamics of the badger in Siberia are as yet unavailable.

The badger has few enemies. It is occasionally prey to direct attack by larger carnivores, e. g., the bear, wolf, tiger, lynx, and others. However, it has many competitors for food. These include all the animals and birds feeding on Muridae, on earthworms, on insects, and on other invertebrates. Badgers are often infested with helminths, ixodic ticks, and numerous species of fleas. The badger catches the same form of plague as afflicts dogs.

Molt occurs once a year, in the summer, beginning about one or one and a half months after the badger comes out of hibernation. According to B. A. Kuznetsov (1952), the underfur is shed first, followed by the guard hair in the scapular area, the molting thereafter involving the entire upper dorsal region and the flanks. In the second half of the summer growth of new fur begins, guard hair first, followed by the underfur. This new growth begins at the dorsal posterior and spreads to the head, and the process terminates by fall.

Practical importance. The badger is only a second-rate fur animal, and does not occupy a high place in the fur trade. Its fur is of little value, as is used for such articles as suitcases, briefcases, etc. The guard hair is used for shaving brushes. Pelts with soft fur go to make collars and cuffs. Some people eat the meat, which is of fair taste and nutritious. The fat is a popular remedy and in addition an excellent lubricant for footwear is made from it.

The animal benefits agriculture and forestry by exterminating harmful animals.

2.   Subfamily L U T R I N A E Baird (1857) — Otters

1857. Lu t r i n a e. Baird, S. F. Mammals of North America, p. 148; Miller, G. S. Catalogue of the Mammals of Western Europe, p. 354, London. 1912; Pohle, H.   Die Unterfamilie der Lutrinae. — Arch. f. Naturgesch, 85, sect. A. No. 9, pp. 1—146, Dec. 1920; Ognev, S. I. Zveri Vostochnoi Evropy i Severnoi Azii (Animals of Eastern Europe and Northern Asia). 2, pp. 505— 506. 1931.

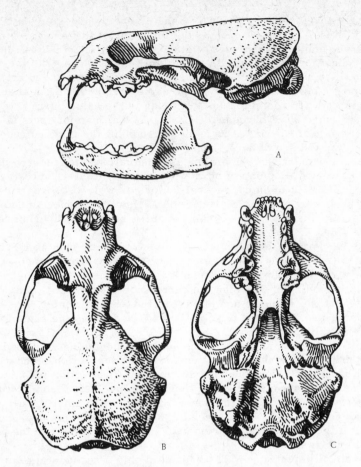

FIGURE 66. Skull of otter Lutra lutra L. (original):

A — lateral view; B — dorsal view; C — ventral view.

Description. Amphibious animals with a distinctive general habitus, characterized by a number of specific adaptations to swimming. Body extremely long and spindle-shaped, somewhat flattened above. Head flattened on top, with broad, short muzzle and small bluntly rounded ears whose apertures are closed by special skin folds during immersion in water. Tail extremely muscular and thick at base, tapering gradually towards end and compressed dorsoventrally or laterally; length of tail at least $^1/_4$ length of body. Limbs plantigrade and very short; toes in most members of subfamily joined by well-developed swimming webs (the African genus Paraonyx Hinton (1921) forms an exception), its forelimbs being unwebbed and its hind limbs being webbed only to the base of the second toe phalanges). Claws short or absent completely. Fur has very dense underfur and usually long guard hair. Fur either of uniform color or somewhat lighter on ventral side than on dorsal side.

Skull (Figure 66) markedly flattened; top almost flat or slightly convex. Rostrum short, its length equally or slightly exceeding its width above the canines. Mastoid processes in most members of subfamily are in form of flattened projections forming a continuation of the occipital crest; in genus Enhydra these are in the form of blunt denticles pointing downwards. Tympanic bullae small and flat.

The number of teeth and the dental formula vary greatly.

Dental formula: $I\frac{3}{2-3}$; $C\frac{1}{1}$; $Pm\frac{3-4}{3}$; $M\frac{1}{2}$ = 34 or 36.

Upper molar frontally broadened; longitudinal axis of tooth crown smaller than transverse axis by one third or even one half; tooth almost as large as or larger than upper carnassial tooth.

Systematic notes. The otters have a very long history. The phosphorites of Quercy (southern France) have been found to contain remains of an extinct genus Amphictis Pomel, which had the dental structure typical for the subfamily save that the upper jaws had two molars. The Lower Miocene of France and North America contain remains of the extinct Potamotherium Geoffroy, distinguished by the fact that, judging by the skeleton of this genus, it was more highly specialized than the contemporary Lutra. Members of this genus occur in the Miocene, Pliocene, and Pleistocene of Europe, North Africa, Asia and North America. This subfamily represents the most primitive martens. Their dental system somewhat resembles that of the raccoon, in that the carnassials have to a great extent lost their cutting function while the molars have become bluntly tuberculomasticatory.

The subfamily includes 8 contemporary genera, and of these 2 are represented in the USSR fauna, both occurring in Siberia.

Geographical distribution. Worldwide except for Australia, Madagascar, islands of the Pacific, and the far Arctic and Antarctic regions.

10.   Genus LUTRA Brisson (1762). Common otters

1762. Lutra. Brisson, M. J. Regnum Animale in Classis 9 distrib., 2, p. 13; Brünnich. Zoologiae Fundamenta, p. 34. 1780; Miller, G. S. Catal. Mamm. West Europe, pp. 354—355. 1912; Satunin, K. A. Opredelitel' mlekopitayushchikh Rossiiskoi imperii (Key to Mammals of the Russian Empire). p. 129, Tiflis. 1911; Ognev, S. I. Zveri Vostochnoi Evropy i Severnoi Azii (Animals of Eastern Europe and Northern Asia). 2, pp. 506—507. 1931; Simpson, G. G. The Principles of Classification and a Classification of Mammals.— Bull. Amer. Mus. Nat. Hist., 85, p. 115. 1945; Ellerman, J. R. and T. C. S. Morrison-Scott. Checklist of Palaearctic and Indian Mammals, p. 275, London. 1951.

1806. Lutris. Duméril.— Zool. Analytique, p. 12.

1815. Lutrix. Rafinesque.— Anal. de la Nature, p. 59.

1843. Lontra. Gray, J.— Ann. Mag. Nat. Hist., 11, p. 118 (for Lutra canadensis Schreber).

1843. Latax. Gray, J.— Ann. Mag. Nat. Hist., 11, p. 119 (for Lutra lataxina F. Cuvier). Nec Latax Glager (1827).

1843. Lataxina. Gray, J.— List Spec. Mamm. Brit. Mus., p. 70 (L. mollis Gray - Lutra lataxina F. Cuvier).

1865. Barangia. Gray, J.— Proc. Zool. Soc. London, p. 123, (B. sumatkana Gray - Lutra barang F. Cuvier).

1865. Lutrogale. Gray, J.— Proc. Zool. Soc. London, p. 127.
(Lutra monticola Hodgson).

1865. Nutria. Gray, J.— Proc. Zool. Soc. London, p. 128.
(Lutra felina Molina).

1867. Lutronectes. Gray, J.— Proc. Zool. Soc. London, p. 180.
(L. whiteleyi Gray-Mustela lutra Linnaeus).

1921. Hydrictis. Pocock, R. I.— Proc. Zool. Soc. London, p. 543.
(Lutra maculicollis Lichtenstein).

Type species. Mustela lutra Linnaeus (1758).

Diagnosis. Dimensions rather large: length of body with head up to
100 cm, length of tail at least 30 cm. Limbs extremely short; toes

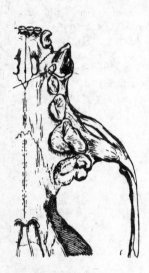

webbed right up to claws. On hind paws middle
toes (II and III) are longest and outer ones (I and
V) shortest. Digits of forepaws developed
normally. Soles bare. Tail flat, being broad
at root and gradually tapering distally. Tail
length more than half length of body. Fur
relatively short, somewhat coarse. Guard
hair on back covers underfur completely.

Skull (Figure 66) relatively large, very low, with
relatively narrow and short facial section and rather
long, broad and flat braincase. Maximum length of
skull 100 — 122 mm and maximum height 35 — 43 mm.
Nasal part gently truncated anteriorly. Nasals
narrow and relatively long. Nasal aperture of
moderate size (transverse diameter about $\frac{1}{3}$
smaller than orbit diameter. Bony palate tapers
markedly behind molars. Tympanic bullae not large,
and are flattened and triangular; diameter of auditory
aperture approximately $\frac{1}{3}$ maximum diameter of
suborbital foramina. Jugular foramina large, being

FIGURE 67. Structure of upper
tooth row of Lutra
lutra L. Arrow points to
premolar (after S. U. Stroganov,
1949)

approximately one half size of upper canine
alveoli. Postorbital processes weakly developed.
Mastoid processes in form of flattened projections
ventrally adjacent to occipital crest and forming
continuation of crest. Infraorbital foramina large,
$\frac{1}{2}$ — 2 times as large as canine alveoli.

Dental formula: I$\frac{3}{3}$; C$\frac{1}{1}$; Pm$\frac{4}{4}$; M$\frac{1}{2}$ = 36.

Molars and premolars have sharp cusps and cutting crests of carnassial
type. First upper premolar (Pm^1) lies outside of tooth row and to the
inside of the canine (Figure 67). Upper carnassial (Pm^4) provided with
large talon occupying no less than $^3/_4$ of inner side of crown. Upper molar
almost equal to or slightly larger than upper carnassial.

Systematic notes. The systematics of the genus have not been
satisfactorily worked out. It includes 5 species, one of which inhabits the
Soviet Union, including Siberia.

Geographical distribution. The range of the genus coincides with that of
the subfamily.

11. **Lutra lutra** Linnaeus (1758). Common or river otter
(Figure 68, Map XI)

1758. M u s t e l a   l u t r a . Linnaeus C. Systema Naturae, 10 ed.,
p. 45.
1777. L u t r a   v u l g a r i s . Erxleben, J. C. Syst. Regn. Anim., 1,
p. 448; Blasius, I. H. Säugethiere Deutschlands, 1857. es 237;
Bichner, E. — Bull. Acad. Imp. Sci., 34, p. 103, St. Petersburg. 1892.
1811. V i v e r a   l u t r a . Pallas, P. S. — Zoographia Rosso-Asiatica, 1,
p. 76.
1823. L u t r a   n a i r . Cuvier G. Dictionnaire des Sci. Nat., 27, p. 247
(Madras, India).
1834. L u t r a   n u d i p e s . Melchior, H. B. Den Danske Stats og Norges
Pattedyr, p. 50 (north Norway).
1834. L u t r a   r o e n s i s . Ogilby, W. — Proc. Zool. Soc. London,
p. 111 (Ireland).
1837. L u t r a   i n d i c a . Gray, J. — Charlesworth's Mag. Nat. His., 1,
p. 580 (Madras).
1837. L u t r a   c h i n e n s i s . Gray, J. — Mag. Nat. Hist., 1, p. 580.
(Canton): Swinchoe, R. — Proc. Zool. Soc. London, p. 624. 1870.
1839. L u t r a   m o n t i c o l u s . Hodgson. — Journ. Asiat. Soc. Bengal,
8, p. 319 (Nepal).
1839. L u t r a   a u r o b r u n n e u s . Hodgson. — Journ. Asiat. Soc.,
Bengal, 8, p. 320 (Kashmir).
1844. L u t r a   k u t a b . Schinz — Syn. Mamm., p. 354 (Kashmir).
1867. L u t r o n e c t e s   w h i t e l e y i . Gray, J. — Proc. Zool. Soc.,
London, p. 181 (Japan).
1897. L u t r a   s i n e n s i s . Trouessart, E. L. Catalogus Mammalium,
1, p. 283 (Canton).
1936. L u t r a   s t e j n e g e r i . Goldman. — Journ. Mamm., 17, p. 164
(Petropavlovsk, Kamchatka).

Type and type locality. Specimens from vicinity of Uppsala in Sweden are
taken as topotypes.
Diagnosis. The features of the species are identical with those of the
genus and are presented in the diagnosis of the latter.
Measurements. Length of body with head 63 — 75 cm, length of tail
41 — 55 cm, length of hind paw 17 — 20 cm, height of ear 20 — 24 cm,
weight 5.8 — 10 kg.
Condylobasal length of skull: males 107.0 — 126.0 mm, females
96.5 — 114.0 mm; zygomatic width: males 65.0 — 83.0 mm, females
61.0 — 72.0 mm; height in area of tympanic bullae: males
35.0 — 43.0 mm, females 36.0 — 40.0 mm; length of upper tooth row:
males 36.2 — 40.0 mm, females 33.0 — 37.2 mm.
Description. In addition to the above-mentioned morphological
peculiarities of the otter, the following should be noted.
Fur short, glossy, and almost equally long throughout body; being shorter
on head, tail and limbs. Winter fur on upper side varies from grayish
brown to dark brown, becoming lighter on ventral side. Head usually
somewhat darker than back. Chin, neck and chest occasionally bear one or
more light patches. Summer fur somewhat duller, darker and shorter
(Figure 68).

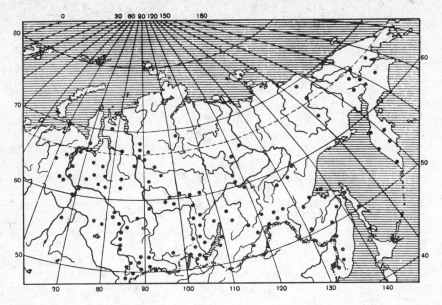

MAP IX. Geographical distribution of the otter Lutra lutra L. in Siberia

Os penis reaches length of 58—65 mm. Tip of bone consists of two rounded lobes divided by a groove, with tips pointing downward; left lobe bears a transverse incisure.

Systematic notes. The otter is a relatively monomorphic species with rather weakly marked geographical variation. The Palearctic and Oriental regions contain about 10 subspecies, these differing in details of fur color. The systematic relationships between the subspecies are as yet insufficiently studied, as museum collections of this species are extremely small. Judging by the material available, a more luxuriant and darker fur color is seen in otters from the northern part of the species' range. No reliable data are available on size.

Geographical distribution. The otter's range takes in North Africa, Europe, and Asia (except for the extreme north), and runs south to Southwest Asia and eastern Indochina.

In the Soviet Union it is distributed almost everywhere outside of the Crimea and the Central Asian deserts.

In Siberia, it ranges from the Urals to the Pacific (Map XI), follows the large rivers northwards to the limit of the forest, and inhabits the frontiers of the Soviet Union.

The following data are available on the otter's distribution in Western Siberia.

For the Yamal there is only one report, by A. N. Dubrovskii (1940) quoting N. V. Provorov and telling of an otter being caught in 1934 on the upper reaches of the Yada River (about 67°N lat.).

It is extremely rare on the lower Ob between Berezovo and Salekhard, according to S. I. Polyakov (1877). According to N. N Spitsyn and others, it

FIGURE 68. The common otter, Lutra lutra L., after a specimen in the Moscow Zoo. Painted by V. A. Vatagin

is rather common in the valley of the Polui River (A. N. Dubrovskii, ibid.). A. A. Dunin-Gorkavich (1910) reported that it is occasionally obtained on the Edy-Yakhe River (a tributary of the Nadym) and reports it in the list of animals inhabiting the valley of the Pura River. Dubrovskii (1940) noted, according to information obtained from V. I. Lapatov, that the otter is found along the Nadym River as high as 65°N lat., on the Aivaseda-Pur and Pyuku-Pur rivers, and in small numbers in the Bol'shaya and Malaya Tydyottam rivers. Telegin collected the otter in 1954 at Pyaku-Pur in the area of Lake Pyakuto (coll. S. U. Stroganov).

According to N. V. Provorov, it was obtained on the Gyda Peninsula — in the tundra along the lower reaches of the Yuribei River (about 71°N lat.).

Further east it occurs in the valley of the Taz River; according to Skalon (1931), "in the Taz area it probably fails to reach the Arctic Circle." Skalon collected the animal on the Ramma River (coll. Zool. Mus. Moscow University). S. P. Naumov (1931) reports that the otter is rare along the middle and upper reaches of the Turukhan River; the author saw two otter pelts in the Yanovoi camp which had been obtained on the Pokatka River.

South of the above-mentioned localities it ranges along all the West Siberian rivers.

It is not abundant in the northern areas east of the Urals. According to Flerov (1933), it is encountered on the Lyapin River, though rarely, and most often along this river's small tributaries, being more common in the Synya River valley.

According to N. A. Abramov (1857), it is found in the Kazym Subdistrict, i. e., in the valley of the Kazym River. Near the village of Sharkaly, which is on the Ob below the mouth of the Sharkalskaya, the otter was obtained in 1909 by D. Vardropper (coll. Zool. Inst. Acad. Sciences USSR).

It occurs in small numbers on the watershed between the Malay Sosva and Konda rivers (on the territory of the former reserve). According to Skalon and to V. V. Raevskii (in litt.), it occurs there permanently only on the two rivers which are most plentiful with fish, the Esse and Em-Egan, visiting the other water bodies only irregularly.

According to N. P. Bulychev (1878), I. Ya. Slovtsov (1892), V. P. Anikin (1902), S. M. Chugunov (1915), and others, it is rare within the southern part of the present Tyumen Region. According to fur supply centers in the Tyumen Region, the only plentiful source of otter pelts is the Yarkovo area, with the Kazym, Uvat, and Yalutorovsk districts and the Khanty-Mansi National District being moderate sources and the Tyumen area a poor one. None of the other districts in the region have yielded otter pelts. According to Telegin, the otter was common in 1950 along the Demyanka River and its tributaries.

According to the above-mentioned authors, the otter has been most frequently encountered on the upper reaches of the Tara River (Novosibirsk Region) and along rivers emptying into the Vasyugan (Tomsk Region); according to my data the animal is common along the taiga tributaries of the Chulym River; according to Yudin it occurs occasionally on the Tagan River (Kozhevnikovo area of the Tomsk Region).

In the Novosibirsk Region, according to the data available to me, it is common along wooded rivers in the Maslyanino, Kyshtovka, Severnyi and Suzun areas, and is occasionally encountered in the Moshkovsk and Bolotino areas (along the Voriya and the Iksa). M. D. Zverev (1932), reports that in the former counties of Novosibirsk and Barnaul the otter is fairly common and occurs occasionally in steppe areas. Cases of deep entry into the open steppe along river valleys are known. Yudin has found traces of the otter in the Iskitim district in the valley of the Berd River.

In the forests on the Upper Ob near Barnaul the otter inhabits the Petrovka, Bol'shaya Rechka, Kamyshenka, and other rivers, but in small numbers.

On the Altai it is among the most common animals. According to A. P. Razorenova (1939), it occurs along the Katun River from Manzherka up to its upper reaches, as well as along this river's tributaries Chemal, Kuba, Samuleta, Kadrin, Eilyaguzh, Urusul, Emurle, Chuya, and Argut. According to F. Gebler (1837), F. A. Kuznetsov (1948) and others, it occurs along the Bukhtarma and its tributaries. Yurlov recorded it in the fall of 1959 in the lower reaches of the Ak-Alakha River (a left tributary of the Dzhazator River).

According to Yurgenson (1938), it is rather rare everywhere in Oirot Jura [now Gorno-Altai Autonomous Region].

In the Altai reserve, the otter has been recorded on the Koksha and its left tributary the Yuzhagan, on the Bol'shoi Abakan and its tributaries Erinat and Konui, and on the Kamga River. Yurgenson (ibid.) observed the otter beyond the limits of the reserve on the Sary-Kokshi River, somewhat above the Ynyrgo River; two otters have been obtained in winter on the Uimen River.

In the Gorno-Altai Region, according to V. N. Savinov (1953), the animal abounds in the Turochak and Choi subdistricts. In the Turochak district, according to material collected by Yudin, the animal is relatively abundant in the valley of the Baigol River and its tributaries Saite, Shuksha, Togun, Titazhak and Klyk. Telegin often encountered (1953) traces of the otter on the Biya River and its tributary the Pyzh. According to the material collected by G. E. Grum-Grzhimailo (1914), it was encountered throughout the northern slopes of the Altai and Sayan mountains and occurred in the valleys of the Tashtyp and Abakan rivers. In the Gornaya Shoriya, according to G. Gol'tsmaier (1935), it occurs in large numbers along all the many rivers with abundant fish.

For the Western Sayan we have a report from Skalon (1936). In the Minusinsk taiga, according to N. Yablonskii and the Kozhanchikov brothers (1924), it is rather common and found throughout (depending on the height of the locality and steepness of the mountains), occurring particularly along the Us, Amyn, and Buiba rivers; it occurs in Buibinskii Pass. Yanushevich and Yurlov (1949) report otter in the wooded regions of the Western Sayan.

It has been reported in the central part of the Eastern Sayan by K. Gromov (1951), and encountered by Yurlov in the valley of the Agul — along that river's tributaries Ulba, Korog, Telegash, Verkhnyaya Krasnaya, Erma, and Katorma, and also from the upper reaches of the Kan River and the sources of its right tributary the Kui.

In the Tuva ASSR, according to Yanushevich (1952), the otter is common in the east Tuva highland, where it was obtained on the

Azas River in the Todzha area. A. Ya. Tugarinov (1916) reported the otter in the upper reaches of the Kemchik River. I. P. Kopylov, A. V. Dobrovol'skii and I. A. Shergin (1940) give the following description of the otter's distribution in the Irkutsk Region: "In the upper reaches of the Lower Tunguska River (Katanga area) the otter occurs along the Tetei, Bol'shaya and Malaya Erema, Nerunga, and Okunaika rivers. In the valley of the Angara, it is known along the Tangui River and its tributary the Tarei, along the Ilim River and most of its tributaries, and along the Voronovaya River (a left tributary of the Angara). The otter abounds in the Sayan area. The known localities here are the Agul, Tagul, Gutara, and Kan (Tofalariya) rivers, and more rarely, the upper reaches of the Biryusa and Tumanshet rivers. It occurs in the valley of the Lena River, along the Notai River, throughout the length of the Tutura River, along the rivers Nazim and Kelor, and along the upper reaches of the Kirenga and its tributaries the Khanga, Mogol, Min, Ichikta, Dalag and Ulkan. It survives further down the Lena along the Bol'shaya and Malaya Tira and on the Kuta. In the southern Baikal area the otter inhabits the rivers on the northern slopes of the Khamar-Daban — the Murina, the Utulik (opposite the mouth of the Shubutui), the Pal'kovka, the Vydrino, and the Kaban'ya, as well as the rivers Bol'shaya Bystraya and Zon-Murin (a tributary of the Irkut). "

According to V. V. Timofeev (1949), in the Irkutsk Region the rivers most abounding in otter are the right tributaries of the Kirenga River and, in the Kazachinskoe-Lena area, the Ilim and Kuta rivers.

The above data agree completely with those presented by B. E. Petri (1930), V. N. Troitskii (1930), and V. B. Podarevskii (1936), among others.

The otter has been reported by I. S. Polyakov (1873) from the basin of the Vitim River and the northern part of the Vitim Plateau, and along the rivers Matukan and Tsipe.

Further to the north, it is not rare near Yeniseisk (Tel', 1880), in the southern part of the Turukhansk territory (Tret'yakov, 1869), and in the area of Turukhansk (Tolstov, 1916).

According to N. P. Naumov (1934), the otter is one of the few game animals in the Tunguska area of the Yenisei's right bank. The otter can be taken to occur generally along the Yenisei and the Stony Tunguska but even here is low in numbers and sporadically distributed. Along the Stony Tunguska the animal's density is highest on the upper and middle reaches of the river — in the area of the Panolik trading post (along the Shoboda River) — and on the Oskoba, Taimba and Bachinskaya rivers. Along the Nencheshemo (near Oskoba) it is abundant. It occurs on the upper reaches of the Komo (a tributary of the Komond) and of the Kamenka (a tributary of the Angara), though in lesser numbers. Further down along the Stony Tunguska the otter occurs only in the lower reaches, along the Erachimo River, at the tip of the Kochumdek River, and on Lake Milchany (below 66°N lat.). It has been obtained at the mouth of the Nidym River.

According to E. Yakovlev (1930), it occurs on the middle reaches of the Kureika River and on Lake Khantai (69°N. lat.). N. N. Urvantev (1931) reported, on the basis of questionnaires, the otter's presence on lakes Lama and Glubokoe (69°N lat.).

It is present on the Khatanga, according to Middendorf (1867), and absent on the watershed between the lower Khatanga and the Lena, according to A. A. Romanov (1941).

On the Vilyui, according to Maak (1886), it is occasionally encountered in the vicinity of the village of Suntar; the author observed traces of the otter on the upper reaches of this river, and the local inhabitants have mentioned rare cases of the otter being found near the rivers Tyun, Tyukan, and Khatanga, as well as along the Lena tributaries Muna and Serne, and in the vicinity of Zhigansk.

According to recent data from V. I. Belyk (1953), it occurs occasionally in Yakutia along the Vilyui, inhabits all principal tributaries of the Tokko, Tyana, Chary and Nyui rivers, and is often seen in the Ust-Maya area. It is known to occur in the Timpton, Tommot, and Uchur areas. The extreme northeastern point reported for the otter in this Republic is the Alazeya River (Sredne-Kolymsk area).

It has been reported as a rare animal in the basin of the Kolyma River by Iokhel'son (1898) and by G. M. Allen (1941), among others. Iokhel'son mentioned evidence of the animal on the Yasachnaya River.

On the Anadyr, according to Portenko (1941), the otter occurs sporadically and is rare. It occurs in small numbers along the Anadyr River and on all the rivers right up to the Apuka. According to Portenko (ibid.), Belopol'skii (1937) and others, the otter is obtained on the Anadyr River and its tributaries the Main, Belaya and Tanyurer, as well as on the Velikaya, Kanchalan and Taivama rivers emptying into its estuary.

Yudin saw signs of otter on the banks of the Anadyr opposite the mouth of the Tanyurer River.

It is probably more numerous to the south of the Anadyr. Portenko had material from the Oklan River, which is south of the village of Penzhino. Near Penzhino the otter has also been recorded by N. P. Sokol'nikov (1927). The animal has been collected by I. G. Volkov (coll. Zool. Mus. Moscow University) on the Penzhina River near Oyanka village, which is about 60 km to the west of Penzhino, and S. D. Pereleshin and others saw it on the Oklan River.

In the Olyutorka area, according to A. A. Samorodov (1939), it is rather common in the upper reaches of small streams far away from the camps of local inhabitants and thus not very much visited by hunters. It has already already been exterminated in the middle and lower reaches of the Apuka River.

It ranges throughout Kamchatka (Slyunin, 1900; Averin, 1948, and others). The collections of the Zoological Institute of the Academy of Sciences of the USSR contain a vast series of otter skulls from Kamchatka obtained by Grebnitskii (in 1884) and by F. P. Ryabushinskii's expedition. In the Kronoki reserve it inhabits all water bodies and is particularly abundant on the Malaya, Bol'shaya, Chazhma, Tyushevka, and Bogachevka rivers and along the lower reaches of the rivers emptying into Lake Kronotskoe.

It occurs all along the coast of the Sea of Okhotsk, but only sporadically, as is the case in most areas of its range.

According to N. Buxton it is no longer encountered near Gizhiga, although it occurred there previously. There are collections of N. V. Slyunin's from this coast (coll. Zool. Mus. Moscow University).

In Transbaikalia it is widely distributed except for the Daurian mountain steppe.

It is common on the northeastern shore of Lake Baikal, according to S. S. Turov (1936). This author observed the animal on the Kudalda River, on the shore of Chivyrkuiskii Bay, and on the Svyatoi Nos. It was collected in the valley of the Sosnovka by Turov and G. F. Svatosh, and in the Barguzin reserve in 1935 by V. K. Timofeev (near the village of Zyryanskoe); (coll. Zool. Mus. Moscow University).

It is extremely rare on the Yablonovyi Range, according to Kuznetsov (1929). It has been taken near Akima on the Veich River.

It is common on the Stanovoi, according to Middendorf (1853), both on the Range itself and on its spurs.

According to N. T. Zolotarev (1934), it is almost absent from the Upper Selemdzhina areas, this being the result of excessive hunting. On the Udskie slopes, particularly on the lower reaches of the Shevli River and along the Uda River, the animal is still abundant.

According to Maak (1859), it is encountered frequently along mountain streams emptying into the Shilka and upper Amur. Radde reported it (1862) near the Bureya River, where he considered it to be quite abundant. I have otter skulls collected in the basin of the lower reaches of the Amur River (collections of M. E. Ashkov). It occurs, but only rarely, in the Ol'doi — Gilgui interfluve, according to G. N. Gassovskii (1927).

It was obtained by K. A. Vorob'ev and V. S. Stakhanov on the Gorin River in 1932. The same authors collected badgers in the upper reaches of the Dekun River on the Koksha, and at the mouths of the Sydyiza and Gyrba (coll. Zool. Mus. Moscow University).

On the Ussuri, according to Maak (1861), it ranges from the mouth of the river to its upper reaches, being encountered often in mountain streams on the Khelchtsyrskii Range, along the Chirk River, on Cape Kalang, at the mouth of the Nor, and on tributaries of the Bikin River, etc.; it also occurs on the southern slopes of the Sikhote-Alin.

According to Przheval'skii (1870) it is encountered in large numbers throughout the Ussuri territory; particularly on the large tributaries of Lake Khanka, for instance on the Lefu. It was collected on Lake Khanka in 1914 by A. I. Cherskii (coll. S. I. Ognev). According to Zolotarev (1936), it is rather rare on the Iman but more common along the Kolumbe, particularly in its upper reaches.

In the southern part of the Maritime Territory, Bromlei has collected badger on the seashore near the mouth of the Chingouz River, on the Taukha and Sandagou rivers, and in the area of Zarya Bay (coll. Zool. Mus. Moscow University).

It occurs on Bol'shoi Shantar Island, where it was obtained in 1925 by G. D. Dul'keit on the Mitina River (Ognev, 1929).

It abounds in all of Sakhalins water bodies (Schrenck, 1858; Nikol'skii, 1889; and others). According to recent data from the Sredne-Sakhalin reserve (Gerasimov, 1951), it has been obtained by Volkova on the Pilenga River (coll. Zool. Mus. Moscow University).

Survey of subspecies. Three subspecies of the otter are distinguished within the Soviet Union. The nominate subspecies ranges in Siberia.

11a. **Lutra lutra lutra** Linnaeus (1758). Common otter

In addition to the synonymy presented in the species description we present the following:

1922. L u t r a   v u l g a r i s   b a i c a l e n s i s. Dybowski, B. — Arch. Tow Nauk. Lvov, 1, p. 349 (nomen nudum. Vicinity of Lake Baikal).

1922. L u t r a   v u l g a r i s   a m u r e n s i s. Dybowski, B. — Loc. cit. (nomen nudum. Amur, Ussuri Territory).

1922. L u t r a   v u l g a r i s   k a m t s c h a t i c a. Dybowski, B. — Loc. cit. (nomen nudum. Kamchatka).

1931. L u t r a   l u t r a   l u t r a. Ognev, S. I. Zveri Vostochnoi Evropy Severnoi Azii (Animals of Eastern Europe and Northern Asia). 1, p. 507.

Type and type locality. See species description.

Diagnosis. Characterized by relatively dark fur which is dense and soft. The winter fur is glossy dark gray or dark brown above, gradually becoming insignificantly lighter on flanks and belly, where it assumes an indistinctly russet hue. The light patch on the gula is absent.

Measurements. See species description.

Systematic notes. There are data indicating that the otters ranging over the vast expanse of Siberia are not subspecifically identical. At any rate, when comparison of otter pelts obtained at corresponding seasons of the year in the northern and southern areas is made, a difference can be seen in fur quality. Those from the northern areas are marked by denser and more luxuriant fur. Kuznetsov (1952) reported that dark and thick-furred otter pelts of particularly high grade are obtained from Yakutia and the Far East. Gol'dman described (1936) the "species" L u t r a   s t e j n e g e r i from a Kamchatka specimen. The 22 skulls and 2 pelts from Kamchatka which I have studied have, however, failed to provide a basis for isolating the Kamchatka otter as a distinct taxon. B. Dybovskii (1922) distinguished between the Kamchatka otters, the Baikal ones, and the Amur ones, regarding these as separate "variations," but failed to provide a diagnosis. At present we do not possess sufficient material for solving this problem, so the otters inhabiting Siberia should conjecturally be associated with the nominate form.

Material studied. The USSR in Europe — 17 specimens, the Caucasus — 5 specimens, Western Siberia — 14 specimens, the Altai — 1 specimen, Sayans — 1 specimen, Barguzin — 4 specimens, Chukchi — 3 specimens, the Kamchatka — 27 specimens, the Okhotsk Coast — 3 specimens, Bol'shoi Shantar Island — 1 specimen, Maritime Territory — 28 specimens. Total — 107 specimens.

Biology. The otter is closely associated with the water, obtaining its food — which consists of various aquatic animals — therein.

At the same time its connection with dry land is considerable, for it there constructs its burrow or den, in which it hides from bad weather, rests, brings its young to life, nurses them, etc.

FIGURE 69. The Pyaku-Pur River, in the basin of the Pur. Otter biotope. Photo by V. I. Telegin

The otter is biotopically confined to the shores of various bodies of fresh water, which it inhabits only if extensive reserves of fish are available throughout the year. In winter, the otter can only visit those water bodies which have air holes and hollows under the ice. The otter is not to be found around those which freeze to the bottom except occasionally in the warm part of the year. The animal also avoids rivers with wide stretches of ice. Turbid or shallow water bodies are also unsuitable for the otter.

In the Arctic tundras, e. g., on the Yamal and Gyda, it lives along large tundra rivers. On Kamchatka it is sporadically encountered along the seashore.

In the lowland taiga it prefers rivers with rapid flow, with sandbars, and with whirlpools, along with river mouths and with lake shores overgrown with forests (Figure 69).

On the Altai it prefers swift, stony-bottomed mountain rivers abounding with fish.

In the Sayans (in the Minusinsk taiga), according to the brothers L. and I. Kozhanchikov (1924), it inhabits all water bodies which contain fish, independent of the height of the locality or the steepness of the mountains (Figure 70).

In the treeless steppe and in the forest steppe, the otter lives along river and lake shores overgrown with shrub thickets or reeds.

In the southwestern part of Transbaikalia, according to A. Cherkasov (1867), the otter prefers ravines and open places in the taiga to ridges and secluded forests.

FIGURE 70. An oxbow of the Kan River, Eastern Sayan. Otter biotope. Photo by K. T. Yurlov

On the Anadyr, according to N. P. Sokol'nikov (1927), it lives in winter on the small tributaries and creeks where the grayling fish abounds (Figure 71).

This seasonal change of biotope is caused by ice conditions on the water body, and on food availability.

In winter, when rivers and lakes are ice-bound, otters migrate from one empty place in the ice to another, often managing to switch from one basin to another. During such seasonal migrations the otters travel dozens of kilometers, overcoming whatever forests or mountains stand in their way. Thus, on the Sayans, according to the Kozhanchikov brothers (1924), with the onset of frost and deep snows the otter will migrate from one small river to another — or even from one region of a large river into another, e. g., going from the Us River valley, where it lived during the summer and fall, into the Amyl River, ascending along the Buiba and forcing the Buibinskii Pass.

At other times the otter does not travel further than $\frac{1}{4}$ km from its water body. It feels less secure on dry land than in water.

The animal uses both temporary lairs and permanent burrows. The temporary lairs are shallow burrows on the shore, washouts under overhanging banks, cavities in the roots of bankside trees, in heaps of stone, in accumulations of driftwood, windbreaks, etc., and sometimes simple hollows under some waterside shrub with overhanging branches.

The otter will pass the day in these lairs if it has traveled far from its permanent home.

The permanent burrow is built beside the water, and consists of a flask-shaped chamber with a main entrance which descend gently and opens under water at a depth of about half a meter. The nesting chamber always lies above water level. One or two narrow ramifications are built out from the nesting chamber to the surface of the earth, probably serving as ventilation. According to observations made by Cherkasov (1867) in southern Transbaikalia, the otter may sometimes occupy another animal's burrows and may also inhabit fissures and cavities in cliffs. The surroundings of the burrow or the nest always show accumulations of fish bones and other small animal bones. According to N. P. Sokol'nikov (1927), on the Anadyr, in winter the otter's burrow is constructed near a "polynya" [an ice-free area], under the brow of a steep bank below the ice surface where an empty space forms between the ice and the water. In the summer, when it gives birth, the otter constructs its abode in heaps of driftwood or in cliffs.

FIGURE 71. The floodplain of the Anadyr River. Otter biotope. Photo by S.S. Yudin

The trails and footprints of the otter are generally similar to those of the badger, the difference being that in the otter the digits are more separate, and the claws markedly weaker, making the prints less sharp. The print of the hind paw is about 9 cm long, while that of the forepaw is 6—7 cm long.

The animal is generally nocturnal, and is only in rare cases active during the day. The entire day is passed in the abode. When resting, like other carnivores it lies in various poses: curled on its side, on its belly, or on its back with paws outstretched.

Hearing, the tactile sense, and sight are the best developed senses, the sense of smell being not as sharp. The otter is an extremely taciturn animal. In rare cases it may make a sound like a loud whistle. The animal is extremely cautious and reticent, and is only rarely seen by humans. Young otters, once caught, are rapidly tamed in captivity and become attached to their masters. Otters usually do not bite in captivity. The otter swims and dives perfectly, twisting and turning in the water with lightning speed, and few fish can escape it. The otter can stay under water for two minutes, swimming a distance of 100 m the while. On dry land the animal is relatively helpless, and its movements are awkward and rather slow — so slow, in fact, that even the least talented dog can easily overtake it within a few dozen meters.

The otter feeds chiefly on fish, but also on other small animals, such as mollusks, frogs, and even water fowl and rodents, etc. In captivity, the otter's daily ration consists of 1 kg of food. The stomach and feces of the otter are found to contain remnants of insects on which the fish eaten by the otter have fed. Cases are known, in water bodies where fish are abundant, of otters hiding fish in secluded places for storage; such stores occasionally reach 8—10 kg (V. P. Teplov, E. N. Teplova, 1947). The animal is known to eat plants. Thus, according to Cherkasov, in Transbaikalia the animal occasionally eats grass, young tree shoots, and bark.

Its reproduction is still unclear, and no concrete data are available on the principal phenomena associated with reproduction. Rut occurs in Western Siberia, according to the available data, in March—April.

In Transbaikalia, according to Cherkasov, rut occurs in February. There are no other observations pertaining to this phenomenon in Siberia. The gestation period is 9—10 weeks (Ognev, 1951). The young are born in April—May. Cases of very late broods — arriving in June to December — are known, but are extremely rare. Brood size can be five, but is most often 2—3. The young are born blind, and the eyes open at about the 5th week of life. Lactation lasts some 3 months. At the age of 2 months the young begin learning to catch fish and other animals, and by winter have become independent. Sexual maturity is reached by females in the second year of life and by males in the third year.

Molt occurs slowly and gradually. The summer fur differs only slightly from the winter fur. The fur of the young is longer and softer than that of the adults, with a less developed underfur.

Practical importance. Otter fur is notable for strength and beauty and is highly valuable, being used for collars, hats and other fur products. Its economic significance is, however, small, due to its relative rarity.

11. Genus ENHYDRA Fleming (1822). Sea otters

1822. Enhydra. Fleming, I. Philosophy of Zoology, 2, p. 187, Edinburgh; Miller, G. S. List of North American Recent Mammals, p. 130, Washington. 1914; Ognev, S. I. Zveri Vostochnoi Evropy i Severnoi Azii (Animals of Eastern Europe and Northern Asia). 2, p. 530. 1931; Simpson, G. G. The Principles of Classification of the Mammals. — Amer.

Mus. Nat. Hist., 85, p. 115. 1945; Ellerman, I. R. and T. C. S. Morrison-Scott. Checklist of Palaearctic Mammals, p. 279, London. (1951).

1827. Latax. Gloger, C. — Nova acta Phys. Med. Acad. Caes. Leop. Carol, 13, 2, p. 511. Satunin, K. A. Opredelitel' mlekopitayushchikh Rossiiskoi imperii (Key to Mammals of the Russian Empire). p. 130, Tiflis. 1914.

1829. Enhydris. Fischer, J. B. Synopsis Mammalium, p. 228.

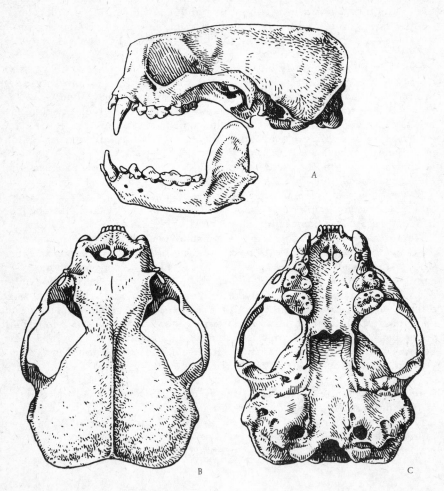

FIGURE 72. Skull of the sea otter, Enhydra lutris L. (original):

A — lateral view; B — dorsal view; C — ventral view.

Type species. Mustela lutris Linnaeus (1758).

Diagnosis. Dimensions extremely large: length of body with head up to 150 cm, length of tail up to 36 cm. Hind limbs similar to flippers and completely covered with short hair. Forepaws have greatly shortened fully fused digits. In hind limbs, outermost toe (V) is longest and innermost shortest. Tail dorsoventrally flattened, and slightly tapered from root to tip. Length of tail constitutes $\frac{1}{4}$ of body length. Fur luxuriant, long, dense and silky. Guard hairs on back extremely sparse and almost invisible against dense underfur.

Skull (Figure 72) resembles in general configuration that of [common] otter but is larger and more massive, being set off by relatively greater height and width as against inconsiderable length. Maximum skull length 120—150 mm, maximum height 56—67 mm. Rostrum anteriorly almost perpendicularly truncate, nasals broad and short. Nasal aperture very large: its transverse width exceeds width of orbit. Bony palate barely tapering behind molars. Tympanic bullae transverse and small; auditory meati extremely small. Jugular foramina extremely large and approximately as long as alveoli of canines. Postorbital processes little marked. Mastoid processes, in form of blunt massive bulges, directed obliquely foreward. Occipital and sagittal crests reach considerable development. Infraorbital foramina either almost of same size as alveoli of upper canines or barely greater.

Dental formula: $I\frac{3}{2}$; $C\frac{1}{1}$; $Pm\frac{3}{3}$; $M\frac{1}{2}$ = 32.

Molars and premolars low and bluntly tuberculate. First upper premolar (Pm^1) occupies usual place for tooth of this category: between canine and Pm^2. Carnassials and molars have polished masticatory surface, smoothed out edges, and bluntly rounded tubercles.

Systematic notes. The sea otters are a distinct genus within the otter subfamily. The degree of differentiation is so great that some students isolate them in a distinct subfamily (Pocock, 1921). There are, however, forms intermediate between the sea and river otters: the African and South Asian genus A o n y x Lesson (1827). Fossil forms with intermediate traits are also known (E n h y d r a r e e v e i Newton from the Pliocene of England). All this compels us to treat the sea otters as an extremely specialized genus within subfamily Lutrinae.

The genus is monotypic.

Geographical distribution. The coasts and islands of the northern part of the Pacific Ocean.

12. **Enhydra lutris Linnaeus (1758). Sea otter**

1751. Lutra marina. Steller, G. W. De Bestis Marinis.— Novi Comment. Acad. Sci. Imp. Petropolit., 2, pp. 367—398 (1749).

1758. Mustela lutris. Linnaeus, C. Systema Naturae, 1, 10 ed., p. 45.

1777. Lutra marina. Erxleben, I. C. Syst. Regn. Anim., p. 445, Leipzig (Kamchatka).

1800. Lutra gracilis. Bechstein, I. M. Uebersicht der Vierfüssigen Thiere, 2, p. 408, Weimar (Kurile Islands).

1811. Phoca lutris. Pallas, P. S. Zoographia Rosso-Asiatica, 1, pp. 100—102.

1816. Pusa orientalis. Oken, L. Lehrbuch d. Naturgesch., 3, Abt. 2, pp. 986—987.

1827. Lutra stelleri. Lesson, R. Manual de Mammologie, Histoire Naturelle des Mammifères, p. 156, Paris.

1850. Enhydris lutris. Simashko, Yu. Russkaya fauna (Russian Fauna), p. 402. 1850. pl. XIV A—XIV F.

1880. Enhydris marina. Brandt, J. F.— Melang. Biol. Bull. Acad. Imp., 11, p. 15, St. Petersburg; Lekh. C. Nekotorye nablyudeniya nad morskim bobrom (Some Observations on the Sea Beaver).— Zapiski Obshchestva Izucheniya Amurskogo Kraya, 10, pp. 1—37. 1907.

1898. Latax lutris. Steineger, L. The Fur Seals and Fur-seal Island, 4, p. 24; Satunin, K. A. Opredelitel' mlekopitayushchikh Rossiiskoi imperii (Key to Mammals of the Russian Empire). p. 131, Tiflis. 1914. figs. 136—139.

1902. Enhydris lutris. Grebnitskii, N. A. Komandorskie ostrova (Commander Islands). p. 18. Sankt-Peterburg, Izdatel'stvo Departamenta Zemledeliya.

1931. Enhydra lutris. Ognev, S. I. Zveri Vostochnoi Evropy i Severnoi Azii (Animals of Eastern Europe and Northern Asia). 2, pp. 531—541. figs. 134—136; Barabash-Nikiforov, I. I. Kalan, ili morskaya vydra (The Sea Otter Enhydra lutris L.). pp. 1—96, Moskva. 1933. figs. 1—26; Barabash-Nikiforov, I. I. Kalan (Enhydra lutris L.); ego biologiya i voprosy khozyaistva (The Sea Otter (Enhydra lutris L.), its Biology and Economic Problems).— In:Sbornik "Kalan," pp. 3—201, Moskva, Izd. Glavnogo upravleniya po zapovednikam. 1947. figs. 1—55; Ellerman, J. R. and T. C. S. Morrison-Scott. Checklist of Palaearctic and Indian Mammals, p. 279, London. 1951; Novikov, G. A. Khishchnye mlekopitayushchie fauny SSSR (Carnivorous Mammals of the Fauna of the USSR). pp. 224—230. Izdatel'stvo AN SSSR. 1956. figs. 148—150.

Type and type locality. The tenth edition of Linnaeus' Systema Naturae (1758) says the following about the distribution of the sea otter: "Habitat in Asia et America septentrionalis"— that and nothing more. I. I. Barabash-Nikiforov (1947) has justly noted that Linnaeus' description of the sea otter was based on data from G. Steller, whose material was almost exclusively from the Commander Islands, and that these islands should therefore be considered the type locality (terra typica) for the animal.

FIGURE 73.

Os penis of the sea otter Enhydra lutris L. (from I. I. Barabash-Nikiforov)

Diagnosis. The features of the species are identical with those presented above in the diagnosis of the genus.

Measurements. Length of body with head 93—150 cm, length of tail 30—36 cm, length of hind paw 20—23 cm, height of ear 2.4—2.6 cm. Weight of males up to 40 kg, and females 23—30 kg.

Condylobasal length of skull: males 130—140.3 mm, females 120.0—128.2 mm; zygomatic width: males 101.0—110 mm, females 90.0—102.6 mm; interorbital width: males 42.0—46.5 mm, females 36.7—42.2 mm; postorbital width: males 28.0 — 36.0 mm, females 27.0—35.5 mm; height in region of tympanic bullae males 56.2—67.5 mm, females 56.0—62.0 mm; length of upper tooth row: males 46.2—51.4 mm, females 44.3—48.6 mm.

Description. Externally resembles the common or river otters, but differs from them in larger size and peculiar structure of hind limbs, these being markedly larger than forelimbs, broad and flat, and similar to flippers in form. Fur varies from russet to intense black. Variation in fur color consists of differing degrees of intensity of general tone and of occurrence and density of gray hair. Conspicuous age variation in fur color. In the newborn otter — the "medvedka" — the fur is a light brownish russet. One-year-olds, known locally as "koshlaki," are intermediate in color between the "medvedka" and the adult animal. Gray hair characterizes all ages. Albino or white-colored individuals are occasionally encountered.

Os penis massive and slightly recurved. Terminal part has small expansion in form of head with groove on lower side. Length of bone reaches 145 mm, basal height 15 mm (Figure 73).

Systematic notes. As shown by Barabash-Nikiforov (1947), the sea otter forms several — at least three — subspecies: the Commander (nominate), the south Kamchatkan, and the Californian. Differences consist in craniological features and fur quality.

Geographical distribution. The range of the sea otter today lies in the northern part of the Pacific. Within Soviet territory, it lives along the shores of the Commander Islands (chiefly off Medny Island), the southern tip of Kamchatka (at Cape Lopatka) and on some islands of the Kurile chain where, according to B. A. Kuznetsov (1949), it occurs in extremely small numbers. In the area of Paramushir Island (near Cape Vasil'ev), sea otters were caught in September 1945. The otter has been found along the coasts of Onnekotan, Shiashkotan, and Musiri islands. It occurs on Urup Island. Outside the Soviet Union, it survives on some of the Aleutians, on the southern coast of Alaska, and locally along the west coast of North America as far south as California.

Survey of subspecies. The number of subspecies has not been precisely established. There are probably at least five. Two or three subspecies inhabit the Soviet Union.

12a. Enhydra lutris lutris Linnaeus (1758). Commander sea otter

1751. Lutra marina. Steller, G. W. De Bestis Marinis.— Novi Comment. Acad. Sci. Imp. Petropol., 2, pp. 367—398. (1749) (partim).
1758. Mustela lutris. Linneaus, C.— Systema Naturae, 10 ed. 1, p. 45.
1947. Enhydra lutris lutris. Barabash-Nikiforov, I. I. Kalan (Enhydra lutris L.), ego biologiya i voprosy khozyaistva (The Sea Otter (Enhydra lutris L.), its Biology and Economic Problems).— In: Sbornik "Kalan," pp. 25—26, Moskva.

Type and type locality. See description of species.
Diagnosis. Characterized by relatively narrow skull. Zygomatic width of skull 71— 80 % of condylobasal length, mastoid width 71—79 % (respective indexes in south Kamchatka sea otter are 85—87 % and 84—86 %). Fur, according to Barabash-Nikiforov, has well-developed guard hair; length of guard hair about 30 mm in middle of back. Fur relatively light, with noticeable grayness.

Measurements. (17 males and 7 females). Condylobasal length of skull: males 130.5—140.3 mm (av. 136.5 mm), females 120—128.2 mm (av. 125.4 mm); zygomatic width: males 101.0—110.0 mm (av. 104.3 mm), females 90.0—102.0 mm (av. 94.3 mm); interorbital width: males 40.2—46.5 mm (av. 43.4 mm), females 36.7—42.2 mm (av. 39.2 mm); mastoid width: males 93.9 — 108.0 mm (av. 99.5 mm), females 88.0 — 95.3 mm (av. 91.4 mm); height in area of tympanic bullae: males 56.2—67.1 mm (av. 62.2 mm), females 56.0 — 62.0 mm (av. 58.8 mm); width between infraorbital foramina: males 44.2—50.2 mm (av. 46.6 mm), females 41.6— 45.5 mm (av. 42.8 mm); length of upper tooth row: males 46.2—51.4 mm (av. 48.3 mm); females 44.3—48.6 mm (av. 46.0 mm).

Systematic notes. The nominate subspecies is readily differentiated craniologically from the south Kamchatka and California sea otters. When compared with the first, the skull is narrower and with the second, smaller. With regard to fur color, the material studied by me (three pelts and one live specimen) is insufficient for any definite conclusion. On the basis of the literature (Brandt, 1881; Barabash-Nikiforov, 1947), the fur of the Commander sea otters is lighter than that of the Kamchatka individuals and is similar in color to that of the American specimens.

Geographical distribution. The Commander Islands. Barabash-Nikiforov (1947) includes in this subspecies the sea otters from the Aleutian Islands and also conjecturally those from the northeastern coast of Kamchatka.

Material studied. The Commander Islands: 26 skulls and 4 pelts.

12b. Enhydra lutris subsp. South Kamchatka sea otter

1947. **Enhydra lutris gracilis.** Barabash-Nikiforov, I. I. Kalan (Enhydra lutris L.), ego biologiya i voprosy khozyaistva (The Sea Otter (Enhydra lutris L.), its Biology and Economic Problems).— In: Sbornik "Kalan," pp. 26—27, Moskva. (nec Bechstein. 1799).

Type and type locality. Skull No. 1/L in the collection of I. I Barabash-Nikiforov, ♂, sen. Cape Lopatka (the southern tip of Kamchatka).

Diagnosis. Differentiated from nominate subspecies by broader skull and darker fur. Zygomatic width of skull 85—87 % of condylobasal length, mastoid width 84—86% [of latter]. Length of guard hair at mid-back about 25 mm (against 35 mm in Commander sea otter). Fur darker, as shows less gray.

Measurements. (5 adult male skulls). Condylobasal length 132.8—133.6 mm (av.133.4 mm); zygomatic width: 113.3—116.4 mm (av. 114.9 mm); interorbital width 46.9 — 49.1 mm (av. 48.0 mm); mastoid width 107.0—112.3 mm (av. 109.5 mm); height in area of tympanic bullae: 52.9—55.0 mm (av. 54.1 mm); width between infraorbital foramina: 50.0 — 52.2 mm (av. 51.1 mm); length of upper tooth row: 46.2—47.0 mm (av. 46.5 mm).

Systematic notes. Differences from nominate subspecies have been given above. The first to assign systematic significance to this otter's

distinctive morphological traits was Barabash-Nikiforov (1947) who,
however, identified it with the sea otter described from one of the islands
in the southern part of the Kurile chain. This kinship between the south
Kamchatka and the Kurile sea otters was made a priori, since the author
had no actual material. The published data also provide no basis for
conclusions about the systematic relationships between these otters. The
south Kamchatka sea otters cannot be included with the south Kurile ones
without an extensive survey of collected material. The south Kurile sea
otter has been incompletely described. It is not to be denied that
systematic differences do occur between this and the south Kamchatka sea
otter, but until specimens of the south Kurile sea otter are studied in
detail I refrain from giving a taxonomic name to the otter inhabiting the
southern tip of Kamchatka.

Geographical distribution. The southern tip of the Kamchatka
Peninsula.

Material studied. One specimen. In addition, data on about 5 of
Barabash-Nikiforov's specimens have been used.

12c. **Enhydra lutris gracilis** Bechstein (1799). South Kurile sea otter

1799. L u t r a   g r a c i l i s. Bechstein, S. M. Uebers. d. vierfüssig.
Thiere, II, p. 408.

Type and type locality. The form as established by modern authors
(Hollister, 1912; Barabash-Nikiforov, 1947) was first described from
material from the southernmost of the Kurile islands, then known as
Statenland.

Diagnosis. Characterized by relatively small size.

Systematic notes. At present we do not possess concrete data
permitting precise diagnosis and description of this form. The data
presented in the above diagnosis are taken from an incomplete description
in Bechstein's work (1800).

The systematic position of the sea otter inhabiting the middle and
northern part of the Kurile chain remains unclear.

Geographical distribution. The southern islands of the Kurile chain.

Material studied. Absent.

Biology. The sea otter's characteristic habitat is along steep
shorelines — in bays containing reefs and large rocks (both above and
below the surface) and having sea kale thickets and an abundance of large
benthic invertebrates. In these shoreline inlets the animals seek shelter
from wind and surf, and lie on the reefs and stones (Figure 74); they rest
in the sea kale thickets, where the sea is relatively calm and which offers
good protection from the killer whale. Migration along the shore has been
noted, and the otter's density at a place varies over time. One cause of
this is the strong wind. A diurnal animal, it sleeps during the night either
ashore or on rocks protruding from the water. Windless summer nights
it sometimes passes in thickets of sea kale. During the day it swims in
search of food, resting intermittently. It swims in schools.

The sea otter feeds chiefly on sea urchins, mollusks, crabs and fish.
From a study of 1,500 specimens, Barabash-Nikiforov (1947) reports

the following percentage breakdown for the sea otter's diet: sea
urchins 59.0%, mollusks 23.3%, fish and crustaceans 16.7%. This author
also noted seasonal changes in the diet associated with seasonal
changes in distribution(i.e., within the biotope) of the animal which
constitute its prey. In winter the diet consists almost exclusively of
sea urchins and mollusks (except for octopus); the diet is supplemented
in summer by fish, crabs, and octopus. The sea otter finds its prey in
shallow water, and lies belly-up in the water as it eats, using its forepaws
like hands. In captivity its daily ration may reach as much as 35 — 40 kg
urchins (weight with the shell, which the sea otter does not eat) or about
10 kg of fish (without bones and innards).

FIGURE 74. The Commander Islands. Biotope of the sea otter. Photo by N.A. Violovich

Reproduction is almost unstudied. Barabash-Nikiforov (1947) saw females
with young throughout the year in the area of Medny island. Courtship
games and mating occurred both in winter and in summer, but these occur
more vigorously in spring (March — May). The gestation period is
supposedly about 8 — 9 months. Before parturition, females collect in
shore inlets protected from the wind and the surf. Parturition occurs on
the shore or on rocks above the water. The litter usually contains one,
and extremely rarely two, young; these are born completely developed,
with eyes open and with teeth cut. The female goes into the sea with the
newborn, though she may sometimes leave it ashore. Swimming on her
back, the female clasps the young to her breast and, when diving for food,
leaves it on the surface. In case of danger she may dive together with her
young. The young live together with their mothers for about one year, and
quite often mature young may stay with the mother even when she has

another newborn.   The sea otter has long been known to migrate, but the nature of this has not been studied closely.

The molt is extremely protracted and not associated with any definite time; the fur displays almost no seasonal change.

Practical importance.   Sea otter fur, known in the fur trade as "Kamchatka beaver," is extremely valuable.   Due to its relative scarcity, hunting the sea otter is at present prohibited.   As shown by the experiment in keeping the sea otter in captivity on the Murman coast, the otter can be bred in enclosures.

12.   Genus MARTES Pinel (1792).   Sables

1792.   M a r t e s.   Pinel, Ph. — Actes Soc. d'Hist. Nat., 1, p. 55, Paris; Thomas, O. — Proc. Zool. Soc. London, p. 139. 1911; Miller, G. S. Catalogue of the Mammals of Western Europe, p. 365, London. 1912; Satunin, K. A. Opredelitel' mlekopitayushchikh Rossiiskoi imperii (Key to Mammals of the Russian Empire). p. 105, Tiflis. 1914; Ognev, S. I. Zveri Vostochnoi Evropy i Severnoi Azii (Animals of Eastern Europe and Northern Asia). 2, pp. 557 — 558. 1931; Bobrinskii, N. A. Otryad khishchnye. Ordo Carnivora. V knige: Opredelitel' mlekopitayushchikh SSSR, pod redaktsiei N. A. Bobrinskogo (Order Carnivores (Ordo Carnivora). In: Key to Mammals of the USSR edited by N. A. Bobrinskii). p. 117, Moskva. 1944; Ellerman, J. R. and T. C. S. Morrison-Scott. Checklist of Palaearctic and Indian Mammals, p. 244, London. 1951; Novikov, G. A. Khishchnye mlekopitayushchie fauny SSSR (Carnivorous Mammals of the Fauna of the USSR). pp. 170 — 171, Moskva-Leningrad. 1956.

1849.   Z i b e l l i n a.   Kaup, J. — Entw. Gesch. und Nat. Syst. europ. Thierw., 1, pp. 31, 34 (M u s t e l a z i b e l l i n a Linnaeus. 1758).

Type species.   M a r t e s d o m e s t i c a Pinel (1792)-M u s t e l a f o i n a Erxleben (1777).

Diagnosis.   Body thin, slender and very lithe.   Muzzle sharp.   Ears quite large, almost triangular, with rounded tips.   Tail extremely bushy,   length about $\frac{1}{2} - \frac{2}{3}$ length of body with head.   Toes slightly webbed.

Skull narrow and long.   Upper skull profile gently convex.   Hamulary processes (processes of the pterygoid bones) not connected by bony bridges with tympanic bullae.   Auditory tubes present (Figure 75). External auditory meatus more or less open above, being covered below by outgrowth of auditory tube.   Distance between jugular

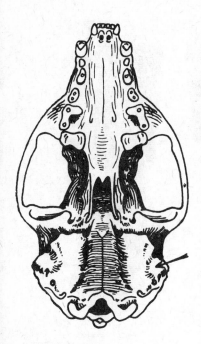

FIGURE 75. The skull of forest or pine marten M a r t e s m a r t e s L.   Arrow shows auditory tube (after S. U. Stroganov, 1949)

foramina markedly greater than half length of tympanic bulla. Paroccipital processes well developed but fail to reach upper side of tympanic bullae. Mastoid processes relatively weakly protruding laterally. Mastoid width exceeds distance from basion to palation. Infraorbital foramina of almost same size as alveoli of upper canines.

Dental formula: $I\frac{3}{3}$; $C\frac{1}{1}$; $Pm\frac{4}{4}$; $M\frac{1}{2} = 38$.

Lower carnassial tooth bears on inner side an additional denticle of moderate size. Talon of upper carnassial tooth provided with large and sharp denticle. Longitudinal axes of upper carnassial crowns lie at angles to each other. Upper molar twice as broad as long, and divided into two parts, the outer smaller and higher, the inner expanded.

Forms are terrestrial and to some extent adapted to movement in crowns of trees.

Geographical distribution. Includes the Northern Hemisphere from the northern forest belt and south to the Mediterranean, India, Malay Archipelago, Japan, Northern California, and New Mexico.

Systematic notes. Genus includes about 10 species. Of these, 4 (united in 2 subgenera) occur in the Soviet Union; all occur in Siberia.

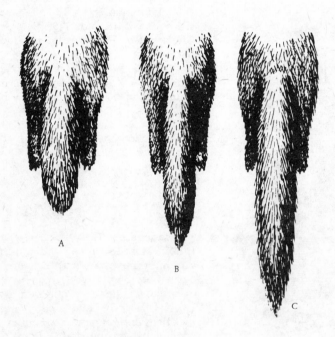

FIGURE 76. Length and form of tail:

A — the sable (Martes zibellina L.); B — the forest or pine marten (Martes martes L.); C — the stone marten (Martes foina Erxleben).

FIGURE 77   Size and form of gular patch:

A — sable; B — forest or pine marten; C — stone marten (after N. A. Bobrinskii).

Key to Subgenera and Species of Genus Martes Occurring in Siberia

1 (2).   Dimensions large: length of body with head 55 — 80 cm; condylobasal length of skull over 100 mm.   Tail not bushy.   Color extremely
vivid and rather motley; upper part of head, back, tail and legs
black, body yellow.   Os penis bears on distal end two paired blunt
protrusions (processes). . . . . Subgenus **Lamprogale** (p. 237)

2 (1).   Dimensions relatively small: length of body with head 30 — 57 cm;
condylobasal length of skull less
than 100 mm.   Tail bushy; color more
of less uniform, no vivid motley
spots.   On anterior end os penis
either forked or bears small open
or closed ring. . . . .

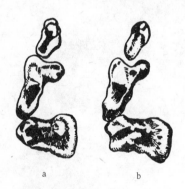

a   b

FIGURE 78.   Size and form of last upper
premolar and first molar:

a — forest or pine marten Martes
martes L.; b — stone marten
Martes foina Erxl. (after
S. I. Ognev, 1931).

. . . . Subgenus **Martes** (p. 213) .

3 (4).   Head above usually colored lighter
than back.   Light gular patch, if
present, rather weakly outlined,
fusing gradually with lateral and
lower parts of neck.   Tail of moderate
length; when extended, less than
final quarter shows past ends
of extended hind legs.
(Figure 76 A).   Distance between
carotid foramina less than one half
distance from anterior edge of
tympanic bullae to posterior edge of
paroccipital process . . . .
Sable-**Martes** s.str.**zibellina** (p. 213). .

4 (3).   Head colored like back.   Light gular patch sharply outlined
(Figure 77).   Tail longer: when extended protrudes markedly
(more than by $\frac{1}{4}$ of its length) beyond ends of extended hind legs
(Figure 76).   Distance between carotid foramina greater than one
half distance from anterior edge of tympanic bulla to posterior
edge of paroccipital processes . . . . 5.

FIGURE 79. The sable Martes zibellina L. After specimen No. 5665 Zool. Mus. Moscow University. Painted by V. A. Varagin

5 (6). Gular patch light yellow or orange (Figure 77); extends back as
        narrow band between forelegs. Soles densely hirsute. Distal
        hairs on tail form tuft with rounded tip. External aspect of upper
        molar lacks vertical groove (or at most has an extremely small one.
        Width of this tooth approximately equals length of upper carnassial
        tooth (Figure 78) . . . . . Pine marten **Martes** s. str. **martes** (p. 227)
6 (5). Gular patch pure white (Figure 77); usually continues back in
        two bands bifurcating onto forelegs. Soles almost bare;
        pads protruding. Distal hairs on tail form tuft with pointed
        tip (Figure 76B). External surface of upper molar with
        well-marked vertical groove. Width of upper molar markedly
        less than length of upper carnassial tooth (Figure 78). . . .
        . . . . Stone marten - **Martes** s. str. **foina** (p. 233)

1.   Subgenus M a r t e s s. str.   True martens

     Synonym.   See description of genus.
     Type species of the subgenus. M u s t e l a f o i n a Erxleben (1777).
     Diagnosis.   Dimensions relatively small: length of body with head
30 — 57 cm, length of tail 15 — 30 cm; condylo-basal length of skull less than
100 mm.   Tail extremely furry.   Color more or less uniform but no vivid
motley areas.   Os penis bears on anterior end a bifurcation or a small
ring which can be closed.
     Three species in the Soviet Union.
     Geographical distribution.   Range of the subgenus coincides with that of
the genus.

13. **Martes** s. str. **zibellina** Linnaeus (1758). Sable

     1758. M u s t e l a z i b e l l i n a . Linnaeus, C   Systema Naturae, 10 ed.
p. 46; Gmelin, J. G. — Nov. Comment. Acad. Petrop., 5, pp. 338 — 339.
1760; Pallas, P. S.   Specilegia Zoologica, Berolini, 14, pp. 54 — 78. 1780;
Auct. cit   Zoographia Rosso-Asiatica, 1, p. 83, Petropoli. 1811 — 1831;
Simashko, Yu. Russkaya fauna (Russian Fauna). 2, p. 338. 1851;
Bogdanov, M. N. Okhotnich'i i promyslovye zveri i ptitsy Evropeiskoi
Rossii i Kavkazskogo kraya (Hunting and Game Animals and Birds of
European Russia and the Caucasian Territory). — Zhurnal Okhoty i
Konnozavodstva, Nos. 9 — 10, p. 186. 1873; Sabaneev, L. P.   Sobol' i
sobolinyi promysel (The Sable and the Sable Trade). pp. 1 — 70.
Moskva. 1875; Satunin, K. A. Opredelitel' mlekopitayushchikh Rossiiskoi
imperii (Key to Mammals of the Russian Empire). p. 108, Tiflis. 1914;
Ognev, S. I. Sobol' (The Sable). — Trudy po Lesnomu Opytnomu Delu
Tsentral'noi Lesnoi Opytnoi Stantsii, otdel biologicheskii i promyshlennoi
okhoty, No. 14 (4), p. 5, Moskva. 1931; Adlerberg, G. P. Khishchnye zveri
(Carnivora Fissipedia) Arktiki (Carnivora Fissipedia of the Arctic). — In:
Zveri Arktiki, pod redaktsiei prof. N. A. Smirnova, pp. 345 — 350, Leningrad,
Izdatel'stvo Glavsevmorputi. 1935; Kuznetsov, B. A. Geograficheskaya

izmenchivost' soblei i kunits fauny SSSR (Geographical Variation of Sables and Martens of the Fauna of the USSR). — Trudy Moskovskogo Zootekhnicheskogo Instituta, 1, pp. 113 — 124. 1941; Ellerman, J. R. and T. C. S. Morrison-Scott. Checklist of Palaearctic and Indian Mammals, pp. 248 — 249, London. 1951; Bannikov, A. G. Mlekopitayushchie Mongol'skoi Narodnoi Respubliki (Mammals of the Mongolian People's Republic). Moskva, Izdatel'stvo AN SSSR. 1954.

1844. Mustela brachyura. Temminck. Faun. Japan. Mamm., p. 33 (Ieso, Japan).

1944. Martes (martes) zibellina. Bobrinskii, N. A. Otryad khishchnye. Ordo Carnivora. V knige: Opredelitel' mlekopitayushchikh SSSR, pod redaktsiei prof. N. A. Bobrinskogo (Order Carnivores (Ordo Carnivora)). In: Key to Mammals of the USSR, edited by Prof. N. A. Bobrinskii). pp. 119 — 120, Moskva; Novikov, G. A. Khishchnye mlekopitayushchie fauny SSSR (Carnivore Mammals of the Fauna of the USSR). pp. 174 — 185, Leningrad. 1956.

Type and type locality. The species has been described from Siberian material. Ognev (1931) thinks that the terra typica is the vicinity of Tobolsk since this yielded the first precise report (Gmelin, 1760) of the sable's range following the publication of the 10th edition of Linnaeus' "Systema Naturae."

Diagnosis. Color of top of head usually lighter than back. Light gular patch, if present, small, of irregular form and not sharply outlined (Figure 77). Tail relatively short, being less than half length of body with head; when extended, tail protrudes slightly beyond paws of extended hind limbs (Figure 76). Distance between carotid foramina up to as large as one half length of tympanic bulla from its anterior side to posterior edge of paroccipital process. Mastoid processes do not protrude beyond lower edge of auditory meatus.

Measurements. Length of body with head (from 142 males and 92 females): males 380 — 560 mm, females 350 — 510 mm; length of tail: males 120 — 190 mm, females 115 — 172 mm; length of hind paw: males 70 — 110 mm, females 60 — 96 mm; height of ear: males 47 — 57 mm, females 43 — 55 mm. Weight: males in winter 880 — 1,640 g, males in summer 940 — 1,800 g, females in winter, 700 — 1,130 g, females in summer 740 — 1,560 g.

Dimensions of skull from measurements of 250 males and 195 females as follows: condylobasal length: males 76.3 — 93.3 mm, females 72.0 — 84.2 mm; zygomatic width: males 42.2 — 56.8 mm, females 39.0 — 48.7 mm; interorbital width: males 13.8 — 18.5 mm, females 12.8 — 17.7 mm; width of rostrum above canines: males 15.0 — 19.8 mm, females 14.0 — 17.0 mm; mastoid width: males 34.4 — 40.3 mm, females 33.5 — 35.8 mm; height in area of tympanic bullae: males 29.8 — 35.0 mm, females 27.0 — 31.2 mm; length of braincase: males 43.0 — 51.3 mm, females 42.0 — 47.7 mm; length of facial part: males 23.0 — 28.2 mm, females 20.8 — 25.0 mm; length of upper tooth row: males 28.8 — 38.7 mm, females 26.7 — 31.2 mm.

Description. General build typically mustelidlike. Body extremely slender, long and agile. Head looks rather broad. Muzzle not very long but markedly pointed at end of nose. Ears relatively large, with rounded tips. Tail length about $\frac{1}{3}$ body length; tail shorter than extended hind limbs. Soles covered with extremely dense and stiff hairs; in winter fur covers claws on hind paws.

Fur long, luxuriant, and silky, with glossy guard hair and dense gray or bluish gray underfur. Fur color subject to individual and considerable geographical variations. General tone of winter fur from light yellow-grayish brown, often with a russet tinge, to dark black-brown. Guard hair sometimes has white tips, which impart to fur a particular "silveriness." Back usually darker than flanks (Figure 79).

Head most often lighter than body and often with ash gray-brown or slight yellowish tinge. Neck usually bears rather diffuse yellowish patch, smaller than on marten and occasionally absent. Tail well furred, and in color like back or darker. Fur on limbs darker than on back. Summer fur appreciably shorter and sparser, with poorly developed underfur; it is dull in color and darker than winter fur.

Individual sharp aberrations in color are encountered: chromic, albinotic, and spotted (with white patches).

In addition to individual variation, fur color and quality are subject to broad geographical variation. Very dark and silky fur characterize sables in Transbaikalia and southern Yakutia, while to the west and east color begins gradually to lighten and fur becomes coarser. Sable inhabiting mountain areas are characteristically darker than those found in the lowlands.

There are no more than 16 tail vertebrae.

Os penis differs from marten's in being much straighter and in lacking upward-arched bend in distal part; end divided into characteristic bifurcation and lacks the marten's distinctive closed ring. Length of os penis 36—40 mm.

Skull (Figure 80) rather long and narrow. Braincase generally egg-shaped, relatively long and high; its length constituting 55—60 % of condylobasal length of skull. Height of braincase about one third less than length. Facial part of skull relatively long; distance from alveoli of middle incisors to line joining ends of postorbital processes constitutes more than 65 % of distance from same line to posterior protrusion of occipital crest. Zygomatic arches relatively thin and expanded posteriorly; zygomatic width equals 50—60 % of condylobasal length. Rostrum relatively narrow, its width above canines equal to or slightly greater than constriction in postorbital area. Postorbital area characterized by conspicuous constriction whose width is markedly less than distance between orbit. Mastoid processes massive; their size varies markedly. Infraorbital foramina rounded and oval; major axis no longer than longitudinal axis of outer canine base. Sagittal crest well developed only in lambdoidal region. Occipital crests conspicuous but low. Occipital condyle massive, projecting sharply behind and below.

Mesopterygoid fossa narrower than in martens. Choanal incisure rudimentary, lacks middle protrusion behind palatine bones. Hamuli of pterygoid bones only slightly elongated, shorter than those of martens.

Tympanic bulla elongated longitudinally and markedly close together, distance between them in area of carotid foramina being no more than one half length of tympanic bulla from its anterior end to posterior side of paroccipital process. Mastoid processes weakly developed and do not project beyond lower edge of external auditory meatus.

Teeth very large, with sharp cusps. Internal part of upper molar (M^1) greatly broadened and has well-developed high torulus on lingual edge.

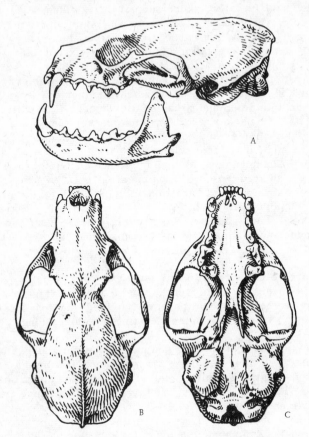

FIGURE 80. Skull of the sable, Martes zibellina L. (original):

A — lateral view; B — dorsal view; C — ventral view.

Biology. The sable is a typical forest-dweller. Recent studies have shown that in the past it inhabited almost the entire forest belt of northern Asia and eastern Europe (Kirikov, 1958). It was only natural that the sable's habitat should then have included the various types of forest, ranging from the Okhotsk taiga and from the broadleaf forests of Manchuria type to the Finnish coniferous forests and the virgin forests of Belorussia and Lithuania.

In Siberia it inhabits the entire taiga, occupying various biotopes in both lowland and mountain taiga. It finds optimal conditions for existence in biotopes associated with secluded taiga thickets having large accumulations of fallen trees interspersed with rock streams, their vegetation including siberian stone or Japanese stone pine with abundant stands of berries and their fauna rich in small rodents. In high mountains it prefers the upper periphery of the forest belt, dissected by tongues of large stone accumulations or by tickets of Japanese stone pine.

FIGURE 81. The West Siberian lowland. Taiga in the valley of the Ob River, sable biotope. Photo by K. T. Yurlov

The density of the sable population in the biotope depends on the combination of specific conditions providing the animal with a stable feeding basis and reliable shelters. In various districts such conditions occur in particular types of biotope, depending on local peculiarities of the taiga. Thus, in the taiga around the Siberian Urals, according to B. F. Koryakov (1948), the continental spruce stands and the large forest tracts with a considerable admixture of Siberian stone pine are the best biotopes for the sable. It lives readily on old burns overgrown with spruce (Figure 81). It is encountered more rarely in pure pine forests, and more rarely still in relatively young burns. These data concur with results of the winter census of sables in the Konda-Sosva reserve carried out V. V. Raevskii (1946). According to this author traces of sable were encountered in spruce and Siberian stone pine stands (71%), on overgrown burns (23%), and in marshes and pinewoods (6%).

This picture of the biotopical distribution of the sable characterizes the taiga of the entire West Siberian plain.

In the Central Siberian Plateau (interfluve of the Yenisei and Lena) it keeps mainly to larch, spruce—Siberian stone pine, and spruce—fir forests having some Siberian stone pine.

In this area, to the north of the Lower Tunguska and on the watershed between the Anabar and the Olenek, it inhabits larch forests occurring

217

outside the limits of distribution of the Siberian stone pine and Japanese stone pine. It also inhabits the alder—willow thickets here. This biotope "consists of thickets of willows and alders, under the canopy of which impassable thickets are formed by red currants and dog rose. Among these thickets are scattered islands of larch taiga whose understory consists of willow and alder. These sites are a feature of the Lena valley and extend for long stretches along the river. This was where the sable lived at the time of its most limited distribution, and this was its original focus of distribution, serving as a basis for the modern population. These habitats are still densely inhabited by the animal" (Timofeev and Nadeev, 1955).

In the Altai it lives chiefly on outfalls of large stones in the upper taiga zone (Figure 82). It does not inhabit the rocks streams outside the taiga, and in pure taiga not divided by stony stretches the sable is found only occasionally.

FIGURE 82. Fir thickets in the valley of the Klyk River, northeastern Altai. Sable biotope. Photo by V.S.Yudin

In the Kuznetsk Ala-Tau, where stony stretches are encountered at every altitude, the sable population is rather dense throughout the taiga extending all along the western slope of the range.

In the Sayans and in the mountains around Lake Baikal and south of Eastern Siberia, the sable occupies a variety of forest types — from the lower belt of dark coniferous taiga up through the thickets of Japanese stone pine in the subalpine zone. However, the animal only very rarely goes above the timberline.

According to V. V. Timofeev and V. N. Nadeev (1955), the highest density of sable population in the Sayans is found in fir—Siberian stone pine taiga lying on shaded slopes of mountains (Figure 83). Higher, in the high mountain taiga consisting of separated stands of larch and Siberian stone pine with some birch, density is still considerable, but less than that in fir—spruce taiga. In light taiga with some spruce, sable is common. Its presence is continuous but scattered in pure larch stands, and it is occasionally encountered in pure pine forests with some birch.

FIGURE 83. Southern slopes of the Kulumys Range in the Western Sayan. Sable biotope. Photo by K. T. Yurlov

In southern Transbaikalia — to the east of Khamar-Daban — P. P. Tarasov determined the sable population density in 1940, to be as follows. On the average, there was one sable per each of the following units of area: in the Siberian stone-pine stands— 1.5 km²; in subalpine areas with dense thickets of Japanese stone pine — 2 km²; in Hylocomiosa — Siberian stone pine forests — 4—10 km^2; and in larch forests — 20—25 km^2 (Nadeev and Timofeev, 1955).

In all forest types the sable prefers to live on rock streams. [These are locally called "kurum."]

In the southwestern part of Transbaikalia, according to Cherkasov (1867), the sable's favorite habitat is in high wooded ranges with cliffs and rock streams

In the northern stretches of Transbaikalia and the Khabarovsk Territory, and in Yakutia and northeastern Siberia (except for Chukotka and Kamchatka), it lives chiefly in variants of the larch taiga. Here as everywhere the sable avoids living in areas of uniform vegetation, e.g., in pure pine and larch forests, avoiding as well bogs, open alpine stretches above the timberline and the tundra.

On Chukotka — in the basin of the Anadyr and on the area inhabited by the Olyutorka koryaks — it lives in floodplain forests consisting of stone birch and of thickets of Japanese stone pine, lying along upper reaches and slopes of rivers.

On Kamchatka it is commonest in forests of Ermans birch which contain many trees with hollows and a dense shrub understory consisting of Japanese stone pine, mountainash, dog rose, and honeysuckle, and others with a luxuriantly developed grass story (Figure 84). Sable density in white birches, poplars, willows, etc., is markedly lower. As illustration of this, we present below results of a survey made among trappers and relating to places where 590 sables had been caught (V. V. Timofeev and V. N. Nadeev; 1955). The sables were obtained in the following biotopes (percentage of overall number of specimens in the census):

Ermans birches	60.5 %
White birches	18.5 %
Poplar stands	18.0 %
Willow stands	2.0 %
Larch stands	1.0 %

On Bol'shoi Shantar Island, according to G. D. Dul'keit (1929), the most inhabited places are mixed spruce—larch forests with some birch, an occasional aspen, and an understory of Japanese stone pine, dwarf birch, mountainash, alder and some other shrubs, or pure dark spruce stands with plentiful wind-broken trees. In such places the animal may even be found on seashore, making its way along the bear trails which girdle the island.

In localities where the sable is not being indiscriminately exterminated it may become quite numerous and extend itself into biotopes not characteristic for it. Thus, according to T. N. Gagina, in the valley of the Upper Angara River the sable has become increasingly common outside the forest — in riverside brush and on tussocky flatland meadows. When not persecuted the sable does not avoid humans and can live close to them. Thus, according to Yu. V. Averin (1948), when food was insufficient on Kamchatka, sables paid visits to a human settlement in the forest and fed on garbage near the dining room in sight of the diners. In some spots in the Sayans the sable may live near gold mines, areas being logged, and other places inhabited by humans.

FIGURE 84. A forest of Ermans birch. Kamchatka. Sable biotope. Photo by
N. A. Violovich

On Sakhalin's Shmidt Peninsula, according to A. I. Gizenko (1954), the
sable winters on the floodplains of rivers near inhabited localities and
may sometimes appear in chicken coops and livestock yards.

The sable leads a sedentary life. Observations in the field and of
banding material have shown that a sable spends its entire life in a definite
area making up its individual range. The size of such a range varies,
depending on the degree of food and shelter availability in the biotope. In
the Eastern Sayan, according to D. K. Solov'ev and V. I. Belousov (1920),
"the area inhabited by an individual sable is relatively small, 2—3
intermingled wooded mounts, the heads of 2—3 neighboring rivulets,
often a mountain taiga stream whose inflows drain, an area of about
22—28 square versts* — this is the area where it is born, lives and dies."
In the Konda-Sosva reserve, according to V. V. Raevskii (1947), the average
area of the individual range in winter is 10.3 km². On Bol'shoi Shantar
Island, according to G. D. Dul'keit (1929), during winter the hunting area of
the sable is 5—22 km² (average 13 km²) and in rare cases it may reach
30 km².

Within its individual range the sable will occupy a given section at a
time. The sizes of these sections vary with the time of year, food conditions
and other factors. In each such section the sable has permanent and
temporary abodes where it rests or in which it hides from inclement
weather or enemies.

The distances between a sable's hunting grounds vary depending on the
nature of the locality. According to observations by V. V. Timofeev in
East Siberia, "in dense massifs in good sable country, particularly where
the relief is smooth, the boundaries of [each of a sable's] separate hunting
grounds touch, forming one continuous area within which the sable has a

* [One verst = 1.067 km]

number of abodes and nests used alternatively. In localities with dissected relief, where areas of dark coniferous taiga or other areas preferred by the sable are interspersed with thin pine forests or separated by open stretches of balds and burns, the hunting ground is distinctly limited. The greatest distances between hunting grounds which we chanced to observe were no more than 10—12 km in a straight line (though such areas are usually separated by small watershed ridges dividing neighboring creeks and branches" (Timofeev and Nadeev, 1955)).

In localities where the sable abounds, individual ranges occasionally overlap.

Periodical seasonal migrations are observed in a few areas. In Kamchatka these are caused by snow accumulation on mountain tops open to winds, which makes catching food difficult. In summer and fall, sables enter the tundra, being attracted by the abundance of berries (Vershinin and Dolgorukov, 1948; Averin, 1948). A number of authors report periodic summer migrations of sables into high mountains and fall migrations into ravines and river valleys (Sabaneev, 1875; Belousov, 1926 et al.). However these reports are not confirmed in studies by other authors (Raevskii, 1947; Nadeev and Timofeev, 1955).

The non-periodic migrations are caused by sharp food scarcity in a given area, intensive lumbering, or natural calamities, e. g., a forest fire or floods. In some years lack of food in a given locality will lead the sable to move into biotopes with more food. According to V. V. Timofeev, "in the Kirensk area of the Irkutsk Region, sables were numerous in the fall in areas near the Lena River. The appearance of sables in the low reaches of the rivers was explained by the fact that food was scarce in mountains, while a good crop of berries was available in the land close to the Lena." Movements of sables down from the mountains is observed in years when a poor crop of Japanese stone pine, Siberian stone pine, and berries coincides with a sharp decrease in numbers of Muridae. Such migrations are usually not for long distances, generally covering only a few dozen kilometers.

Migration of the animal due to extreme causes, e. g., forest fires, is quite a different matter. According to D. K. Solov'ev and V. I. Belousov (1920) forest fires raged particularly in 1915 in the Yeniseisk Province. The dense fog from the smoke was so thick that the movement of boats along the Yenisei towards Minusinsk stopped temporarily. Forests were burning everywhere, bringing animals down in various directions to the side opposite the approaching fires. Inhabitants of Erargash village observed, on 15 July, two sables swimming across the Yenisei from the right bank to the left. Judging by the nature of the locality, the sables, in order to reach the Yenisei here, "must have traveled a minimum of 50 versts from their home taiga."

In fall 1949, in the Bratsk area of the Irkutsk Region, forest fires raged in the center of a large sable focus and the sables, to save themselve moved to the periphery. In 1947, movement of sables caused by extensive forest fires was observed in the Barguzin reserve.

There is no doubt that in a forest fire the bulk of the sables perish, and that only few manage to save themselves.

In Kamchatka, sable migration was caused in winter 1944/1945 by the eruption of the Klyuchevskaya Volcano, which resulted in the snow being covered by a thick layer of ash. The sables traveled far from the area [of the eruption].

The sable prevents as far as possible the intrusion of its fellows into its individual area, and chases such intruders out of its territory. Fierce fights may occur between sables for this reason. In rare cases a male may allow a female to live in its area. Male and female have been observed in the same nest outside the period of rut in very rare cases, but never were two males observed in the same nest.

The sable adopts various natural covers for its shelter: cavities under stones among vegetation, under roots of trees, hollows in standing or already fallen trees, under logs, etc. It does not dig a burrow, but may occasionally widen the entry or clean the nesting chamber proper. In the winter it constructs passages through the snow (up to 10 m long) leading to its abode.

V. V. Raevskii (1947), who studied 120 nests and abodes of sables in the Konda-Sosva reserve, distinguished the following types: permanent nests, and temporary and occasional abodes. The particular type of shelter utilized by the sable depends on the season or the local situation.

The permanent abodes or nests are divided into winter and maternal ones. In the former, all sables pass the winter; in the latter, females give birth and nurse their young.

Sables pass the winter from December to April in their winter nests. These are constructed in burrows, among roots of trees and stumps, under logs, in cavities in tussocks and mounds, and in hollows of the lower parts of trees. The nest consists of a round chamber, 30×35 cm in size, rarely larger, into which leads a burrow about $15 - 100$ cm long and about 10 cm in diameter, serving as nest entry and exit. The entry, the burrow, and the nest proper are usually under the trunk or roots of a tree.

The most frequent variant of the nest is one constructed in a hollow low down in a tree, the lined part lying in a special hollow in the bottom while the burrow runs among the roots. Another variant is found under a log, the characteristic nest position being in the angle formed by the trunk and roots. Nests in hollow tussocks and under raised roots of overturned trees are not so common. The nest may also occur in cavities among entaglements of Siberian stone-pine roots on tussocks, but due to the large size of these cavities and the mass of dark "back alleys," it has been difficult to discover them. "Every time, I had to retreat when the trail of the sable led to such a place " (V. V. Raevskii).

Similar permanent abodes occur in the West Siberian plain and such abodes are also preferred in the Maritime taiga of the Far East.

In mountain areas — on the Altai, Kuznetsk Ala-tau, Sayans, and Vitim Plateau, where numerous rock streams and cliffs occur — the sable, according to V. V. Timofeev prefers to build its abode in fissures between stones. Such abodes may lie deep in the rock. Timofeev writes: "We had to dig in such stone accumulations and sometimes did not manage to reach a nest even at a depth of over 9 meters... In areas where large amounts of hollow trees and logs are present together with stone accumulations, the sable may use both" (Timofeev and Nadeev, 1955).

In extreme cases the sable's nest may occur in quite unexpected places. Raevskii discovered the winter nest of a sable in the Konda-Sosva reserve under a plank bed in an abandoned hunter's hut. Timofeev discovered an abode in the Irkutsk Region constructed "under an old overturned dog-trough already embedded in the earth, preserved near a discarded and rotting hunting shack." In the Bodaibo area a sable wintered under the building of a rest house closed for the winter.

The winter nest of the sable is protected from the snow. The nesting chamber is always half filled by a soft and dry lining consisting of vole nests, moss, leaves, and trash. Occasionally feathers are found, along with dried paws and tails of murids.

Sable nests accumulate a large amount of fleas and ticks. Raevskii (1947) found in one nest as many as 88 fleas, some hundreds of their larvae and several dozen ticks. The presence of fleas can indicate the extent to which the nest is inhabited.

A dug-out sable nest, even in severe frost and after numerous hours of the animal's absence, preserves a rather high temperature. The lining is warm to the touch and the fleas move actively.

Excrement never occurs in the nest. It accumulates in cavities adjacent to the nesting chamber, in extensions of the snow passages, and at particular spots on the surface, [either] openly or under some cover, and 10—15 m or more from the entry.

FIGURE 85. Sable tracks (Martes zibellina L.). Eastern Sayan. Photo by K. T. Yurlov

The sable never disguises the approach to its nest. Trails made by the animal, sometimes several meters long, usually lead to this and afterwards diverge in various directions. Sometimes underground passages lead to the nest, the diameter of these being 10 cm and the length 0.5 to 10—15 m.

The majority of winter abodes are given away by the entanglement of sable trails near them (Figure 85). However, on stony stretches it is extremely difficult to find the abode since the sable passes through a labyrinth formed by fissures and cavities among the stones before emerging to the surface.

In severe frosts the sable will stay in the nest, sometimes for several days in succession. In the Urals, according to L. P. Sabaneev (1875), "in the Bogoslovskii District it remains in its dens for the 10—15-day-period of intensest cold between Christmas and Epiphany, having prepared a store of chipmunks, squirrels, jays and nutcracker." (Figure 86). During this time of year in the area east of the Urals, Raevskii (1947) observed sables returning to the nest after going out for more than 200 meters. He established that one sable remained for more than 4 days in the nest without leaving it. Similar data are reported by Timofeev for the sables of Eastern Siberia. According to Solov'ev and Belousov (1920), in the Sayans "long periods of inclement weather or the danger of being brought to bay compelled the sable to remain starving in its burrow for days on end. We know of a case where a sable brought to bay hid for 6 days until the hunter grew weary of waiting, lifted the siege and went away." The sable, however, cannot stand long starvation. According to Timofeev, individuals may roam in even the most inclement and cold weather. Special areas provided by humans for sables are visited by the animals in any weather Timofeev has found stores of food in sable shelters which could be used during long times of forced residence in the nest.

FIGURE 86. Traces of sable's successful hunt for the Siberian jay. Telegash Range, Eastern Sayan. Photo by K. T. Yurlov

By the end of February and early March, when the weather becomes milder, the sables begin to emerge more often, and sometimes rest far from the nest in temporary abodes.

In April, in the West Siberian plain, floodwater may penetrate sable nests constructed on the ground and often moistens linings of hollows near the butt end of the tree, sometimes flooding the entire nest chamber. The sables are compelled to leave their winter nests and switch to drier abodes — hollows in logs or live trees, or hollowed logs which are high above the ground.

The sable continues into the spring in its winter abode only in localities where no dampness arises, e, g., in fissures in cliffs and among stone accumulations.

In summer, males and barren females often use several abodes, these being more or less permanent, temporary, and occasional.

The maternal, or brood, nests are placed under completely dry cover. A female whose winter nest was in the root of a tree may switch in spring to a hollow in the tree's trunk. Raevskii (1947) reports such a case. On 4 September 1940 he saw (on the Em-Egan River) a sable nest built in a woodpecker hole 12 m up the trunk of a live larch. Judging by the excrements, the nest lining and the composition of its insect fauna, the characteristic sable claw marks on the bark, and some other features, the author concluded that the hollow had been inhabited by a sable family. The brood had dispersed and "the nest had been left some one and a half months ago." A typical winter sable nest was present in the roots of the same larch Judging by all available data, this had been uninhabited since spring. The nest lining was already rotten and none of the fleas so characteristic of recently abandoned sable nests were found. The female who probably had lived in this nest had moved in spring to a drier and safer place — a tree hollow, in which she had passed the winter and managed successfully to raise her progeny.

The female and her newborn young may remain in the maternal nest till as late as August, i, e., till the time when the family is dispersed.

Unlike the lining of the winter nest, that of the maternal nest is extremely sparse, consisting chiefly of rotten wood from the same hollow. The nest almost always contains food remnants of varying degrees of freshness, and some excrement. It also contains a sizable fauna of invertebrates.

A sable's permanent nests may be located anywhere within its individual area.

The sable uses its permanent nests for several years in succession; cases are known where, after the death of the owner, its nest is occupied by another sable. Timofeev has mentioned the case of a male occupying one nest permanently for two years and in the third year using this same nest as a temporary abode. In another case, a female left her winter nest for unkonown reasons and built a new nest in another abode lying not far from the old one.

The sable uses these temporary nests for resting in autumn, usually from September through November; but it may use them even during the summer and on warm days after the frost.

The temporary nests are built near the winter nests, also in tree-, log-, and stump-hollows. Unlike the winter nests, they have no special lining, no food remnants, and few, if any, nest parasites. Raevskii (1947) discovered fleas only in three out of six hollows occupied by sables as temporary nests, and only 1—3 fleas, per nest.

According to the same author, in contrast to the microclimatic conditions of winter nests with their even dampness and insignificant temperature fluctuations, the temporary nests are either dry and cold (stump hollows), or else very damp (hollows in rotting logs).

With the onset of cold the sable switches to warmer winter nests.

The sable uses temporary nests for short rests throughout the year. It seldom returns to these. Any cover can provide an occasional nest → a squirrel's nest or a den dug in the snow by the sable itself. Such a den is often found near a large prey which the sable has found or caught.

14. **Martes** s. str. **martes** Linnaeus (1758). Forest or pine marten (Map XII)

1758. M u s t e l a m a r t e s. Linnaeus, C. Systema Naturae, 1, 10 ed. p. 46; Pallas, P. S. Zoographia Rosso-Asiatica, 1, pp. 85 — 86, Petropoli. 1811 — 1831; Simashko, Yu. Russkaya Fauna (Russian Fauna). 2, pp. 351 — 354, Sankt-Peterburg. 1851. tabl. 13, fig. 1.

1827. M a r t e s v u l g a r i s. Griffith. Cuvier's Anim. Kingd., 5, p. 123.

1865. M a r t e s a b i e t u m. Gray. — Proc. Zool. Soc. London, p. 104.

1935. M a r t e s m a r t e s. Adlerberg, G. P. Khishchnye zveri (Carnivora Fissipedia) Arktiki (Carnivores (Carnivora Fissipedia) of the Arctic). — In: Zveri Arktiki, pod redaktsiei prof. N. A. Smirnova, pp. 345 — 350, Leningrad, Izdatel'stvo Glavsevmorputi; Ellerman, J. R. and T. C. S. Morrison-Scott. Checklist of Palaearctic and Indian Mammals, p. 245, London. 1951.

1944. M a r t e s (m a r t e s) m a r t e s. Bobrinskii, N. A. Otryad khishchnye. Ordo Carnivora (Order Carnivores (Ordo Carnivora)). — In: Opredelitel' mlekopitayushchikh SSSR, pod redaktsiei prof. N. A. Bobrinskogo, pp. 120 — 121, Moskva; Novikov, G. A. Khishchnye mlekopitayushchie fauny SSSR (Carnivorous Mammals of the Fauna of the USSR). pp. 185 — 193, Moskva-Leningrad. 1956.

Type and type locality. The species has been described from a Swedish specimen. The vicinity of Uppsala is taken as terra typica.

Diagnosis. Gular patch distinctly outlined, and extends backwards as terminally tapering band passing between forelegs. Color varies from light yellow to orange. Tail extends markedly (by more than $1/4$ of its length) beyond paws of outstretched hind limbs. Plantar pads, in winter, completely hidden by dense hair. Distance between carotid foramina greater than half distance from anterior edge of tympanic bullae to posterior side of paroccipital process. Mastoid processes project slightly outward beyond lower edge of auditory meatus. Anterior edge of choanal fissure has conspicuous middle protrusion. Upper molar with highly expanded internal part; external surface either lacks vertical groove or (more rarely) has a poorly developed one.

Measurements. The general measurements of the forest marten's body and limbs, according to the literature and to measurements of three males from the Tobolsk Region, are as follows: length of body with head 450 — 580 mm, length of tail 160—240 mm, length of hind paw 62—90 mm, height of ear 40—45 mm.

Measurements of skull (32 males and 15 females) are as follows: condylobasal length: males 78.3 — 86.6 mm, females 71.0 — 81.2 mm; zygomatic width: males 42.9—53.0 mm, females 40.0—48.3 mm; interorbital width: males 19.0—23.0 mm, females 17.8—20.0 mm; postorbital width: males 17.5—21.8 mm, females 14.0—19.3 mm; width of rostrum above canines: males 15.2—18.0 mm, females 14.3—16.7 mm; mastoid width: males 36.0—41.5 mm, females 34.0—37.7 mm; height in area of tympanic bullae: males 30.3—33.6 mm, females 27.0—31.3 mm; length of braincase: males 44.0—48.6 mm, females 38.2—45.0 mm; facial length: males 24.0— 27.7 mm, females 22.0—26.6 mm; length of upper tooth row: males 29.8—33.0 mm, females 26.2—30.0 mm.

Description. Has general appearance of sable but with longer tail and looks less powerful. Tail longer than outstretched hind limbs. Head seems less broad in frontoparietal area, muzzle shorter.

Paws covered by dense hair, less stiff than in sable: winter fur does not cover claws completely.

Winter fur luxuriant and silky, gray-brown or chestnut to gray-brown, often with more or less conspicuous dark brown or light grayish brown-yellowish tinges. Underfur light, whitish gray with soft grayish brown tinge. Tail somewhat darker than back. Head gray-brown. Limbs brown, dark yellow near paws and sometimes blackish to grayish brown. Chest and lower neck have a light yellowish patch with occasional orange tinge.

Summer fur characterized by short and coarse hair, with sparse underfur. Color duller and more monotonous, brown or grayish brown with an earthen tinge. Gular patch more vivid.

Os penis curved distally, and bears in adults a closed ring at anterior end. Length of os penis 35—40 mm.

Number of caudal vertebrae 20—22.

Skull (Figure 87) similar in form and in structural features to the sable's, differing only in details. Braincase relatively shorter and broader. Postorbital area lacks conspicuous compression. Nasals only slightly narrowed in middle, without sharp constriction characteristic of stone marten. Postorbital processes massive but short. Frontal area more or less convex. Skull crests, particularly sagittal, poorly developed; choanal incisure with very conspicuous median protrusion. Mesopterygoid fossa relatively broader than sable's. Hamular processes of pterygoid bones relatively longer. Tympanic bullae not so close together and not as long in longitudinal direction as in sable. Distance between tympanic bullae in area of carotid foramina greater than one half distance from anterior end of bullae to posterior side of paroccipital process. In contrast to stone marten, tympanic bullae are longer, their length being greater than distance between external edges of jugular foramina.

Upper molar (M^1) relatively large, with markedly widened internal lobe as in sable, and with well-developed high torulus extending lingually. External side of tooth either lacks vertical groove or has only poorly developed one. Internal side of anterior upper premolar (Pm^3) convex in back half, external side of base of crown slightly concave.

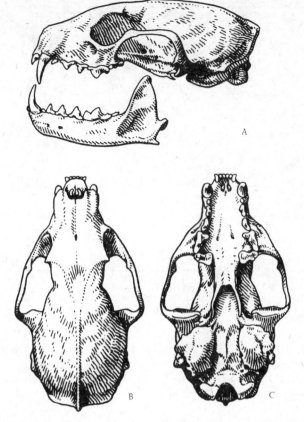

FIGURE 87. Skull of the pine marten, Martes martes L.
(original):

A — lateral view; B — dorsal view; C — ventral view.

Systematic notes. The pine marten is craniologically closer to the sable (M. zibellina) than to the stone marten (M. foina). Such important features, as the structure of the tympanic bullae, the form of the choanal incisure, and in particular the traits of the upper molar (M[1]) show more similarity than difference between the pine marten and the sable. These differ from each other less than each differs from the stone marten.

Over its large range the pine marten is divided into a number of intraspecific forms differing chiefly in size and fur color. Seven subspecies are differentiated, including 5 in the USSR (Kuznetsov, 1941; P. B. Yurgenson, 1947; Ellerman and Morrison-Scott, 1951).

The pine martens ranging in Transuralian Siberia probably belong to M. m. uralensis Kuznetzov (1942), described from the southern Urals.

Geographical distribution. Distributed mainly in the forest belt and mountain forest areas of Europe, the Caucasus, and Transuralia.

In the Soviet Union the area of distribution lies chiefly in the forest and wooded steppe zone of the European part, in the wooded mountain areas of the Carpathians, the Caucasus, the Urals, and Transuralia.

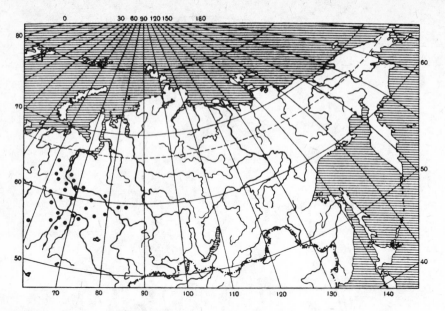

MAP XII. The geographical distribution of the pine marten, Martes martes L., in Siberia

In Siberia it occurs from the edge of the Urals in the western areas of the Tyumen Region eastwards to the lower middle reaches of the Ob River and the basin of the lower Irtysh River. The distribution pattern of the pine marten in Siberia is given above in Map XII, and the details are as follows.

It was reported from the Northern Urals by Brandt (1845) in his list of the animals of this territory. According to Flerov (1933), it is rare in the Arctic Urals. Ognev (1931) thinks that in the Urals it probably ranges as far north as 65°N lat., and that from here the northeastern boundary descends sharply to the south and extends along the eastern slope of the Urals, passing near the sources of the Vol'ya, Nyais and Northern Sosva rivers; the boundary then descends in a southeasterly direction towards the upper reaches of the rivers Tapsui (a right tributary of the Northern Sosva), Ess and Konda, emerges in the basin of the Nyaginegan River, and crosses the Ob River in the area of Lake Vandmtor. On the right side of the Ob River the range extends north to about 63°N lat., and proceeds from here eastwards to the source of the Nazym River and to the south along the right bank of this river to the lower reaches of the Irtysh River. The boundary then runs eastwards from the Surgut District towards the basin of the Vakh River (recorded by V. N. Skalon in 1928 — the yurts at Nizhne-Vartovskie), and from here turns in a southwesterly direction in the Vasyugan area, where Skalon found the animal at about 59°30'N lat., and 46°E long. The pine marten is extremely rare here occurring only sporadically.

Between the Ob and the Irtysh it is encountered occasionally in the basins of the Dem'yanka and Tartas rivers, where it is, however, also rare.

The southern boundary in Siberia extends from the Vasyugan westwards towards the basin of the lower reaches of the Ishim River and thence via the districts of Golyshmanovo and Yalutorovsk (about 56°30'N lat.) runs southwestwards towards the Urals as far as Shchadrinsk, continuing further north of the railroad to Sverdlovsk (which it skirts from the north), and then turning abruptly south to Mias and the upper reaches of the Ural River (Kuklin, 1937).

The animal is encountered sporadically within the range delineated by the above-mentioned boundaries and probably avoids living in dark coniferous taiga and in areas occupied by the sable. Concrete data on its distribution in Siberia are given by I. Ya. Slovtsov (1892). According to this author, the animal has occasionally been obtained in the Yalutorovsk and Ishim districts and is also encountered on the watersheds between the Tura and Tavda. In the 1880 s it began to penetrate further north along the Pelymka River. According to fur-trade records, it occurs in the southwestern part of the Khanty-Mansii National District and in the Uvat area, and abounds in the Tobolsk area. It also figures in the take from the Vagai, Golyshmanovo, Baikal, Velizhany and Yalutorovsk areas (F. D. Saposhnikov, 1956, in litt.).

Survey of subspecies. Within Siberia it appears to be the Ural pine marten which is encountered.

14a. **Martes s. str. martes uralensis** Kuznetsov (1941).
Ural pine marten

1941. M a r t e s m a r t e s u r a l e n s i s. Kuznetsov, B. A. Geografi-cheskaya izmenchivost' sobolei i kunits fauny SSSR (Geographical Variation of Sables and Martens in the USSR Fauna).— Trudy Moskovskogo Zootekhnicheskogo Instituta, 1, pp. 126—127, Moskva.

Type and type locality. No. 20170 of the collections of the Zoological Institute of the Academy of Sciences of the USSR, winter 1927; from the collections of Karutskii. Vicinity of the city of Mias, southern Urals.

Diagnosis. Characterized by relatively large size (condylobasal length of male skull about 83.6 mm, as against 80.2 mm in M. m. r u t h e n a Ognev) and rather light color of winter fur. General tone of back fur grayish brown, somewhat lighter on flanks. Gular patch extremely light and sometimes pure white. Fur luxuriant and soft.

Measurements. B. A. Kuznetsov (1941) gives the following measurements (from 7 males and 2 females). Condylobasal length: males 79.8 — 87.0 mm (av. 83.6 mm), females 74.9 — 75.0 mm; zygomatic width: males 45.0—49.1 mm (av. 47.1 mm), females 43.0—44.2 mm; interorbital width: males 20.0—21.2 mm, females 18.2—19.0 mm; occipital width: males 35.7 — 39.5 mm (av. 38.3 mm), females 35.5 mm; height of skull: males 31.8—34.9 mm (av. 33.0 mm), females 29.4—31.6 mm; width of rostrum: males 16.6— 18.1 mm, females 14.8 —15.4 mm; length of bullae osseae: males 16.2—17.3 mm (av. 16.6 mm).

Systematic notes. I have studied about five dozen commercial pine marten pelts obtained in the Uvat and Tobolsk areas. Judging by fur color these are subspecifically identical with M. m. u r a l e n s i s. I think it completely justified to isolate the martens inhabiting the Urals and Transuralian Siberia as a subspecies.

Geographical distribution. This subspecies ranges throughout the Urals and the wooded parts of Bashkiria and Transuralian Siberia. The distribution pattern there has been given above.

Material examined. Forty-six commercial pelts obtained in the Uvat and Tobolsk areas. In addition, three sukulls from the Tobolsk area.

Biology. The pine marten is a true stenotopic animal closely associated with the woods. It lives chiefly in extensive old forests, both coniferous and broadleaf, where numerous hollow trees are available. It is encountered, but relatively rarely, in pine woods. In Kazakhstan it lives in floodplain broadleaf forests.

The animal is a nocturnal carnivore and is encountered rarely during the day. On its night-time search for food it may cover some 20—30 km. The day is passed in the nest. The animal is better adapted than the sable to arboreal life, climbing trees very adroitly and pursuing squirrels into the crowns.

Observations show that the animals live in pairs occupying neighboring areas. During the nuptial period, the neighboring areas of the male and female merge. The marten has several nests within its area. For its nest it prefers tree hollows and, more rarely, squirrels' nests or even the abandoned nests of large raptorial birds. Temporary abodes are provided by heaps of wood, branches and logs, and by cavities under uprooted trees.

The animal has excellent smell and hearing, and rather sharp sight.

The animal feeds chiefly on Muridae, as well as on chipmunks, squirrels, birds and other small animals, including insects (beetles, bees, wasps, etc.). The daily average amount of meat is about 150 g (Novikov, 1956). It likes honey and searches assiduously for hollows occupied by wild bees. The pine marten also devours large amounts of various fruits and berries. Depending on the composition of the local fauna and flora, the diet may vary geographically and seasonally. Particularly important in the northeastern areas of its range are red voles, squirrels and chipmunks; in the Caucasus fat dormice; in the Kola Peninsula the white hare, capercaillie and willow ptarmigans. Among the plants consumed are various berries and fruit: European whortleberry, cloudberry, mountainash, Siberian stone pine nuts, etc. The food remnants are stored by the animal.

Reproduction differs little from that of the sable. The rut occurs in summer. The period of gestation, including the latent period, is 230—275 days. The brood size is 2—8 sometimes, most often 3—5. The eyes open on the 32nd—36th day. Lactation lasts 6—7 weeks, and the brood stays together until fall. Mortality of the young in infancy is rather high. The yearly population renewal is no more than 90% the number of sires. The young grow rapidly. Longest known life span is about 15 years.

Periodical migrations are known and are probably associated with migrations of the squirrel and with bad yields of murids. The marten's diseases are little studied. Pulmonary, intestinal and frontal sinus helminths are known. It suffers from skin diseases and various forms of plague.

Molt is poorly studied. From late August through September, summer fur begins to be replaced by a winter coat; the complete winter fur usually grows in late October and November.   The spring molt occurs in March, beginning with the shedding of the guard hair on the flanks.

Practical importance.   The pine marten is an important fur animal. Its fur has excellent qualities and is highly valuable.   In Siberia it is trapped in small numbers and is bred on State animal breeding farms.

By attacking game animals (hare and squirrel) and birds (hazel hen and capercaillie), the pine marten inflicts a certain small loss on the hunting economy.

15. **Martes** s. str. **foina** Erxleben (1777). Stone or
beech marten

1777. Mustela foina.   Erxleben. Syst. Regn. Anim., p. 458; Eversmann, E. A. Estestvennaya istoriya Orenburgskogo kraya (Natural History of the Orenburg Territory). Vol. 2, p. 58. 1850; Simashko, Yu. Russkaya fauna (Russian Fauna). 2, p. 354. 1851. tabl. 3, fig. 2, tabl. A, figs. 1—2.

1792. Martes domestica.   Pinel, Ph. — Actes Soc. d'Hist. Nat. 1, p. 55, Paris (France).

1873. Mustela intermedia.   Severtsov, N. A.   Vertikal'noe i gorizontal'noe raspredelenie turkestanskikh zhivotnykh (Altitudinal and Horizontal Distribution of Turkestan Animals). — Izvestiya Obshchestva Lyubitelei Estestvoznaniya, Antropologii i Etnografii, Vol. 8, No. 2, p. 61 (Tien-Shan); Satunin, K. A. Opredelitel' mlekopitayushchikh Rossiiskoi imperii (Key to Mammals of the Russian Empire). pp. 108—109, Tiflis. 1914.

1879. Martes leucolachnea.   Blanford, W. T.   Scientific Results of the Second Yarkand Mission. — Mammalia, p. 26 (Yarkand).

1941. Martes foina.   Kuznetsov, B. A.   Geograficheskaya izmenchivost' sobolei i kunits fauny SSSR (Geographical Variation of Sables and Martens in the USSR Fauna). — Trudy Moskovskogo Zootekhnicheskogo Instituta, 1, pp. 108—132; Ellerman, J. R. and T. C. S. Morrison-Scott.   Checklist of Palaearctic and Indian Mammals, pp. 236—247, London. 1951.

1944. Martes (martes) foina.   Bobrinskii, N. A.   Otryad khishchnye.   Ordo Carnivora (Order Carnivores (Ordo Carnivora)). — In: Opredelitel' mlekopitayushchikh SSSR, pod redaktsiei prof. N. A. Bobrinskogo p. 121, Moskva; Novikov, G. A.   Khishchnye mlekopitayushchie fauny SSSR (Carnivorous Mammals of the Fauna of the USSR). pp. 193—197, Moskva-Leningrad. 1956.

Type and type locality.   The species was first described from a German specimen.

Diagnosis.   Gular patch distinctly delineated and usually continuing backward in two bands branching on to forelegs (Figure 77).   Color of patch pure white.   Tail pointed distally (Figure 76), markedly longer than extended hind limbs.   Sole pads on paws only thinly covered with hair in winter and readily seen.   Distance between carotid foramina greater than half distance from anterior edge of tympanic bullae to posterior edge of paroccipital process.   Mastoid processes protrude slightly outward beyond lower edge of external auditory meatus. Anterior edge of choanal incisure usually without median protrusion. Upper molar with sligthly expanded internal part; external surface of this has well-marked vertical groove.

Measurements. According to data in literature, the overall dimensions of males are as follows: length of body with head 430—540 mm, length of tail 230—300 mm, length of the hind paw 85 —100 mm, and height of ear 34 — 47 mm.

Skull sizes are as follows: Condylobasal length: males 78.8—85.1 mm, females 73.0— 78.0 mm; zygomatic width: males 45.3 — 49.4 mm, females 45.0— 49.0 mm; interorbital width: males 20.9 — 23.0 mm, females 19.2 — 20.5 mm; postorbital width: males 17.0 — 19.2 mm, females 16.7 — 18.0 mm; width of rostrum above canines: males 17.1 — 18.0 mm, females 15.2 — 17.2 mm; mastoid width: males 37.2 — 42.2 mm, females 34.8 — 38.2 mm; height in area of tympanic bullae: males 30.0 — 32. mm, females 27.3 — 30.0 mm; length of braincase: males 42.3 — 47.5 mm, females 42.0— 45.0 mm; facial length: males 24.5 — 28.0 mm, females 21.0— 24.3 mm; length of upper tooth row: males 30.0 — 31.6 mm, females 26.3 — 28.8 mm

Description. Similar to the pine marten but differing in form and in pure white color of the gular patch, in relatively longer tail, and other features. End of tail extends markedly beyond hind limbs when all are extended; distal hair on tail forms tuft with pointed tip. Ears broader, shorter and more rounded than in pine marten. Soles covered with sparse and short hair, through which pads stand out markedly.

Fur generally coarse, with springy guard hair; underfur less dense than in pine marten.

The winter fur varies from pale grayish brown to intensely dark brown or gray-brown. Underfur very gray or whitish. Tail and legs somewhat darker than back. Gular patch varies from pure white to straw yellow-white; and often bifurcates on chest extending onto the forelimbs in diverging bands.

Summer fur relatively sparse, stiffer and darker.

Skull (Figure 88) has general traits of pine marten. Craniological differences consist in the following structural peculiarities: nasals have pronounced median constriction; tympanic bullae short and more widely separated; length of bullae shorter and rarely equal to distance between external edges of jugular foramina.

Upper molar (M^1) relatively small. Internal part slightly expanded. External side of tooth with conspicuous vertical groove. Internal side of upper anterior premolar (Pm^3) evenly convex both internally and externally

Systematic notes. The stone marten is a considerably polymorphic species. Occupying a vast area with different natural conditions, from the plains of Eastern Europe and the mountains of Northern Asia to the mountains of South Asia, from Spain in the west to Manchuria in the east, the stone marten is subdivided into numerous subspecies differing in the nature of the coat, in color, and to some extent in morphological features. The differences between the intraspecific forms are extremely small.

Geographical distribution. The range includes most of Europe, the Caucasus, Asia Minor, Iran, Afghanistan, mountains of Central and Middle

(Soviet) Asia,* Tarbagatai, the southern Altai, Mongolia, Northeast China, and probably some mountains of North China.

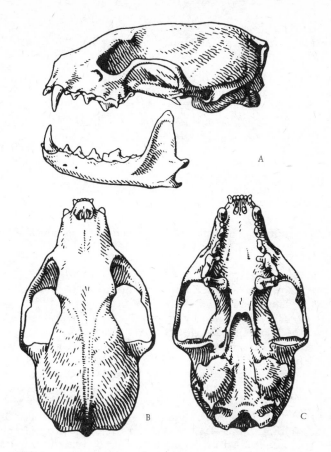

FIGURE 88. Skull of the stone or beech marten, M a r t e s f o i n a Erxleben (original):

A — lateral view; B — dorsal view; C — ventral view.

The distribution in Siberia has been little studied. On the Altai the animal was first found in 1840 by P. Romanov, taxidermist for Prof. E. A. Eversmann. It was later reported by N. F. Kashchenko (1889, 1900). A. M. Kolosov (1939) includes it in a list of animals of the southeast Altai although he does not give concrete data about its distribution. According to N. M. Berger (1946) single specimens have been obtained in the Bukhtarma slopes of Oirotiya. According to A. A. Sludskii, it occurs throughout the southern Altai. It has been recently obtained in the valleys of the Ulba, Bukhtarma and Kurchum rivers. It also extends into the Tarbagatai and Saur ranges (A. A. Afanas'ev, V. S. Bazhanov and others, 1953). A. G. Bannikov (1954) recorded the animal in the Mongolian Altai but it is "rather rare here."

* [i.e., both Soviet Central Asia and the Chinese parts of Central Asia.]

Survey of subspecies. Twelve subspecies are known at present, 4 of these in the fauna of the Soviet Union. The animal occurring in Siberia belongs to the Tien Shan form.

15a. **Martes** s. str. **foina intermedia** Severtsov (1873).
Tien Shan stone or beech marten

1873. Mustela intermedia. Severtsov, N. A. Vertikal'noe i gorizontal'noe rasprostranenie turkestanskikh zhivotnykh (Altitudinal and Horizontal Distribution of Turkestan Animals).— Izvestiya Obshchestva Lyubitelei Estestvoznaniya, Antropologii i Etnografii, Vol. 8, No. 2, p. 61; Auct. cit.— Ann. Mag. Nat. Hist., 18, p. 45. 1876.
1879. Martes leucolachnea. Blanford, W. T. Scientific Results of the Second Yarkand Mission.— Mammalia, p. 26 (Yarkand).
1914. Martes foina altaica. Satunin, K. A. Opredelitel' mlekopitayushchikh Rossiiskoi imperii (Key to Mammals of the Russian Empire). p. 111, Tiflis (Altai).
1931. Martes foina intermedia. Ognev, S. I. Zveri Vostochnoi Evropy i Severnoi Azii (Animals of Eastern Europe and Northern Asia). 2, pp. 626—631, Moskva-Leningrad.

Type and type locality. Described from a specimen in the collections of N. A. Severtsov kept in the Zoological Institute of the Academy of Sciences of the USSR. Tien Shan.
Diagnosis. Characterized by rather large dimensions (see measurements) and general light color of winter fur, varying from gray-brown to brown. Tail dark brown. Gular patch extremely variable in outline and size.
Measurements. Skull dimensions (7 males and 4 females) are as follows: condylobasal length: males 81.2—84.6 mm (av. 83.2 mm), females 77.5—78.0 mm (av. 77.7 mm); zygomatic width: males 49.6—52.0 mm (av. 51.4 mm), females 46.2—47.4 mm (av. 46.8 mm); interorbital width: males 21.0—22.8 mm (av. 21.8 mm), females 19.0—19.7 mm (av. 19.4 mm); height in area of tympanic bullae: males 30.5—32.7 mm (av. 31.6 mm), females 29.2—31.2 mm (av. 30.6 mm); width of rostrum above canines: males 17.2—18.0 mm (av. 17.8 mm), females 15.7—16.2 mm (av. 16.0 mm).
Systematic notes. The animal is systematically closer to its Central Asiatic relatives than to forms inhabiting Europe, the Crimea and the Caucasus, having lighter and softer fur than these.
Geographical distribution. Mountains of Central (Soviet) Asia and south of Western Siberia. Ranges beyond the USSR in Afghanistan, Kashmir and Mongolia.
Material studied. Crimea — 4 specimens, Caucasus — 7 specimens, Tien Shan — 9 specimens, Dzhungaria — 1 specimen, Tadzhikistan — 6 specimens, Tibet — 3 specimens. Total 30 specimens.
Biology. In contrast to the sable and the pine marten, it is not associated with the forest. More precisely, the forest is not an indispensable element in its habitat. It inhabits mountains, climbing to 4,000 m, and prefers rocky places and ravines with accumulations of

stones. It is encountered more rarely in forests. On plains it prefers wooded ravines and gorges and occasionally may inhabit old burrows and forests. It is known to inhabit human settlements sometimes and, like the black polecat, may live in attics, stony ruins, and various other constructions. For its nest it uses fissures in cliffs voids among stones, tree hollows, etc.

The senses are well developed and the animal can orient itself excellently. If pursued and depending on the circumstances, it will either try to escape underground from its attacker or will hide in any available shelter. It is no less agile than the sable and can climb trees and move with perfect ease on cliffs and rock streams. It is generally crepuscular and nocturnal, but may occasionally be active during the day as well.

It feeds on various small animals, chiefly rodents and birds, as well as on various fruits and berries. In the mountains of Kazakhstan and Central Asia it hunts various rodents (even marmots), rock partridges and other small birds, and eats lizards, beetles, bumblebees and large amounts of different berries.

Its reproduction pattern is apparently similar to that of the pine marten. Rut is observed in mid-summer. Gestation time is 236—274 days. The brood size can be 8 but is on the average 3—4.

The molt process is similar to that of the pine marten.

Practical importance. This is a commercial fur animal; its pelt is rated somewhat lower than that of the pine marten. Occasional specimens turn up in Siberia.

16. **Martes (Lamprogale) flavigula** Boddaert (1785).
Yellow-throated marten; kharza (Figure 89)

1785. M u s t e l a f l a v i g u l a. Boddaert. Elench Anim., 1, p. 88.
1792. M u s t e l a m e l i n a. Kerr, R. Anim. King., p. 183 (type locality not indicated).
1800. V i v e r r a q u a d r i c o l o r. Shaw. Gen. Zool. Mamm., 1, 2, p. 429 (type locality not indicated).
1800. M u s t e l a l e u c o t i s. Bechstein. Uebers. Vierf. Thiere, 2, p. 375 (type locality not indicated).
1811. V i v e r r a a t t e r i m a. Pallas, P. S. Zoographica Rosso-Asiatica, 1, p. 81. (Uda-Amur interfluve).
1828. M u s t e l a h a r d w i c k e i. Horsfield.— Zool. Journ., 4, p. 238. pl. 8. (Nepal).
1842. G a l i d i c t i s c h r y s o g a s t e r. Smith, H.— Jardine's Nat. Lib., 35, Mamm., 1, p. 167. (North India).
1866. M a r t e s c h r y s o s p i l a. Swinhoe.— Ann. Mag. Nat. Hist., 18, p. 286. (central Taiwan).
1918. L a m p r o g a l e f l a v i g u l a. Pocock, R. J.— Ann. Mag. Nat. Hist., 6, p. 309.
1922. C h a r r o n i a m e l l i. Matschie.— Archiv. f. Naturgesch., 88, A, 10, pp. 17, 34 (Kwantung, South China).
1930. C h a r r o n i a y u e n s h a n e n s i s. Shih.— Bull. Dept. Biol. Sun Yatsen Univ., Canton. No. 9, p. 3 (Hunam, China).

1941. Charronia flavigula. Pocock, R. J. Fauna British India. 2. Mamm., p. 330.

1944. Martes (Lamprogale) flavigula. Bobrinskii, N. A. Otryad khishchnye (Order Carnivores). — In: Opredelitel' mlekopitayushchikh SSSR, pod redaktsiei prof. N. A. Bobrinskogo, p. 121, Moskva. tabl. 8, map 21; Novikov, G. A. Khishchnye mlekopitayushchie fauny SSSR (Carnivorous Mammals of the Fauna of the USSR). pp. 197 — 200, Moskva-Leningrad, Izdatel'stvo AN SSSR. 1956.

1951. Martes flavigula. Ellerman, J. R. and T. C. S. Morrison-Scott. Checklist of Palaearctic and Indian Mammals, pp. 249 — 250, London.

Type and type locality. Type not given by author. Nepal thought to be terra typica.

Diagnosis. Length of tail reaches about two thirds length of body; tail not bushy, covered throughout with relatively short hair of uniform length. Color highly varied: head black-brown or black above, chin white, chest golden yellow; fore part of back and of flanks, together with all of underpart, mainly yellowish; posterior back, legs and tail black. Os penis bears distally 4 blunt paired processes.

Measurements. Length of body with head 48 — 65 cm, length of tail 37 — 45 cm, length of hind paw 8.0 — 10.4 cm, length of ear 3.7 — 4.9 cm. Weight about 2.5 kg.

Condylobasal length of skull: males 100.0 — 112.4 mm, females 95.0 — 109.0 mm; zygomatic width: males 54.0 — 68.0 mm, females 53.9 — 59.4 mm; mastoid width: males 43.6 — 49.4 mm, females 42.0 — 48.2 mm; height of skull in area of tympanic bullae: males 36.0 — 41.4 mm, females 34.0 — 38.6 mm; interorbital width: males 21.8 — 23.7 mm, females 21.2 — 22.7 mm; postorbital width: males 23.5 — 28.3 mm, females 20.5 — 28.0 mm; length of upper tooth row: males 34.0 — 36.8 mm, females 32.0 — 34.7 mm.

Description. Yellow-throated marten is the largest and most variably colored member of genus Martes. Body long, muscular and agile. Head with relatively broad forehead, pointed muzzle, and rather large wedge-shaped ears with rounded tips. Paws of moderate length, with pads on soles not hidden by hair (Figure 89). Toes connected by rudimentary webs. Tail relatively long, attaining about two thirds length of body and markedly greater than length of extended hind legs.

Fur short, sparse and coarse. Tail covered throughout its length by hair of uniform length, not bushy. Color distinctive, being vivid and very motley. Winter fur running along top of head to occiput (and past ears on neck) varies from dark brown to black. Ears black but tips and insides of ear conchae gray-yellow. Cheeks russet gray. Lower lip and chin white. Neck (on each side and below), as well as chest area intense golden yellow with orange tinge. Forepart of back, dorsal surface of neck and flanks ocher yellow, this color darkening rearwards and gradually merging with the brownish black back, pelvic area, hind legs and tail. Ventral side light yellow. Vibrissae glossy black. Claws horny, yellowish.

Summer fur shorter and coarser than winter fur, lacking glossiness; has darker tones with less orange-golden tinges on chest and back. Color of young is dull, markedly lighter than that of adults and generally characterized by faded and duller colors.

FIGURE 89. Kharza [yellow-throated marten], Martes flavigula Bodd. After specimen No. 12884, Zool. Museum of Moscow University. Painted by V.A. Vatagin

Skull (Figure 90) large, bulky and moderately elongated. Upper profile
has form of slightly convex arch somewhat compressed in middle and
convex in frontal area. Rostrum somewhat concave above. Back of head
descends almost vertically. Length and width of rostrum and braincase
proportional to those of true marten's skull. Sagittal crest conspicuous
in completely adult and old individuals. Width of skull in postorbital area
slightly greater than interorbital width, and markedly greater than width
of rostrum above canines. Zygomatic arches relatively well developed
and widely parted. Tympanic bullae of moderate size and relatively
weakly inflated. Longitudinal axes of bullae not parallel, instead diverge
slightly toward back. Bony palate rounded back in area of mesopterygoid
fossa and does not form sharp triangular projection. Infraorbital
foramina somewhat roundly triangular, their largest diameter about
equal to that of alveoli of upper canines. Talon of upper carnassials of
almost uniform width throughout.

Number of tail vertebrae 21 — 24.

Structure of os penis (according to Pocock, 1918), characterized by
sharply arched distal end of bone having four paired processes. Compressed groove is visible ventrally. Length of os penis 78 mm.

Systematic notes. Systematically this marten represents a distinct
species in the Soviet mammalian fauna, one with clearly marked diagnostic
features. The intraspecific forms have not yet been worked out.
Mammalogists recognize about five subspecies differing in color and size,
but the systematic relationships between these are as yet little studied.
Judging by available data, the sizes vary geographically, increasing from
south to north; intensity of fur color also varies, becoming more vivid in
the more northern animals.

Geographical distribution. The range takes in the southern parts of
Asia and extends from Manchuria and the basin of the middle reaches of
the Amur in the north to India, Indochina and the Malayan Archipelago
in the south; from Kashmir, India, and Indochina in the west it stretches
to Taiwan, Korea, and the Maritime Territory in the east.

In the Soviet Union there is one variety of this marten — namely, the
kharza, Ussurian [yellow-throated] marten — and that only in the Far East.

Maak (1861) thinks that the northern boundary of the kharza's range is
probably 49°N lat. Radde (1862) reported the animal in the Bureya
Mountains and says that it occurs rarely on the Amur and in the lower
Ussuri. According to Przheval'skii (1870), it occurs along the middle
reaches of the Amur.

According to recent data of G. F. Bromlei (1953), it ranges north along
the Sikhote-Alin to the sources of the Koppi, Votcha and Tumin rivers, which
originate on the eastern slopes of this range. West of the Sikhote-Alin,
the northern boundary extends to the Khungari basin, crossing the middle
reaches of the Kura, Urma, Bira, Bidzhan, Zeya and Bureya rivers and
reaching northwest to the Oldoi River, whence it extends beyond the Soviet
frontier. In the south, according to Maak, it is extremely rare in the
Kekhtsyr Mountains and in the basin of the lower Ussuri River. It is
commoner in the Ussuri basin south of the mouth of the Nora River.
It is more common in the Khara, Duma, Kyung and Kirka mountains, and
is rather numerous in the mountains of Akuli and near the mouth of the

Ussuri. These data agree with the data of Przheval'skii (1870). The latter famous explorer also noted that the animal was particularly abundant in the southern parts of the Sikhote-Alin Range. It has been collected in the Ussuri territory by N. A. Smirnov, A. D. Baturin and other students (coll. Zool. Inst. Acad. Sciences USSR). According to N. T. Zolotarev (1936), it occurs in the Iman River valley. In addition, it has been collected from the following localities: by A. A. Emel'yanov near the village of Chernigovka south of Lake Khanka; by V. Velichkovich in the valley of the Volkha River (coll. Zool. Inst. Acad. Sciences USSR); and by Bromlei in the Sikhote-Alin and the Sudzukhe reserves (coll. Zool. Mus. Moscow University). It also occurs in the Suptinsk reserve (Bromlei and Gutnikova, 1955).

Survey of subspecies. Of the five subspecies of the yellow-throated marten, only one occurs in Siberia, the Ussurian [yellow-throated] marten or "kharza."

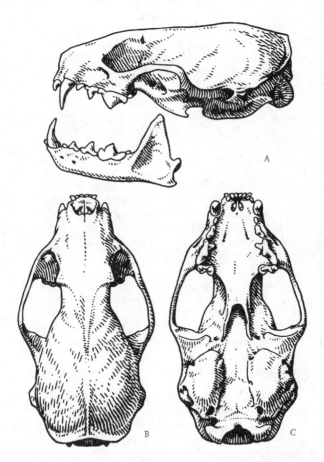

FIGURE 90. Skull of the kharza [Ussurian yellow-throated marten], Martes flavigula Bodd. (original):

A — lateral view; B — dorsal view; C — ventral view.

16a.　Martes (**Lamprogale**) **flavigula aterrima** Pallas
(1811). Ussurian yellow-throated marten or kharza

1811. Viverra aterrima. Pallas, P. S.— Zoographia Rosso-
Asiatica, 1, p. 81.
1862. Mustela (Martes) flavigula var. borealis. Radde, G.
Reisen im Süden von Ost-Sibirien, 1, Die Säugethierfauna, pp. 19, 24.
(Burein Mountains).
1870. Mustela flavigula. Przheval'skii, N. M. Puteshestvie v
Ussuriiskom krae (Journey in the Ussuri Territory). p. 247, Sankt-
Peterburg.
1901. Mustela flavigula borealis. Bonhote, J.— Ann. Mag.
Hist., Ser.7, 7, p. 345; Satunin, K. A. Opredelitel' mlekopitayushchikh
Rossiiskoi imperii (Key to Mammals of the Russian Empire). pp. 106—107,
Tiflis. 1914.
1931. Martes (Lamprogale) flavigula borealis. Ognev, S. I.
Zveri vostochnoi Evropy i Severnoi Azii (Animals of Eastern Europe and
Northern Asia). 2, pp. 636—641; Zolotarev, N. T. Mlekopitayushchie
basseina reki Imana (Mammals of the Iman River Basin). pp. 94—95,
Moskva-Leningrad, Izdatel'stvo AN SSSR. 1936.
1951. Martes flavigula aterrima. Ellerman, J. R. and
T. C. S. Morrison-Scott. Checklist of Palaearctic and Indian Mammals,
p. 250, London.

Type and type locality. Pallas's type has not been preserved. The
subspecies has been described from material collected on the
Uda-Amur.
Diagnosis. Differs from nominate form in relatively more vivid and
intense general color.
Measurements. See above description of the species.
Systematic notes. Comparing the data presented above for the yellow-
throated marten with data for its subspecies the "kharza," it must be
concluded that the Ussuri subspecies is larger than its relatives inhabiting
China and India; however, more extensive material is needed. I had
only five adult specimens indicating sex; with so few data reliable
conclusions cannot be guaranteed.
Ellerman and Morrison-Scott (1951) include in this subspecies the
marten inhabiting Korea, which the Japanese T. Mori (1922) had isolated
in distinct subspecies M. f. koreana. I lack the material to judge where
the truth lies.
Geographical distribution. The range within Siberia is given above
in the description of the species.
Material studied. The Soviet Far East — 9 specimens, Szechwan —
2 specimens, Kashmir — 1 specimen; total 12 specimens.
Biology. The kharza is a forest animal, and usually keeps to secluded
taiga thickets far from inhabited points. According to observations made
by Bromlei (1953), it prefers coniferous forests situated on the slopes of
ranges having a few cliffs and rock streams. In the broadleaf forest zone
covering the mountains forces it to descend. Przheval'skii (1870) also
noted the animal's attraction to coniferous mountain vegetation, and

according to him the kharza is very common in the coniferous forest covering the principal axis of the southern parts of the Sikhote-Alin Range.

The kharza is a typical flesh-eater. Its staple diet is small animals, chiefly ungulates weighing 10—12 kg. It attacks the musk deer, the young of Manchurian deer, of elk, of roe deer, and of spotted deer, and more rarely of gorals and of wild boars. It devours hares, pikas, squirrels, murids and birds and their clutches. Occasionally it may attack the sable, the raccoon dog and other small carnivores. The animal makes rare use of plant food, such as Siberian stone pine nuts and berries.

"The food," writes Bromlei, "consists during the year 50% of small ungulates, about 30% of large rodents (from the Russian flying squirrel down to the hare), and only 5% mice and voles, and this chiefly in the snowless time of the year. The diet also includes plants."

It is both terrestrial and arboreal. It moves rapidly and in a variety of gaits on the ground, climbs trees well, maneuvers about in their crowns, and can jump from one to another and to the ground. When necessary it can travel like a squirrel, jumping from tree to tree for a distance of 100 m or more. V. P. Sysoev (1952) while hunting saw one jump from tree to ground. If pursued by dogs it may leap up into a tree and escape along the branches. If the animal cannot travel via the upper route, it climbs to the very tip of the tree and jumps from there to the ground; gliding during the fall it may cover some 20—30 m.

It runs down its prey. When the young become somewhat older, they accompany the mother in searching for food and in attacking large prey. Sysoev writes that he encountered several animals traveling in company in the Ussuri taiga. Bromlei (1953) describes the yellow-throated marten's pursuit of the musk deer in the following manner: "The carnivores usually chase the frightened musk deer in groups and not individually, trying to cut off their prey's escape route or jumping on it from above as it runs under some tree. At times when an ice cover has formed on the rivers the animals, like wolves, try to chase the musk deer onto the ice, where they are readily caught." The pursuit of musk deer is even more successful in March when there is an ice cover on the ground.

The reproduction of the yellow-throated marten has not been studied in detail and no reliable data are available. According to Sysoev, the animals mate in June and July and the young are born in spring. The litter size is 2—3. Other data quote as many as 5 young (Naumov, Lavrov, 1948). N. T. Zolotarev (1936), quoting hunters, reports that rut occurs in March and that the young are born in August.

The replacement of winter fur by summer fur occurs in the spring, in March. The fall molt occurs in October.

Practical importance. The commercial value is insignificant and the pelt is of low value. It is taken in small amounts. No special methods of hunting exist. It is occasionally shot, or caught in snares set for other animals. The animal is undoubtedly a negative element in the game fauna, since it exterminates a number of commercially valuable species. The scale of the harm it inflicts on the game fauna is indicated by the following facts given by Bromlei (1953). "In voyaging on the Sitsa River (Sikhote-Alin reserve), on a number of different winters, generally 4—15 carcasses of musk deer killed by the yellow-throated marten were encountered per 30 km. In one case the zoologist Yu. A. Salmin, on a 200 km trip, discovered 26 carcasses of musk deer half devoured by the yellow-throated marten."

13. Genus GULO Storr (1780). Gluttons

1780. G u l o. Starr, G. G. Prodrom. Meth. Mamm., p. 34. Tubingae.
tabl. A; Pallas, P. S. Spicilegia Zoologica etc., 2, p. 25. fasc. 14,
Berolini; Blasius. Säugethiere Deutschlands, p. 208. 1857; Miller, G. S.
Catal. Mamm. Western Europe, p. 433, London. 1912; Ognev, S. I. Zveri
SSSR (Animals of the USSR). 3, p. 85. 1935; Ellerman, J. R. and
T. C. S. Morrison-Scott. Checklist of Palaearctic and Indian Mammals.
p. 250, London. 1951.

Type species. M u s t e l a g u l o Linnaeus (1758).
Diagnosis. Distinguished from other members of Mustelinae by large
size (see measurements in species description), peculiarities of skull
structure, and dental system. Sagittal crest extremely powerful,
protruding backwards far beyond back of head, which it overhangs as a large
projection. Mastoid processes in form of digitate protrusions, point
obliquely forward and down. Tympanic bullae relatively small, thick-
walled, and somewhat inflated internally.

Dental formation: $I\frac{3}{3}$; $C\frac{1}{1}$; $Pm\frac{4}{4}$; $M\frac{1}{2}$ = 38.

Dental system essentially similar to that of other true martens, differing
only in some structural details. Uper carnassial tooth extremely large, with
relatively small talon occupying no more than $\frac{1}{4}$ to $\frac{1}{5}$ of internal side;
longitudinal axis of tooth parallel to skull's longitudinal axis.
Geographical distribution. The Boreal regions of Eurasia and North
America.
Systematic notes. Some authors (Miller, 1912; I. Ognev, 1935) isolate the
gluttons into a distinct subfamily — Guloninae. On the other hand,
Miller (loc. cit.) has pointed out their kinship to the true martens
(Mustelinae). Ellerman and Morrison-Scott (1951) include the glutton
within subfamily Mustelinae, and rightly so. If we take as the basis for
the systematic division of the Mustelinae, their odontological features —
and there is no other solid basis — then this linking of gluttons and true
martens represents nothing extravagant; on the contrary, it shows the
kinship between these animals more correctly.
Extinct members of genus G u l o Storr are encountered in the
Pleistocene of Europe and North America.
A monotypic genus.

17. **Gulo gulo** Linnaeus (1758). Glutton (Figure 91,
Map XIII)

1758. M u s t e l a g u l o. Linnaeus, C. Systema Naturae, ed. X, p. 45
(Lapland).
1780. G u l o s i b i r i c a. Pallas, P. S. Spicilegia Zoologica, 14, p. 35.
tab. 2 (Upper Tura and Upper Ob rivers).

1811. M e l e s g u l o. Pallas, P. S. Zoographia Rosso-Asiatica, 1, p. 73, Petropoli.

1816. G u l o v u l g a r i s. Oken, L. Lehrbuch der Naturgesch., 3, p. 1004, pt. 2 (name instead of g u l o).

1820. G u l o b o r e a l i s. Nilsson. Skand. Faun. i. p. 95 (name instead of g u l o); Blasius. Säugethiere Deutschlands, p. 209. 1857; Greve, C. Die geographische Verbreitung der jetzt lebenden Raubthiere, p. 163, Halle. 1894.

1820. G u l o a r c t i c u s. Desmarest. Mammalogie, p. 174 (name instead of g u l o).

1829. G u l o a r c t o s. Kaup.— Entw. Gesch. Nat. Syst. Europ. 1, Thierw., 1, p. 68.

1910. G u l o l u s c u s. Trouessart, E. L. Faune des Mammifères d'Europe, p. 71. (nec U r s u s l u s c u s Linnaeus, 1766).

1914. G u l o g u l o. Satunin, K. A. Opredelitel' mlekopitayushchikh Rossiiskoi imperii (Key to Mammals of the Russian Empire). p. 104, Tiflis; Adlerberg, G. P. Khishchnye zveri (Carnivora Fissipedia) Arktiki (Carnivores (Carnivora Fissipedia) of the Arctic).— In: Zveri Arktiki edited by Prof. N. A. Smirnov, Leningrad, Izd. Glavsevmorputi, p. 325. 1935; Bobrinskii, N. A. Otryad khishchnye (Order Carnivores).— In: Opredelitel' mlekopitayushchikh SSSR, p. 130, Moskva. 1944; Ellerman, J. R. and T. C. S. Morrison-Scott. Checklist of Palaearctic and Indian Mammals, p. 250, London. 1951; Novikov, G. A. Khishchnye mlekopitayushchie fauny SSSR (Carnivorous Mammals of the Fauna of the USSR). p. 200. Izdatel'stvo AN SSSR. 1956.

1918. G u l o b i e d e r m a n n i. Matschie, P. Sechs neue Arten der Gattung G u l o. Sitzungsb. der Gesellsch. naturf. Freunde z. Berlin, 5, p. 145 (Altai mountains to the south of Lake Teletskoe).

1918. G u l o w a c h e i. Matschie, P. Op. cit., p. 147 (Altai to the north of Belukha, the upper reaches of the Katum River).

1922. G u l o k a m t s c h a t i c u s. Dybowski.— Arch. Tow. Nauk., 1, p. 349, Lvov (nom. nud).

Type and type locality. The type has been described from a Lapland specimen.

Diagnosis. Diagnostic features of the species have been given above in the diagnosis of the genus.

Measurements. Length of body with head 70—105 cm, length of tail 18—23 cm, length of hind paw 17—19 cm, height of ear 5—6 cm; weight 12—19 kg.

Condylobasal length of skull: males 145—158 mm, females 134—148 mm; zygomatic width: males 101—106 mm, females 98—108 mm; interorbital width: males 39—44 mm, females 35—42 mm; postorbital width: males 31—37 mm, females 33—36 mm; width between infraorbital foramina: males 42—47 mm, females 39—45 mm; width of rostrum above canines: males 41—46 mm, females 37—42 mm; height in region of tympanic bullae: males 56—65 mm, females 54—60 mm; length of upper tooth row: males 53—60 mm, females 49—56 mm.

Description. In general habitus this is a giant marten of heavy build. Head is large, with broad forehead, moderately long muzzle, and small roundly blunted ears. Tail short and shaggy. Limbs massive, digitiplantigrade. Claws powerful, semiretractile; length of claws on forepaws 24 — 26 mm, on hind paws 22 — 24 mm. Soles bear six naked pads, with rest covered by fur.

Fur color on body and limbs principally brown-dark brown, sometimes with predominating dark blackish or lighter russet brown tinges.

FIGURE 91. The glutton, Gulo gulo L. (original)

Head dark brown; area between eyes and ears bears on each side a diffuse light grayish yellow patch which in some individuals merges on the forehead, forming a large and broad transverse band. A broad light band extends on both flanks from shoulders to tail, and these bands fuse in the caudal area to form a horseshoe-like figure (the so-called "train") surrounding a dark field on back (the "saddle"). Color of "horseshoe" varies from pale yellowish to russet, brown, and dark brown. In last case color of "trains" weakly visible against general black background. Underparts covered with black-brown fur. Chest and neck often have small pure white patches. Tail and leg coloration like that of back parts of saddle, or somewhat darker. Summer fur shorter and coarser than winter fur. Underfur markedly less developed. Color relatively dull, less glossy (Figure 91).

Skull large (Figure 92) and bulky, somewhat resembling that of a bear in miniature. Upper skull profile in middle area shows rather convex arch. Sagittal crest powerfully developed, fuses behind with upper occipital crest, and overhangs back of head as powerful projection protruding markedly posteriorly. Frontal area relatively convex. Orbits relatively small, with diameter about equal to transverse axis of nasal aperture. Braincase relatively high and narrow, but markedly widens to rear, reaching its maximum breadth in area of mastoid processes. Nasal part relatively short, with length only slightly greater than width of rostrum above canines. Zygomatic arches extremely massive. Postorbital processes moderately developed. Paroccipital processes pyramidal, large and high, protruding sharply above low posterior part of auditory capsule. Mastoid processes, in form of massive digitate protrusion, point obliquely downward and forward behind auditory apertures. Auditory capsules have thick walls, relatively small, and inflated internally. Longitudinal axes of auditory capsules widely divergent to sides and rearwards. Auditory tubes well developed. Size of auditory meatus equal to or somewhat greater than that of infraorbital foramina. Infraorbital foramina small, ovally long, and $\frac{1}{4}$ to $\frac{1}{5}$ times size of alveoli of upper canine. Bony palate extends beyond molars for distance equal to about one half width between these teeth.

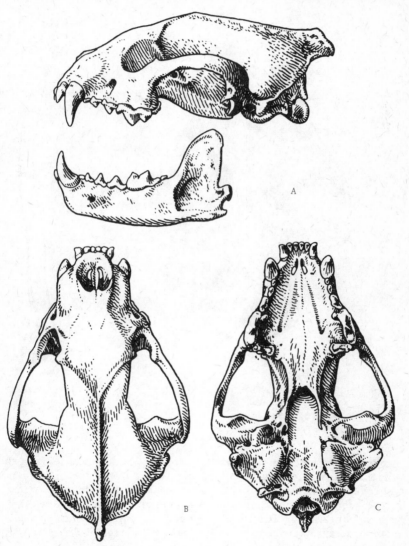

FIGURE 92. Skull of the glutton, G u l o g u l o L. (original):

A — lateral view; B — dorsal view; C — ventral view.

Teeth large and powerful. Upper carnassial tooth extremely large but provided with small talon occupying no more than $\frac{1}{4} - \frac{1}{5}$ internal aspect of crown (Figure 93); longitudinal axes of crowns of these teeth lie parallel to each other. Upper molar tooth small and markedly widened, being twice as wide as long. When jaws are closed, denticles of carnassials are widely separated, the denticles of the upper carnassials lying markedly to the front of the denticles of the corresponding lower teeth. The two anterior premolars, upper and lower, do not touch when the jaws are closed.

Os penis very large, terminally expanded, and recurved in distal third (Figure 94); length of bone is 80 mm.

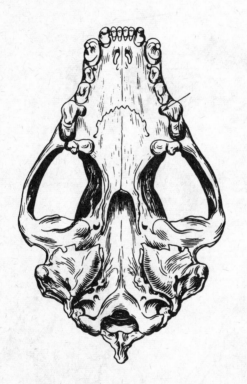

FIGURE 93. Skull of glutton, Gulo gulo L. Ventral view. Arrow shows talon of upper carnassial tooth (after S. U. Stroganov, 1949)

FIGURE 94. Os penis of glutton, Gulo gulo L. (original)

Systematic notes. The gluttons ranging the European part of the Soviet Union and in Western and Central Siberia differ neither in color nor in size as proven by available material, and should be considered identical. As can be seen from the diagnosis presented above, dark-colored individuals predominate among those relatively small animals. As one approaches northeastern Siberia a tendency is observed toward increase in size and in frequency of occurrence of light-colored individuals, the latter predominating in the East Siberian population.

The subspecific position of the gluttons found in southern Yakutia, Transbaikalia, and the Maritime Territory is as yet unclear. Perhaps forms which can be subspecifically isolated occur there.

Geographical distribution. This includes the tundra and forest zones of northern Scandinavia, of Eastern Europe, and of Northern Asia.

In Siberia it occurs in the tundra and in both the plain and mountain taiga (Map XIII).

According to I. F. Brandt (1856), it occurs in the northern and central Urals. K. K. Flerov (1933) listed the animal as one of the most widely distributed game animals of the Northern Urals.

The author met gluttons many times on the Syn and Lyapin rivers, and collected them on the upper reaches of the Mana River.

Details of distribution in Siberia are as follows:

In Western Siberia it is widely distributed in the tundra and the taiga. On the Yamal, according to B. M. Zhitkov (1913), it occurs throughout the peninsula. According to A. N. Tyulin (1938), it has been obtained on the northernmost tip of the Yamal, from which it may occasionally cross to Belyi Island. N. V. Provorov observed trails of the animal on the northern tip of the Mogui-Sale Peninsula (Dubrovskii, 1940). According to D. Wardropper, it occurs in the area of Taz Bay (Slovtsov, 1892). V. I. Telegin (in litt.) has seen traces of the animal on the western shore of the Taz Peninsula near the Sedaya Khorvuta factory and on the lower reaches of the Nyda River.

S. P. Naumov (1931) observed glutton on the Gyda Peninsula, right up to the shore of the Kara Sea (Figure 95). It was also encountered in the valley of the middle reaches of the Yuribei River (70°N lat.); the author observed relatively rare traces of the animal on the Uder-Yakha River (67°N lat.) and much higher numbers near Lake Khassein-to. According to I. Ya. Slovtsov (1892), it occurs in the Berezovo and Surgut territories throughout the Pelym and Turinsk subdistricts, and relatively rarely in the Tyumen Region. S. M. Chugunov (1915) reported glutton in the valley of the Yugan River. According to I. N. Shukhov (1928), it occurs in the basins of the Tui, Ui, Shish, Urna and Demyanka rivers.

According to data for the Tyumen Region presented by F. D. Shaposhnikov (in litt.), the glutton occurs in large numbers in the Khanty-Mansiisk National District, and in the Uvat, Tobolsk and Kazym districts; it is rare in the Yamal-Nenets National District and in the following areas: Baikalovo, Golyshmanovo, Dubrovnoe, Novo-Zaimka, Polnovat, Tyumen and Yarkovo.

In the Tomsk area it occurs more often in northern areas than in southern ones. According to a survey made by V. P. Anikin (1902), it is rather common in the Narym territory, particularly on the left bank of the Ob River. My data show that it occurs in the Ket river valley and its tributaries, in the taiga along the right shore of the lower reaches of the Chulym River, and occasionally in secluded forest thickets in the Tomsk and Shegarka areas. Ioganzen (1923) reported it for the Chulym taiga, saying that it abounds on the rivers Chicka-yulu, Malaya and Bol'shaya Yuksa. Yudin (1956) reported it for the Kozhevnikovo area, but it is extremely rare here, occurring only in secluded localities along the Baksa River.

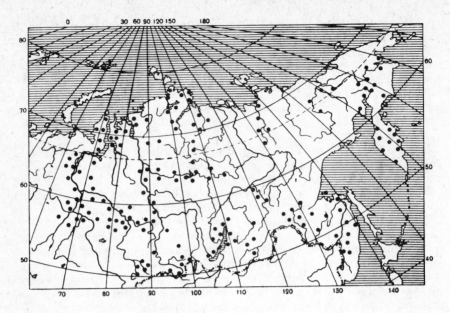

MAP XIII. Geographical distribution of the glutton, Gulo gulo L., in Siberia

P. Stepanov (1886) listed the animal as very rare in the taiga forests along rivers in the area of the upper Om' and Tartas rivers.

In the Novosibirsk Region, according to K. T. Yurlov (personal communication), it is common in a number of localities in the area of Kyshtova, Severnoe, Mikhailovo and Kolyvan (Figure 96). In 1957 (both winter and summer) Yurlov reported finding it along the Uz River, south of Lake Karas'e, in the Tara marshes, on the River Bol'shaya Icha, near lakes Peshkovo and Ichkalinskoe, on the right shore of the Tartas River opposite Stepino village, on the forest island called "Cheremshanka" (on the Tartas — Tara watershed), on the upper reaches of the Om' and Shegarka, and near Lake Teniz. North of the Tara River it proved to be more abundant in the winter in almost all watershed marshes containing some islands of forest.

In the Altai Territory it occurs in wild taiga thickets and in the tundra belt above the timberline. A. P. Razorenova (1939) says that the glutton occurs in very secluded places along the rivers Chemal, Kuba, Argut, Kadrin, and Ilgumen, as well as on the Uimen and in the dense thickets of Siberian stone pine along the Kuragan River. N. F. Kashchenko (1899) mentions a specimen of the animal obtained by V. V. Sapozhnikov on the Kalguty River. A. M. Nikol'skii (1883) mentions that the animal was hunted by the inhabitants of Uimen village. In the Ust-Koksa area, according to A. A. Nasimovich (1949), it is not rare in wooded localities. According to P. B. Yurgenson (1938), it occurs occasionally within the former Altai reserve, and he gives the following data on its occurrence in the reserve. In 1933 two animals entered the reserve from the heights dividing the Baigom River (basin of the Lebed' River) from the Kamga. They roamed along the Kamga River valley and entered the Bol'shoi and Malyi Shaltan rivers, then going via the coastal ranges to the Yurga River and the Karatash site. They also appeared in the tundra belt above the Albas timberline. Traces of the animal abounded throughout the territory of the reserve in 1934 — 1935, and became common in the valleys of the Kyga and Karasu rivers near Lake Teletskoe in 1936.

FIGURE 95. Forest tundra, Gyda Peninsula. Glutton biotope. Photo by V.I. Telegin

In Gornaya Shoriya, according to G. Gol'tsmaier (1936), it ranges everywhere. In the taiga of the Khakass Autonomous Region, according to P. Polikevich (1923), it apparently occurs in low numbers. According to G. Tel (1880), it may be found near Minusinsk.

In the Western Sayan, according to L. and I. Kozhanchikov (1924), it occurs everywhere but is nevertheless not particularly common, and sometimes even rare. Yanushevich and Yurlov (1949) describe the animal as rare in the taiga and alpine areas of the Western Sayan. It is known from the Sayan reserve in the central part of the Eastern Sayan (Gromov, 1951) (Figure 97). Yurlov encountered signs of glutton in winter 1952 on the upper reaches of the Kungus River, on the divide between the Kungus and Agul rivers, and along the valley of the Agul

River from near Sakharnoe village to the upper reaches of the Erma and Katorma.

According to I. N. Shukhov (1825), it occurs along the upper Lesser and Greater Yenisei. According to A. Ya. Tugarinov (1916), it occurs in the mountain taiga of the Tuva Autonomous Region; it is rare along the upper reaches of the Kemchik and in Tannu-Ola. Yanushevich (1952) reports that in the Tuva Autonomous Region the animal is obtained chiefly on the east Tuva highland.

FIGURE 96. Forest islands within watershed bogs. Northern District of the Novosibirsk Region, Glutton biotope. Photo by K. T. Yurlov

In the Uda-Angara District (the former Kansk, Krasnoyarsk and Tulun subdistricts), according to V. N. Troitskii (1930), the animal probably occurs in low numbers. In the former Kirensk Subdistrict, according to A. A. Pogudin (1930), it is rare and obtained only occasionally.

It is no rarity in the Yenisei basin, occurring throughout the great expanses of taiga; it is also reported to occur between the cities of Yeniseisk and Turukhansk. According to N. P. Naumov (1934), it is common in the Tunguska District (basin of the Lower Tunguska). E. O. Yakovlev (1930) writes that it occurs along the lower reaches of the Kheta and the Kanga rivers. I. I. Kolyushev (1933), quoting people who wintered at Yenisei Bay, says that traces of the animal have been observed north of Gol'chikha village near the Zyryanka River, and in the area of Shirokaya inlet, where it inflicted damage to the Arctic fox trade. According to Middendorf (1867), it occurs in the valley of the Boganida, near the city of Khatanga, and extends further north deep into the tundra, reaching as far as the Novaya River (about 72°N lat.). Ognev (1935) reports data on the animal's occurrence on the Taimyr in the area of Omulevaya Bay (72°N lat.), as well as at the mouth of the Khura, a left tributary of the Pyasina River (73°N lat.). It is not rare near Lake Zhessei and on the southern shore of Lake Taimyr (74°N lat.), and is encountered on numerous occasions in the northern part of the Brekhovskie Islands.

L. P. Shastin (1939) mentions a 1937 catch of glutton specimens in Ust-Taimyr. It was encountered by L. N. Popov (1939) on the east coast of Taimyr, but is rare there. A specimen was caught in a trap set by staff members of the Arctic Station who were wintering at Pronchishchevaya inlet. At the northern tip of the Chelyuskin Peninsula a glutton was encountered by G. L. Rutilevskii (1939) near the Arctic Station of the Arctic Institute, at about 77°N lat.

FIGURE 97. The Agulsk Range, the Eastern Sayan. Glutton biotope. Photo by K. T. Yurlov

According to A. A. Romanov (1941), the glutton occurs on the interfluve of the lower Khatanga and Lena, "chiefly in the forest zone near the tundra. It may occasionally enter the tundra and penetrate further from the shores of the Laptev Sea." The author observed an animal deep in the tundra drained by the Kharabyl River — near the mouth of the Maian River (72°N lat.). Near its northern boundary fresh traces were encountered on the Sardakh River (a right tributary of the Khorgukhuongka River, 72°N lat.), on the Udzha River (near the mouth of the Onghuchakh River, 71°N lat.), on the Piligai River (near the mouth of the Arylakh River, 71°N lat.) and on the Rossokha River (near the mouth of the Sakh-Yuryakh River, 71°N lat.). Further south, on the way from Saskylakh to the Vilyui River, Romanov encountered (March and April of 1935) traces of five or six gluttons over a 1,500 km route.

It was extremely rare in the Vilyui River valley and tributaries, according to Maak (1859, 1886). According to V.I. Belyk (1935), it is also rare at present in the Vilyui valley and, of course, in the central agricultural areas of Yakutia. It is common in the southern part of the Republic in the valleys of the Olekma, Aldan, Chara, and Tokko rivers. It is rather common in the forest tundra areas and may enter the tundra.

I.S. Polyakov (1873) describes the glutton as one of the common species on the Olekma-Vitim upland; it is encountered in the northwestern areas of Baikalia and in the valleys of the Golustnaya and Bugul'deika rivers, occurring in the vicinities of Kachuga and Verkholensk.

According to Bunge (1887), it is distributed sporadically throughout the Yana River basin, is not too rare near the Kazach'e, is encountered somewhat more often near the tundra belt, and sometimes may penetrate the tundra of the delta to the seashore.

On the Kolyma, south of Sredne-Kolymsk, according to V.I. Iokhel'son (1898), it was encountered relatively rarely but had previously been taken quite often. These data are also confirmed by S.A. Buturlin's report (1913), according to which the glutton is only "occasionally encountered" in the Verkhoyansk Range and on the Kolyma above the mouth of the Omolon River. Ognev's collections include a glutton skull (from E.V. Shmit) collected in 1932 on the Omolon River some 70 km from its mouth.

On the Anadyr, according to N.L. Gondatti (1897), N.P. Sokol'nikov (1927), and other authors, the animal occurs throughout the territory. According to L.A. Portenko (1941), it is a common but not abundant carnivore, ranging chiefly in the western part of the Anadyr and being very rare in the maritime belt. Portenko provides a list of localities where the glutton had been obtained or where its traces had been observed: vicinity of Markovo village, the Shchuchinskie and Gorelovy mountains, and on the Shchuch'ya, Velikaya, Ubienka and Chernaya rivers; south of Markovo village traces of the animal were encountered on the road to Penzhino. Portenko writes: "On November 26, 1931, I encountered traces of the glutton at Shchechki, north of the Orlov huts.... S.D. Pereleshin considered the glutton scarce in the Penzhino area. I have not observed the animal in the central part of the Anadyr territory." L.O. Belopol'skii, during his winter voyage along the Anadyr, encountered traces from the mouth of the river up to Eropol, some 40—50 km above Ust-Belaya; he saw many traces on the Maina between the villages of Vaeg and Vikarino. According to N.P. Sokol'nikov (loc. cit.), gluttons have been obtained near the Anadyr estuary. Gondatti obtained a glutton on the Bol'shaya River and on Mt. Dionisii (coll. Zool. Inst. Acad. Sciences USSR). Buxton purchased two specimens caught in the vicinity of Kamenskoe on Penzhina Bay (J.A. Allen, 1903). Yudin reported that the animal frequents the area of the Tanyurer River, but in low numbers.

In the Koryak National District, according to the observations of A.V. Samorodov (1939), it occurs rather often, and 25—27 specimens are obtained throughout the year.

It is widespread in Kamchatka. S.P. Krasheninnikov (1949), a pioneer of the scientific study of the peninsula, wrote as follows:

"Glutons are rather abundant on Kamchatka... More so near Karaga, Anadyr and Kolyma..." According to N. V. Slyunin (1900), some 40—50 gluttons are obtained yearly on Kamchatka. According to V. N. Tyushev (1906) they occur on the western shore of Kamchatka. Yu. V. Averin (1948) reported that the animal inhabits the mountains and the shore of the entire peninsula; this author collected the animal in Kronoki near the mouth of the Povorotnaya River and observed it throughout the reserve.

On the Okhotsk coast of Siberia it has been obtained by N. V. Slyunin (coll. Zool. Mus. Moscow State University). In the area of Gizhiga, according to Buxton, it occurs quite rarely (J. A. Allen, 1903). In the valley of the Uda and in the upper Selemdzha, according to N. T. Zolotarev (1934), the animal occurs throughout but in low numbers.

Numerous authors report the animal from Transbaikalia. According to Turov (1936), it ranges throughout the northeastern shore of the lake, probably occurring on Svyatoi Nos. Doppel'maier (1926) reports the animal from the Barguzin reserve. According to A. Cherkasov (1867), it is rare in the southern and southwestern part of Transbaikalia. On the upper reaches of the Chita River, according to E. Pavlov (1948), it is extremely rare. According to B. A. Kuznetsov (1929) it occurs in the mountain taiga of the Yablonovyi and Undinskii ranges, being common on the former range and rare on the latter.

According to G. N. Gassovskii (1927), it occurs in the area of the Oldoi — Gilyui interfluve. South of the Tukuringra Range only a few traces have been encountered, on the middle reaches of the Lagunaya River. Gassovskii discovered signs of the glutton's presence along the Malyi Dzheltulak River, particularly along the Gilyui and in neighboring areas. Traces of it are also encountered on the middle and lower reaches of the Mogot River and lower down the valley of the Mogot and its right tributary, the Tsyganka River.

In the Soviet Far East the glutton is common, being distributed everywhere though in low numbers. According to Schrenck (1958), it has been encountered on the mainland south to 48° N lat., as well as in the Geonsk and Vand mountains, the southern boundary of the animal's range here. It also occurred on the upper reaches of the Bureya and Zeya. In the Iman basin, according to N. T. Zolotarev (1936), it is extremely rare. According to V. K. Arsen'ev (1923), it ranges in the Ussuri territory south to 44°N lat., and is common on the Sikhote-Alin. Ognev (1935) reported the following data given by V. S. Stakhanov (from a manuscript dated 1933) about the distribution of the glutton: "The glutton ranges in the Amur territory in the Okhotsk-Ayan type of taiga, and in mixed coniferous and larch—birch forests, inhabiting the Amgun' River, the lower Amur, the vicinity of lakes Chlya and Orel, and the taiga from Cape Litke to the Bureya slopes. To the south it ranges in the area of Lake Udyl', the rivers Bichi, Pil'di and Limuri, on the Goryun River, in the Mnovocha Range, along the tupper reaches of the Kur, Uryash, and Bira rivers, in the northern part of the Malaya Khingan, [and] on the Bureya, Selemdzha and Zeya. Its limit of distribution is everywhere formed by the zone of transition between forests of Okhotsk-Ayan type and the Manchurian flora.

"Thus, for instance, in the vicinity of Lake Bolon-Odzhal' it is rare along the lower reaches of the Goryun River. In the northen part of the Sikhote-Alin Range it is common, reaching south along the eastern slope of this range to the Botchi River and along the western slope to the upper reaches of the Iman."

It occurs on Bear Island and on Bol'shoi Shantar Island (Dul'keit, 1927).

It was reported from Sakhalin in 1858 by L. Schrenck according to whom it descended along the mountain ranges to the southern tip of the island. In the northern part of the island, according to P. I. Suprunenko (1890), it is rather common. In the southern part of the island, according to F. Shmidt (1862), it is very rare. This is confirmed by recent data of Japanese scientists (N. Kuroda, 1928). Ognev (1935) reports the following data furnished by N. R. Obrekht (from a 1933 manuscript) on its distribution in Sakhalin. "The glutton is not numerous; it is obtained only occasionally, and is not a commercial animal. In 1931, a hunting expedition discovered several dens and broods of the animal near the city of Aleksandrovsk and the Oktyabr'skii mine. Obrekht himself saw an excellent specimen, obtained on the eastern shore in the vicinity of Katangli, and saw glutton tracks near the village of Onora (in central Sakhalin)." M. V. Gerasimov (1951) reported the glutton among the animals in the Central Sakhalin reserve.

Survey of subspecies. The systematics of the intraspecific subdivisions of the glutton have yet to be worked out to any degree of adequacy. The animal is another of those polymorphic species with broad age, individual, and geographical variations, as well as with sexual and seasonal dimorphism. It is very poorly represented by collected material, so much so that the material available does not permit solution of the complicated problem of the forms of Gulo gulo inhabiting Eurasia. The nominate subspecies and the northeastern glutton could be considered as more or less distinct forms, since they differ in fur color and dimensions.

17a. **Gulo gulo gulo** Linnaeus (1758). Common glutton

The synonymy and data on the type habitat are presented above in the species description.

Diagnosis. Characterized by rather large dimensions of "saddle" and slight development of horseshoe-shaped pattern, whose lateral bands are relatively narrow and are not fused in scapular area. Dimensions of skull relatively small: condylobasal length averages 148 mm (as against 155 in East Siberian form). Dark type predominates in populations.

Measurements. Condylobasal length of skull: males 144.0—150.0 mm (av. 148.0 mm), females 134.0—138.0 mm; zygomatic width: males 96.0—107.2 mm (av. 102 mm), females 89.0—93.0 mm (av. 91.3 mm); interorbital width: males 38.7— 43.0 mm (av. 40.8 mm), females 35.0 — 37.2 mm (av.. 36.0 mm); postorbital width: males 36.2—37.0 mm (av. 35.6 mm), females 32.0—35.2 mm (av. 33.4 mm); mastoid width: male 84.9—93.1 mm (av. 88.5 mm), females 81.3—91.6 mm (av. 83.3 mm);

height of skull in area of tympanic bullae: males 55.2—61.0 mm (av. 59.5 mm), female 54.0—56.2 mm (av. 54.8 mm); length of upper tooth row: males 51.0—56.3 mm (av. 53.7 mm), females 49.0—52.0 mm (av. 50.2 mm).

Geographical distribution. Western and Eastern Siberia northeast as far as Chukotka and Kamchatka, and southeastwards to approximately the southern areas of Yakutia and the Baikal area.

Material studied. European part of the USSR — 7 specimens, Western Siberia — 34 specimens, the Altai — 3 specimens, Far Eastern Territory — 1 specimen, Sakhalin — 1 specimen. Total 46 specimens.

17b. **Gulo gulo albus** Kerr (1792). Northeastern glutton

1792. Ursus gulo albus. Kerr, R.— Anim. Kingd. Syst. Cat., No. 381, p. 190.

1922. Gulo kamtschaticus. Dybowski.— Arch. Tow. Nauk., 1, p. 349, Lvov (nom. nud., Kamchatka).

1935. Gulo gulo gulo. Ognev, S. I. Zveri SSSR i prilezhashchikh stran (Animals of the USSR and Adjacent Countries). 3, pp. 85—106 (partim).

1948. Gulo gulo kamtschaticus. Averin, Yu. V. Nazemnye pozvonochnye Vostochnoi Kamchatki (Terrestrial Vertebrates of Eastern Kamchatka).— Trudy Kronotskogo Gosudarstvennogo Zapovednika, 1, pp. 145—148, Moskva (mouth of the Povorotnaya River, Kronotskii reserve).

Type and type locality. The subspecies has been described from a Kamchatka specimen.

Diagnosis. Differs from nominate subspecies in a having lighter color, smaller "saddle" and marked development of saddle-shaped pattern ("trains"), whose lateral bands usually fuse in scapular area to form closed ring. Dimensions of skull large. Condylobasal length on average 155 mm (against 148 mm in nominate form). Light-colored type predominates in populations.

Measurements. Condylobasal length of skull: males 149.0—158.0 ; n (av. 155.0 mm), females 142.0—149.0 mm (av. 146.0 mm); zygomatic v lth: males 101.0—108.0 mm (av. 105.0 mm), females 98.0—103.0 mm (av. 99.0 mm); interorbital width: males 41.9—44.2 mm (av. 43.0 mm), females 40.0—42.3 mm (av. 41.2 mm); postorbital width: males 31.0—35.2 mm (av. 33.7 mm), females 30.0 — 33.6 mm (av. 32.6 mm); mastoid width: males 89.2—93.2 mm (av. 90.6 mm), females 84.2—88.8 mm (av. 86.0 mm); height of skull in area of tympanic bullae: males 56.7—65.2 mm (av. 60.4 mm), females 54.0—60.0 mm (av. 57.3 mm); length of upper tooth row: males 54.5—79.7 mm (av. 57.2 mm), females 54.2—56.8 mm (av. 55.3 mm).

Systematic notes. Light fur color as a characteristic trait of gluttons inhabiting Kamchatka was noted by scientists long ago. Thus, even S. P. Krasheninnikov (8th ed., 1949) in his "Description of the Land of Kamchatka" mentioned "white glutton fur with a yellow tinge" being used by the local population for decorating festive clothes. R. Kerr (1792) described the Kamchatka glutton, characterizing it as a lightly colored and almost white form.

This trait of Kamchatka gluttons was later noted by K. A. Satunin (1914) and by Ognev (1935, 1941). The collections of L. A. Portenko from the Anadyr territory also show the light type of "saddle" color.

Yu. A. Averin has recently (1948) described the Kamchatka glutton as a new subspecies, giving it the name G. g. kamtschaticus.

Study of 12 specimens collected on Chukotka and Kamchatka shows that gluttons from these localities are indeed distinguished by light color and relatively large size. These differences are rather characteristic and undoubtedly can serve as grounds for subspecific rank for this form.

Concerning nomenclature, the Kamchatka or northeastern subspecies should, according to the rule of priority, be called Gulo gulo albus Kerr (1792) and not G. g. kamtschaticus Averin (1948).

Geographical distribution. The extreme northeast of Siberia and Kamchatka. The limits of the range towards the south and west can not yet be established due to lack of collected material.

Material studied. Kamchatka — 4 specimens, Anadyr — 8 specimens. Total 12 specimens.

Biology. The glutton's characteristic habitat is the taiga and tundra, it inhabits both forested lowland, and tundra plains, and also various mountain landscapes up through mountain tundra and the alpine zone above the timberline.

On the northern Urals, according to K. K. Flerov (1933), it occurs both in the taiga and in the mountain-tundra area.

In the tundras of northwestern Siberia, according to A. N. Dubrovskii (1940), the glutton is encountered throughout the year and sites its dens in deep ravines. In the West Siberian taiga zone, according to my observations, it prefers unpopulated forest thickets with areas of broken trees and forest bogs cut by rivers and streams. South of the taiga zone in the Tara River valley, according to K. T. Yurlov (personal communication), it lives on forest islands lying within marshy watershed areas. It may enter forest steppe areas. In the valley of the Lower Tunguska, according to N. P. Naumov (1934), glutton sites are highly variegated, but it prefers forest ridges and river valleys.

On the Altai, according to G. D. Dul'keit (1953), it lives in various types of forest stands, in river valleys, bog-shrub tundra, and on rocks.

In the Minusinsk taiga of the Sayans, according to observations by the Kozhanchikov brothers (1924), it is encountered in all mountain zones, its traces being found both in treeless localities and in the thickets of the low taiga (Figure 98).

It prefers to live on gentle and soft crests, avoiding abrupt and stony mountains.

In the southwestern areas of Transbaikalia, according to A. A. Cherkasc (1867), the glutton lives year-round in secluded taiga and on high mountair ranges overgrown with dense forests and containing rocks and rock stream The above-mentioned author writes: "It does not like meadow places, and is never encountered near the steppes, even in dense forests."

On the Yablonovyi and Undinskii ranges, according to B. A. Kuznetsov (1929), it lives in the most secluded and inaccessible places among rocks and thickets. On the upper reaches of the Chita River, according to E. Pavlov (1948), it inhabits larch forests, northern mountain slopes with accumulations of stones, and stream valleys, particularly the upper reaches of the river.

On the Anadyr, according to L. A. Portenko (1941), it lives in winter chiefly in floodland stands. The burrows, according to N. P. Sokol'nikov (1927), are in mountain rocks.

FIGURE 98. A glutton on its trail. Sources of the Vasyugan River, West Siberian lowland. Photo by K. T. Yurlov

In Kamchatka, according to observations of Yu. V. Averin (1948), during the snowless time of year and when food is readily available, it inhabits various biotopes from the seashore to mountain localities at a height of about 2,000 m. In winter, when most of the summer food resources become unavailable, the animal sticks chiefly to areas where deer and sheep pass the winter, and these are its sole source of food at this time. The glutton will nest in caves, in hollows among stones and roots of trees, in broken wood, accumulations of dry twigs, ets. It may occasionally occupy burrows of foxes, badgers, marmots, and other animals. The glutton is a secretive animal rarely seen by humans, and leads a nocturnal life; occasionally, however, particularly in bad weather, it may also be active during the day.

During the winter it roams widely over its territory, covering 20—45 km a day. At this time of year a glutton's individual territory may be as large as 1,000 km^2. A peculiar trait of the animal is that it may cover some 10—15 km without resting when searching for prey, carrion, or a wounded animal. The glutton's individual range is smaller in summer. Its size

depends on topographic conditions, composition of local fauna, etc.
In plains the range is larger than in mountains, where the rugged and
varied landscape creates highly favorable food conditions and provides
ready nests.

The glutton feeds on various animals which it catches either on the
trail or by lying in wait. It is known to attack reindeer, Manchurian wapiti
marals, roe deer, musk deer, goats, [wild] sheep, and young elk, which it
stalks or pursues in the deep snow until the prey is brought to exhaustion.
It devours various rodents and occasionally birds or other animals. As to
plants, it may eat Siberian stone pine nuts and various berries, but only
in small amounts. It even eats carrion. In a number of areas it eats in
winter mainly carrion and food left behind by other animals. The results of
studies by G. D. Dul'keit (1953) on the nature of the glutton's winter feeding
in the Altai, show that in only 26.6% of the cases did the food consists of
ungulates killed by the glutton itself.

In the Altai, the glutton's winter diet was determined from traces to be,
according to Dul'keit, as follows (percent from total of 30 cases):

Maral	16.7
Roe deer	3.3
Musk deer	3.3
Mountain goat	3.3
Capercailzie	6.7
Carrion	66.7

Ungulates become the usual prey of the carnivore in the second half of
winter, when the deep snow cover makes their movement difficult but
does not distrub the glutton too much.

The small prey are gnawed and eaten completely. Several gluttons
may accumulate near a large carcass in winter, fighting fiercely for it. Th
carcass of a dead bear was visited in February by three gluttons. Four
poisoned gluttons were found near remnants of a maral which had been
killed by strychnine pills. All the gluttons within a radius of 10—15 km
may accumulate near the carcass of a large animal.

Direct attacks by gluttons on adult and healthy reindeer, maral, wapiti
and other large animals have never been observed. The glutton mainly
attacks sick animals, gravid females, and young. Yurlov (personal
communication), in examining the valley of the upper reaches of the Tara
River in the winter of 1957, discovered the remains of reindeer in places
where glutton lurk and traced two animals skulking about in areas where
capercailzies passed the night in forest glades.

In Kamchatka, according to Averin (1948), the glutton will in winter attack
reindeer and bighorn sheep. Gluttons are always encountered on the
latter's cliffside wintering sites. Remains of bighorn sheep killed by
glutton are not rare.

The glutton is distinguished by keen observation and orientates itself
rapidly in its surroundings. It can find carrion quickly thanks to the
behavior of its kin, as well as to that of ravens, magpies, gulls and other
animals. The glutton occasionally hides and stores food which it has not finish

Middendorf (1875), quoting traders, reported that in North Siberia store of glutton food discovered after the snow thaw would contain 8—20 killed Arctic foxes and some 100 or more willow ptarmigans.

Glutton reproduction has not been studied sufficiently. Rut occurs in late summer and early fall. Mating times probably vary with geographical location, but at any rate by the time the snow cover has begun to form, the rut is already ending. In Western Siberia rut takes place in September—October. On the Altai, where the snow falls early, the rut terminates (Dul'keit, 1953) by September. In the valley of the Lower Tunguska, according to N. P. Naumov (1934), rut begins in late September and lasts to the second half of October; phenologically, the time of rut approximately coincides with the period of rut in wild reindeer, and begins after the yellowing and shedding of the larch needles.

The birth of young takes place at the very end of the winter or in the first half of spring. On the Lower Tunguska, the young are born in April (N. P Naumov, 1934). The litter size is 1—5, usually 2—3. Lactation lasts for 2½—3 months, but at the same time, from the middle of the lactation period, the mother gradually trains the young to eat ordinary adult food. The young remain with the mother till autumn, i. e., till the beginning of the rut. The role of the male in raising the brood is not clear, and according to some observations, he participates.

The young reach adult size by about the end of their first year of life. Sexual maturity sets in at the age of two years.

Times of the spring and autumn molt are as yet not established.

Practical importance. The glutton's commercial value is insignificant since only small quantities are taken. The fur has no valuable qualities; the hair is coarse, though rather beautiful in color and luster. No standards or grades have been established for this animal's fur. It harms the [fur] trade through destroying animals caught in traps.

14. Genus MUSTELA Linnaeus (1758). Weasels and ermines

1758. M u s t e l a. Linnaeus, C. Systema Naturae, 1, p. 45, 10 ed., Thomas, O.— Proc. Zool. Soc. London, p. 138, 1911; Miller, G. S. Catalogue of the Mammals of Western Europe, p. 384, London. 1912; Satunin, K. A. Opredelitel' mlekopitayushchikh Rossiiskoi imperii (Key to the Mammals of the Russian Empire). p. 132, Tiflis. 1914; Ognev, S. I. Zveri SSSR i prilezhashchikh stran (Animals of the USSR and Adjacent Countries). 3, pp. 7 — 9, Moskva-Leningrad. 1935.

1829. A r c t o g a l e. Kaup, J.— Entw. Gesch. Nat. Syst. Europ., Thierw. 1, p. 30. (M u s t e l a e r m i n e a Linnaeus).

1829. I c t i s.. Kaup, J.— Entw. Gesch. Nat. Syst. Europ., Thierw. 1, pp. 35, 40, 41. (M u s t e l a v u l g a r i s Erxleben = M u s t e l a n i v a l i s Linnaeus. Nec Schinz. 1824—1828).

1841. G a l e. Wagner, J. A.— In: Schreber, I. Ch. Naturgesch. der Säugethiere, Suppl. 2, p. 234 (M u s t e l a v u l g a r i s Erxleben = M u s t e l a n i v a l i s Linnaeus).

1871. Mustelina. Bogdanov, M.N. Ptitsy i zveri chernozemnoi polosy Povolzh'ya (Birds and Animals of the Chernozem Belt of the Volga Area). — Trudy Obshchestva Estestvoispytatelei pri Imperatorskom Kazanskom Universitete, 1, p. 167. (erminea vulgaris).

1899. Eumustela. Acloque. Faune de France, Mammifères, p. 62 (Mustela vulgaris and M. erminea).

Type species. Mustela erminea Linnaeus (1758).

Diagnosis. The smallest species, markedly smaller than other members of subfamily. Body very thin, long, and slender. Head relatively flat above, with pointed muzzle. Ears small, ovally rounded. Tail about one half or less length of body with head covered with short hair. Legs very short. More or less developed webs present between toes.

Skull long, narrow, short in facial area and slightly expanded in occipital region. Width in area of tympanic bullae less than one half condylobasal length. Tympanic bullae long, ovally lenticular. Distance between jugular foramina approximately one half length of tympanic bullae. Hamulary processes of pterygoid bones not connected by bony bridges with tympanic bullae. Mastoid processes weakly developed and projecting slightly on either side. Paroccipital processes not developed.

Dental formula: $I\frac{3}{3}$; $C\frac{1}{1}$; $Pm\frac{3}{3}$; $M\frac{1}{2}$ = 34.

Lower carnassial lacks additional denticle on internal surface of middle cusp. Longitudinal axes of crowns of upper carnassials lie at angles to each other.

Terrestrial forms, not adapted to aquatic or arboreal life.

Geographical distribution. Europe, North Africa, Asia, North America and the north of South America.

Systematic notes. Genus Mustela comprises a rather homogenous group of small martens, readily characterized by a uniform dental formula and by such craniological features as structure of mastoid region, tympanic bullae, etc.

The grouping of the species into subgenera, adopted by certain authors (Satunin, 1911, 1914; Ognev, 1931), is in my opinion plausible, since it promotes better orientation in the systematics of the genus. There is no doubt that the Siberian weasel and the Altai weasel are closer to each other than to their other relatives. The weasels and ermines stand in an approximately similar relation.

The number of species within genus Mustela cannot be decided without a revision of the entire group of mustelids according to new data. Some ten of these are recognized today. The fauna of the Soviet Union includes five species, and these also occur in Siberia.

Key to Subgenera and Species of Genus
Mustela Occurring in Siberia

1 (4) Distinctly bicolored, the brown upper side being marked off from the contrasting white underparts. Winter fur in northern forms white. Length of tail appreciably less than one half length of body

with head.   Infraorbital foramen larger than alveoli of upper canine.
. . . . Subgenus Mustela s. str. (p. 264)

2 (3).   Tail bicolored, distal third or half of tail being always black; basal part brown in summer and white in winter.   Length of tail about one half length of body with head.   Posterior part of bony palate usually appreciably wider than space between tympanic bullae.   Os penis does not form hooklike curvature distally . . . .
. . . . Ermine-Mustela (s. str.) erminea

3 (2).   Tail monocolored: completely white in winter and brown in summer (insignificant addition of black or white hair may occasionally occur at tip of tail).   Tail appreciably shorter than one half length of body with head.   Posterior part of bony palate no wider than space between tympanic bullae.   Os penis hooklike, curved in distal part . . . . Weasel-Mustela (s. str.) nivalis (p.290)

4 (1).   Color uniformly russet throughout body, except for lips and for white spot on throat and chest.   Fur does not whiten for winter. Length of tail more than half length of body with head.   Infraorbital foramina smaller than alveoli of upper canines . . . .
. . . . Subgenus Kolonocus (p. 309)

5 (8).   Dark, coffee-brown coloration of muzzle; and of orbital area forms characteristic "mask."   Upper lips pure white.   Postorbital constriction of skull elongated, with sides lying almost parallel. Condylobasal length of male skull at least 55 mm, and of females — 49 mm 8

6 (7).   White area on lower lip and chin sharply marked off from yellowish-russet color of throat and neck.   Legs colored like body.   Under-parts same color as back or slightly lighter.   Bony palate extends backwards beyond level of backs of molars for a distance which is less than width of palate between these teeth.   Tympanic bullae moderately expanded rearwards on inner side.   Distance between jugular foramina about one half length of longitudinal axis of bullae · · ·
. . . . Siberian weasel-Mustela (Kolonocus) sibirica (p. 309)

7 (6).   Whitish coloration of lower lips and chin fuses with pale yellow throat, lower part of neck and chest.   Legs darker than body. Underpart lighter than back.   Bony palate extends backwards beyond level of molars for a distance greater than width of palate between these teeth.   Tympanic bullae markedly expanded rearwards on inner sides.   Distance between jugular foramina about two thirds of length of longitudinal axis of bullae . . . .
. . . . . Japanese weasel or itatsi-Mustela (Kolonocus) itatsi (p. 335)

8 (5).   Facial "mask" lacking.   Upper lips whitish or whitish straw-yellow. Postorbital constriction of skull short, usually with constricted "waist" and with lateral edges diverging posteriorly.   Condylo-basal length of male skull no more than 53 mm, of female 48 mm . .
. . . . Altai weasel-Mustela (Kolonocus) altaica (p. 341)

1. Subgenus M u s t e l a s. str. True weasels (ermines
and weasels)

Synonymy. See description of the genus.

Type species of the subgenus. M u s t e l a e r m i n e a Linneaus (1758).

Diagnosis. Dimensions very small. Tail short, its length less than half
length of body with head. Fur relatively short. Summer fur distinctly
bicolored; brown upper part marked off from contrasting white underparts. Winter fur white in northern forms. Tympanic bullae lie parallel
to each other, their inner sides diverging backward only in extreme
cases and then only slightly. Infraorbital foramina longer than alveoli of
upper canines. Os penis varies in different species.

Two species in the Soviet fauna.

Geographical distribution. Eurasia from the Arctic coastlines
southwards to North Africa and Asia Minor inclusively (occurs on the
Balearic Islands, Corsica, Sicily, Sardinia, Malta, and in Algeria and
Egypt). Found further east in Iran, Baluchistan, Afghanistan, Kashgaria,
and in the Himalayas (through to Nepal). Probably also occurs in Tibet.
Encountered in Northeast China, Korea, on Sakhalin, and in north Japan.
Found in America from the northern tip of Alaska to Panama,
Columbia, and northwestern Ecuador.

18. **Mustela** (s. str.) **erminea** Linnaeus (1758). Ermine
(Figure 99, Map XIV)

1758. M u s t e l a e r m i n e a. Linnaeus, C. Systema Naturae, X ed.,
1, p. 46; Kerr, R Animal Kingdom, p. 181. 1792; Adlerberg. G. P.
Khishchnye zveri (Carnivora Fissipedia) Arktiki (Carnivores
(Carnivora Fissipedia) of the Arctic). — In: Zveri Arktiki, edited by Prof.
N A. Smirnov, pp. 370 — 377, Leningrad, Izdatel'stvo Glavsevmorputi. 1935;
Yurgenson, P. B. — Byulleten' MOIP, otdel biologicheskii, Vol. 45, No. 3,
p. 239; Ellerman, J. R. and T. C. S. Morrison-Scott. Checklist of Palaearctic
and Indian Mammals, pp. 253 — 256, London. 1951.

1811. M u s t e l a e r m i n e u m. Pallas, P. S. Zoographia Rosso-
Asiatica, 1, pp. 90 — 94, Petropoli.

1816. M u s t e l a h e r m i n e a. Oken. Lehrb. Nat., 3, p. 1026 (instead
of e r m i n e a).

1851. P u t o r i u s e r m i n e a. Simashko, Yu. Russkaya fauna (Russian
Fauna). Mlekopitayushchie, 2, pp. 366 — 372.

1871. M u s t e l i n a e r m i n e a. Bogdanov, M. N. Ptitsy i zveri
chernozemnoi polosy Povolzh'ya (Birds and Animals of the Chernozem Belt
of the Volga Area). — Trudy Obshchestva Estestvoispytatelei pri
Imperatorskom Kazanskom Universitete, 1, p. 167.

1873. F o e t o r i u s e r m i n e u s. Severtsov, N. A. — Izvestiya
Obshchestva Lyubitelei Estestvoznaniya Antropologii i Etnografii, 8, No. 2,
pp. 7 and 61.

1896. P u t o r i u s a r c t i c u s. Merriam, C. H. Synopsis of the Weasels
of North America. — North American Fauna, No. 1, pp. 15 — 16 (Cape
Barrow, Alaska).

1898. P u t o r i u s (I c t i s) e r m i n e u s. Trouessart, E. L. Catalogus
Mammalium, 1, p. 278.

1900. Mustela (Eumustela) erminea. Acloque. Faune de France. Mammifères. p. 62.

1908. Mustela whiteheadi. Wroughton.— Journ. Bombay Nat. Hist. Soc., 18, p. 882 (North India).

1911. Ictis ermineus. Satunin, K. A. K sistematike semeistva Mustelidae. Vidy i podvidy roda Ictis (The Systematics of Family Mustelidae. Species and subspecies of Genus Ictis).— Izvestiya Kavkazskogo Muzeya, 5, pp. 7—8, Tiflis.

1912. Mustela lymani. Hollister, N. New Mammals from the Highland of Siberia.— Smiths. Misc. Coll., Vol. 63, No. 14, pp. 5—6, Washington. (Taipucha).

1914. Mustela kanei. Allen, G.— Proc. New England Zool. Club, Vol. 5, p. 58. (Nizhne-Kolymsk; nec Baird 1857).

1926. Arctogale erminea. Ognev, S. I. Mlekopitayushchie Severo-Vostochnoi Sibiri (Mammals of Northeastern Siberia). pp. 59—64, Vladivostok.

1944. Mustela (Mustela) erminea. Bobrinskii, N. A. Otryad khishchnye. Ordo Carnivora (Order Carnivores (Ordo Carnivora)).— In: Opredelitel' mlekopitayushchikh SSSR, edited by Prof. N. A. Bobrinskii pp. 129—130, Moskva; Novikov, G. A. Khishchnye mlekopitayushchie fauny SSSR (Carnivorous Mammals of the Fauna of the USSR). pp. 127—134. Moskva-Leningrad, Izdatel'stvo AN SSSR. 1956.

Type and type locality. The species has been described from a Swedish specimen.

FIGURE 99. The ermine, Mustela erminea L. (original)

Diagnosis. Basal part of tail same color as back: brown in summer, white in winter; terminal half or third always black. Length of tail about one half length of body with head. Posterior part of bony palate usually markedly broader than area between tympanic bullae. Os penis does not form hamate curvature distally.

Measurements. Length of body with head (from measurements of 75 males and 47 females): males 187—325 mm, females 170—270 mm; length of tail: males 75—120 mm, females 65—106 mm; length of hind paw: male 40.0—48.2 mm, females 37.0 — 47.6 mm; length of the ear: males 18.0—23.2 mm, females 14.0—23.0 mm. Weight: males up to 258 g, females 180 g.

Skull measurements (from 213 males and 136 females): condylobasal length: males 39.3—52.2 mm, females 35.7—43.8 mm; zygomatic width: males 21.0—30.6 mm, females 18.2—24.2 mm; interorbital width: males 9.1—13.2 mm, females 7.9—10.9 mm; mastoid width: males 19.1—26.3 mm females 16.8—21.7 mm; maximum width of infraorbital foramina: males 2.3—3.6 mm, females 2.3—3.4 mm; length of upper tooth row: males 11.3—14.2 mm, females 9.8—12.8 mm.

Description. Dimensions small (see measurements). Fur color shows clearly marked seasonal variation. In summer entire dorsal part grayish brown to brown of varying intensity, underparts white or lemon-white, and bicolored — base same color as back, and terminal third or half black (Figures 99, 100). Winter fur completely snow white except for terminal part of tail, which is black throughout year. Winter fur longer and more luxuriant than summer fur.

FIGURE 100. The ermine, Mustela erminea L. Photo by B.S.Yudin

Os penis weakly sigmoidally curved: lacks distal hamate bend (Figure 101). Length of os penis 20.5 — 46.7 mm.

Skull (Figure 102) in general structure similar to that of Siberian weasel but less elongated, and comparatively broader and higher in area of braincase, having less elevated frontal area and shorter postorbital compression. Skull more massive in facial section and rather strongly and evenly swollen in area of braincase. Upper profile approximates a straight line from interorbital area back to lambdoidal area, becoming markedly lower from forehead to tip of nose. When viewed from above, the lateral contours closely resemble the corresponding outlines of the skull of the mottled polecat (Vormela peregusna Güldenstaedt), but with the difference that in ermine the braincase is markedly longer, less expanded posteriorly, and has a very slight lateral projection of the mastoid processes. Area of postorbital compression, in contrast to that of Siberian weasel, is extremely short, making facial section of skull from level of maximal constriction of postorbital area to end of rostrum markedly shorter than cranial section lying behind this point. Nasals appreciably extended forward. Width of rostrum above canines markedly less than interorbital width. Mastoid width approximately one half condylo-basal length. Postorbital processes small though massive. Zygomatic arches relatively thin and weak. Sagittal crest generally slightly developed; in adults, especially old individuals, it may be conspicuous, particularly posteriorly. Occipital crest as a rule well marked even in relatively young individuals. Infraorbital foramina large and round; transverse axis of foramen markedly greater than longitudinal axis of upper canine base. Tympanic bullae lenticular, evenly inflated, and elongated in direction of longitudinal skull axis; bullae almost one half as wide as long. Inner sides of tympanic bullae parallel to each other. Width of hard palate at level of choanal incisure markedly greater than space between tympanic bullae. Paroccipital processes only slightly developed, their tips not elevated above posterior edge. Ends of hamular processes of pterygoid bones markedly divergent.

Sexual dimorphism manifested in dimensions and in modeling of skull. Skull smaller in females than in males (see measurements). Outlines rounder, and sutures (sagittal and occipital) markedly less noticeable. Female skulls generally endowed with definite juvenile traits.

Craniological variation with age is, as in other mustelids, rather marked. Skulls of young ermine with milk dentition (i. e., aged 2—3 months) characterized by general round oval form and by absence of occipital and sagittal crests, are more elevated in parietal area than skull of adult, and extremely short rostrally. Infraorbital foramina narrower and elongated on either side. Sutures well marked. After replacement of milk teeth by permanent teeth, i. e., at age of about 6—7 months, concresence of sutures occurs, expcept for those which delineate nasals. Sagittal and occipital crests appear. At age of 11—12 months surface of bones becomes thicker and concentric protuberances become distinguished with crests on roof of braincase sharply marked. Skull loses juvenile traits, becoming almost indistinguishable from adult skull.

Systematic notes. The systematics of the ermine's intraspecific forms needs revision and rearrangement. The literature contains many descriptions of different forms of the animal. The catalogue of Ellerman and Morrison-Scott (1957) includes for the Palaearctic alone 21 subspecies, 14 for the USSR, and 9 for Siberia. Most of these are unsatisfactorily

characterized and remain unchecked. These notions of the extensive
variety of the ermine's intraspecific forms do not stand up when actual
material is studied with attention given to age, sex, and individual
variation. Geographical variation is expressed only in an insignificant
decrease in size towards the east and in development of long hair and
thick and luxuriant fur in the northern and northeastern parts of the species'
Eurasian range.

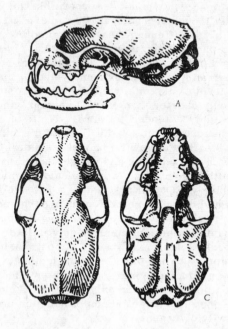

FIGURE 101. Os penis
of ermine (Mustela
erminea L.) (after
S. I. Ognev, 1931)

FIGURE 102. Skull of the ermine, Mustela
erminea L. (original):

A — lateral view; B — dorsal view; C — ventral
view.

Geographical distribution. Eurasia, except for its southern regions,
and North America. Distributed almost throughout the Soviet Union except
for Crimea and Transcaucasia. Occurs throughout Siberia, from western
boundaries to northern and eastern shorelines, as well as on Kotelny,
Shantar, and Sakhalin, among other islands (Map XIV).

We present below a survey of the accumulated data on the ermine's
distribution in the Soviet Union.

In Western Siberia the ermine occurs from the northern periphery of
the tundra zones to the forest steppe and steppe zones and the Altai
Mountains, inclusively. It is more abundant in the valleys of large rivers
and in the forest steppes (Figure 103). On the Yamal, according to
B. M. Zhitkov (1913), A. N. Dubrovskii (1940) and other authors, the ermine is
found throughout the peninsula. Common in the lower Ob, it has been

collected there by I. S. Polyakov. In some years it is abundant further east, to the Yenisei. According to available material, it occurs on the lower reaches of the Polui, Nadym, and Pur rivers. Ermine were collected in the Taz River valley by R. E. Kol's in 1927 (coll. S. I. Ognev). Skalon (1931) considers it a common species in the Ob-Taz region, and S. P. Naumov (1931), in traversing the Gyda Peninsula, encountered ermine from the typical forest zone (Turukhansk—Yanov-Stan) to the extreme north. Telegin collected it in 1956 on the Malaya and Bol'shaya Kheta rivers (collections of S. U. Stroganov). According to A. N. Dubrovskii (1940), it inhabits the island of Sibiryakov and probably enters the islands of Olenii and Shokalskii in years in which lemmings are scarce.

South of the above-mentioned localities it occurs ubiquitously, but is more common in large river valleys and the wooded steppe zone.

According to information collected by me it is rather common in the Tyumen, Tomsk, Kurgansk, Omsk, Novosibirsk and Kemerovo regions, and in the Altai and Krasnoyarsk territories, as well. In these regions and territories ermine pelts figure in the take in every district.

It has been collected in the Tyumen region by the following: I. S. Polyakov (1887) on the lower Ob and in the valley of the Irtysh River (coll. Zool. Acad. Sciences USSR); D. Wardropper near the city of Perezov (coll. Zool. Inst. Acad. Sciences USSR); D. M. Vyazhlinskii in 1936 on the upper reaches of the Northern Sosva River near the village of Neksimvol'; V. V. Raevskii in 1940 in the valley of the Malaya Sosva; and S. M. Chugunov (1915) in the valley of the Yugan River.

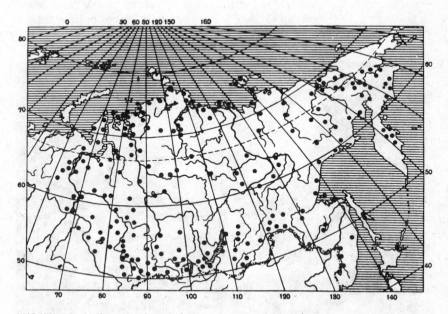

MAP XIV. Geographical distribution of the ermine, Mustela erminea L., in Siberia

FIGURE 103. Tundra in the vicinity of Gizhiga. Ermine biotope. Photo by K.T.Yurlov

According to S. Shvetsov (1888), it occurs in the Surgut taiga, and according to Sadovnikov (1911) it is plentiful along the Vakh River. The Zoological Museum of Moscow University has collections of ermine taken in 1936 in the Maslyanino, Golyshmanovo, and Ishim areas.

FIGURE 104. A glade in a birch forest in the vicinity of Lake Teniz, West Siberian lowland. Ermine biotope. Photo by K.T.Yurlov

In the Tomsk area ermine has been collected as follows: by
M.G. Vladimirskii in 1946 in the Aleksandrovskoe District (coll. Zool.
Inst. Acad. Sciences USSR); by V.P. Anikin (1902) near the city of
Narym, by S.U. Stroganov in 1949—1950 in the Verkhne-Ketskoe, Kolpashevo,
Asino and Tomsk areas; by V.G. Kazanskaya in 1950 near Tomsk city;
and by I.N. Glotov and B.S. Yudin in 1955—1956 in the Kozhevnikovo area.

In the Omsk Region it was collected by V. Ushakov in 1909 in the Tara
River valley; collections are also available from the Murom, Tyukalinsk
and Pavlodar (the village Bogodukhovka) districts (coll. Zool. Museum of
Moscow University).

In Novosibirsk Region (Figure 104) it has been collected by V. Gubar' in
1928 in the Legostaevo and Vengerovo districts; A.A. Maksimov in 1950
in the Kargat District (the village Rovenskoe); M.G. Vladimirskii in 1949
in the Ordynskoe District; N.V. Nadeev in 1949 in the Chany area; by
Stroganov in 1952 in the Kashlamskii pine forest; and by Telegin in 1955
near the city of Novosibirsk (Figure 105).

In the Kemerovo Region Yudin collected it in 1953 in the Yashkino area
(the Zyryanka village).

It occurs throughout the Altai territory (Savinov, 1953). G.N. Likhachev
(1930) reported it in the Upper Ob pine forest. According to my material
it is common in the Barnaul and Troitskoe areas, and not rare in the
Biisk District.

In the Gornaya Shoriya, according to G. Gol'tsmaier (1935) it is a rare
species. It has been seen and collected on the Altai by numerous students.

P.B. Yurgenson (1938) encountered it all the way from Oirot-Tury to
Artybash. A.P. Razorenova (1939) reported a catch of ermine in the
Khanzara River valley. Hollister (1912) described a distinct subspecies
of ermine from material collected near the village of Topuchii on the Chuya
trail.

For the Ust-Koksa area of the Gorno-Altai Autonomous Region,
A.A. Nasimovich (1949) reports that the average of fur trade figures over
the years show the ermine to hold the first place among carnivores collected.

On the upper Uimen, the animal was collected in 1897 by A.A. Silant'ev.
In the Chuya canyons (Kosh-Agach) the noted explorer G. Potanin took
specimens in 1884 (coll. Zool. Inst. Acad. Sciences, USSR).

In the former Altai reserve, according to Yurgenson (1938), it is
widely (though unevenly) distributed, being more common in the Chulyshman
valley than in localities around Lake Teletskoe. In the valley of the
Chulyshman it has been collected at Kok-Pash and on the Shepish-Oyuk
River. Yurgenson obtained it on the Chechenek, on the Chiik (a left
tributary of the Koksa), near the mouth of the Kamga River, at the sites
Yailyu, Chulyush, and Chiri, and at the mouths of small streams emptying
into Lake Teletskoe (Figure 106).

In the Western Sayan, Yanushevich and Yurlov (1949) have reported
the ermine as being common in all landscape zones except the steppe
areas of the Minusinsk valley depression, where it is rare. It has been
found in the Khakass Autonomous Republic (N.A. Kokhanovskii, personal
communication). In the Tuva Region, according to Yanushevich (1952),
it is common. In the Minusinsk taiga, L. and I. Kozhanchikov report

(1924) that the ermine is common all the way up to the subalpine zone along the Kazyr and Kizyr rivers. On the northeastern slopes of the Easter Sayan, as well as in the area of Krasnoyarsk, it has been collected by M. E. Kibibort and V. Torgashev, among others. It is a very characteristic member of the mammal fauna of the central parts of the Sayans (Gromov, 1951), where it has been collected by V. K. Timofeev (coll. Zool. Mus. Moscow University). In the taiga between the Eastern Sayan and the valley of the lower reaches of the Amgara and its tributaries the ermine is common and plays an important role in the fur trade (Troitskii, 1930). In the Irkutsk Region, according to M. P. Kopylov (1948), it is common both in the plain and in the mountains.

FIGURE 105. Edge of a pine forest near Novosibirsk. Ermine Biotope. Photo by B. S. Yudin

The ermine is widespread in Trans-Yenisei Siberia north of the above mentioned localities, and we have the following details on its occurrence there:

On the Stony Tunguska P. Valdeev obtained it near the village of Baikit (coll. Zool. Inst. Acad. Sciences USSR).

In the valley of the Lower Tunguska N. P. Naumov collected it (1934) near the Taimur trading post, the Tur and Vivi rivers. Near the mouth of the Niva River it was obtained in 1925 by Penin (coll. Zool. Mus. Moscow University). On the Moiero River (the valley of the lower reaches of the Kotui River) it was obtained by A. L. Chekanovskii (coll. Zool. Inst. Acad. Sciences USSR). Schmidt (1872) encountered the animal in large numbers along the Yenisei from Turukhansk to Dudinka.

FIGURE 106. Valley of the Agul River in its middle reaches. The Eastern Sayan. Ermine biotope. Photo by K.T. Yurlov

On the Taimyr it has been reported by all investigators beginning with Middendorf (1869), who encountered it on the Taimyr River at around 73°N lat.

On the east side of Yenisei Bay A. Ya. Tugarinov obtained it near the mouth of the Glubokaya River.

Collections are known from the Golchikha, Cape Isachenko, and Tolstyi Nos (Naumov, 1934; Kolyushev, 1933).

On Dickson Island and neighboring parts of the mainland, according to V.G. Geptner (1936), it is rather common, and in years of lemming outbreaks may even occur in larger numbers. It was collected on Dickson in 1951 by V.S. Sokolov (coll. Zool. Mus. Moscow University).

In the northwestern part of the Taimyr Peninsula, according to L.P. Shastin (1939), it is encountered rarely, particularly to the southeast of the Nordenskiold Archipelago; it is encountered with greater frequency in the southern part of the Nordenskiolds (recorded on Chebak and Taimyr islands) and further west along the mainland shore. In the area of Taimyr Bay the author has seen ermine tracks on the Lower Taimyr River near Lake Engelgard, and near Cape Vega. According to G.L. Rutilevskii (1939), the ermine apparently inhabits the entire Taimyr Peninsula right to its northern tip, i.e., to 77°N lat. Isolated individuals cross over via the ice to the offshore islands. On 29 April 1933, Rutilevskii personally observed an ermine crossing the ice separating the mainland and Fram Island (Mod Bay). On the east side of the peninsula L.N. Popov (1939) obtained ermine in the area of Pronchishchevaya inlet, and according to him the animal is probably not rare there.

On the Khatanga River it was collected in 1931 by A. F. Chirkova (coll. Zool. Moscow University). In the country stretching from the lower reaches of the Khatanga to the mountains of the Kharaulakh Range (inclusively), according to A. A. Romanov (1941), the ermine occurs throughout the taiga to the shores of the Laptev Sea. It is also encountered on the Begichev and Salkai islands and on the islands in the Lena River delta and the mouth of the Olenek River. According to A. A. Chekanovskii (1873), it is encountered all along the Olenek, but Romanov (1941) says that the ermine's distribution in this area is extremely uneven. It is relatively abundant in the forest near the tundra, being encountered in large numbers in mountain tundra and in lesser numbers in lowland tundra.

Further to the east and south it is widespread throughout Yakutia and is encountered on the Lyakhov and Novosibirsk islands (Belyk, 1953) and on the island Kotelnyi (Birulya, 1907). In the delta of the Yana River, according to Bunge (1887), it is a common species. It was taken by the Russian Arctic Expedition near the village of Kazach'e and in the Verkhoyansk area (coll. Zool. Inst. Acad. Sciences USSR). In the Indigirka valley, according to N. M. Mikhel' (1938), it was encountered in large numbers everywhere except in the tundra.

On the Kolyma the ermine is rather common, according to S. A. Buturlin (1913), who wrote that "its numbers increased as we crossed over the Alazeya Range into the Kolyma area on our way to the east." Buturlin collected ermine at Sukharnoe (a village near the mouth of the Kolyma), near the town of Sredne-Kolymsk, near the post Krestovaya, and at the village of Pokhodskii (coll. Zool. Inst. Acad. Sciences USSR). Near Nizhne-Kolymsk, according to G. Allen (1914), it was obtained by Koren.

On the Vilyui, according to Maak (1886), it is encountered more often than any other mustelid; A. I. Ivanov describes the ermine as one of the most important components of the local fur trade (Tugarinov, Smirnov and Ivanov, 1934).

According to recent data of V. I. Belyk (1953), ermine are particularly abundant in the northeastern areas of Yakutia, the yield being highest there. It is also high in the agricultural areas: those on the Vilyui and the central ones in the Amga—Lena interfluve, which have the second highest ermine yields. The animal is numerous in the southern area (near the Lena and the Aldan), but is there insufficiently exploited.

Ermine distribution in the northeast part of Siberia is reported by numerous authors, both past and contemporary.

N. L. Gondatti (1897) wrote that ermine were more often encountered along the upper and middle reaches of the Anadyr River. According to N. P. Sokol'nikov (1927), they range throughout the Anadyr territory, but in small numbers.

L. O. Belopol'skii (1937) considered the ermine to be particularly abundant on the Anadyr and to play an important role in the fur trade there.

According to L. A. Portenko (1941), the ermine is more or less common everywhere in the Anadyr territory, being more abundant in the western part though nevertheless not as numerous as along the Kolyma. According to information collected by this author, it abounds on the Anyui and th Omolon and is obtained in large numbers. Portenko has collected the animal near the villages of Eropol and Oselkino and around Markovo near Modinskaya Povarnya and the village Penzhino. Sokol'nikov (1927) collected it on the Anadyr near the village of the same name and near Markova. Traces of the animal have been observed in the valley of the Ubienkovaya River, near the Gorelovye Mountains, and at the mouth of the Tanyurer. An extensive series of ermine was collected in 1954 and 1958 in the area of the Anadyr and the Tanyurer by B. S. Yudin and V. I. Telegin. S. D. Pereleshin obtained it on the lower reaches of the Penzhina. The ermine is common on the Velikaya River and abounds on the Main River.

According to A. V. Samorodov (1939), it ranges in large numbers throughout the Olyutorka Koryak country and has been collected by this author in the valleys of the Achaivam (a tributary of the Apuka), the Ilka, and the Pakhaga (coll. Zool. Mus. Moscow University). On Karagin Island it was collected in 1913 by M. P. Rozanov (coll. Zool. Mus. Moscow University).

On Kamchatka it was reported back in the days of Krasheninnikov (see 1949 edition). All subsequent investigation have reported the animal as widespread there. Extensive series have been collected on Kamchatka by N. A. Grebnitskii, A. D. Baturin (coll. Zool. Inst. Acad. Sciences USSR), and others.

It abounds in the Kronoki reserve in the valleys of the Bol'shaya Chazhma, Malaya Chazhma, Tyushevka, Ol'ga, Tatyana, Bogachevka and Shumnaya. It is encountered in large numbers in the basin of Lake Kronetskoe and on the lower reaches of rivers flowing into Kronotskii Bay, and is known from the Uzon caldera.

It is widespread along the shore of the Sea of Okhotsk. According to N. V. Slyunin (1900) it was obtained in small numbers in Gizhiga and Okhotsk. The Zoological Museum of Moscow State University contains material from the area of Magadan. In the area of Verkhne-Kolymsk it has been collected by I. D. Cherskii (coll. Zool. Inst. Acad. Sciences USSR), and A. Torin obtained it along the upper reaches of the Kolyma.

The ermine is quite common in Transbaikalia. On the Khamar-Daban it has been obtained by S. S. Turov and on the Sosnovka, Kudalda, and Shuminikha by Z. F. Svatosh. It occurs on the northern and southern Muiya Ranges and throughout the Vitim Plateau (Polyakov, 1873).

In Eastern Transbaikalia, according to B. A. Kuznetsov (1939) it is rare; this author found it on the Yablonovyi Range (at Kyker village) and among its foothills (at Zyulzikan village), in the forest steppe along the Nercha River (at the city of Nerchinsk), and on the Undinskii Range (at the village of Kalinino). On the upper Chita River, according to E. Pavlov (1948), it is rare. According to Radde (1862), it is common along the middle reaches of the Onon and occurs, though more rarely, in the mountain steppes of Dauria; it is common in the valley of the upper Amur.

On the Stanovoi Range Middendorf (1869) found the ermine to be a common species. G. N. Gassovskii (1927) reports that it is widely distributed in the interfluve between the Oldon and the Gilyui. The author observed the animal on the Stanovoi in the valley of the Mogota River, on the Tynda and Getkan, and on the Oldoi near the mouth of the Zimovicha.

The ermine is reported from the valley of the upper Selemdzha and the Uda by N. T. Zolotarev (1934). From Bureya Range it is reported by Radde (1862), and it inhabits the entire valley of the Ussuri River (Maak, 1861). According to N. M. Przheval'skii (1870) it is rare in the Ussuri territory, and this famous explorer never obtained it.
V. K. Arsen'ev collected ermine on the Samarka River (coll. Zool. Inst. Acad. Sciences USSR). It occurs (sparsely) throughout the valley of the Iman River, according to Zolotarev (1936), and inhabits the Sudzukhe reserve (Bromlei, 1951).

It has been collected on the Shantar Islands by Baturin, Dul'keit, and others (Ognev, 1929).

On Sakhalin it is encountered throughout the island, and L. Schrenck (1858) found it in the valley of the Tym River. According to P. I. Suprunenko (1890) the ermine is encountered along river valleys on the island, but in low numbers. M. V. Gerasimov (1951) includes it in a list of animals inhabiting the Central Sakhalin reserve (the southern slopes of the Vostochnyi [Eastern] Range). According to A. I. Gizenko (1954), it is common on Shmidt Island.

It occurs on the Kurile Islands. B. A. Podkovyrkin (1958) observed ermine on Shumshu Island, but it is rare here.

Survey of subspecies. The total number of ermine forms cannot be determined at present even approximately. Preliminary data indicate that Siberia is inhabited by six subspecies.

18a. **Mustela** (s. str.) **erminea tobolica** Ognev (1922).
West Siberian ermine

1922. Arctogale erminea tobolica. Ognev, S. I. Materialy po sistematike russkikh mlekopitayushchikh. Novyi podvid gornostaya (Data on the Systematics of Russian Mammals. A New Subspecies of the Ermine).— Biologicheskie Izvestiya Gosudarstvennogo Nauchno-Issledovatel'skogo Instituta im. Timiryazeva, Vol. 1, pp. 112—113.

1935. Mustela erminea tobolica. Ognev, S. I. Zveri SSSR i prilezhashchikh stran (Animals of the USSR and Adjacent Countries). Vol. 3, pp. 25—27, Moskva-Leningrad; Ellerman, J. R. and T. C. S. Morrison-Scott. Checklist of Palaearctic and Indian Mammals, p. 225, London. 1951.

Type and type locality. No. 1957 in the collection of the Zoological Museum of Moscow University; collected November 1919 by V. E. Ushakov near the city of Tara in Tobolsk Province (the locality lies in the present Omsk Region).

Diagnosis. Differentiated from European ermine M. e. aestiva Kerr by higher, denser and more silky winter fur. Summer fur is also somewhat longer, denser and softer.

Measurements. Length of body with head (from 43 males and 35 females): males 200—300 mm (av. 260 mm), females 200—270 mm (av. 230 mm); length of tail: males 50—120 mm (av. 90 mm), females 50—100 mm (av. 70 mm); length of hind paw: males 40—48 mm (av. 45 mm), females 34—42 mm (av. 37 mm); height of ear: males 18—22 mm (av. 20 mm), females 14—18 mm (av. 16 mm).

Skull measurements (from 45 males and 40 females). Condylobasal length: males 43.4—50.1 mm (av. 48.3 mm), females 49.6—45.6 mm (av. 43 mm); zygomatic width: males: 24.8—30.0 mm (av. 27.7 mm), females 21.4—26.8 mm (av. 24.2 mm); interorbital width: males 10.4—13.2 mm (av. 12.0 mm), females 9.2—12.0 mm (av. 10.8 mm); postorbital width: males 9.6—12.1 mm (av. 11.2 mm), females 8.2—11.1 mm (av. 9.2 mm); mastoid width: males 21.2—25.2 mm (av. 23.6 mm), females 19.3—22.2 mm (av. 21.0 mm); facial length: males 12.1—13.1 mm (av. 12.8 mm), females 10.0—11.1 mm (av. 10.7 mm); length of braincase: males 25.6—30.3 mm (av. 28.5 mm), females 26.3—28.3 mm (av. 15.3 mm); length of tympanic bullae: males 14.0—16.7 mm (av. 15.3 mm), females 13.1—14.4 mm (av. 13.7 mm); width of tympanic bullae: males 7.4—10.1 mm (av. 8.7 mm), females 7.2—8.7 mm (av. 7.8 mm); length of upper tooth row: males 13.2—14.9 mm (av. 14.3 mm), females 11.7—13.1 mm (av. 12.2 mm).

Systematic notes. Peculiarities of fur quality, not craniological features were the basis for the isolation of the West Siberian ermine. According to S. I. Ognev (1922 and 1935), M. e. tobolica is differentiated from the European subspecies M. e. aestiva by relatively greater zygomatic width, longer upper tooth row, larger infraorbital foramina and greater width of the nasal apertures, which are more broad than high.

Examination of extensive craniological material (about 300 skulls obtained in Western Siberia, and more than 450 specimens from the central regions of the European part of the USSR) has failed to confirm the indicated features.

For example the ratio of zygomatic width to condylobasal length (as a percentage) is as follows: 54.2—28.1% (n = 75) in M. e. aestiva, 54.6—58.1% (n = 45) in M. e. tobolica; length of upper tooth row is 27.8—31.8% in aestiva, 28.2—31.7% in tobolica. In addition, the size of the infraorbital foramina and the ratio between the width and the height of the nasal apertures vary markedly and have no systematic significance.

The sole feature characterizing tobolica is thus the quality of the fur, whose peculiarities were presented in the diagnosis.

Geographical distribution. The West Siberian lowland eastwards to the Altai and the Yenisei.

Material studied. Tundra zone of Western Siberia — 5 specimens; taiga zone — 75 specimens; wooded steppe — 190 specimens. Total 270 specimens, including 85 skulls with pelts.

18b. **Mustela** (s. str.) **erminea lymani** Hollister (1912).
Altai ermine

1912. Mustela lymani. Hollister, N. New Mammals from the Highland of Siberia. — Smiths. Misc. Collect., Vol. 63, No. 14, pp. 5—6.
1935. Mustela erminea lymani. Ognev, S. I. Zveri SSSR i prilezhashchikh stran (Animals of the USSR and Adjacent Countries). Vol. 3, pp. 28—29, Moskva-Leningrad; Yurgenson, P. B. Materialy k poznaniyu mlekopitayushchikh priteletskogo uchastka Altaiskogo gosudarstvennogo zapovednika (Contributions to the Study of Mammals of the Lake Teletskoe Area of the Altai State Reserve). — Trudy Altaiskogo Gosudarstvennogo

Zapovednika, No.1, pp.116—124, Moskva. 1938; Ellerman, J.R. and
T. C. S. Morrison-Scott. Checklist of Palaearctic and Indian Mammals,
p. 255, London. 1951; Bannikov, A. G. Mlekopitayushchie Mongol'skoi
Narodnoi Respubliki (Mammals of the Mongolian People's Republic).
pp. 97 — 98. Moskva, Izdatel'stvo AN SSSR. 1954.

Type and type locality. Described from a specimen preserved in the
National Museum of the USA and found at Tapuchai in the Altai.

Diagnosis. Distinguished from West Siberian ermine by less dense fur.
Summer fur color characterized by slightly marked russet-brown tone,
sometimes by complete lack of deep tone. Zygomatic width of skull about
55 % of condylobasal length (against 57.7% in tobolica).

Measurements. Length of body with head (from 10 males and 5 females):
males 218—295 mm (av. 258 mm), females 185—260 mm (av. 220 mm);
length of tail: males 45—105 mm (av. 75 mm), females 40—90 mm
(av. 60 mm); length of hind paw: males 37—48 mm (av. 44), females
32—42 mm (av. 36 mm).

Skull measurements (from 14 males and 12 females). Condylobasal
length: males 44.0—49.4 mm (av. 48.4 mm), females 41.2—45.2 mm
(av. 43.7 mm); zygomatic width: males 24.4—28.7 mm (av. 27.3 mm),
females 20.8—26.2 mm (av. 24.4 mm); interorbital width: males
11.8—12.6 mm (av. 12.2 mm), females 9.9—12.0 mm (av. 11.3 mm);
postorbital width: males 10.0—12.8 mm (av. 11.4 mm), females
9.0—11.7 mm (av. 10.2 mm); mastoid width: males 21.3—25.3 mm
(av. 23.6 mm), females 19.2—23.0 mm (av. 21.1); facial length: males
11.8—12.9 mm (av. 12.6 mm), females 9.9—10.8 mm (av. 10.4 mm); length
of braincase: males 26.8—30.5 mm (av. 28.2 mm), females 26.0—28.1 mm
(av. 27.0 mm); length of tympanic bullae: males 14.2—15.2 mm
(av. 14.8 mm), females 13.1—14.4 mm (av. 13.8 mm); width of tympanic
bullae: males 8.8 — 9.9 mm (av. 9.4 mm), females 8.2—9.4 mm
(av. 8.7 mm); length of upper tooth row: males 12.2—14.2 mm
(av. 13.8 mm), females 10.6—13.0 mm (av. 12.4 mm).

Systematic notes. Judging from craniometric data, the Altai ermine is
close to the Transbaikalian, being differentiated however by having longer,
relatively sparser, and less silky fur.

Geographical distribution. Includes the mountains of Southern Siberia
eastwards approximately to Baikalia.

Materials studied. Altai — 18 specimens; the Sayans — 6 specimens;
Tuva — 2 specimens; total 26 skull and pelt specimens.

18c.   **Mustela** (s. str.) **erminea ognevi** Jurgenson (1932).
Central Siberian or Turukhan ermine

1932. **Mustela erminea ognevi.** Jurgenson, P. B. Das Hermelin
aus dem Turuchans-Gebiete.— Zoolog. Anzeig., Bd. 98, H 1/2, pp. 11—19;
Ognev, S. I. Zveri SSSR i prilezhashchikh stran (Animals of the USSR and
Adjacent Countries). Vol. 3, pp. 27—28, Moskva-Leningrad. 1935;
Ellerman, J. R. and T. C. S. Morrison-Scott. Checklist of Palaearctic and
Indian Mammals, p. 255, London. 1951.

1931. Mustela erminea tobolica. Naumov, S. P. Mlekopitayushchie i ptitsy Gydanskogo poluostrova (Mammals and Birds of the
Gyda Peninsula).— Trudy Polyarnoi Komissii AN SSSR, No. 4, pp. 25—27
(nec Ognev, 1929).
1934. Arctogale erminea orientalis. Naumov, N. P. Mlekopitayushchie Tungusskogo okruga (Mammals of the Tunguska area).
Trudy Polyarnoi Komissii AN SSSR, No. 17, pp. 31—33, 36—37. (nec. Og
Ognev, 1928).
1938. Mustela erminea naumovi. Yurgenson, P. B. Materialy
k poznaniyu mlekopitayushchikh priteletskogo uchastka Altaiskogo
gosudarstvennogo zapovednika (Contributions to the Study of Mammals of the
the Lake Teletskoe Area of the Altai State Reserve).— Trudy Altaiskogo
Gosudarstvennogo Zapovednika, No. 1, p. 124, Moskva.

Type and type locality. No. M. 3530 of S. I. Ognev's collection (preserved
in the Zool. Mus. of Moscow University) [collected] January 1927, [by]
R. E. Kol's. Delta of the Taz River.
Diagnosis. Differentiated from West Siberian ermine by smaller skull
size and by relatively narrow zygomatic width. Condylobasal length
of male skull about 45.6 mm, with ratio of zygomatic width to this
averaging 55%; the respective indexes in M. e. tobolica being 48.3 mm
and 57.7%.
Measurements. Dimensions of skull (from 36 males and 30 females).
Condylobasal length: males 40.6—49.8 mm (av. 45.6 mm), females
37.8—46.7 mm (av. 40.8 mm); zygomatic width: males 20.0—29.2 mm
(av. 25.5 mm), females 19.2—27.0 mm (av. 22.0 mm); interorbital width:
males 9.6—12.5 mm (av. 11.3 mm), females 8.2—11.8 mm (av. 9.6 mm);
postorbital width: males 9.5—12.5 mm (av. 10.6 mm), females
8.6—11.8 mm (av. 10.0 mm); mastoid width: males 18.7—24.1 mm (av.
22. 5 mm), females 17.5—23.0 mm (av. 20.0 mm); facial length: males
12.0—13.4 mm (av. 12.6 mm), females 9.9—11.0 mm (av. 10.5 mm); length
of braincase: males 27.6—30.7 mm (av. 29.2 mm), females 26.5—29.2 mm
(av. 27.6); length of tympanic bullae: males 13.0—15.9 mm (av. 14.8 mm),
females 11.6—15. 2 mm (av. 13.5 mm); width of tympanic bullae: males
8.2—9.9 mm (av. 9.3 mm), females 8.0—9.1 mm (av. 8.7 mm); length of
upper tooth row: males 10.6—13.8 mm (av. 12.4 mm), females 9.7—12.4 mm
(av. 10.9 mm).
Systematic notes. This subspecies is closely related to the West
Siberian ermine, differing only slightly in having a generally smaller skull
and less broad zygomatic width. It is nearer craniometrically to
M. e. lymani, but has a denser and silkier coat.
Geographical distribution. The valley of the Taz River, the lower
Yenisei, Lower Tunguska, and Khatanga, eastwards probably to the Lena,
and northwards to the sea.
Material studied. Basin of the Taz River — 6 specimens; Gyda
Peninsula — 3 specimens; Taimyr — 4 specimens; lower Yenisei — 12
specimens; basin of Lower Tunguska — 36 specimens; Khatanga — 3
specimens; lower Lena River — 3 specimens. Total — 67 specimens,
including 35 skulls with pelts.

18d. Mustela (s. str.) **erminea arctica** Merriam (1896).
East Siberian ermine

1896. Putorius a r c t i c u s. Merriam, C. H. Synopsis of the Weasels
of North America.— North Amer. Fauna, No. 14, pp. 15—16; Ognev, S. I.
Novye dannye po sistematike i geograficheskomu rasprostraneniyu
nekotorykh vidov semeistva Mustelidae (New Data on the Systematics and
Geographical Distribution of Some Species of Family Mustelidae). —
Memuary Zoologicheskogo Otdela Obshchestva Lyubitelei Estestvoznaniya,
Antropologii i Etnografii, No. 2, pp. 14—15, Moskva. 1928; Ognev, S. I.
Zveri SSSR i prilezhashchikh stran (Animals of the USSR and Adjacent
Countries). Vol. 3, pp. 31—33, Moskva-Leningrad. 1935; Ognev, S. I.
Zametki po sistematike anadyrskikh mlekopitayushchikh (Notes on the
Systematics of Anadyr Mammals). — In: L. A. Portenko. Fauna
Anadyrskogo kraya,. Part 3, Mlekopitayushchie, pp. 96—98, Leningrad-
Moskva, Izdatel'stvo Glavsevmorputi. 1941; Ellerman, J. R. and
T. C. S. Morrison-Scott. Checklist of Palaearctic and Indian Mammals, p. 25
London. 1951.

1914. M u s t e l a k a n e i. Allen, G. Notes on the Birds and Mammals
of the Arctic Coast of East Siberia, Mammals.— Proc. New Engl. Zool.
Club, Vol. 5, p. 58 (Nizhne-Kolymsk, nec. Baird, 1857).

1922. P u t o r i u s e r m i n e a var. k a m t s c h a t i c a. Dybowski.—
Arch. Tow. Nauk., Vol. 1, p. 349, Lvov (nom. nud.).

1926. A r c t o g a l e e r m i n e a subsp. Ognev, S. I. Mlekopitayushchie
Severo-Vostochnoi Sibiri (Mammals of Northeastern Siberia). pp. 59—64.
Vladivostok.

1928. M u s t e l a e r m i n e a o r i e n t a l i s. Ognev, S. I. Novye danny
po sistematike etc. (New Data on the Systematics, etc.).— Memuary
Zoologicheskogo Otdela Obshchestva Lyubitelei Estestvoznaniya,
Antropologii i Etnografii, No. 2, pp. 15—16 (Pokhodskoe village on
the Kolyma River); Ognev, S. I. Zveri SSSR etc. (Animals of the USSR, etc.)
Vol. 3, pp. 33—34, Moskva-Leningrad. 1935; Ellerman, J. R. and
T. C. S. Morrison-Scott.— Loc. cit., p. 255. 1951.

1944. M u s t e l a e r m i n e a d i g n a. Hall, R.— Proc. Calif. Acad.
Sci. Vol. 23, p. 559 (Kamchatka).

Type and type locality. Described for the first time from a specimen
from the vicinity of Point Barrow, Alaska.

Diagnosis. Distinguished from those subspecies already described by
relatively pale summer fur with grayish brown-yellowish tinges of varying
intensity. Condylobasal length of male skull averages 46.0 mm, and ratio
of zygomatic width to condylobasal length is about 56.0%.

Measurements. Length of body with head (from 22 males and 7 females
males 213—325 mm (av. 260 mm), females 176—222 mm (av. 212 mm);
length of tail: males 70 —100 mm (av. 86.0 mm), females 67—77 mm
(av. 72.0 mm); length of hind paw: males 40—48 mm (av. 43 mm), female
33.0—43.0 mm (av. 38.0 mm); length of ear: males 20—22 mm (av. 21 mm
females 18—20 mm (av. 19.0 mm).

Skull measurements (from 24 males and 23 females). Condylobasal
length: males 44.0—49.2 mm (av. 46.0 mm), females 38.9 —44.3 mm
(av. 40.9 mm); zygomatic width: males 24.0—28.8 mm (av. 26.2 mm),

females 20.0 — 25.2 mm (av. 22.3 mm); interorbital width: males
10.1 — 13.2 mm (av. 11.4 mm), females 8.8 — 10.0 mm (av. 9.5 mm);
postorbital width: males 10.0 — 12.5 mm (av. 11.0 mm), females
8.7 — 10.9 mm (av. 10.7 mm); mastoid width: males 20.1 — 24.7 mm
(av. 22.5 mm), females 18.0 — 20.2 mm (av. 19.2 mm); facial length: males
10.7 — 13.0 mm (av. 11.7 mm), females 9.2 — 10.0 mm (av. 9.6 mm); length of
braincase: males 26.1 — 30.2 mm (av. 28.1 mm), females 24.2 — 29.9 mm
(av. 25.0 mm); length of tympanic bullae: males 14.0 — 16.1 mm (av. 15.0 mm),
females 12.7 — 14.8 mm (av. 13.4 mm); width of tympanic bullae: males
8.0 — 9.9 mm (av. 9.3 mm), females 7.0 — 8.3 mm (av. 7.4 mm); length of
upper tooth row: males 12.2 — 14.3 mm (av. 13.1 mm), females
10.5 — 12.8 mm (av. 11.4 mm).

Systematic notes. M. e. arctica differs from West Siberian and Central
Siberian ermines only slightly, the difference being a slight lightening of
summer fur. This property is well borne out by the material. No persistent craniological differences have been found on the material studied.

Geographical distribution. Includes the central and northeastern areas
of Yakutia, plus Chukotka, Kamchatka, and the coast of the Sea of Okhotsk
south to approximately the latitude of the Shantar Islands.

Material studied. Central Yakutia — 5 specimens; Yana River — 3
specimens; Indigirka River — 8 specimens; Kolyma River — 10 specimens;
Anadyr River — 36 specimens; Kamchatka — 25 specimens; Sea of Okhotsk
coast — 4 specimens. Total 87 [sic] specimens, including 40 skulls with
pelts.

18e. Mustela (s. str.) erminea karaginensis
Jurgenson (1936). Karagin ermine

1936. Mustela erminea karaginensis. Yurgenson, P. B. O
gornostayakh Dal'nevostochnogo kraya (Ermines of the Far Eastern
Region). — Byulleten' Moskovskogo Obshchestva Ispytatelei Prirody, otdel'
biologicheskii, Vol. 45, No. 3, pp. 239 — 243; Ellerman, J. R. and
T. C. S. Morrison-Scott. Checklist of Palaearctic and Indian Mammals,
p. 256, London. 1951.

Type and type locality. No. 8989, collection of the Zoological Museum
of Moscow State University, winter 1930 — 1931, collected by M. P. Rozanov.
Karagin Island in the Bering Sea.

Diagnosis. Distinguished from M. e. arctica by smaller skull
dimensions. Condylobasal length of male skull 40.5 — 43.7 mm (av.
42.7 mm), as against 44.0 — 49.2 mm (av. 46.0 mm) in M. e. arctica.

Measurements. Yurgenson (1936) gives the following measurements
for male skulls. Condylobasal length: 40.5—43.7 mm (av. 42.7 mm);
zygomatic width: 21.6 — 23.7 mm (av. 23.0 mm); interorbital width:
9.8 — 11.0 mm (av. 10.1 mm); maximum width: 19.3 — 21.6 mm (av. 20.3 mm);
length of tympanic bullae: 12.9 — 13.0 mm (av. 13.1 mm); length of upper
tooth row: 11.1 — 11.8 mm (av. 11.3 mm).

Systematic notes. This is a small insular form not known to us from
the field. Yurgenson (1936) places it close to M. e. arctica.

Geographical distribution. Known only from Karagin Island off the
northeast coast of Kamchatka.

18f. Mustela(s. str.) erminea transbaicalica Ognev
(1928). Transbaikalian ermine

1928. M u s t e l a e r m i n e a t r a n s b a i c a l i c a . Ognev, S. I. Novye
dannye po sistematike i geograficheskomu rasprostraneniyu nekotorykh
vidov semeistva Mustelidae (New Data on the Systematics and Geographical
Distribution of Some Species of Family Mustelidae). — Memuary Zoologi-
cheskogo Otdela Obshchestva Lyubitelei Estestvoznaniya, Antropologii i
Etnografii, No. 2, p. 14; Ognev, S. I. Zveri SSSR i prilezhashchikh stran
(Animals of the USSR and Adjacent Countries). Vol. 3, pp. 29 — 30,
Moskva-Leningrad. 1935; Ellerman, J. R. and T. C. S. Morrison-Scott.
Checklist of Palaearctic and Indian Mammals, p. 255, London. 1951.

1929. M u s t e l a e r m i n e a b a t u r i n i . Ognev, S. I. Mlekopitayushchie
Shantarskikh ostrovov (Mammals of the Shantar Islands). — Izvestiya
Tikhookeanskoi Nauchno-Issledovatel'skoi Stantsii, Vol. 2, No. 5, pp. 9 — 10,
Vladivostok (Bol'shoi Shantar Island) ; Ognev, S. I. Zveri SSSR etc.
(Animals of the USSR etc.). Vol. 3, pp. 30 — 31, Moskva-Leningrad. 1935;
Ellerman, J. R. and T. C. S. Morrison-Scott. Loc. cit., p. 255.

Type and type locality. No. 11 in S. I. Ognev's collection (kept at
the Zoological Museum of the Moscow State University), adult male,
23 December 1923, collected by Z. F. Svatosh at Sosnovka in the Barguzin
reserve on the eastern shore of Lake Baikal.

Diagnosis. Distinguished from West Siberian ermine by relatively
short and sparse fur and by smaller skull. Condylobasal length of male
skull 39.3 — 46.1 mm (av. 43.6 mm) and ratio of zygomatic width to
condylobasal length being 51.6%, as against 43.4 — 50.1 mm (av. 48.3 mm)
and 57.7% in M. e. t o b o l i c a.

Measurements (skull measurements from 94 males and 26 females).
Condylobasal length: males 39.3 — 46.1 mm (av. 43.6 mm), females
35.7 — 41.7 mm (av. 38.2 mm); zygomatic width: males 21.0 — 24.5 mm
(av. 23.2 mm), females 18.2 — 23.7 mm (av. 19.5 mm); interorbital width:
males 9.1 — 11.6 mm (av. 10.8 mm), females 7.9 — 10.0 mm (av. 8.7 mm);
postorbital width: males 9.3 — 12.0 mm (av. 11.0 mm), females
8.3 — 10.7 mm (av. 10.1 mm); mastoid width: males 19.1 — 22.1 mm (av.
21.0 mm), females 16.8 — 21.8 mm (av. 18.1 mm); facial length: males
9.2 — 11.4 mm (av. 11.0 mm), females 7.6 — 10.7 mm (av. 8.7 mm); length of
braincase: males 25.5 — 29.6 mm (av. 27.8 mm), females 23.6 — 27.1 mm
(av. 25.4 mm); length of tympanic bullae: males 13.0 — 15.7 mm (av.
14.9 mm), females 11.8 — 14.2 mm (av. 12.1 mm); width of tympanic bullae:
males 7.2 — 9.1 mm (av. 8.6 mm), females 6.1 — 8.8 mm (av. 7.1 mm);
length of upper tooth row: males 11.3 — 13.1 mm (av. 12.4 mm), females
9.8 — 10.9 mm (av. 10.1 mm).

Systematic notes. The subspecies is readily distinguished (but, as
with other ermine forms, [only] on series material) by its relatively
short and sparse hair and by craniometric features. The latter are
clearly seen when comparison is made with similar indices for some
other Siberian ermines.

The following table shows the relation of the principal craniometric
measurements to the condylobasal length of the skull in a number of
ermine subspecies (Table 7).

TABLE 7. Relation (in %) of various skull measurements to condylobasal length in certain ermine subspecies (upper line — average, lower line — range of variation)

	M.e. tobolica n = 45	M.e. ognevi n = 36	M.e. arctica n = 24	M.e. lymani n = 14	M.e.trans- baicalica n = 94
Zygomatic width	57.7 54.6—62.3	55.1 52.6—56.1	56.0 53.4—59.5	55.1 52.5—58.1	51.6 50.3—55.5
Interorbital width	25.5 22.8—28.4	25.4 22.9—26.3	25.2 20.3—28.6	24.9 22.6—26.8	23.3 21.4—26.1
Postorbital width	23.7 19.1—26.7	23.6 20.3—27.8	23.2 20.8—26.1	24.8 20.1—28.0	24.5 20.7—29.7
Mastoid width	48.7 45.5—50.4	48.5 24.0—52.0	48.5 42.1—51.7	48.3 45.5—51.6	47.5 45.1—48.5
Length of facial section. . .	26.1 25.1—26.7	25.3 24.0—26.5	25.2 23.6—26.8	25.3 24.0—27.1	24.7 22.3—25.5
Length of braincase	58.4 55.5—60.8	61.7 52.4—68.2	60.2 57.2—65.7	50.5 57.1—62.9	63.7 56.6—67.5
Length of tympanic bullae.	32.1 30.0—35.0	32.0 29.2—34.8	32.2 28.5—34.1	31.8 29.1—33.9	32.7 30.1—35.2
Width of auditory bullae . .	18.1 16.4—20.4	18.4 17.2—20.9	18.9 17.2—21.1	19.4 18.2—20.6	18.9 16.6—20.6
Length of upper tooth row .	29.4 28.2—31.7	28.2 26.8—29.0	28.5 27.0—29.2	27.7 24.8—29.7	28.2 26.2—29.9

The data presented in Table 7 show the proportional relationships between salient cranial features to be generally similar in the ermine subspecies studied. The divergence between extreme variants and the average is small and does not exted beyond the limits of individual variation. At the same time, the small skull dimensions in M. e. transbaicalica are readily seen.

Study of ermines from Transbaikalia, the Amur area, the Maritime Territory, and the Shantar Islands shows them to be systematically identical.

The systematic status of the ermine inhabiting Sakhalin and the Kurile Islands is as yet unclear. I had no material from these places.

Geographical distribution. Transbaikalia, Amur area, Maritime Territory, and Shantar Islands.

Material studied. Transbaikalia — 60 specimens; Amur area — 7 specimens; Maritime Territory — 3 specimens; Shantar Islands — 75 specimens. Total — 145 specimens, including 72 skulls with pelts.

Biology. The ermine inhabits a variety of landscapes, from the Arctic tundras to the southern alpine mountain zones. With respect to biotopical conditions it is extremely adaptable, and can be encountered in the most varied places, avoiding only true desert (and being relatively rare deep in the taiga).

According to V. M. Sdobnikov (1937), in the boreal tundras of Western Siberia it occupies woods and brush, chiefly along the shorelines of rivers and lakes. In the Gyda Peninsula tundra S. P. Naumov (1931) observed the animal to be commonest in winter in scrub or in the fissured slopes of the mainland, it being attracted thither by the abundance of rodents.

At the northern tip of the Taimyr (Chelyuskin Peninsula), according to G. L. Rutilevskii (1939), ermine tracks are in the snowy period most often encountered in ravined river valleys and near high, fissured coastal precipices. In the snowless part of the year the ermine concentrates in shaly stretches.

In the Lena-Khatanga territory, according to A. A. Romanov (1941), it inhabits river valleys and lacustrine depressions in the lowland tundra. The ermine is commonest here along river terraces, particularly on terrace edges and along main slopes with crumbled earth clumps. On watersheds in the lowland tundra the animal is occasionally encountered in summer but is absent in winter, occurring only during its journeys from one river valley to another.

In the Lena River delta and along the shore of the Laptev Sea, Romanov usually encountered the ermine in driftwood heaps and on precipitous shores of islands with earthy hillocks remaining after deglaciation.

These tundra biotopes are characterized by an abundance of murids, which the ermine readily catches in winter in coastal fissures, within hollows in piles of turf, and in driftwood heaps.

The ermine's winter absence from watersheds, gentle slopes, and flat depressions in the tundra Romanov explains as being due to the great snow density making it difficult to catch lemming. In the nomads' winter camping area, along the northern boundary of the forest, in localities with very dense snow accumulations, he [Romanov] observed ermine tracks on reindeer pastures. The hollows which the deer make in the snow make it easier for the ermines to catch the murids living under the snow.

In the forest belt near the tundra the ermine is commonest along river and stream valleys and on sloping lakeshores overgrown with willow and dwarf birch. It is also not rare in larch stands having a dense understory of willow and dwarf birch, particularly if these are greatly obstructed by brushwood. In areas poor in understory the ermine is rare. It is encountered in large numbers on regenerating burns.

In mountain areas of the forest zone ermines are particularly numerous in the subalpine belt, in alder thickets, and on rock streams. In mountain areas above the timberline the commonest ermine habitats are river-valley slopes, cliffs, and steep riverbanks.

In the woods near the tundra the ermine hunts, in addition to voles and lemmings, the many pikas which there abound.

In the Anadyr territory, according to L. A. Portenko (1941), the ermine keeps throughout the year chiefly to river valleys and lake shores. It is particularly attracted to bare river- and stream-banks where various snags, fissures, and soil irregularities provide many cozy hiding places. In mid-November 1931, when the snow was not very thick near Markovo and one could walk without skis, ermines frequented the heaps of driftwood brought to the shingle-covered sandbars where pikas occurred. "In mid-winter, it could be concluded from their tracks that ermine were roaming widely throughout the scrub, particularly in the alder and the clumps of poplar and Korean willow, but were definitely avoiding the open stretches of tundra" (Portenko, 1941). Numerous ermine were encountered in the Japanese stone pine forest on Modinskaya Sopka. The animals occurred in Markovo itself, and in other inhabited places.

The biotopes are particularly varied in the taiga belt. In the Arctic Urals and the adjacent areas of Northwest Siberia the ermine keeps to bankside thickets (Flerov, 1933). In the Surgut territory, according to the observations of I.D. Kiris (1934), it lives both in island Siberian stone pine stands in the Ob River valley and in the mainland taiga (Figure 107). In the Siberian stone pine stands on islands it lives mainly in glades full of fallen trees and in alluvial forests. When searching for food it may also go deep into the islands. In mainland Siberian stone pine forests it keeps mainly to those glades which are near the "sor" [the underwater portion of a partly submerged valley], where the water vole abounds. It is much rarer in other types of taiga.

In the basin of the Demyanka River, according to I.I. Barabash-Nikiforov (1937), it is commonest in streamside scrub, about burns, and in general in places abounding in Muridae, particularly the water vole.

In the northern part of the Tomsk Region, according to I.P. Laptev (1953), it usually keeps to the open parts of floodplains covered with scrub thickets, or to the high grass, but may occasionally inhabit the woods.

In the Narym taiga, according to my observations, the ermine lives in various types of forest, manifesting a rather high level of ecological variety; at the same time it prefers cluttered places, independent of forest type. It particularly likes localities abounding in windbroken branches, stumps, and uprooted trees and in brushwood and assorted debris as well, provided these localities are densely inhabited by the rodents, ground-dwelling birds, and other small animals which form the ermine's prey. The floodplain areas of rivers and streams provide habitats for the animal in thickets of willow and other shrubs. In similar biotopic conditions ermine also occur in the southern periphery of the taiga in the Omsk, Novosibirsk and Kemerovo regions.

In the valley of the Lower Tunguska, according to observations of N.S. Naumov (1934), the ermine inhabits various biotopes, but most often river- and stream-banks, the edges of patches of wooded tundra, and small streams, i.e., localities where large thickets of scrub are common or which have rock streams abounding in pikas. Its numbers generally increase towards the north in the forest tundra belt. It is rarer in dense and uniform taiga.

In Kamchatka, according to Yu. V. Averin (1948), the ermine inhabits the entire forest belt, being most abundant in the floodplains of the river valleys and rarer in the sparse scrub bordering the plateau. It occurs at altitudes of about 1,300 m, but does not go out onto the treeless heights.

On the Altai, according to Yurgenson (1938), the ermines in the area of Lake Teletskoe avoid the dark coniferous forest taiga, keeping to the river floodplains and to some extent to the terraces above the floodplains. In the wooded taiga zone the ermine's habitat is associated with the distribution of the water vole. The ermine most often inhabits lacustrine terraces which are more or less occupied by hay meadows and agricultural crops, as well as areas fringing the mouths of small rivers emptying into Lake Teletskoe, where the various Muridae serving as food for the ermine abound. High numbers of ermine are also observed in the alpine tundra belt above the timberline and in the developed alpine landscape, where it gravitates to the large rock streams with their plentiful pikas (Ochotona alpina).

In the Minusinsk taiga, according to observations of L. and I. Kozhanchikov (1924), the ermine, like the Siberian weasel, inhabits the entire taiga. But in contrast to the Siberian weasel, which prefers lowlands, the ermine population increases with height, and the animal is common in the alpine zone where pika (locally called "shadak") abound.

In the mountain taiga zone of the Irkutsk Region, according to I. P. Kopylov (1948), the ermine inhabits valleys, mountains, and clearings in the lower and middle mountain belts, as well as rock streams on the boundaries of Siberian and Japanese stone pines and the high mountain tundra (Figure 108).

FIGURE 107. Floodplain thickets of willow in the valley of the Ob River near the village of Yoronovo. Ermine biotope. Photo by B.S. Yudin

In the southwestern part of Transbaikalia, "the ermine likes to live far from human habitation, chiefly in stony stretches and cliffs" (Cherkasov, 1867). In the taiga of the Yablonovyi Range, the ermine also "usually lives on rock streams and in the alpine tundra belt above the timberline, where feeds on pikas and Siberian chipmunks" (Kuznetsov, 1929).

In the forest steppe zone of Siberia, ermine biotopes are associated with birch groves, ravines with overgrown slopes, reed thickets along shores of lakes and marshes, river floodlands with willows and other osiers, copses among ploughlands, and human habitations.

In the Kirensk polecat sanctuary near the city of Barnaul, according to observations of G. A. Velizhanin (1931), the ermine is commonest on meadows sited either in large birch groves, in ravines, or in marshes, being on the open steppe. Its burrows here lie on high crests (Figure 109).

FIGURE 108. Mountain tundra. The Idarskoe Belogor'e in the Eastern Sayan. Ermine biotope. Photo by K. T. Yurlov

"The ermine is quite frequently encountered in old buildings, inhabiting not just isolated scattered farmsteads and huts but often large villages or even cities" (Zverev, 1931).

The ermine is generally a sedentary animal. Small-scale movements from one type of biotope to another are more or less regular, being associated with seasonal changes in the biotopic habitats of the rodents which serve as its food. Mass migrations are also known and will be discussed later.

The animal makes its nest in clefts in stones, in fissures in cliffs and on the ground, in hollows among and under the roots of trees, in tussocks, in old haystacks and straw, in ricks and in the burrows of other animals as well. The nest chamber is lined with soft, dry grass, with moss, and with feathers and the fur of small animals. The animal also makes use of concealed places for temporary shelter.

Ermine tracks resemble those of the Siberian weasel, but are distinguished by being markedly smaller and somewhat more closely spaced.

The length of the ermine's leap is about 30—50 cm, and in extreme cases as much as 82 cm, but even this is not the limit since on compact snow the ermine may leap 150 cm or more (Nasimovich, 1948). The pawprints often lie in pairs. Ermine tracks run over the snow in an intricate and tangled line with numerous loops, and are often interrupted, because in pursuit, the animal plunges into the snow and pushes along under it for a certain distance.

FIGURE 109. Islands in the Irtysh River near the village of Pyatoryzhskoe. Ermine biotope. Photo by K.t. Yurlov

According to M. D. Zverev (1931), "in soft snow (in the West Siberian forest steppe — S.S.) ermine tracks differ only slightly from those of the polecat. Among shrubs and reeds the ermine makes special trails in th loose snow which can be used for passage even after snowfall. When hunting rodents in deep snow it burrows through the snow like a polecat. These ermine 'burrows' differ from those of the polecat in that the animal usually emerges again to the surface of the snow not via the hole through which it entered but through a new hole made from below after it has traveled under the snow for sometimes several dozen meters."

The ermine is endowed with keen hearing, a good sense of smell, and extremely swift reactions. It can even hear—at distances of dozens of meters — the rustlings of small animals on the move, and can sense what is happening in burrows covered by a layer of soil or snow. The ermine attacks its prey immediately. It does not see badly, but has (along with other animals) the peculiarity of spotting, at considerable distances, any moving or even barely stirring object but of being unable to see any animal which stands (or lies) motionless.

The ermine's voice varies with the circumstances: on suddenly meeting a large carnivore, e.g., a dog, it hisses or sniffs, and sometimes the sounds emitted are reminiscent of a magpie's chirping. When frightened it may produce a shrill and loud squeaking.

The ermine's movements are notably agile and quick. Like its nearest relatives, it moves by leaping. It climbs trees well. If necessary it can also swim. Its lithe and slender body, narrow head, and very short limbs enable it to penetrate very narrow fissures and the burrows of relatively small animals. The burrows of small voles, mice, and shrews are however not always accessible to the ermine, and these animals it catches when they leave their nests and emerge to the surface.

It is courageous and resolute in attacking, and often attacks animals markedly larger in size, for instance adult hares and capercailzies. A case is known of an ermine's biting through the neck of a capercailzie. The terrified bird flew away with its enemy still attached, but finally fell exhausted. The ermine then finished it off very quickly. In a similar manner it attacks willow ptarmigans, black grouse, and hazel hens.

The ermine is a nocturnal animal but may be active during the day as well, particularly in summer. Being an extremely cautious animal, it is very rarely seen by humans. During snowy periods its activity is mainly indicated by the tracks it leaves on the snow. In searching for food the animal scrutinizes every place where a living thing could be encountered. It will crawl into any burrows it has found, under snow, logs, and fallen branches, into cliff overhangs, etc. A. A. Nasimovich (1948) has reported the following observations of V. I. Osmolovskaya on ermine which were out hunting lemmings in the Yamal tundra. The animal searches the locality "shuttlewise" and kills the lemmings in the clumps of moss. A. A. Romanov (1941) spent two hours watching an ermine catch mice in a rock stream in the Lena-Khatanga territory. During these two hours the ermine searched the rock streams within an area of $80-100 \, m^2$. Romanov writes: "The ermine searches in a nervous and irregular way, scrutinizing the same locality several times and often sitting down on stones and looking around."

Acccording to Yu. V. Averin (1948), in Kamchatka the ermine hunts for hours in winter under the snow and in hollows under barren shale and large stones. Thus its trails, particularly when the snow cover is deep, are rather rare on the daytime surface and often extend under the snow. The ermine marches as much as $10-15 \, km$ a night, and occasionally even more.

The animal feeds on various small animals, eating plants only in rare cases and in extremely low quantities.

A clear picture of the composition of the ermine's diet in the West Siberian forest steppe has been gained from the mass dissections and content analyses carried out by Yu. N. Klimov (1940) on the stomachs and intestines of 1,600 ermines. The material was collected in the winters of 1928 and 1929 in a number of districts in the Omsk and Novosibirsk regions and in the former Slavgorod and Biisk subdistricts of the Altai territory. The food composition (in percentages) turned out to be: mammals — 97.2%; birds — 1.3%; birds' eggs — 1.1%; insects and other components — 0.4%.

Thus, mammals are the staple food of the ermine, the percentage of other animals being insignificant. The species make-up of the mammal aggregation devoured by the ermine depends on the relative proportions of the various small species in the fauna at the given time, but the ermine relies mainly on mammals. The food composition thus changes seasonally and biotopically.

19. Mustela (s. str.)nivalis Linnaeus (1766).
Weasel   (Figure 110, Map XV)

1766. Mustela nivalis. Linnaeus, C. Systema Naturae, XII ed., p. 69; Adlerberg, G. P. Khishchnye zveri (Carnivora Fissipedia) Arktiki (Carnivores (Carnivora, Fissipedia) of the Arctic).— In: Zveri Arktiki, pod redaktsiei Prof. N. A. Smirnova, pp. 377—383, Leningrad, Izdatel'stvo Glavsev morputi. 1935; Ellerman, J. R. and T. C. S. Morrison-Scott. Checklist of Palaearctic and Indian Mammals, pp. 256—259, London. 1951.

1777. Mustela vulgaris. Erxleben. Systema Regni Animal., 1, p. 471 (vicinity of Leipzig); Simashko, Yu. Russkaya fauna (Russian Fauna).— Mlekopitayushchie, 2, p. 372. 1851.

1800. Mustela boccamala. Bechstein. Pennant, Uebers. vierf. Thiere, 2, p. 395. (Sardinia).

1811. Mustela gale. Pallas, P. S. Zoographia Rosso-Asiatica, 1, p. 94 (instead of vulgaris).

1820. Mustela minor. Nilsson, S. Skandinavisk Fauna, 1, p. 35. (instead of nivalis).

1833. Mustela subpalmata. Hemprich et Ehrenberg.— Symb. Phys. Mamm., 3, 2 (Cairo, Egypt).

1853. Putorius minutus. Pomel, A. Catal. Meth. et Descript. Vertebr. Foss. Loire, p. 51. (Near Paris, France).

1855. Putorius numidicus. Pucheran.— Rev. Mag. Zool., 7, p. 393 (Tangiers, Morocco, Africa).

1869. Foetorius pusillus. Fatio. Faune Vertebr. Suisse, 1, p. 332 (nec De Kay. 1842).

1873. Mustelina gale. Bogdanov, M. N. Okhotnich'i i promyslovye zveri i ptitsy Evropeiskoi Rossii i Kavkazskogo kraya (Game and Hunting Animals and Birds of European Russia and Caucasian Territory).— Zhurnal Okhoty i Konnozavodstva, Nos. 11—12, p. 283.

1877. Mustela stoliczkana. Blanford, W. T.— Journ. Asiat. Soc. Bengal, 46, 2, p. 260 (Dzharkent, Chinese Turkestan); Blanford, W. T. Scient. Results of the Second Lark Mission, Mammalia, pp. 30—31. 1879.

1889. Putorius stoliczkanus. Radde, G. and A. Walter.— Wissensch. Ergebn. der in Transkasp. ausg. Expedition, 1, p. 31; Satunin, K. A. Obzor mlekopitayushchikh Zakaspiiskoi oblasti (Survey of Mammals of the Transcaspian Region), p. 19. 1905.

1899. Mustela nikolskii. Semenov, A. P. Neskol'ko soobrazhenii o proshlom fauny i flory Kryma (Some Thoughts about the Past of the Fauna and Flora of Crimea).— Zapiski Imperatorskoi Akademii Nauk, Ser. 8, Vol. 8, No. 6, p. 14 (vicinity of Simferopol).

1901. Mustela (Ictis) dombrowskii. Matschie. Sitzungsb. der Gesellsch. d. Naturforsch. Freunde z. Berlin, pp. 231—232 (Rumania).

1903. Putorius (Arctogale) pygmaeus. Allen, J. Report on
the Mammals.— Bull. Amer. Mus. Nat. Hist., 19, pp. 176—178 (Gizhiga).

1910. Arctogale nivalis. Ognev, S. I. and S. N. Gorbachev.
Mlekopitayushchie yugo-vostoka Orlovskoi gubernii (Mammals of the
Southeastern Part of Orel Province), p. 39.

1911. Mustela russeliana. Thomas, O.— Abstr. Proc. Zool. Soc.,
London, p. 4 (Szechwan, China).

1911. Ictis nivalis. Satunin, K. A. K sistematike semeistva
Mustelidae (On the Systematics of Family Mustelidae).— Izvestiya
Kavkazskogo Muzeya, 5, p. 17.

1926. Mustela punctata. Domaniewski J.— Neue Säugetiere aus Nord-
asien.— Ann. Zool. Mus. Polon. Hist. Nat., 5, pp.55—56 (Darasun, East Transbaikalia).

1937. Mustela trettaui. Kleinschmidt.— Falco, 33, 2. (Germany).

1944. Mustela (Mustela) nivalis. Bobrinskii, N. A. III. Otryad
khishchnye Ordo Carnivora (Order Carnivora (Ordo Carnivora)).— In:
Opredelitel' mlekopitayushchikh SSSR, edited by prof. N. A. Bobrinskii,
p. 130, Moskva; Novikov, G. A. Khishchnye mlekopitayushchie fauny SSSR
(Carnivorous Mammals of the Fauna of the USSR). p. 134. Moskva-
Leningrad, Izdatel'stvo AN SSSR. 1956.

Type and type locality. Vesterbotten Province, Sweden.

Diagnosis. Tail color matches back color right to tip of tail
being brown in summer and white in winter. Length of tail less than
half length of body with head. Posterior part of bony palate narrower than or
same size as distance between tympanic bullae. Os penis has distal
hooklike bend.

Measurements. Length of body with head (from 110 males and 85
females): males 130—260 mm, females 114— 204 mm; length of tail:
males 20—78 mm, females 17—60 mm; length of hind paw: males
20—36 mm, females 17—33 mm; length of ear: males 10.0—16.0 mm;
females 8.8—12.8 mm. Weight: males 62 —250 g, females 40—117 g.

FIGURE 110. The weasel Mustela nivalis L. (original)

Skull measurements (from 75 males and 55 females). Condylobasal length: males 31.7—47.2 mm, females 29.5—36.7 mm; zygomatic width: males 15.1—25.7 mm, females 14.2—19.2 mm; interorbital width: males 6.4—9.7 mm, females 5.5—7.8 mm; mastoid width: males 14.1—21.1 mm, females 13.0—18.9 mm; maximum width of infraorbital foramina: males 1.6—3.2 mm, females 1.5—2.2 mm; length of upper tooth row: males 8.2—12.5 mm, females 7.8—11.8 mm.

Description. In general build and fur color similar to the ermine, differing in extremely small size and in having a shorter tail, the latter completely uniform in color.

The fur as in the ermine, is subject to pronounced seasonal variation, except in the southern areas, where it does not whiten completely. Summer fur is dark brown with a chocolate tinge. On the flanks this color contrasts sharply with the pure white color of the underparts. Individuals are occasionally encountered with irregularly scattered, small dark brown patches of various sizes and outlines on the underparts. The tail color is similar to that of the back. In extreme cases (in aberrant individuals) the very tip may bear a small admixture of black or white hair. The summer fur on the back gets to be as long as 10 mm, the winter fur, 15—16 mm (Figure 110).

The os penis is distinctly differentiated from that of the ermine (Figure 11), being very similar in form to that of the Siberian weasel and differing only in its small size. The bone is not sigmoidally recurved as in the ermine, its tip having a hooklike bend as in the Siberian weasel. The length of the os penis is 13.0—19.5 mm.

The skull (Figure 112) of the weasel is similar in general configuration to that of the ermine, but is smaller. It is really an ermine skull in miniature but more slender, with thinner bones and several specific structural features. The most stable of these are the narrowness of the posterior part of the bony palate, the mesopterygoid fossa, and the size of the infraorbital foramina. The width of the bony palate at the level of the choanal incisure is approximately equal to the distance between the tympanic bullae. The mesopterygoid fossa is correspondingly narrower than in the ermine. The infraorbital foramina are relatively small, the width of each being approximately as great as that of the alveolus of the upper canine.

The view of some authors (Adlerberg, 1935; Kuznetsov, 1944; Novikov, 1956) that the facial section is broader in the weasel than in the ermine is erroneous. Out of several dozen weasel skulls examined, only one exhibited a rostrum width above the canine which was as large as the interorbital distance (specimen No.1811 in the Stroganov collection, female, 3 March 1950. the Vakhsh Valley, Tadzhikistan). In all the other skulls the rostrum width was, as in the ermine, less than the interorbital distance.

Sexual dimorphism is clearly manifested. The female skull is smaller and weaker than the male, the crests, particularly the sagittal and the occipital, being less conspicuous and the general outlines of the skull being smoother.

Craniological variation with age is manifested in the weasel to the same degree and develops in the same sequence as in the ermine. The skull of a young weasel — of a juvenile with milk dentition — is characterized by disproportion of the parts, by unfused sutures, and by the absence of crests, except for the occipital, which is rudimentary. The postorbital processes are rudimentary. The facial section is extremely short and compressed, while the cranial section is on the contrary extremely long and wide. The distance from the anterior side of the premaxillary bone to the level of the postorbital processes is some 20—30% of the distance from the same point to the upper edge of the foramen magnum (in adults this index is 45—55%). The rostrum and the interorbital area have attained ratio characteristic of adults.

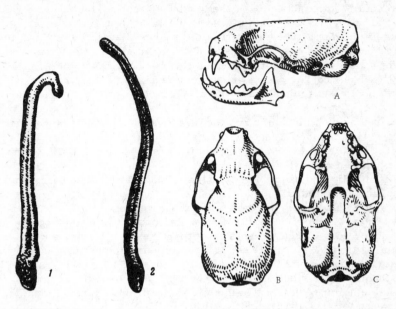

FIGURE 111. Os penis of true weasels and ermines:

1 — The weasel, Mustela nivalis L.; 2 — the ermine, Mustela erminea L. (after S. U. Stroganov, 1949).

FIGURE 112. Skull of the weasel, Mustela nivalis L. (original):

A — lateral view; B — dorsal view; C — ventral view.

In the subadult stage, with the final dentition, the skull is characterized by a pronounced expansion of the braincase, with sutures remaining only in the rostral part between the frontal maxillary and nasal bones and between the premaxillary, maxillary, and nasal bones. The occipital crests are extremely small; the mastoid process is already present, the zygomatic arches extremely weak and narrowly spread, and the postorbital processes are small.

Systematic notes. Geographical variation in the weasel takes the form of variations in the size and proportions of individual body parts and in craniometric details, as well as of differences in color and in the nature of seasonal color variations. These variations show a certain regularity, the weasels being smaller towards the north, having shorter tails and keeping the white winter fur for longer periods, while towards the south they are larger and manifest a tendency to preserve the fur's brown color throughout the year.

The weasels of the northern part of Eastern Europe and the Western Siberian lowland (except for the tundra zone) are characterized by rather small size, by relatively short tails (these being only somewhat longer than the hind paw), and by a generally darker summer coat. The length of the planta is some 63—95% of the length of the tail. In extreme cases the planta may be as long as the tail or even a bit longer.

Weasels inhabiting the tundra part of Siberia, Eastern Siberia to the south of the Transbaikalia steppes, and the area around the Amur are somewhat smaller in size, the tail being very short, shorter than the planta (the length of the planta being some 105—140% the length of the tail) and have a denser and softer coat. The color of the summer fur is paler.

The area around the Amur and the Maritime Territory is inhabited by a small, darkly colored weasel with a tail somewhat longer than in the East Siberian form (the length of the tail being greater than the length of the planta).

Transbaikalia and eastern and central Mongolia are inhabited by an as yet insufficiently studied, moderate-sized and generally light-colored weasel which belongs among the short-tailed weasels.

The second group of M. nivalis forms consists of very large, light-colored, long-tailed weasels inhabiting Western Europe and the southern parts of Asia. Here the tail is almost twice as long as the planta, the latter being no more than 55—60% the length of the tail (Figure 113).

Geographical distribution. The weasel's range broadly coincides with that of the ermine, and takes in the whole of Europe, North Africa, Asia (except for the south), and North America.

The Soviet Union lies almost completely within the range of the weasel, it being absent only on some islands and in the depths of the Central Asian deserts.

In Siberia it ranges all over the mainland and on some adjacent islands (Dickson, Begichev, Lyakhov, and Sakhalin) as well (Map XV).

The following details are available on weasel distribution in Siberia.

In Western Siberia it is numerous everywhere except in the northern areas of the tundra and the steppe zones, where it is rare.

On the Yamal it was found by B. M. Zhitkov (1913) near Lake Nei-To on the Se-Yakh River, at about 70°N lat. T. N. Dunaeva and V. V. Kucheruk (1941) discovered weasel remains in droppings of the long-tailed skua on the Khe-Yakh River.

In the northern part of the Transurals it occurs everywhere on the Lyapin and the Syn, according to K. K. Flerov (1933), but not frequently. Flerov also obtained the animal on the lower reaches of the Ob River near Muzhi village (coll. Zool. Inst. Acad. Sciences USSR).

It has been obtained near the mouth of the Taz River on the Gyda Peninsula, and on the middle reaches of the Yuribei River, at about 70°47'N lat. (Naumov, 1931).

It is widespread south of the above-mentioned localities, but concrete data about its occurrence there are scanty.

FIGURE 113. The weasel Mustela nivalis L. Northwestern Altai. Photo by B.S. Yudin

It was obtained by V. N. Skalon and V. V. Raevskii (coll. Zool. Mus. Moscow University) within the Sosva reserve on the divide between the Malaya Sosva and the Konda.

S. M. Chugunov (1915) reported the weasel in the former Surgut County. Two specimens were obtained within the city of Surgut.

According to data collected by F. D. Shaposhnikov (personal communication), the weasel is caught in the Khanty-Mansiisk National District, as well as in the following districts of the Tyumen Region: Uvat, Tobolsk, Vagai, Tyumen, Yalutorovsk, Novo-Zaimska, Uporovo, Golyshmanovo and Maslyanskoe. V. I. Telegin collected it on the Demyanka River.

In the Tomsk Region, according to my data, it is common in all areas. According to V. P. Anikin (1902), it is encountered rather frequently in the Narym Territory. I encountered the animal in the Verkhne-Ketsk, Kolpashevo, Asino and Tomsk districts and within Tomsk city itself. Yudin has obtained the weasel in the Kozhevnikovo area.

It is widely distributed in the Kurgan, Omsk and Novosibirsk regions, where it is particularly abundant in the forest steppe zone. Around Novosibirsk the animal has been collected by V. V. Nikolaev, by Telegin, and by Yudin. Our collection contains a specimen taken in December 1959 in the city of Novosibirsk.

In the Altai Territory, according to V. N. Savinov (1953), it occurs ubiquitously. According to G. N. Likhachev (1930), it is encountered in the upper Ob pine forest. It was collected there by Yudin in 1953 near the

295

village of Borovlyanka in the Troitskoe area. It was also encountered in the Biisk and Solton districts.

In the former Zmeinogorsk County the weasel was collected in 1913 by an amateur zoologist, the precentor A.I. Lavrov (coll. Zool. Inst. Acad. Sciences USSR).

On the Altai it is encountered everywhere and was long ago reported as being common by J. Gebler, N.F. Kashchenko, and A.M. Nikol'skii, among others. Weasel collections are available from the Gornaya Shoriya, the valley of Lake Teletskoe, and the Chulyshman alpine plateau (coll. Zool. Mus. Moscow University).

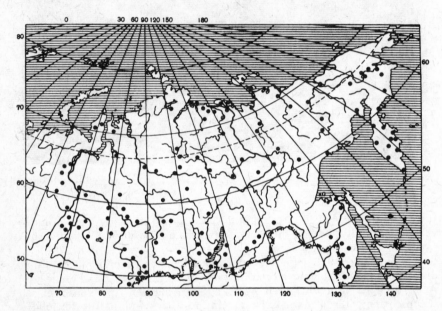

MAP XV. Geographical distribution of the weasel, Mustela nivalis L. in Siberia

Kashchenko (1889, 1902) reported encountering the weasel in Cherga and on the Komurl River. A.P. Razorenova (1939) obtained it near the village of Khankhara.

In the Ust-Koksa area, according to A.A. Nasimovich (1949), the weasel is obtained in large numbers. The animal is encountered on the southeastern Altai, where A.M. Kolosov (1939) informs us that it figures in the fur trade at Kosh-Agach. Kolosov obtained the weasel in the vicinity of the village of Artybash.

In the former Altai reserve it is, according to Yurgenson (1938), widespread. This author observed the animal and its trails on the banks of the Chechenek River and in the floodplain of the Okporok River. In Khakasiya the animal is common and in some places very abundant.

In the Western Sayan, according to Yanushevich and Yurlov (1949), the weasel is common in all landscape zones except for the steppe areas of the Minusinsk basin, where it is rare.

In the Tuva ASSR Yanushevich (1952) reports the weasel as being considerably more rare than the ermine.

Data on the weasel in the Irkutsk Region are provided by M. P. Kopylov, A. V. Dobrovol'skii and I. A. Shergin (1940), according to whom the animal is most frequently encountered on the upper reaches of the Lower Tunguska and in the areas around the Angara and the Sayan, and more rarely in the valleys of the Lena and Vitim. The animal was collected in the vicinity of Irkutsk by V. Ch. Dorogostaiskii (coll. Zool. Inst. Acad. Sciences USSR). According to A. A. Pogudin (1930), it abounds in the former Kirensk District.

The weasel's range encompasses the entire Yenisei River valley. N. P. Naumov (1934) reported that the animal is rare in the valley of the Lower Tunguska; this author observed and obtained the animal at the mouth of the Vivi River, and also reports on specimens collected on the Lower Yenisei in the vicinity of the villages Tolstyi Nos and Yakuta. According to S. M. Tolstov (1916), it is very common in the area of Lake Essei. The Zoological Institute of the Academy of Sciences of the USSR has a specimen taken by Tolstov near the Avash post on the lower Yenisei.

The weasel is extremely rare on the Taimyr. Middendorf supposed that the northern boundary of its range runs south of that of the ermine. This is, however, not confirmed by recent data. Cases are known where the weasel has been obtained in the northernmost part of the ermine's range, right up to the Soviet Arctic coast and on the islands beyond. For example, Heptner (1936) reports a weasel catch on Dickson Island and thinks that the animal, although extremely rare, should probably be considered part of the local fauna.

On the interfluve between the lower reaches of the Khatanga and of the Lena, according to A. A. Romanov (1941), the weasel's range, like that of the ermine, extends northwards to the shore of the Laptev Sea, including the islands of the Lena Delta, the mouth of the Olenek, and the Salkai and Begichev islands. Romanov collected the weasel on the Sobo-Sige Islands in the delta of the Lena (72°N lat.), near Lake Ebelyakh (72°N lat.), near Lake Ulakhan-Sistyakh, and on the upper reaches of the Kumakh-Yurvakh, a left tributary of the Khangalas-Yuel (72°N lat.). Komanov saw signs of weasel on all his routes along the northern timberline and through the forest tundra zone. The weasel is encountered here more rarely than the ermine, there being an average of 8 — 10 ermine prints for every weasel print.

I. I. Kolyushev (1936) mentions takes of weasel pelts along the lower Lena and Olenek.

The Zoological Institute contains weasel collections from Bol'shoi Lyakhov Island (A. N. Smesov) and from the Yana River, where the following have collected it: S. A. Buturlin (near Ust-Yansk), E. V. Toll' (near the village of Kazach'e), and A. Bunge (near Verkhoyansk).

It is encountered on the lower reaches of the Indigirka (N. M. Mikhel', 1938). Buturlin has collected it on the Kolyma and also on Cape Enraukun in the area of Krestovskaya, near the Nizhne-Kolymsk in the vicinity of Timkin, at the site Olbut, on the Antoshkina River, and in the vicinity of Sredne-Kolymsk (coll. Zool. Inst. Acad. Sciences USSR).

South of the above-mentioned localities, the weasel is reported for the rest of Yakutia between the valleys of the Anabar and the Lower Kolyma. Maak (1886) mentioned a weasel caught by him on the Olenek River (about 68°N lat.) and reports that it occurs rather often along the entire Vilyui. The Zoological Institute of the Academy of Sciences of the USSR contains a weasel specimen collected by A. F. Middendorf in 1844 near Yakutsk. According to A. I. Ivanov, it occurs everywhere within Yakutia and is most abundant on the Vilyui and in the central areas of the republic (Tugarinov, Smirnov and Ivanov, 1934). According to V. I. Belyk (1953), the weasel, like the ermine, reaches the Arctic shore but is obtained in relatively large quantities [only] in the southern agricultural areas of Yakutia.

In the Anadyr territory, according to L. A. Portenko (1941), the weasel is "a rare, perhaps even very rare, species in various localities" of the territory. N. P. Sokol'nikov (1927) obtained four specimens near Markovo village, where traces of the animal were observed twice in February 1932 by Portenko. According to a survey conducted by L. O. Belopol'skii, weasels are extremely rare near the post Snezhnaya on the Anadyr (above Ust'-Belaya) and on the Maine. Yudin and Telegin collected a series of weasels in 1958 in the vicinity of the Anadyr, where they were abundant.

In the Olyutor Koryak country, according to A. V. Samorodov (1939), the weasel is rare. The annual fur take from the territory of the Apuka River valley contains only 2 — 4 pelts.

On Kamchatka it was noted back in the days of Krasheninnikov, the weasels being, according to this author "caught by nobody, except by chance... The weasels live in granaries and extermine mice like cats." Yu. V. Averin (1948) reports that weasels are caught every year (12 — 15 pelts) in all areas of Kamchatka except for the Bystrinsk District in the mountains. Within the Kronoki reserve the weasel is an extremely rare species. This author encountered traces of the animal at the following localities in the reserve: the Malaya Chazhma and Shumnaya valleys, the shore of Lake Kronotskoe, the lower reaches of the Listvennichnaya, the Severnaya gorge, near the sources of Kronotskaya River, Olga Bay, and the Krasheninnikovo caldera (at heights of 1,000 m above sea level). Averin obtained three weasel specimens at the following localities: the city of Petropavlovsk, the mouth of the Kronotskaya River, and the mouth of the Povorotnaya River.

I. A. Allen (1903) described the East Siberian or lesser weasel subspecies from a specimen obtained by N. Buxton near Kushka post in the area of Gizhiga. This animal is extremely rare.

A common species in Transbaikalia and in the southwestern part of the country, according to A. Cherkasov (1867), the weasel occurs more often than the ermine. P. S. Mikhno collected it in the area of Troitskosavsk, now Kyakhta, near the village Gudzhartui (coll. Zool. Inst. Acad. Sciences USSR). It was obtained on the Khamar-Daban by A. S. Fetisov.

On the upper Chita River, according to E. Pavlov (1948), it is probably not very rare and is most often encountered in river valleys and on meadows. A. B. Domanevskii (Domaniewski, 1926) studied a weasel specimen obtained near the city of Darasun in the Chita Region.

According to B. A. Kuznetsov (1929), it occurs throughout eastern Transbaikalia, but infrequently.

Traces of the weasel were observed by G. N. Gassovskii (1927) at the divide of the Aldan and Gilyui rivers, on the southern slopes of the Tukuringra Range, and along the Getkan River.

In the Khabarovsk Territory, according to V. P. Sysoev (1952), it ranges throughout.

In the Far East the weasel is in places encountered more often than the ermine. L. Schrenck obtained it in the area of the mouth of the Amur in 1858. N. N. Rukovskii sent for my examination a weasel specimen obtained in the Sikhote-Alin reserve (in the area of the Kamennyii spring on the Sunya River). According to N. T. Zolotarev (1936), the weasel occurs in the valley of the Iman more or less regularly. About three dozen weasel pelts turn up in each year's fur take. In the area of Lake Khanka the weasel was obtained by Maak (1861, at about 45°N lat.) and by A. I. Cherskii (on the western shore near Kamen'-Rybolov village; coll. Zool. Inst. Acad. Sciences USSR). It was encountered by Przheval'skii (1870) in the valley of Lake Khanka and on the Ussuri River.

To the south of the Khanka it has been obtained by A. A. Emel'yanov near the Chernigovka village (coll. Zool. Inst. Acad. Sciences USSR). In the valley of the lower reaches of the Tumangan it has been obtained by Cherskii (coll. S. I. Ognev).

In the Maritime Territory's Suputinska reserve the weasel occurs rarely, according to G. F. Bromlei and Z. I. Gutnikova (1955), but is common in neighboring areas near inhabited localities.

On Sakhalin it ranges throughout the island but is not abundant. It was reported in the southern part of Sakhalin by Kishida (1936). According to A. I. Gizenko (1954), the weasel is not abundant, but inhabits the territory all the way to the Schmidt Peninsula. Similar data were reported to me by N. A. Violovich (in litt.). The weasel is probably encountered on the Kurile Islands.

Survey of subspecies. The intraspecific taxonomic picture for M. niv a l i s is still far from complete. A large number of forms whose nature is as yet unclear have been described. Ellerman and Morrison-Scott (1951) report 15 subspecies for the Palaearctic and India. Nine subspecies, including two for Siberia, have been described for the Soviet Union. According to my data no less than three subspecies of the weasel occur in Siberia.

19a.   **Mustela (s. str.) nivalis nivalis** Linnaeus (1766).
Common weasel

1766. M u s t e l a n i v a l i s. Linnaeus, C. Systema Naturae, XII ed., p. 69.

1912. M u s t e l a n i v a l i s n i v a l i s. Miller, G. S. Catalogue of the Mammals of Western Europe, pp. 402—405, London; Ognev, S. I. Novye dannye po sistematike i geograficheskomu rasprostraneniyu nekotorykh vidov semeistva Mustelidae (New Data on the Systematic and Geographical Distribution of Some Species of Family Mustelidae).— Memuary Zoologicheskogo Otdela Obshchestva Lyubitelei Estestvoznaniya, Antropologii i Etnografii, No. 2, pp. 19—20, Moskva. 1928; Ognev, S. I. Zveri SSSR i prilezhashchikh stran (Animals of the USSR and Adjacent

Countries). Vol. 3, pp. 40—48, Moskva-Leningrad. 1935; Adlerberg, G. P. Khishchnye zveri (Carnivora Fissipedia) Arktiki (Carnivores of the Arctic).— In Zveri Arktiki, pod redaktsiei Prof. N. A. Smirnova, pp. 382—383, Leningrad, Izdatel'stvo Glavsevmorputi. 1935; Ellerman, J. R. and T. C. S. Morrison-Scott. Checklist of Palaearctic and Indian Mammals, p. 256, London. 1951.

Type and type locality. See above in description of species.

Diagnosis. A small (see measurements), relatively short-tailed, dark-colored weasel. Tail usually longer than hind paw. Summer fur of upper part of body dark brown, winter fur snow white.

Measurements. Length of body with head (from 60 males and 54 females): males 130—208 mm (av. 165 mm), females 114—167 mm, (av. 142 mm); length of tail: males 23—40 mm (av. 31 mm), females 18—35 mm (av. 28 mm); length of hind paw: males 20 — 27 mm (av. 23. 4 mm), females 17—24 mm (av. 20.0 mm); height of ear: males 9.3—14.0 mm (av. 12.4 mm), females 9.0—13.6 mm (av. 12.0 mm).

Skull measurements (from 32 males and 24 females). Condylobasal length: males 32.0—37.0 mm (av. 34.6 mm), females 30.0—34.7 mm (av. 31.7 mm); zygomatic width: males 14.9—19.2 mm (av. 17.4 mm), females 14.2—17.8 mm (av. 15.5 mm); interorbital width: males 6.4—8.8 mm (av. 7.2 mm), females 6.2—7.4 mm (av. 6.7 mm); maximum width of skull: males 13.8—17.5 mm (av. 15.4 mm), females 14.2—16.2 mm (av. 14.6 mm); width between infraorbital foramina: males 7.8—9.1 mm (av. 8.3 mm), females 6.5—7.3 mm (av. 6.8 mm); length of upper tooth row: males 7.8—10.0 mm (av. 9.0 mm), females 7.6—9.7 mm (av. 8.3 mm).

Systematic notes. M. n. nivalis is nearest to M. n. pygmaea. The two forms are similar in size, nature of coat, and seasonal variation of fur color. The radical difference between the forms consists in the ratio between tail and plantar lengths, the nominate subspecies having the tail longer than the planta while in pygmaea it is shorter. Series of M. n. nivalis sometimes contain individuals in which the tail and planta are equal in length, but these aberrant individuals occur extremely rarely (some 2—3% of the population) and are nothing more than a manifestation of individual variation.

M. n. nivalis differs from the southern weasel M. n. vulgaris Erxleben in its relatively small size and short tail. The following measurements characterize vulgaris. Length of body : males 200—220 mm, females 140—160 mm; length of tail: males 45—60 mm, females 40—44 mm; length of planta: males 26—32 mm, females 20—24 mm; condylobasal length of skull : males 36.3—40.0 mm.

Comparison of measurements of M. n. vulgaris with those of M. n. nivalis shows that they overlap to a certain degree, undersized individuals of M. n. vulgaris being smaller than large M. n. nivalis; but this overlap is insignificant. The differences between these subspecies are clearly manifested in series by average indices. Thus the average condylobasal length reaches 40.0 mm in M. n. vulgaris but only 34.6 mm in M. n. nivalis.

The systematic position of the weasels inhabiting the Altai, the Sayans, Tuva, and the mountains around Lake Baikal is still unclear. The collections contain only a few individuals from these localities, not enough for definite systematic conclusions. Judging by the few data available, the weasels from the various mountain areas of Southern Siberia display essential differences in structure and color of fur.

It is possible that the weasel in this part of the country is divided into a number of subtly differing forms, but additional material is needed to elucidate this.

Geographical distribution. The central and northern regions of the European USSR, and the West Siberian lowland (except for the tundra belt) eastwards probably to the Yenisei. Extends south to North Kazakhstan inclusively.

Material studied. European USSR — 46 specimens, West Siberian lowland — 72 specimens; mountains of South Siberia — 10 specimens; North Kazakhstan — 16 specimens. Total 114 [sic] specimens.

19b. Mustela (s. str.) nivalis pygmaea J. Allen (1903).
Siberian least weasel

1903. Putorius (Arctogale) pygmaeus. Allen, J. Report on the Mammals.— Bull. Amer. Mus. Nat. Hist., Vol. 19, pp. 176—178.

1913. Putorius vulgaris pygmaeus. Zhitkov, B. M. O kollektsii mlekopitayushchikh sobrannykh Kolymskoi ekspeditsiei (On the Mammals Collected by the Kolyma Expedition).— Dnevnik Zoologicheskogo Otdeleniya Obshchestva Lyubitelei Estestvoznaniya, Novaya Seriya, 1, No. 5, pp. 274—276.

1922. Ictis nivalis var. kamtschatica. Domaniewski, I.— Arch. Tow. Nauk., Vol. 1, p. 349, Lvov (nomen nudum).

1926. Arctogale nivalis pygmaea. Ognev, S. I. Mlekopitayushchie severo-vostochnoi Sibiri (Mammals of Northeastern Siberia). pp. 56—59, Vladivostok.

1928. Mustela nivalis pygmaea. Ognev, S. I. Novye dannye po sistematike i geograficheskomu rasprostraneniyu nekotorykh vidov semeistva Mustelidae (New Data on the Systematics and Geographical Distribution of Some Species of Family Mustelidae).— Memuary Zoologicheskogo Otdela Obshchestva Lyubitelei Estestvoznaniya, Antropologii i Etnografii, No. 2, p. 21, Moskva; Ognev, S. I. Zveri SSSR i prilezhashchikh stran (Animals of the USSR and Adjacent Countries). Vol. 3, pp. 56—58, Moskva-Leningrad. 1935; Adlerberg, G. P. Khishchnye zveri (Carnivora Fissipedia) Arktiki (Carnivores of the Arctic).— In: Zveri Arktiki pod redaktsiei Prof. N. A. Smirnova, p. 383, Leningrad, Izdatel'stvo Glavsevmorputi. 1935; Averin, Yu. V. Nazemnye pozvonochnye Vostochnoi Kamchatki (Terrestrial Vertebrates of East Kamchatka).— Trudy Kronetskogo Gosudarstvennogo Zapovednika, No. 1, pp. 144—145, Moskva. 1948; Ellerman, J. R. and T. C. S. Morrison-Scott. Checklist of Palaearctic and Indian Mammals, p. 258, London. 1951.

1933. Mustela rixosa pygmaea. Allen, G. M. The Least Weasel, a Circumpolar Species.— Journ. of Mammal., Vol. 14, No. 4, p. 19.

Type and type locality. No. 18322, of collection of the American Museum of Natural History, adult female, 2 October 1900, collected by N. G. Buxton.

Diagnosis. Extremely small and short-tailed weasel. Length of body: males 175 mm, females 145 mm (against respectively, 208 and 165 mm in

M. n. n i v a l i s); condylobasal length of skull: males 33.4 mm, females 32.6 mm (against 37.0 and 34.7 mm in M. n. n i v a l i s). Tail shorter than hind paw. Summer fur dorsally brownish with more or less marked dull russet tinges. Winter fur snow white.

Measurements. Length of body with head (from 23 males and 16 females): males 138 — 175 mm (av. 152 mm), females 124 — 145 mm (av. 136 mm); length of tail: males 16.2 — 23.0 mm (av. 18.8 mm), females 13.4 — 17.5 mm (av. 15.4 mm); length of hind paw: males 19.0 — 23.0 mm (av. 19.9 mm), females 17.0 — 21.0 mm (av. 18.6 mm); height of ear: males 9.0 — 12.0 mm (av. 9.6 mm), females 8.0 — 11.4 mm (av. 9.0 mm).

Size of skull (from 16 males and 10 females). Condylobasal length: males 31.0 — 34.4 mm (av. 32.8 mm), females 27.5 — 32.6 mm (av. 30.3 mm); zygomatic width: males 14.3 — 17.8 mm (av. 16.3 mm), females 14.0 — 17.0 mm (av. 15.7 mm); interorbital width: males 6.8 — 8.4 mm (av. 7.3 mm), females 6.0 — 7.0 mm (av. 6. 7 mm); maximum width: males 14.4 — 16.0 mm (av. 15.2 mm), females 14.0 — 15.0 mm (av. 14.3 mm); width between infraorbital foramina: males 8.2 — 9.2 mm (av. 8.7 mm), females 7.0 — 8.1 mm (av. 7.8 mm); length of upper tooth row: males 7.9 — 9.2 mm (av. 8.6 mm), females 7.8 — 8.6 mm (av. 8.3 mm).

Systematic notes. M. n. p y g m a e a is undoubtedly a valid subspecies characterized, as mentioned above, by small size, distinct shortness of tail, and relatively pale summer fur, the fur being dense and silky. The systematic relationships between M. n. p y g m a e a and M. n. n i v a l i s have been discussed above.

The systematic position of the weasel inhabiting the Transbaikalian steppes remains unclear. In color of summer fur the Transbaikalian weasel, admittedly studied from scanty material (only 5 pelts), seems to be light-haired. There are no measurements available for the body and skulls of these specimens.

A. B. Domanevskii (Domaniewskii, 1926) described, from a specimen from eastern Transbaikalia (area of Darasun), in his opinion a new species of weasel which he termed M u s t e l a p u n c t a t a. Now, the specimens on which this description is based were in molt, and had white patches on their shoulders. These features (not specific from the systematic point of view) were used by the author to diagnose his M. p u n c t a t a. It is clear that no scientific value can be attached to this p u n c t a t a; the author does not even mention the presence of any concrete deviating variant exceeding normal individual variation.

A. G. Bannikov described a subspecies M. n. k e r u l e n i c a for central and east Mongolia, from a specimen from the Kerulen River (vicinity of Undurkhan). In his extensive paper devoted to Mongolian mammals this author (1954) supposes that this form of weasel may inhabit eastern Transbaikalia. This has not been confirmed so far.

The Siberian least weasel is readily differentiated from the weasel inhabiting the Amur area and the Maritime Territory (M. n i v a l i s subsp.) by its paler and duller summer color and shortness of tail.

Geographical distribution. Embraces the tundra belt of Western and Eastern Siberia, including Kamchatka. The southeastern part of Baikalia and Western Transbaikalia, judging by material studied from the vicinity of Irkutsk, Troitskosavsk [now Kyakhta] and Barguzin reserve, are also inhabited by this subspecies of weasel.

The southern boundary of its range in the eastern Transbaikalia and Amur areas has so far not been established.

Material studied. Western Siberian tundra — 7 specimens; right bank of the Yenisei — 15 specimens; area of Lake Baikal — 7 specimens; Yakutia — 24 specimens; Chukchi Peninsula — 12 specimens; Kamchatka — 2 specimens; shore of Sea of Okhotsk—3 specimens. Total—70 specimens.

19c. **Mustela**(s. str.)**nivalis** subsp. Far Eastern weasel

Diagnosis. Distinguished from M. n. p y g m a e a by dark color of summer fur and longer tail.

Back is saturated dark gray brown. Winter fur is pure white. Tail is longer than hind paw.

Measurements. Length of body with head (from 7 males and 5 females): males 153 — 175 mm (av. 169 mm), females 140 — 160 mm (av. 152 mm); length of tail: males 29 — 37 mm (av. 34 mm), females 25 — 32 mm (av. 29 mm); length of hind paw: males 21 — 26 mm (av. 24 mm), females 20 — 23 mm (av. 22 mm); height of ear: males 10.7 — 12.0 mm (av. 11.3 mm), females 10.0 — 12.0 mm (av. 11.2 mm).

Skull measurements (from 7 males and 5 females). Condylobasal length: males 33.9 — 36.2 mm (av. 34.8 mm), females 31.0 — 33.6 mm (av. 32.7 mm); zygomatic width: males 16.7 — 18.2 mm (av. 17.7 mm), females 15.3 — 17.3 mm (av. 17.0 mm); interorbital width: males 6.8 — 7.6 mm (av. 7.3 mm), females 6.7 — 7.2 mm (av. 6.9 mm); maximum width: males 15.9 — 16.8 mm (av. 16.3 mm), females 14.7 — 16.3 mm (av. 16.0 mm); length of upper tooth row: males 8.8 — 11.0 mm (av. 9.2 mm), females 7.9 — 9.3 mm (av. 9.0 mm).

Systematic notes. The Far Eastern weasel is readily differentiated as a subspecies. Its differences from p y g m a e a are reported above in the diagnosis. It is readily differentiated from the Mongolian weasel M. n. k e r u l e n i c a by the darker color of the summer fur. In addition, the winter fur is white, while in M. N. k e r u l e n i c a, according to A. G. Bannikov (1954), the winter fur is as a rule only somewhat lighter than the summer fur.

As to the nomenclature of the Far Eastern weasel, this problem should remain open until its systematic relationships with the Korean weasel M. n. m o s a n e n s i s Mori (1927) are elucidated. We have so far no material from Korea, and the limited description of m o s a n e n s i s is not enough to solve the problem.

The Sakhalin weasel has been described as a subspecies under the name M. n. c a r a f t e n s i s Kishida (1936), but it is not known to me in nature.

Geographical distribution. Includes the Amur area and the Maritime Territory.

Material studied. Total of 12 specimens, collected at various points in the range.

Biology. The Far Eastern weasel lives in very varied biotopic conditions, inhabiting any place where small rodents, its staple food, are available. It is encountered in all landscapes from the boreal tundras to the southern deserts, and at altitudes ranging from the lowlands to the alpine zone.

In the tundra it occupies various kinds of tree and scrub vegetation, both along river valleys and on watersheds. It lives in thickets located along riverbanks, in lacustrine depressions, on hills. In mountain tundra it prefers river-valley slopes, cliffs, and steep riverbanks (Figure 114).

On the seashore of northern Siberia, according to A. N. Dubrovskii (1940), A. A. Romanov (1941), and others, weasel tracks are fairly often encountered amid the driftwood on steep, crumbling shores.

In the northern tundras it is nevertheless considerably rarer than the ermine. Thus, according to Romanov (1941), when pawprints were counted along routes in the Lena and Khantanga tundras, an average of 8 — 10 ermine prints occurred for each weasel print.

In the taiga zone it prefers sparsely vegetated areas abounding in Muridae and having plentiful half-decayed voles, uprooted trees and stumps, brushwood, and various plant debris. The weasel population density for any given biotope is directly proportional to the degree of clutter and the number of murids. The weasel also inhabits forest clearings (Figure 115), forest glades, forest borders, and the edges of marshes and other water bodies (Figure 116). It is more rare in dense vegetation with tall trees than in sparse forests. On the Lower Tunguska, where the weasel is generally rare, N. P. Naumov (1934) encountered its tracks most often on the edges of patches of forest tundra and near small bogs.

In the forest steppe zone the weasel prefers small insular groves of aspen or birch and shrub, ravines, tussocks, and meadows. In the steppe it inhabits river valleys, where it prefers localities occupied by curtains of scrub, reeds, or gullies overgrown with various vegetation.

In mountains the weasel lives in all zones up to and including the alpine belt.

All landscapes with cultivated soils are inhabited by the weasel — the fringes of fields, and gaps and islands of virgin land within ploughland where masses of murids concentrate (Figures 117, 118).

The weasel often inhabits buildings, not just solitary huts but also buildings in large villages and even in such cities as Novosibirsk. It often inhabits hedges, weedy patches, grassland, and also haystacks, woodpiles, field camps, dumps, livestock sheds, etc., being attracted by the large numbers of voles, mice and rats.

In the southwestern part of Transbaikalia, according to A. Cherkasov (1867), weasels "often live outside human habitations but mostly, like the Altai weasel, under the floors and in the cellars of old village buildings, store-houses, barns, and other agricultural places, where they fiercely attack and exterminate many mice." The weasel cannot and does not dig its own burrow, since its paws and claws are too weak and are unsuitable for this sort of work. For its abode and nest it occupies rodent burrows or hollows between tree roots, under tiles, among stones, in heaps of brushwood, lumber stacks, hay and straw stacks, low-lying hollows of trees, under buildings, etc. The nest is lined with dry grass.

FIGURE 114. Tundra in the Anadyr River valley. Weasel biotope. Photo by B.S. Yudin

FIGURE 115. Forest glades with birch copses in vicinity of Novosibirsk. Weasel biotope. Photo by B S. Yudin

FIGURE 116. An oxbow in the Alei River valley, northwest Altai. Weasel biotope. Photo by B. S. Yudin

FIGURE 117. Steppe near Lake Uchum in Uzhur District of Krasnoyarsk Territory. Weasel biotope. Photo by K. T. Yurlov

The weasel leads a sedentary life while nursing its young and also when a given biotope contains sufficient amounts of small rodents for food. Should the food sources deteriorate, it may move to another biotope. Within its individual range each weasel, like other mustelids, makes use of several burrows or other temporary abodes where it can hide at any moment from danger or bad weather, or just rest.

The tracks of a large weasel, according to A. N. Formozov (1936), are indistinguishable from those of a small ermine, the sole difference being length of the route. The weasel usually avoids traveling far, its trails usually appearing at one vole burrow and soon disappearing into another. The average length of a weasel leap is 20 — 25 cm, the maximum about 35 — 40 cm.

The weasel has well-developed senses — an excellent sense of smell and good hearing, but its sight is not very sharp.

The weasel moves quickly and tirelessly. It typically runs in jumps, this being a characteristic of all members of the weasel and ermine genus. It climbs well and is able to swim. When attacking prey it is as swift as lightning.

The weasel is extremely attentive to its surroundings and orients itself excellently in any situation, thus being able to live unnoticed in human habitations. It has an extremely curious nature. When encountering humans it tries to examine them by standing on its hind legs, often changing position in order to facilitate observation.

The weasel is generally a nocturnal animal, but in places where it is not bothered may often hunt by day as well. In localities where the weasel is persecuted it hunts by night, emerging during the day only in extreme cases and then very cautiously.

The weasel's diet is little different from that of the ermine. Its food consists chiefly of small rodents, mice, voles, hamsters, pikas, and other mammals, also of birds, insects, etc.

According to Yu. N. Klimov, who examined the contents of 88 weasel stomachs collected in February and March in the forest steppes of Western Siberia (in the former Omsk District), the following food percentages are observed: mammals — 78.6%, fish — 2.4%, and carrion — 19.0%.

The following mammals were found: water vole — 3.0%, other voles — 42.4%, striped field mouse — 21,2%, Dzhungarian hamster — 6.1%, mice of undetermined type — 3.0%, and undiagnosed small rodents — 24.3% (Zverev, 1931).

The contents of 8 weasel stomachs collected during winter in the steppe and forest steppe zones of Transbaikalia were found by A. S. Fetisov (1942) to contain feathers of passerine birds (12.5%), voles (62.5%), and common field mice (25%).

Whenever the possibility arises, the weasel will kill animals in markedly greater quantities than it can devour, being stimulated by a kind of hunting frenzy. It follows rodents relentlessly. Having a long, slender, snakelike body, a narrow head, and short limbs, the weasel can easily penetrate the narrow burrows of small rodents and catch the latter. In winter the weasel catches mice and voles, mostly under the snow, penetrating there through the passages made by the animals. When the catch is abundant it gnaws through the head of the prey, eating the brain only. It occasionally stores food.

FIGURE 118.   Valley of the Chuya River in the Altai.   Weasel biotope.   Photo by K.T. Yurlov

In the spring it may occasionally raid birds' nests and attack the young.
The literature reports that relatively large birds, for instance the black
grouse, are sometimes attacked by the weasel.   S. T. Aksakov (Zapiski
ruzheinogo okhotnika [Notes of a Gun Hunter], p. 395, 1857) was witness
to such an attack.   According to Cherkasov (1867), the weasel "attacks
black grouse and may often rise with the grouse into the air, killing it
high in the air and then falling with it to the ground... It may even
strangle hares, attacking them in their dens and in their snow burrows."
    The biology of weasel reproduction is as yet little known.   Rut,
according to some authors, occurs in March — April, but in the opinion
of others it is not associated with definite dates and extends over
extremely long periods, since young have been found from May to
January.   The gestation period is not known.   The brood size is 3 — 9,
most often 4 — 7.   In years of mass murid proliferation, when the
weasel is provided with abundant food, fertility increases.
    The weasel's enemies are the stronger carnivores, the large diurnal
birds of prey, and owls; but these all attack the weasel only rarely.   They
present a more serious danger to the weasel as competitors for food, and
in this respect all mammals and birds which feed chiefly on small rodents,
and primarily on mice and voles, are its enemy.   These are: the ermine,
buzzards, small owls, and a large number of other carnivorous animals.
    The diseases and parasites of the weasel are almost unknown.
In Westen Siberia weasels are often infested with the nematode

Skrjabingulus nasicola Leuckart (1842), which parasitizes the frontal sinuses.

Molt occurs twice a year, in spring and autumn. In Siberia this is accompanied by seasonal changes in the fur. In spring, when the snow is thawing, the winter fur is shed and the summer fur starts growing. In Western Siberia all weasels acquire their summer fur by the end of April. With the first autumn frosts the summer coat is gradually replaced by winter fur, and by the time the snow cover is permanent all weasels are white. In Western Siberia weasels in winter fur are usually encountered in late October and the first half of November.

Practical importance. The commercial importance of the weasel is insignificant, since its pelt is of slight value. In agricultural areas the weasel makes itself useful by exterminating obnoxious rodents, but in commercial game areas it is harmful since it limits the food resources of such valuable fur-bearing species as the ermine by its extermination of rodents. It is known that the ermine and the weasel cannot stand each other's competition, and that in localities where weasel numbers are high, ermine numbers are low, and vice versa.

2. Subgenus Kolonocus Satunin (1911).
Siberian weasels

1911. Kolonocus. Satunin, K. A. K sistematike semeistva Mustelidae (On the Systematics of Family Mustelidae). — Izvestiya Kavkazskogo Muzeya, 5, p. 23; Auct. cit. Opredelitel' mlekopitayushchikh Rossiiskoi imperii (Key to Mammals of the Russian Empire). p. 124, Tiflis. 1914; Ognev, S. I. Zveri Vostochnoi Evropy i Severnoi Azii (Animals of Eastern Europe and Northern Asia). 2, pp. 714— 715, Moskva-Leningrad. 1931.

Type species of the subgenus: Mustela sibirica Pallas (1773).
Diagnosis. Larger than weasels. Tail somewhat longer, being one third or one half length of body with head. General color more or less russet, uniform throughout body, or brown-yellow, gradually lightening below and becoming whitish or light sandy on underparts. Surroundings of mouth and chin covered by light field. Small white patches occasionally occur on neck and chest. Seasonal variation of fur color poorly marked and fur does not whiten for winter. Tympanic bullae lie longitudinally. Infraorbital foramina smaller than alveoli of upper canines.

Os penis has form similar to that of weasel, but larger; length of bone is 30—33 mm.

Three species in fauna of the Soviet Union, all occurring in Siberia.

Geographical distribution. North (Soviet), Central, Middle, and East Asia and the eastern areas of the European USSR, westwards to about Kirov and the valley of the lower Kama.

20. **Mustela (Kolonocus) sibirica** Pallas (1773).
Siberian weasel

1773. Mustela sibirica. Pallas, P. S. Reise durch verschiedene Provinzen des Russischen Reiches, 2, p. 701; Auct. cit. Specilegia

Zoologica, Fasc. 14, Vol. 2, pp. 86—94, Berolini. 1780; Adlerberg, G. P. Khishchnye zveri (Carnivora Fissipedia) Arktiki (Carnivores of the Arctic).- In: Zveri Arktiki, pod redaktsiei Prof. N. A. Smirnova, pp. 365—370, Leningra Izdatel'stvo Glavsevmorputi. 1935; Ellerman, J. R. and T. C. S. Morrison-Scott. Checklist of Palaearctic and Indian Mammals, pp. 260 — 262, Londor 1951; Sludskii, A. A. — In: Afanas'ev, A. V., V. S. Bazhanov et al. Zveri Kazakhstana, pp. 339 — 343, Alma-Ata, Izdatel'stvo AN Kazakh SSR; Bannikov, A. G. Mlekopitayushchie Mongol'skoi Narodnoi Respubliki (Mammals of the Mongolian People's Republic). pp. 91—93. Moskva, Izdatel'stvo AN SSSR. 1954.

1851. Putorius sibiricus. Simashko, Yu. Russkaya fauna (Russian Fauna). Mlekopitayushchie, 2, p. 365, tabl. XII, fig. 3.

1911. Kolonocus sibiricus. Satunin, K. A. K sistematike semeistva Mustelidae (On the Systematics of Family Mustelidae). — Izvestiya Kavkazskogo Muzeya, 5, p. 266; Yurgenson, P. B. Materialy k poznaniyu mlekopitayushchikh priteletskogo uchastka Altaiskogo gosudarstvennogo zapovednika (Contributions to the Study of the Mammals of the Lake Teletskoe Area of the Altai State Reserve). — Trudy Altaiskogo Gosudarstvennogo Zapovednika, No. 1, pp. 114—116, Moskva. 1938.

1944. Mustela (Mustela) sibirica. Bobrinskii, N. A. III. Otryad khishchnye Ordo Carnivora (Order Carnivores (Ordo Carnivora)). — In: Opredelitel' mlekopitayushchikh SSSR, edited by Prof. N. A. Bobrinskii, p. 128, Moskva.

1956. Mustela (Kolonocus) sibiricus. Novikov, G. A. Khishchnye mlekopitayushchie fauny SSSR (Carnivorous Mammals of the Fauna of the USSR). pp. 139—144. Moskva-Leningrad, Izdatel'stvo AN SSSR.

Type and type locality. Tigeretskii Post near Ust'-Kamenogorsk in the Altai.

Diagnosis. Dark coffee-brown on muzzle and orbital area forms characteristic mask. White field on lips and chin clearly delineated and sharply outlined against general dark brown and russet background of entire head. Underparts same color as back or slightly lighter. Feet same color as body. Frontal area of skull humplike, bulging Postorbital constriction elongated, surfaces lateral almost parallel. Bony palate extends backwards beyond end of last molar for a distance less than width of palate between these teeth.

Condylobasal length of skull at least 55 mm in males, 49 mm in females.

Measurements. Length of body with head (from 47 males and 38 females): males 280 — 390 mm, females 250—305 mm; length of tail: male 155—210 mm, females 133—164 mm; length of hind paw: males 53.6—68.0 mm, females 48.0—52.0 mm; length of ear: males 22.0 — 29.5 mm, females 18.8—23.0 mm. Weight: males 650 — 820 g, females 360—430 g.

Skull measurements (from both males and females): Condylobasal length: males 58.0 — 67.3 mm, females 49.8 — 62.7 mm; zygomatic width: males 28.7 — 35.7 mm, females 26.4 — 32.1 mm; width of rostrum above canines: males 12.0—14.9 mm, females 11.0—13.6 mm; interorbital width: males 11.7—13.9 mm, females 10.5—13.0 mm; postorbital width: males 11.4—14.0 mm, females 11.0—13.3 mm; mastoid width: males 26.8—31.0 mm, females 23.0—27.0 mm; height in area of tympanic bullae: males 22.0—24.2 mm, females 18.7—23.0 mm; length of braincase: males 32.0—37.3 mm, females 30.2— 35.3 mm; facial length: males 12.3—17.5 mm, females 11.5—14.4 mm; length of upper tooth row: males 17.2— 20.0 mm, females 15.6—18.6 mm.

FIGURE 119. Siberian weasel (M u s t e l a s i b i r i c a Pall.) after specimen No. 27885, Zoological Museum of Moscow University.   Painting by V. A. Vatagin

Description.   Similar in general build to the polecat but differs from it in smaller size, more luxuriant tail, and in monotone russet color throughout the body.   Body is long, muscular, slender, and short-legged. Head is not flattened in the fronto-parietal part, and has moderately pointed muzzle.   Tail about one half length of body with head (Figure 119).

Fur is long and soft.   Guard hair of winter fur, in rear part of back 25—28 mm long.

Color monotone, being in winter a bright ocher—straw yellow with an occasional red rusty tinge.   Flanks and underparts less saturated and lighter.   Tail luxuriant vivid russet.   Legs similar in color to body. Lips and chin silvery white, head occasionally bears irregular white patch or several small patches.   Color usually darkens on head from forehead to nose,

311

acquiring gray brownish tone (Figure 120). Guard hairs rather long and glossy. Underfur dense, compact straw yellow-gray. Vibrissae brownish, with golden russet ends.

FIGURE 120. Sibirian weasel, Mustela sibirica Pallas (original)

Summer fur shorter, coarser, and relatively sparse. Darker than in winter, being ocher rusty. Underfur grayer and duller. Cinnamon brown color on head more intense and involves a larger area.

Young animals are a markedly darker light brown than adults. With development of russet ocher guard hair, seen through the grayish to gray brown underfur, color becomes bright.

Os penis, as in weasel, has hooklike bent tip, but is larger in agreement with size of animal (Figure 121). In contrast to Radde's weasel and the Japanese weasel (itatsi), the baculum is more recurved in distal third. Length of bone is 32.0 — 35.8 mm; width at base being 0.6 — 3.7 mm; and height at base 2.0 — 5.3 mm.

General form of skull (Figure 122) intermediate between ermine and mink, being larger and more elongated than the first and not as flattened as the second. Looks long and narrow from above. Upper profile wavy, forming from occipital crest to approximately level of front of tympanic bulla a more or less convex arch, being then usually slightly concave, to the postorbital constriction, from which it forms a highly convex arch running about the elevated forehead and abruptly descending to the end of the nose. Rostrum slightly flattened. Frontal area appreciably convex, forming slight hump above rostrum and cranial section. Length of brain-case 55—60% of condylobasal length. Mastoid width appreciably less than distance from lower edge of foramen magnum to anterior edge of choanal incisure (from basion to palation). Height of braincase in area of tympanic bullae 75—85% of width of skull between mastoid processes. Postorbital constriction elongated with almost parallel lateral sides. Sagittal crest usually poorly developed, being most marked in lambdoidal area and only barely visible anteriorly near bregma. Occipital crests conspicuous. Bones of braincase bulge slightly above and laterally. Zygomatic arches relatively long and slender. Infraorbital foramina are up to as large as alveoli of upper canines. Choanal incisure usually lacks reverse medial protrusion of bony palate. Mesopterygoid fossa relatively long, its length from level of posterior end of hamular processes of pterygoid bones being approximately as long as bony palate from choanal incisure to level of posterior sides of molars. Posterior edge of bony palate extends backward beyond level of backs of molars for a distance sometimes as long as (more often shorter than) width of palate between these teeth.

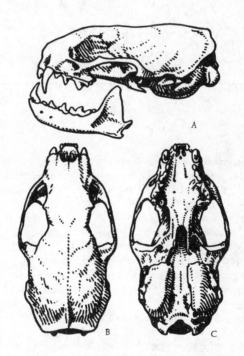

FIGURE 121. Os penis of the Siberian weasel, Mustela sibirica Pallas (after S. I. Ognev 1931)

FIGURE 122. Skull of the Siberian weasel, Mustela sibirica Pall. (original):

A — lateral view; B — dorsal view; C — ventral view.

Tips of hamulary processes diverge slightly outward and seldom form hamate curvature. Tympanic bullae relatively elongated, with inner sides moderately extended posteriorly; width of bullae less than half their length; distance between jugular foramina approximately half length of longitudinal axis of bullae. Teeth, particularly canines, are large.

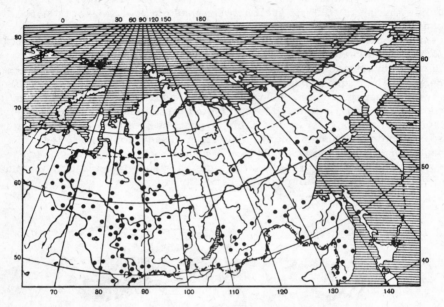

MAP XVI. Geographical distribution of the Siberian weasel, Mustela sibirica Pallas, in Siberia

Systematic notes. The intraspecific systematic differentiation of the Siberian weasel is generally quite clear, but the scale of difference is slight. Ellerman and Morrison-Scott's catalogue (1951) presents 14 sub-species ranging the Palaearctic and India. The systematic interrelationships are not yet completely clear. Several independent species related to the Siberian weasel may have been included. The systematic status of Mustela itatsi Temminck (1844), which, according to the material examined by us, is an independent species, is a case in point.

Geographical distribution. The areas around the Urals in Europe and Asia except for the tundra zone, and south to the Himalayas, inclusively.

Within the Soviet Union the range extends from the valley of the rivers Vyatka, lower Kama, Belaya, and upper Ural rivers east to the shores of the Sea of Okhotsk and the Sea of Japan.

In Siberia it ranges throughout the taiga, both in lowlands and in the mountains, but is absent from Kamchatka (Map XVI).

We present below some reported details on the distribution of the Siberian weasel in Siberia.

In Western Siberia it inhabits the entire taiga and forest steppe zones, penetrating locally into the steppes along riverbanks overgrown with scrub.

S. A. Kuklin (1937) lists the Siberian weasel as a relatively rare animal for the northern taiga areas of the Transurals. It occurs in the upper reaches of the Lozova [Loz'va] River.

FIGURE 123. Pine—larch forests on the upper reaches of the Pyaku-Pur River. Biotope of the Siberian weasel. Photo by V. I. Telegin

N. Telishchev (1931) reports the animal in the Berezovo area, where it is rather rare. It was obtained in the Poludennaya Mountain on the left side of the Ob River. It occurs north of the Nizemskie yurty [R. Nazym]. According to B. G. Chalikov and K. P. Samko (1926), it is known in "the area of the urman-bog* subzone," these authors sketching the northern boundary of this zone as somewhat north of Berezovo. A few specimens were encountered near the villages Sherkaly and Keushki. In the valley of the Koinskaya River, the animal is already common (V. N. Skalon, personal communication). I. S. Polyakov (1877) reported the animal as inhabiting the valley of the Nadym River.

In the valley of the Vakh River the number of Siberian weasels reaches commercial level, but at the mouth of the Kolik-Egan (a right tributary of the Vakh) and on the upper reaches of the Agan and Pur the animal is extremely rare (V. N. Skalon, personal communication).

In the Taz River valley, according to E. O. Yakovlev (1930), the northern boundary reaches the Sidorovaya Pristan (66° 30' N. lat.). Skalon (in litt.) reported a Siberian weasel obtained even further north, namely in the

* [Urman — thick coniferous forest in Western and Central Siberia.]

Merovo area, which is some 80 km higher up on the Taz River, and on the upper reaches of the Turukhan River (Figure 124).

South of these areas it is locally abundant.

In the Central Transurals, according to S. A. Kuklin (1937), the animal is very abundant in the southern part of the taiga and in the forest steppe and occurs in almost all areas except the extreme southern ones. Within the southern Transuralian steppes the animal is rare except in localities lying near the mountains.

FIGURE 124. Fir—Siberian stone pine taiga in the Vartovskaya River valley, Aleksandrovsk District of the Tomsk Region. Biotope of the Siberian weasel. Photo by K. T. Yurlov

The literature contains the following data from earlier authors on the distribution of the animal in the Ob River valley.

Within the former Konda-Sosva reserve, distribution of the Siberian weasel is sporadic, the animal being obtained in the following areas: the upper reaches of the Tugr River, the mouths of the Malaya Sosva, Nercha Egan,

Bol'shaya Eva, and Sorem-Puze and near Timk-Paul on the Tapsui. On the Konda it occurs more regularly. On the Egot'ya River the animal already has a trade value. It was obtained on Mulym'ya and Tapu (tributaries of the Konda River), and near the Em-Egen River, a right tributary of the Malaya Sosva River (V. N. Skalon and V. V. Raevskii, in litt.).

According to I. Ya. Slovtsov (1892), it is encountered in the Tobolsk area and in greater numbers in the subdistricts of Samarovskaya and neighboring districts, throughout the Tyumen and Turinsk areas to the upper Pelymka, and is rather common in the Kozhegalsk area of the Tyumen Region and in the Vasyugan marshes. In the former Tyumen County, the Siberian weasel was collected in 1905 by D. Wardropper (coll. Zool. Inst. Acad. Sciences USSR). According to S. M Chugunov (1915), it occurs in the former Surgut County; this author mentions a specimen he examined which was obtained on the Yugan River. In the Surgut area, according to I. D. Kiris (1934), the animal is widespread and this author obtained the animal there. According to Sadovnikov (1911), the Siberian weasel is encountered in large numbers along the Vakh River.

It was reported by V. V. Vasil'ev (1929) in the valley of the Dem'yanka River. According to hunting data, and as reported to me by F. D. Shaposhnikov (in litt.), it is obtained throughout the Tyumen Region except for the Yamal-Nenets National District.

It inhabits all districts of the Tomsk Region in large numbers. In the Narym taiga, according to V. P. Anikin (1902), it is the most common carnivore and is obtained in large quantities. The author collected the animal near the city of Narym and the village of Kal'nak. G. E. Ioganzen (1923) reported the animal to be extremely common along the Chulym River. According to my data, it is very common in the upper Ket', Kolpashevo, Asino, Tomsk, Shegarka, and Kozhevnikovo areas (Figure 125).

It ranges sporadically in the Kurgan and Omsk regions, in small, insular groves of aspen or birch. Around the city of Tara it was collected by V. Ushov (coll. Zool. Mus. Moscow University), and I. S. Polyakov obtained it in the valley of the Irtysh (coll. Zool. Inst. Acad. Sciences USSR).

In the Novosibirsk area it is far more common in the northern taiga areas than in the southern forest steppe and steppe areas. In the upper reaches of the Tartas and Tara rivers, according to P. Stepanov (1886), it is hunted as game. There are collections made by various persons in the Tatarsk and Legostaevskii areas, and from Bol'shoe Lake (coll. Zool. Mus. Moscow University). Our collection contains specimens from the area of Lake Chany (Baraba) and from Novosibirsk.

In the Kemerovo Region the animal's density is extremely high. It has been obtained in the area of the Suzun mines (coll. Zool. Mus. Moscow University). Yudin collected the Siberian weasel in 1953 in the Yashkinskii area near the village Zyryanskoe (coll. S. U. Stroganov). In the Gornaya Shoriya, according to G. Gol'tsmaier (1936), it is a commonly hunted species. According to M. D. Zverev (1932), it is rather abundant in the forest and forest steppe regions along the Turkestan-Siberia Railroad from Novosibirsk to Semipalatinsk.

It is encountered throughout the Altai Territory (except in the open steppe) and is particularly abundant in the mountain taiga and in the forest steppe (Savinov, 1953).

It was collected near the city of Barnaul by F. V. Gabler in 1841 (coll. Zool. Inst. Acad. Sciences USSR). B. S. Yudin collected the animal in 1958 near the village of Pavlovsk and in the Kosikha area near the village of Bobrovka (coll. S. U. Stroganov). In the Upper Ob pine forest, according to G. N. Likhachev (1930), it is commoner than any other carnivore. Each hunter obtains some 5—30 animals yearly.

Pallas described the Siberian weasel from material from the Tigeretskii Range in the western part of the Altai. According to N. F. Kashchenko (1899) it is common in the northern Altai to the Seminskii Pass, and probably rare in more southern localities. According to A. M. Nikol'skii (1884), it occurs near Uimen. A. P. Razorenova (1939), on the basis of a questionnaire, reported the animal's presence in the Ongudai, Ist'-Kan, Uimen, Ulagan and Chemal counties of the Gorno-Altai Region. Numerous pelts of the Siberian weasel are obtained in Elekmonar and Maima. In the Ust'-Koksa area it occupies a paramount place in the fur trade (Nasimovich, 1949).

FIGURE 125. The southern taiga. Valley of the Baksa River, in the Tomsk Region. Biotope of the Siberian weasel. Photo by B. S. Yudin

In the southeastern Altai, according to A. M. Kolosov (1939), the Siberian weasel is extremely rare, and only a few pelts a year reach the fur depots at Kosh-Agach. Within the territory of the former Altai reserve, according to P. B. Yurgenson (1938), the Siberian weasel is very abundantly and widely distributed. This author lists the following localities where the animal occurs: Artybash village, the Oior and

Koldon rivers, the Aka Range, Yailyu (from the Yurga River to the Chichilgak Cape), the Chechenek and Okporok rivers (middle and lower reaches), the watershed range between the Kamga and the tributaries of the Lebed River, the rivers Kamga, Bol'shoi Shaltan and Malyi Shaltan the upper reaches of the Klyk River, and the Chelyush and Chili areas.

It was collected in Khakasia in 1936 by E.Shmyrin, in the Bol'shoi Abakan River valley (coll. Zool. Mus. Moscow University). P. Polikevich (1923) writes that the animal occupies the territory of the former Minusinsk County and of the Uryankhai Territory [now Tuva ASSR]. According to A. I. Yanushevich (1952), the animal is encountered in the Tuva ASSR, throughout the forest zone, and penetrates the steppe via river valleys; Yanushevich observed and collected the animal on the northern steppes of the Tannu-Ola, and in the valley of the Terekhtyg River (a tributary of the Yenisei), and along the Khadyk River (a tributary of the Buren River).

It was reported from the Minusinsk taiga by L. and I. Kozhanchikov (1924). K. I. Gromov (1951) says that the Siberian weasel is the most typical mammal species in the Sayan reserve (central part of the Eastern Sayan). It was collected on the Sayan Range in 1940 by V. Timofeev, in the valley of the Gutara River (coll. Zool. Mus. Moscow University).

In the area of Krasnoyarsk it is encountered in large numbers, and we have studied materials collected there by M. E. Kibort, who obtained the Siberian weasel in 1892—1894 in the valleys of the Medvezh'ya, Sliznev, Bazaikha, Kaltat, Mana and Negdet rivers and on the Bezhet Creek, as well as in the Chernaya Sopka (Karatal) and around Krasnoyarsk (coll. Zool. Inst. Acad. Sciences USSR). V. A. Gorokhov (1951) reports the Siberian weasel from the "Stolby" reserve. Our collection contains animals collected there by G. D. Dul'keit.

In the Birilyussk area of the Krasnoyarsk Territory it was collected in 1937 by V. Torgashev on the Mendel River. It was obtained on the Yenisei in 1931 by K. A. Yudin near the Shivera River, some 60 km below the city of Krasnoyarsk, and near the village of Khloptunov some 90 km below the above-mentioned city (coll. Zool. Mus. Moscow University).

In the territory of the former Kansk District, lying between the River Kan and the valley of the lower reaches of the Angara River, it was reported by V. N. Troitskii (1930) as being a commonly hunted species. According to G. Radde (1862), in the upper reaches of the Oka River (a tributary of the Angara) the Siberian weasel is rare, becoming more common further down this river some 300 km from the Okinskii [Oka] frontier post. It inhabits the entire Irkutsk Region, including the high mountain tundras of Tofalyariya (Kopylov, Dobrovol'skii and Shergin, 1940).

The distribution of the Siberian weasel on the Yenisei is mentioned both by old and modern authors. Its density on the biotopes decreases northwards.

A. F. Middendorf (1867) reported the Siberian weasel up to the Turukhansk territory. Ul'rikh and Ostrovskikh collected it in 1894—1899 around the city of Turukhansk (coll. Zool. Inst. Acad. Sciences USSR). According to A. L. Chekanovskii (1873) it is encountered on the Lower Tunguska, but not very frequently.

According to N. P. Naumov (1934) it is more abundant in mountain areas on the right bank of the Yenisei than in the territory of the West Siberian lowland. The animal is common throughout the valley of the Stony Tunguska, particularly in its upper reaches, where it is obtained in large numbers. On the Lower Tunguska it abounds chiefly in the lower reaches.

In the Yenisei River valley it is encountered in commercial quantities to the area of Karasino village; near the villages Sushkovo and Igarka it is still obtained, though rarely, and a few individuals are encountered as far up as Khantaika, at about 68°N lat. More to the east it penetrates even further north, being encountered occasionally in the area of lakes Kita and Khantaika. It is very rarely encountered on the upper reaches of the Kureika River, but becomes more abundant further down this river. It is also found very rarely at the tip of the Kochechuma River, the northern limit of distribution in this area being the Tura (a left tributary of the Kochechuma). E. O. Yakovlev (1930) reported the Siberian weasel on the southern shore of Lake Pyasino.

As to the distribution of the Siberian weasel in the Vilyui River valley, Maak (1859, 1886) wrote that around the sources of the river he saw no sign of the animal, and began to meet it only near the mouth of the Chona. He found the animal common enough in the Vilyui valley itself, but it became rare the further north he went. Quoting local inhabitants, Maak reports that, on the northern tributaries of the Vilyui, the Siberian weasel does not occur at all, or at any rate is extremely rare. N. P. Naumov (1934) communicates that his Tungus friend F. S. Khukochar saw tracks of the Siberian weasel at the head of the Vilyui River, at about 65° N lat. According to K. E. Vorob'eva, the Vilyuisk area yielded about five thousand pelts of Siberian weasel in 1925—1926, representing about one third of the total take from Yakutia (Tugarinov et al., 1934).

According to I. S. Polyakov (1873) the weasel is common on the Lena and along the Vitim, and particularly abundant in the Muya Range.

According to recent data provided by V. I. Belyk (1953), it ranges over the central and the Vilyui areas of Yakutia (Nyurba, Verkhne- Vilyuisk), the northern boundary coinciding approximately with the northern boundary of the Kobyai area. Its range extends eastwards to the slopes of the Verkhoyansk Range.

Finds of the Siberian weasel are, however, known outside these boundaries. According to A. I. Ivanov, it is encountered north of the Verkhoyansk Range a rarity. A specimen is known from the Malaya River, 50 km from Verkhoyansk (Tugarinov, Smirnov and Ivanov, 1934). V. N Skalon (in litt. has kindly informed me that in the 1930s three specimens were obtained south of Zhigansk and two specimens taken near the sources of the Yana. In 1932 two pelts figured in the take from the Oimeikon area (upper Indigirka). In the same year a pelt was processed in the Bulun area, though it is possible that this was an imported specimen.

Information on the animal's eastern distribution is extremely scarce. N. V. Slyunin (1900) reported it in his list of the animals of the Okhotsk area but does not mention any specific localities where the animal occurs. S. I. Ognev (1931) thinks that the animal occurs along the Okhotsk coast to 60°—62° N lat. S. P. Naumov and N. P. Lavrov (1941) report information obtained from S. I. Snigirevskii on the Siberian weasel's occurring along the Okhotsk coast to the upper reaches of the Ul'ya River, about 59° N lat.

V. P. Sysoev (1952) reports the animal in the Okhotsk area. It is absent on Kamchatka.

It ranges throughout Transbaikalia and the Far East, but with uneven density.

On the northeastern shore of Lake Baikal, according to S. S. Turov (1936), it occurs only rarely and is seldom obtained. Z. V. Svatosh collected it in the Sosnovka River valley. V. K. Timofeev obtained the animal in the Barguzin reserve, on the Bol'shaya River (coll. Zool. Mus. Moscow University). It was found by Turov (1923) on [Cape] Svyatoi Nos. Kashchenko (1910) examined collections of the Siberian weasel from the vicinity of Kiberet' in the former Verkhneudinsk County [now Ulan Ude].

In the Kyakhta vicinity it was obtained in 1907 by P. K. Kozlov (coll. Zool. Inst. Acad. Sciences USSR).

On the upper reaches of the Chita River, according to E. Pavlov (1948), it occurs everywhere and is regularly hunted. It occurs in the Aginsk Steppe (N. P. Kashchenko, 1912). Radde (1862) encountered it on the Yablonovoi Range and in the floodplain of the Onon River.

According to P. A. Kuznetsov (1929), it is common in eastern Transbaikalia in the taiga zone, much more rare in the forest steppe, and extremely rare in the steppe belt, where it keeps to scrub thickets along the shores of the Onon, Aga, Turga and other rivers. This author discovered it in the Yablonovyi and Unda ranges, near the villages of Kyker, Zilzikan and Kalinin, as well as in the Onon River valley.

In the interfluve between the Oldon and the Gilyui, according to G. N. Gassovskii (1927), it is one of the most widely distributed carnivores, being particularly abundant along the southern slopes of the Tukuringra Range; it is encountered in large numbers along the Gilyui and the latter's western and northern tributaries, and more rarely in the valley of the Oldoi.

In the basin of the upper Selemdzha and Uda, according to N. T. Zolotarev (1934), it ranges ubiquitously but with low density.

In the Amur basin it was encountered as far back as the days of Schrenck (1858), and particularly often by Maak (1859). The Zoological Institute of the Academy of Sciences of the USSR contains collections of Siberian weasel made by V. K. Soldatov along the lower reaches of the Amur by P. Koloskov in the area of Kazakevich village, and by M. A. Menzbir at Vyazemskii village on the Far Eastern Railroad line. I have examined collections of Siberian weasel from the Svobodnyi area and from the vicinities of Blagoveshchensk, of Komsomol'sk on the Amur, and of Khabarovsk. On the Khor River it was collected in 1932 by K. A. Vorob'ev and V. S. Stakhanov (coll. Zool. Mus. Moscow University). It was reported by Maak (1861) for the Ussuri River valley. According to the observations of M. N. Przheval'skii (1870), it occurs in large numbers throughout the Ussuri territory and is present both in forests and in meadow steppes, being in the latter most often encountered in winter.

In the Maritime Territory it occurs in all districts. N. T. Zolotarev (1936) reports that it is encountered throughout the valley of the Iman but that it becomes more abundant in the lower half of the valley. It was collected on the Iman by N. I. Shingarev (coll. Zool. Inst. Acad. Sciences USSR). In the Maritime Territory it has been collected by A. Salmin in the Sikhote-Alin reserve and in the Ternei Bay area, by V. K. Timofeev in the "Kedrovaya Pad'" reserve, and by G. F. Bromlei in the Sudzukhe reserve (coll. Zool. Mus. Moscow University).

In the Suputinka reserve, according to Bromlei and Z. I. Gutnikova (1955), it occurs more often than do other representatives of the mustelid family.

V. K. Arsen'ev obtained the Siberian weasel on the Naina River in 1907. A. A. Emel'yanov collected it in 1914 near the village of Chernigovka, south of Lake Khanka. M. I. Chikovskii obtained the animal near Sidemi Bay in 1883 (coll. Zool. Inst. Acad. Sciences USSR).

It is absent from the Shantar Islands and Sakhalin.

Survey of subspecies. Of the 14 subspecies of the Siberian weasel registered by Ellerman and Morrison-Scott (1951), two occur in the fauna of the Soviet Union, and both in Siberia.

20a. Mustela (Kolonocus) sibirica sibirica Pallas (1773).
Siberian weasel

1773. Mustela sibirica. Pallas, P. S. Reise durch verschiedene Provinzen des Russischen Reiches, 2, p. 701.

1911. Kolonocus sibiricus australis. Satunin, K. A. K sistematike semeistva Mustelidae (On the Systematics of Family Mustelidae). — Izvestiya Kavkazskogo Muzeya, 5, p. 23 (Tyumen County); Auct. cit. Opredelitel' mlekopitayushchikh Rossiiskoi imperii (Key to Mammals of the Russian Empire), p. 126, Tiflis. 1914.

1914. Kolonocus sibiricus sibiricus. Satunin, K. A. Opredelitel' mlekopitayushchikh Rossiiskoi imperii (Key to Mammals of the Russian Empire). pp. 125—126, Tiflis; Ognev, S. I. Zveri Vostochnoi Evropy i Severnoi Azii (Animals of Eastern Europe and Northern Asia). Vol. 2, pp. 716—726, Moskva-Leningrad. 1931.

1951. Mustela sibirica sibirica. Ellerman, J. R. and T. C. S. Morrison-Scott. Checklist of Palaearctic and Indian Mammals, p. 260, London.

1956. Mustela (Kolonocus) sibiricus. Novikov, G. A. Khishchnye mlekopitayushchie fauny SSSR (Carnivorous Mammals of the Fauna of the USSR). p. 144, Moskva-Leningrad.

Type and type locality. See above description of the species.
Diagnosis. Characterized by relatively small size (condylobasal length is about 61.3 mm) and by nature of coat. Winter fur moderately long and rather dense, though coarse. Color generally dull yellow-russet, more saturated on back and tail and slightly paler on flanks and on underparts. Underfur straw yellow-gray. Summer fur shorter and stiffer. Summer color on back is dark russet-reddish, with marked rusty brownish tinge; on flanks and belly, somewhat lighter.
Measurements. Dimensions of skull (from 33 males and 15 females). Condylobasal length: males 58.0—63.5 mm (av. 61.7 mm), females 49.8 — 56.3 mm (av. 52.8 mm); zygomatic width: males 28.7—35.2 mm (av. 32.5 mm), females 26.4—29.6 mm (av. 27.8 mm); width of rostrum above canines: males 12.1—14.2 mm (av. 13.2 mm), females 11.0—13.5 mm (av. 11.8 mm); interorbital width: males 11.7—13.2 mm

(av. 12. 5 mm), females 10.5 — 12.2 mm (av. 11.0 mm); postorbital width: males 11.4 — 13.0 mm (av. 12.5 mm), females 11.0 — 12.5 mm (av. 11.6 mm); mastoid width: males 26. 8 — 28.7 mm (av. 27.5 mm), females 23.0 — 26.1 mm (av. 24.3 mm); height of skull in area of tympanic bullae: males 22.0 — 23.3 mm (av. 22.7 mm), females 18.7 — 22.5 mm (av. 21.8 mm); length of braincase: males 32.0 — 37.0 mm (av. 34.8 mm), females 30.2 — 34.6 mm (av. 31.5 mm); facial length: males 12.3 — 15.1 mm (av. 14.2 mm), females 11.5 — 13.0 mm (av. 12.2 mm); length of upper tooth row: males 17.2 — 18.9 mm (av. 18.2 mm), females 15.6 — 18.0 mm (av. 16.2 mm).

Systematic notes.   The Siberian weasels inhabiting Siberia from the Urals to [Lake] Baikal form both in craniological respects and in fur color a rather monotypic population belonging to the nominate subspecies.   The Siberian weasels from the Altai Territory and the neighboring mountain areas of Kazakhstan do, however, possess a denser and more silky fur than do those from the southern part of the Novosibirsk and Kemerovo regions.   This difference is but small; nevertheless, it is worth recording it in the systematics by restoring Satunin's K o l o n o c u s   s i b i r i c u s   a u s t r a l i s Satunin (1911), described from material from the former Tyumen District and reduced by Ognev, but as a "natio" of the typical subspecies and with a somewhat modified diagnosis.

The Siberian weasel ranging west of the Urals is accepted as being taxonomically distinct from the West Siberian form.   However, 12 pelts I studied from the northern part of Bashkiria (obtained from S. I. Snigirevskii) possessed a definitely sparser and coarser coat than in the West Siberian form.   The color of these was also lighter.   Unfortunately the pelts were without skulls, were undated, and lacked precise indication of the locality from which they were obtained.   No conclusions based on such material can be taken as reliable.

We present below a newly compiled diagnosis of the above-mentioned form of the West Siberian weasel.

20b.   Mustela (Kolonocus) sibirica sibirica natio australis
Satunin (1911). West Siberian weasel

1911.   K o l o n o c u s   s i b i r i c u s   a u s t r a l i s.   Satunin, K. A.   K sistematike semeistva Mustelidae (On the Systematics of Family Mustelidae). — Izvestiya Kavkazskogo Muzeya, 5,   p. 23; Auct. cit. Opredelitel' mlekopitayushchikh Rossiiskoi imperii (Key to Mammals of the Russian Empire). p. 126, Tiflis. 1914.

Type and type locality.   No. 96 (collector's) in the collection of the Zoological Institute of the Academy of Sciences of the USSR, 10 November 1905, from the collection of D. Wardropper.   Antropovskii Subdistrict in the Zhiryakovo village of the [former] Tyumen County.

Diagnosis.   Distinguished from mountain Altai weasels by somewhat less luxuriant fur.

Geographical distribution.   West Siberia eastwards to Lake Baikal, and neighboring areas of Kazakhstan.

The distribution of n a t i o   a u s t r a l i s is such that its range occupies the West Siberian lowland except for those parts of the Altai Territory and of the Novosibirsk and Kemerovo regions which lie near the Altai mountains.

Material studied. Altai — 27 specimens; Sayans — 60 specimens; West Siberian lowlands — 80 specimens; Central Siberian Plateau — 15 specimens: Total 192 [sic] specimens, plus about 300 pelts from commercial sources.

20c.   Mustela (**Kolonocus**) **sibirica miles**   Barret-Hamilton (1904). Transbaikalian Siberian weasel

1904.   M u s t e l a   s i b i r i c a   m i l e s.   Barret-Hamilton, G. E.   Notes and Description of Some New Species and Subspecies of Mustelidae. — Ann. Mag. Nat. Hist., Ser. 7, 13, p. 391.

Type and type locality.   Type specimen in the British Museum; from collections of V. K. Tachanovskii.   Dauria, Transbaikalia.
Diagnosis.   Distinguished from nominate subspecies by relatively more luxuriant and vividly colored winter fur.   General tone of back is russet with slightly developed reddish tinge.   Underparts somewhat lighter, with slight orange-russet tinge.
Measurements.   As in nominate subspecies.
Systematic notes.   Nearer to the nominate subspecies than to the Far Eastern.   Color less intensive and size smaller.
Systematic relationships with Mongolian and Manchurian types as yet unclarified.
The systematic position of the Siberian weasels ranging Yakutia and the Okhotsk coast is as yet unclear.   Judging by the scanty material available (just 6 specimens, collected at various seasons and in different areas), the animal inhabiting this area is light-colored and small.
Geographical distribution.   Transbaikalia eastwards to the valley of the Zeya River.
Material studied.   Total from various areas of Transbaikalia — 17 specimens.

20d.   Mustela (Kolonocus) sibirica subsp.   Far Eastern Siberian weasel

1931.   K o l o n o c u s   s i b i r i c u s   c o r e a n u s.   Ognev, S. I.   Zveri Vostochnoi Evropy i Severnoi Azii (Animals of Eastern Europe and Northern Asia).   Vol. 2, pp. 726 — 727, Moskva-Leningrad   (nec. Domaniewski, 1926).
1936.   M u s t e l a   s i b i r i c a   c o r e a n a.   Zolotarev, N. T.   Mlekopitayushchie basseina reki Imana (Mammals of the Basin of the Iman River).   p. 95, Moskva-Leningrad   (nec. Domaniewski. 1926).
1944.   M u s t e l a   (M u s t e l a)   m a n c h u r i c a.   Bobrinskii, N. A. Otryad khishchnykh.   Ordo Carnivora (Order Carnivores (Ordo Carnivora)). — In: Opredelitel' mlekopitayushchikh SSSR,   p. 128, Moskva.
1956.   M u s t e l a   (K o l o n o c u s)   s i b i r i c u s   m a n c h u r i c u s. Novikov, G. A.   Khishchnye mlekopitayushchie fauny SSSR (Carnivorous Mammals of the Fauna of the USSR).   p. 144.   Moskva-Leningrad.

Diagnosis. Distinguished from those subspecies already described by large size (condylobasal length of skull about 65.4 mm) and by even more vivid and colorful fur. The winter fur is long, dense but coarse, and russet, with a characteristic reddish rusty tinge. The underfur is redder and more vivid than in the nominate form. The summer fur is shorter, sparser, and stiffer. The fur is darker, with well developed rusty-grayish brown tones.

Measurements. Dimension of skull (from 16 males and 12 females). Condylobasal length: males 63.8 — 67.3 mm (av. 65.4 mm), females 57.2 — 62.7 mm (av. 61.2 mm); zygomatic width: males 32.3 — 35.7 mm (av. 34.3 mm), females 27.0 — 32.1 mm (av. 30.5 mm); width of rostrum above canines: males 13.5 — 14.9 mm (av. 14.2 mm), females 12.2 — 13.6 mm (av. 12.9 mm); interorbital width: males 12.3 — 13.9 mm (av. 13.2 mm), females 11.0 — 13.0 mm (av. 12.7 mm); postorbital width: males 13.2 — 14.0 mm (av. 13.6 mm), females 12.0 — 13.3 mm (av. 12.7 mm); mastoid width: males 28.2 — 31.0 mm (av. 29.5 mm), females 24.0 — 27.0 mm (av. 25.0 mm); height in area of tympanic bullae: males 22.5 — 24.2 mm (av. 23.7 mm), females 20.2 — 23.0 mm (av. 21.8 mm); length of braincase: males 34.9 — 37.3 mm (av. 33.0 mm), females 32.1 — 35.3 mm (av. 33.4 mm); facial length: males 14.9 — 17.5 mm (av. 15.7 mm), females 13.2 — 14.4 mm (av. 13.6 mm); length of upper tooth row: males 18.2 — 20.0 mm (av. 19.3 mm), females 16.1 — 18.6 mm (av. 17.3 mm).

Systematic notes. The Siberian weasel found in the Amur Region and the Maritime Territory is taxonomically distinct, and represents a consolidated subspecies characterized by peculiarities of fur color and by large size. It is more distinctly differentiated systematically than are the West Siberian and Transbaikalian subspecies, and of these it is closer to the Transbaikalian form, differing, however, in having more colorful and vivid winter fur and in being larger.

The relationships between the Soviet Far Eastern Siberian weasel and the forms inhabiting the neighboring parts of Korea and China are still undetermined, due to lack of sufficient material for a comparative study. A number of subspecies from these countries have been described: Mustela sibirica coreana Domaniewski, 1926 (Seoul, Korea), M. s. fontanierii Milne-Edwards, 1871 (Peking), M. s. mandschurica Brass, 1911 (S. Manchuria), M. s. charbinensis Lovkashkin, 1934 (Krestovskii Island on the Sungari near Harbin), etc.

The Greater Khingan, as shown by specimens furnished by D. V. Putyata, is inhabited by a lighter-colored form which is undoubtedly not identical with those occurring in Siberia.

A difficulty has arisen with regard to the name of the Soviet Far Eastern Siberian weasel. S. I. Ognev (1931) presented it under the name P. s. coreanus, but without arguments to support this. According to Ya. B. Domanevskii (1926), who described P. S. coreanus, the latter is characterized by extensive development of the dark mask on the head and by a wider circumoral white field. These features cannot be confirmed without a comparison between pelts, and the collections of the Soviet Museum contain no specimens of Siberian weasels from Korea. Ognev (1931) was not sure that the Soviet Siberian weasel is identical with the Korean one and did not insist categorically on the correctness of the name M. s. coreana, taking it as a provisional one pending the accumulation of more material. The name M. s. mandschurica Brass, introduced by

B. A. Kuznetsov (1944), is also unfounded, since the correct relationships between the Soviet Far Eastern Siberian weasel and the Korean and Manchurian ones, and between the latter two, are as yet unclear.

The nomenclature for intraspecific taxonomic units should indicate not only the purely formal side of a given taxon's designation, but should also reflect as far as possible the genetic relationships between these units. These subtle forms not only concretely illustrate the phenomenon of intraspecific variation, but also furnish indispensable material for resolving problems of genetics, of evolution, and of stratigraphy, etc. Therefore, such unjustified indentification of subspecies as that which has occurred, for instance, with respect to the Far Eastern, Korean, and Manchurian Siberian weasels, far from deepening our knowledge of nature, on the contrary hinders it.

FIGURE 126. Pine forest in the vicinity of the city of Novosibirsk. Biotope of the Siberian weasel. Photo by K. T. Yurlov

Therefore none of the names proposed for the Siberian weasels of the Soviet Far East can be retained as valid, for the reason given above, and the problem should be left open pending the study of sufficient actual material.

Geographical distribution. The entire Amur-Ussuri area west to the valley of the lower reaches of the Zeya River.

Material studied. Fifty pelts and 72 skulls from various districts of the Maritime Territory, of the southern part of the Khabarovsk Territory, and of the eastern part of the Amur Region.

Biology. The Siberian weasel is chiefly a forest dweller. The most characteristic biotopes are various types of forest, from the dark

326

coniferous taiga to the broadleaf forests of the Maritime Territory and the birch copses of the East Siberian forest steppe (Figure 126). Altitudinally the biotopes extend to the subalpine zone, inclusively. Outside the wooded zone the animal inhabits the vast reed thickets along lake shores.

In the vast taiga expanses of Western Siberia the Siberian weasel's preferred areas are spots cluttered by windfall, old overgrown burns, shores of bogs and lakes, and, above all, river valleys and scrub thickets.

In the forest steppes of Western Siberia it lives in insular birch groves, along shores of rivers and lakes, and also in ravines overgrown with birch, osier, birdcherry, black currants, bramberry and luxuriant grass (Figures 127, 128).

In the Baraba Steppe it lives in the vast beds of reeds along the numerous lakes. According to M. D. Zverev and I. M. Zalesskii (1935), "the Siberian weasels [here] have so changed their mode of life that they can freely navigate the lakes, sit on the floating islands of reed, and when in pursuit of water voles swim from one island to another, jumping from the water into broken reed beds. They negotiate the water-covered reed ditches with amazing rapidity and agility."

FIGURE 127. Sphagnum—pine bog on the watershed between the Vasyugan and Tara rivers. Biotope of the Siberian weasel. Photo by K. T. Yurlov

In the mountain taiga belt of Siberia the animal is universally present, but in greater numbers in the biotopes not occupied by the sable or where the latter is quite scarce. All other conditions being equal, it prefers wooded places to open ones and particularly prefers riverain localities and mountain streams.

In the area of the Altai reserve, according to observations of P. B. Yurgenson (1948), the weasel does not climb above the timberline

(Figure 129). In the eastern Sayan, according to the Kozhanchikov brothers (1924), it is occasionally encountered in the sparse subalpine forest. In the Olekma-Vitim mountain country it lives in summer mainly on rock streams where pikas are abundant, and for the winter returns to the forest, where it keeps to the banks of streams and small rivers (Polyakov, 1873).

In eastern Transbaikalia, according to B. A. Kuznetsov (1929), the preferred habitats of the Siberian weasel in the mountain-taiga area are rock streams, where it hunts pikas, and river valleys. In the region of insular forests it lives in birch stands situated along river valleys and streams. In the steppe area it is encountered exclusively in thickets of viburnum, birdcherry, poplar, willow, and other tree species along river shores.

In the Ussuri territory, according to Przheval'skii (1870), it inhabits both forests and meadows, preferring the meadows in winter.

The nest is constructed in broadened burrows of the Siberian chipmunk and other animals, under stumps or fallen wood, under tree roots, in cavities between stones, in tree hollows, and under buildings. The nest chamber is lined with fur, feathers, and dried out plants.

The tracks of the Siberian weasel are similar to those of other small mustelid species (Figure 130). They are appreciably larger than those of the ermine and smaller than those of the polecat. The senses of the Siberian weasel are well developed, particularly hearing, smell and taste; the sight is not as good.

Its nature and habits are similar to those of polecats. The animal is bloodthirsty and vicious, merciless when attacking, and will kill many more animals than it can manage to eat. Those not eaten are stored.

The Siberian weasel not only gets along easily near humans, but in forest steppe areas actually gravitates to inhabited points, being encountered not only in small villages but even in cities. For example, it has been caught many times in central parts of such Siberian cities as Tomsk and Novosibirsk.

The movements of the Siberian weasel are dexterous and swift; it swims well, and when in pursuit of its prey (frogs, small fish and water voles) dives into the water. Should the necessity arise, it can climb trees quite well.

The Siberian weasel is active mostly in crepuscular and night hours, but may occasionally be active during the day as well. In winter snowstorms and during severe frosts it may not leave its den for several days in succession.

The animal will cover a large area at night while hunting for some animal to eat. To illustrate this, I present here a slightly edited extract from the diary of M. D. Zverev about the nocturnal peregrinations of the Siberian weasel in Western Siberia.

"On February 10 a fresh night trail of Siberian weasel was discovered in the morning at the exit from the village. After following the trail for half a kilometer, it was discovered that the weasel had emerged from a burrow hidden in the roots of a rotten, snow-covered stump near the steep bank of a taiga stream. It had sat near the stump on its hind paws, jumped onto the stump, and then jumped off again and gone leaping over the ice of the river, keeping close to the right, steep bank with its

overhanging bushes. Keeping the same gait, the animal had veered
sharply towards shore, heading straight for the village threshing floor
via thickets of willows, honeysuckle and hawthorn. Following the
wattle fence, it had reached the threshing floor barn, circled it, and,
with bounds twice those it had come by, run back to the river, keeping to the
bushes and almost retracing its old trail (which lay a few meters to the
side). Along the riverbank the weasel had, without descending onto the
ice, proceeded along via the same easy bounds as those it had used on
emerging from its burrow. At the same time it often veered aside, away
from its main direction along the river, in order to jump onto a stump or
fallen tree, sitting there on its hind paws.

"In the course of an hour's tramping (on skis) along some 3 km of the
animal's trail, no signs were found that it had caught any prey. The
animal had zigzagged over the ice from bank to bank, in two places trying
to dig at something in the bank, but had soon stopped and resumed its
previous gait. The animal's trail reached, on the right bank of the river,
a small bridge leading to hay fields. It had performed a rather large
leap into the snow under the bridge, following a mouse trail which stopped
there, and a piece of wool stuck under a sedge gave evidence that a red
vole had probably been the Siberian weasel's first prey that night. The
snow under the bridge was so trampled by the animal that it was impossible
to see what it had done, but it had apparently searched for additional mice;
in one place the snow was dug out to the very ground.

FIGURE 128. Northern forest steppe in the Novosibirsk Region. Biotope of the Siberian weasel.
Photo by B. S Yudin

"From the bridge the trail ran back onto the ice of the river following
the steep right bank for about one km, and diverging once — veering to
the left, to follow a [common] weasel's track and reaching the place where

the latter had dived under the snow, then resuming its former route along the river (and often disappearing under the snowdrifts between ice and riverbank, where long cracks ran for many meters). The Siberian weasel had next jumped abruptly ashore (in two large leaps) and proceeded several meters, perhaps crawling, since marks of its fur remained on the ice, after which it had taken several more large leaps and landed among the holes of some hazel grouse sleeping in the snow (3 animals). The snow was entirely trampled here, and several fresh bird feathers were found. No traces of blood or other signs showing that the Siberian weasel had managed to catch the hazel grouse were discovered.

"From the hazel grouse's sleeping place, the Siberian weasel had leaped in large bounds to the side of the river, probably in an attempt to chase the hazel grouse which had flown away and alerted by the noise made by the birds as they settled down in the trees; in two places some 50 meters apart in the snow many fresh dry twigs, pine needles, and a single hazel-grouse feather were found. Here the frightened birds had tried to pass the night, and owing to their poor sight had knocked down some twigs before setting down. The Siberian weasel had apparently climbed up into one of these fir trees in an attempt to catch a hazel grouse, but without result, since the trail showed it had to jump back down to the snow and had then resumed its bounding along the river. We did not manage to find the place where the hazel grouse settled down again, nor where the third hazel grouse sat. Being more frightened than the others, it probably flew further away.

"The gait of the Siberian weasel soon switched back to the usual short bounds and meandered for a long time along the edge of a bog overgrown with birch. The trail then ran out onto the ice of a small lake and was lost. On the rim of the lake it reappeared — right near the shore, where there was a fishing hole cut in the ice. Examination of this place showed traces of clawmarks, and some meters from here the animal's trail reappeared on the shore, having emerged from the lake. The animal had then taken a long route through the marsh, following the tracks of an ermine to the place where the ermine had gone under the snow. Here, not far from the edge of the marsh, the trail of the Siberian weasel disappeared into the snow under an uprooted tree, and the animal had crawled into some burrow It probably caught something here since, after emerging from under the roots, it had rolled for a long time in the snow, sat, and lain down, probably cleaning and licking itself.

"Two or three black-brown hairs, probably belonging to a water vole, were found at the place where the animal had wallowed in the snow; the vole was probably caught and eaten under the roots.

"The tracks resumed with appreciably shorter leaps, and soon encountered those of a shrew which ran in the opposite direction and tried to jump aside, but the track of the Siberian weasel trampled the entire glade, leaving only here and there some prints of the shrew, with the marks of its tail dragging after it. The impression was that the Siberian weasel had had its fill and had played cat-and-mouse with the shrew. In the middle of the glade was the carcass of the shrew, with large bruises on the back and flanks (discovered when the hide was flayed). Leaving the shrew, the Siberian weasel turned back sharply and went into the fir stands about 1 km from the river. It climbed fir trees twice, but jumped back. After going some $1\frac{1}{2}$ or 2 km in an almost straight line, the animal turned back to the river and, without making any loops, disappeared under the roots of a fallen tree. There were no tracks coming out, meaning that the animal was still down there. Hence, with all the convolutions of its path the Siberian weasel had covered a full 8 km during the night."

FIGURE 129. Riverain deciduous forest strip on the Charysh River, northwestern Altai. Biotope of the Siberian weasel. Photo by B. S. Yudin

The Siberian weasel is a typical carnivore, its diet being based on various animals, primarily small rodents. Among the latter, first place is occupied by whatever species occur most often during a given season in the weasel's habitat and are the most available to it. The weasel, however, does not disdain any animal, including fish and frogs, and will also eat carrion.

An idea of the composition of its winter diet in different parts of Siberia has been gained from study of stomach contents (Table 8). The data presented in Table 8 show that the composition and percentages of the food items differ in the various areas of the Siberian weasel's range and depend on the composition of the local fauna. Thus, in Western Siberia the water vole predominates in the diet, while the pika predominates in Transbaikalia. The water vole is absent from the Transbaikalian fauna, while the pika is absent from the West Siberian fauna. In neighboring parts of North Kazakhstan jerboas made up 14% and mole rats (Myospalax) 24% of the contents of the stomachs examined.

The birds it catches include not only small passerine species, but large birds as well, for instance black grouse, willow ptarmigans, and capercailzie. During the nesting season it destroys birds' nests, eating the eggs and fledglings.

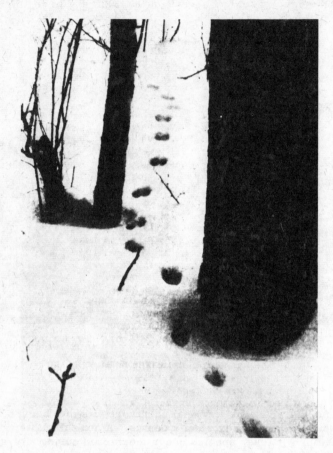

FIGURE 130.   Tracks of a Siberian weasel on loose snow. Vicinity of Pavlovka village in the Altai Territory. Photo by B.S. Yudin

In the Far East it eats large amounts of chum salmon and humpback salmon.

Material concerning the Siberian weasel's diet during the snowless part of the year is rather scant — 10 items, made available by F. D. Shaposhnikov (1956) and collected in the northeastern part of the Altai. These data are presented in Table 9.

According to hunters' observations, in summer and autumn Siberian weasels also eat berries and the nuts of the Siberian stone pine (Naumov and Lavrov, 1941). However, Shaposhnikov (who made a special study of this subject and examined 108 data collected over three years) never found any plant material in the Siberian weasel's diet.

TABLE 8. Occurrence of different types of food in stomachs of Siberian weasels from different parts of Siberia (percentage of number of stomachs examined)

Composition of diet	Taiga of Western Siberia 43 specimens	Forest steppe of Western Siberia, 45 specimens	Western Trans-baikalia, A. S. Fetisov, 406 specimens	Northeastern Altai, F. D. Shaposhnikov, 98 specimens
Small murid rodents	15	23	31	63
Water voles	46	67	—	1
Hamsters	—	3	—	—
Susliks	—	1	1	—
Chipmunks	—	—	10	—
Squirrels	—	—	1	1
Hares	8	—	1	—
Pikas	—	—	38	—
Shrews	15	5	3	49
Birds	—	5	14	9
Frogs	—	1	—	—
Fish	15	—	1	—

TABLE 9. Composition of summer diet of Siberian weasel on the Altai

Type of food	Frequency of occurrence	Percentage of occurrences
Red voles.	2	20
Gray voles	3	30
Murids, without further details	2	20
Water voles	1	10
Chipmunks	1	10
Pikas	3	30

Rut occurs at the very end of winter and in early spring (end of February — March). The Siberian weasel is a polygamous animal. Several males chase one female. They roam broadly in search of females. According to M. D. Zverev and I. M. Zalesskii (1935), the nature of the Siberian weasel trails undergoes a marked change during this period. "For several kilometers, through the most "micy" tracts, the Siberian weasel will make no attempt to hunt, leaving the hazel-grouse holes unexamined. The trail of a Siberian weasel in rut changes direction continuously, making loops, turning back, stopping in the same place, etc. Double and triple trails running for long distances commemorate the males' chase after the female." Fierce fights for a female occur often between males. Coitus lasts several minutes.

The gestation period is 28 — 30 days. Young are found in the West Siberian forest steppe in April. In the southwestern part of Transbaikalia, according to A. A. Cherkasov (1867), the young appear at the end of April and in early May. Later broods are, however, known — late spring and even early summer ones. V. N. Skalon (in litt.) obtained gravid Siberian-weasel females at Tomsk in mid-June and around Yakutsk on 22 May. The litter size is 2—12. Skalon (in litt.), performing an autopsy on a female obtained in the vicinity of Yakutsk, discovered 14 embryos. Telegin and Yudin obtained, in an aspen hollow in the vicinity of Novosibirsk on 16 May 1958, a female Siberian weasel with 11 pea-sized embryos. O. V. Grigor'ev, in June 1959, obtained a female with brood in the Aleksandrov District of the Tomsk Region. The young (6) were still blind. As in other Mustelidae, they are born blind and completely helpless. Growth and development are rather rapid. The eyes open at the age of one month. By the time they are several days old, a dense and soft fur of a light yellow color has grown out. By the beginning of autumn, the young are almost indistinguishable in fur color from adults. Lactation lasts about two months. By the end of August the mother leaves the young and they abandon the maternal nest. At the beginning of their independent life the young roam with the entire brood, but the latter gradually disperses and by the end of autumn the young Siberian weasel is leading a solitary life.

The animal numbers are subject to fluctuations, and depend on variations in food conditions and on diseases. Thus, in a number of regions of Western Siberia the Siberian weasel population increases or decreases in proportion to the changes in population of the water vole (Lavrov, 1937).

Mass mortality due to disease has been observed (Naumov and Lavrov, 1941). Regular seasonal migrations associated with food conditions have been observed in a number of areas. Thus, according to I. S. Polyakov (1873), on the watershed between the Olekma and the Vitim the Siberian weasel passes the summer chiefly in hunting the numerous pikas on the rock streams. In the fall, when the pikas go into hibernation, the Siberian weasels migrate down into the valleys, where they keep to river and stream-banks abounding in murids.

The literature contains reports of mass migrations of the Siberian weasel, probably due to the same causes as similar migrations in other animals. Zverev and Zalesskii (1935) write about a considerable migration of Siberian weasels in 1928 near the city of Tomsk. A mass movement of the animal from west to east was noted. Numerous cases have been recorded of the animals appearing in the city of Tomsk. They have been found on heaps of firewood and bark, in buildings, etc.

V. Belousov (1929) also reports migrations of the animal. According to this author, "Siberian weasels and ermines began to migrate almost simultaneously with chipmunks, by late August and September. They migrated in about the same direction as the chipmunks. They were seen only rarely, but dogs often caught them in the fields."

The Siberian weasel has rather few enemies, these being certain carnivorous animals (the glutton, sable, fox and wolf), stray dogs, and large birds of prey and owls. It has many food competitors, however, including all birds and animals feeding on small rodent species.

In a number of places where the Siberian weasel lives together with the sable, e.g., in the northeastern Altai, direct antagonism between them is observed. The sable drives the Siberian weasel from the wooded biotopes into the open stretches of river valleys and scrub tundra. The sable will stubbornly pursue the Siberian weasel down its trails. While trailing sable Shaposhnikov (1956) came separately upon three dead Siberian weasels, and found the latter's fur more then once in sable excrements.

Molt occurs twice a year. The spring molt usually occurs in early March. The shedding of winter hair and the growth of summer hair is usually very rapid. Spring molt begins and ends at the head and legs, gradually extending backwards to the upper parts and flanks and then to the tail. The autumn molt takes place from late August till early November, involving a complete replacement of the summer coat by the winter fur. Autumn molt begins from the tail and upper parts of the body and gradually moves to the head, flanks, underparts and legs.

Practical importance. The Siberian weasel is a commercial fur-bearing animal. Its pelt bears good-quality fur and is used both in its natural form and as imitation sable fur. The hair of the Siberian weasel's tail is used for making excellent paintbrushes for water colors.

The Siberian weasel occupies a rather high place in the fur take in most of the forested areas of Siberia. The number of pelts could be increased with correct planning and organization of the trade.

Fur standards classify the Siberian weasel in eight grades, differing in their commercial qualities.

The Siberian weasel performs a service by exterminating noxious rodents. In isolated cases it will attack domestic fowl, but is then never satisfied with one or two chickens and will go on to kill a dozen or more. This is usually done by animals who have fallen into the habit of visiting inhabited points, and these are easily caught.

Attempts to acclimatize the Siberian weasel in the Gorki Region and in Kirgizia were made in prewar years.

21. Mustela (Kolonocus) itatsi Temminck (1844).
Japanese weasel or itatsi

1844. **Mustela itatsi.** Temminck, C.J. Fauna Japonica. Mamm., 34, pl.7, fig.2.
1951. **Mustela sibirica itatsi.** Ellerman, J.R. and T.C.S. Morrison-Scott. Checklist of Palaearctic and Indian Mammals, p.261. London.

Type and type locality. Described from Japan.
Diagnosis. Dark coffee-brown color on muzzle and circumorbital area forms characteristic mask. Whitish color of lower lip and chin fuses with pale straw-yellow color of throat, lower neck, and chest. Underparts lighter than back. Feet are darker than body. Bony palate extends backwards beyond level of molars by a distance which exceeds width of palate between these teeth. Tympanic bullae markedly broadened posteriorly on inner sides. Distance between jugular foramina approximately two thirds the length of longitudinal axis of bullae.
Measurements (from 9 male specimens and 2 females). Length of body with head: males 510—550 mm, females 341—465 mm; length of tail:

335

males 145 — 165 mm, females 93 — 101 mm; length of hind paw: males
57 — 65 mm, females 39 — 46 mm; height of ear: males 15 — 21 mm, females
11 — 16 mm; weight: 554 — 874 g.

Condylobasal length of skull: males 57.2 — 61.9 mm, females
47.6 — 47.9 mm; zygomatic width: males 31.3 — 33.2 mm, females
28.9 — 29.1 mm; width of rostrum above canines: males 12.7 — 13.5 mm,
females 8.2 — 8.9 mm; interorbital width: males 12.0 — 12.8 mm, females
9.1 — 9.8 mm; postorbital width: males 10.5 — 12.1 mm, females
10.2 — 10.8 mm; height in area of tympanic bullae: males 19.0 — 21.4 mm,
females 16.0 — 16.8 mm; length of upper tooth row: males 15.7 — 17.3 mm,
females 12.9 — 13.3 mm.

Description. The itatsi is similar to the Siberian weasel. The
differences are in length and in bushiness of tail, quality and color of
hair, and in craniological structural features.

The itatsi body, like the Siberian weasel's, is long, agile, slender, and
short-legged. Head is more flattened, with moderately pointed muzzle.
Tail shorter, its length no more than one third length of body with head.

Fur sparser, lower, and stiffer. Winter fur darker than that of
Siberian weasel, almost color of Siberian weasel's summer fur. General
tone of upper parts towards rear of body brick red to intense red-brown,
flanks a trifle lighter. Underparts pale russet with more or less marked
isabella tinge. Brick brown tinge very prominent in forepart of scapular
area and gradually changes into earth gray-brown color of upper parts of
forepart of neck, extending from here to back of head, ears and upper
part of head to forehead and eyes. Muzzle and orbital region form
characteristic dark coffe brown mask. Upper lips pure white. Lower lips
and chin whitish, gradually fusing with pale straw-yellow color of throat
and lower neck (and occasionally of anterior parts of chest). Neck has
one or more white patches of varying size and outline. Tail is similar in
color to back, but sometimes has more intense hue. Limbs are earth
brown.

Os penis similar in form to that of M. sibirica, save that in the itatsi
the bone in its distal third is usually straight, lacking the curve characteristic of the Siberian weasel. Tip of bone has hooklike bend as in the Siberian
weasel. Length of bone is 30.0 — 34.2 mm.

Skull closer in configuration to a small mink's than to a Siberian
weasel's. Is also flattened, rather long, and compressed laterally, as in
minks, but more slender, not as massive, and of more pronounced
configuration. Upper profile of skull forms slightly bulging arc markedly
lowered in rostral part. Frontal area, in contrast to that of Siberian
weasel, is flat, not forming humplike elevation. Length of braincase
53 — 57% of condylobasal length. Mastoid width usually only slightly
shorter or slightly longer (by ± 0.5 — 2.5 mm) than distance from basion to
palation. Height of braincase in area of tympanic bullae is 65 — 75% of
mastoid width. Postorbital constriction long, with parallel or posteriorly
slightly divergent lateral sides. Sagittal crest clearly delineated but
never reaches considerable development. Occipital crests markedly more
developed. Roof of braincase bulging. Zygomatic arches shorter and
more massive than those of Siberian weasel. Infraorbital foramina
approximately equal to alveoli of upper canines. Choanal incisure usually

with small reverse median protrusion in form of sharp process of bony palate. Mesopterygoid fossa relatively short; length of fossa from level of posterior end of hamulary processes markedly shorter than length of bony palate from choanal incisure to level of posterior sides of molars. Posterior edge of bony palate extends posteriorly beyond level of molars by distance which exceeds width of palate between internal sides of molar crowns. Tips of hamulary processes diverge externally and show hooklike bend. Tympanic bullae relatively shorter and less inflated than those of Siberian weasel, with inner sides markedly divergent posteriorly; width of bullae markedly more than half their length; distance between jugular foramina approximately equal to two thirds length of longitudinal axis of bullae. Teeth usually weaker than those of Siberian weasel.

Systematic notes. The systematic status of the itatsi is still unclear. It had been described by Temminck (1884) from material from Japan as an independent species, but subsequent studies left its exact taxonomic position rather undetermined. Various students have assigned it different ranks and positions within family Mustelidae.

V. Blasius (1884) and F. Lataste (1887) included it in the polymorphic genus Putorius Cuvier (1817), placing the itatsi taxonomically close to the members of subgenus Putorius s. str., in which subgenus, however, the minks and the Siberian weasel were not included.*

N. Kuroda (1924) considered the itatsi an independent species in genus Lutreola.

Ellerman and Morrison-Scott (1951) provisionally included the itatsi among the subspecies of M. sibirica, but with no valid motivation. Judging by the taxonomic principles these authors used for establishing variants among Palaearctic mammals, they based themselves on general formal data of the geographical distribution of the itatsi and the Siberian weasel. We cannot agree with so narrow an approach, and feel it quite fails to resolve the question.

Mustela itatsi occupies, on the basis of its taxonomic features, a position intermediate between the common Siberian weasel, Mustela sibirica Pallas, and the Altai weasel, M. altaica Pallas, being nearer to the first. At the same time, it should be noted that craniological features and, to some extent, the external features (e. g., the color and various shades of the fur) show that the itatsi and the common Siberian weasel differ markedly more from each other than does the Siberian weasel from the Altai weasel, the steppe from the forest polecat, the European mink from the American mink, or the forest marten from the sable.

The differences between M. itatsi and M. sibirica are thus rather deep and involve fundamental features.

For the sake of clarity, we present here a comparison of the most characteristic specific features of the itatsi and the Siberian weasel.

* The minks and the Siberian weasel were included by these authors in the subgenus Lutreola Wagner (1841).

Mustela itatsi	Mustela sibirica

1. Circumoral field whitish in area of lower lips and chin, and gradually merging with pale yellow color of throat and lower neck.

2. Ventral part of body markedly lighter than back.

3. Feet darker than body (are earth brown).

4. Skull elongated, moderately broad and long: length of braincase 53 – 57% of condylobasal length; mastoid width approximately equal to distance from basion to palation; height in area of tympanic bullae 65 – 75% of mastoid width (Figure 131).

5. Frontal area flat, not forming a humplike elevation.

6. Bony palate extends back beyond posterior ends of molars by distance greater than width of palate between these teeth.

7. Choanal incisure usually has small reverse median protrusion in form of sharp process of bony palate.

8. Mesopterygoid fossa relatively short, being markedly shorter than length of bony palate from posterior edge to molars.

9. Tips of hamulary processes of pterygoid bones diverge markedly outwards and show sharp hooklike bend.

10. Tympanic bullae lie behind jaw articulation at distance approximately equal to one-half length of bullae.

11. Tympanic bullae short, with markedly posteriorly-divergent inner sides: width of bullae more than one-half length; distance between jugular foramina approximately equal to two thirds length of longitudinal axis of bullae.

12. Os penis usually straight, without curve in distal third.

---

1. Circumoral field pure white, clearly delineated, and markedly separated from yellowish russet color of throat and neck.

2. Ventral part of body same color as back or slightly lighter.

3. Color of legs usually similar to that of body.

4. Skull elongated, narrow and rather high; length of braincase 55 – 60% of condylobasal length; mastoid width appreciably smaller than distance from basion to palation; height in area of tympanic bullae 75 – 85% of mastoid width.

5. Frontal area humplike, bulging, and elevated markedly above nasal section and braincase.

6. Bony palate extends back beyond posterior ends of molars by distance less than width of palate between these teeth.

7. Choanal incisure often without any reverse median protrusion of bony palate.

8. Mesopterygoid fossa long. Length approximately equal to length of bony palate from posterior edge to molars.

9. Tips of hamulary processes of pterygoid bones diverge slightly outwards and usually lack hooklike bend.

10. Tympanic bullae lie behind jaw articulation at distance approximately equal to one-quarter length of bullae.

11. Tympanic bullae elongated, with moderately posteriorly-divergent inner sides: width of bullae less than one-half length; distance between jugular foramina approximately one-half length of longitudinal axis of bullae.

12. Os penis highly recurved in distal third.

The differences listed, except for items 7, 9, and 12, are rather constant. No individuals have been found which could be called "transitional" on the basis of this group of features. With regard to the features in Item 7 (absence or presence of median protrusion of bony palate on choanal incisure), Item 9 (degree of curvature of tips of hamulary processes), and Item 12 (curvature of os penis in distal third), the material may show deviations to either side, but these are only deviations and should be regarded as such.

The greatest value for systematic purposes here lies in the craniological features listed, primarily via the structure of the auditory area, where a small (for adults) amplitude of individual variation and an absence of geographical variation are seen. Throughout the vast extent of the Siberian weasel's range, no essential differences were observed in the structure or position of the auditory bullae, or in the dislocation of the components of the pterygoid area and of the post-palatine part of the skull. Similar

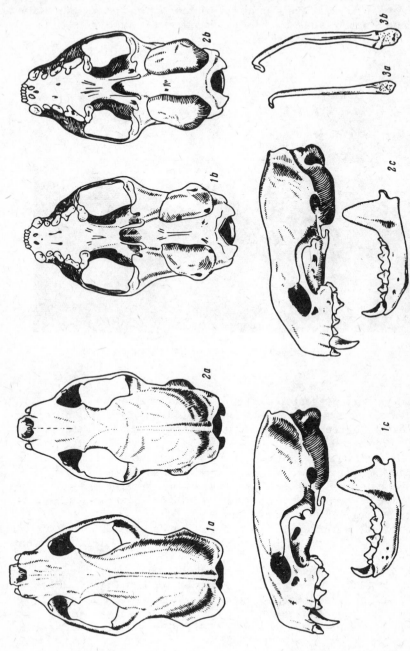

FIGURE 131. Structure of the skull (dorsal, ventral, and lateral view) and of the os penis in the itatsi and in the common Siberian weasel:

1a—1c: skull of Mustela itatsi Temminck, from specimen No. 645, collection of the Sakhalin Combined Institute of the Siberian Branch of the Academy of Sciences of the USSR; from southern Sakhalin, collected by B. F. Spitsyn; 2a — 2c: Skull of Mustela sibirica Pallas, from specimen No. 3712, collection of S. U. Stroganov from the Tomsk Region, (vicinity of Kozhevnikovo village), collected by B. S. Yudin; 3a: os penis of M. itatsi; 3b: os penis of M. sibirica.

features, judging from the material studied, are also characteristic of the itatsi.

Thus, judging by craniological features (the disposition, form and size of the tympanic bullae, and the structure of the posterior part of the bony palate and the pterygoid area), a distinct hiatus exists between the itatsi and the common Siberian weasel, and the animals can be distinguished on the basis of these features at first sight.

FIGURE 132. Southern Sakhalin. Itatsi biotope. Photo by N. A. Violovich

A hiatus is also present in the color. In the Siberian weasel all subspecies are similar patch by patch. Aside from size, they differ not in color but in degree of intensity of the general tone. The itatsi differs from the common Siberian weasel in color. As shown above the two species display structural differences in the circumoral field and uneven coloring in the upper- and underparts and in the limbs.

The above-listed differences are features of a specific order. On this basis, I have to conclude that the itatsi and the common Siberian weasel are not to be included in the same species.

Geographical distribution. A number of the Japanese islands, including Hokkaido, Honshu, Shikoku, Kyushu, Yakushima, Tanegashima and some others.

In the Soviet Union the itatsi lives in southern Sakhalin, where it was introduced in 1932. According to information published by S. D. Pereleshin in 1957, the itatsi then inhabited the areas of Korsakov, Kholmsk, Nevel'sk and other localities. During the 1954—1955 hunting season some 11 itatsi specimens were obtained in the area of the districts of Staraya Russa, Sokol, and Berezniki.

Material studied. Eleven specimens (pelts with skulls) collected on Sakhalin.

Biology. Information available on the mode of life of the itatsi on Sakhalin is restricted to fragmentary data collected by S. D. Pereleshin (1957). According to him, the animal lives near water (Figure 132). The hunter V. F. Spitsyn obtained 11 animals during the 1954—1955 season in the area of Ataraya Russa, Sokol and Berezniki. According to his impression, itatsi numbers are ten times as high as those of the ermine. Judging by its tracks, the animal is more active in the summer than in the spring, since it cannot withstand severe frost; during frost it may remain up to two weeks in its burrow. If caught in a trap the itatsi soon freezes. The itatsi can climb trees, but does so much more rarely than does the Siberian weasel. It is less mobile and less vigorous than the Siberian weasel, but does not fear swimming in nonfreezing rivers and streams. It feeds on various small animal (fish and Muridae). It gladly eats carrion, even when highly decomposed.

Practical importance. Due to its narrow range, the itatsi has no practical significance. The Japanese regard the animal as beneficial since it exterminates rats and mice. Its fur is of low value, and is used in Japan to imitate that of the mink. Several dozen pelts are processed yearly on Sakhalin.

22. **Mustela (Kolonocus) altaica** Pallas (1811).
Altai weasel (Figure 133, Map XVII)

1811. Mustela altaica. Pallas, P. S. Zoographia Rosso-Asiatica, 1, pp. 98 — 99, Petropoli; Ellerman, J R. and T. C. S. Morrison-Scott. Checklist of Palaearctic and Indian Mammals, p. 259, London. 1951; Sludskii, A. A. — In: Afanas'ev, A. V. , V. S. Bazhanov et al. Zveri Kazakhstana (Animals in Kazakhstan). pp. 343—351, Alma-Ata, Izdatel'stvo Akademii Nauk Kazakhskoi SSR. 1953; Bannikov, A. G. Mleko-pitayushchie Mongol'skoi Narodnoi Respubliki (Mammals of the Mongolian People's Republic). pp. 93—95, Moskva, Izdatel'stvo AN SSSR. 1954.

1823. Mustela alpina. Gebler, Fr. Le Putois des Alpes.— Mem. Soc. Imp. Nat., Mosc., 6, pp. 212—213 (Ridder mines on the Altai).

1851. Putorius alpinus. Simashko, Yu. Russkaya fauna (Russian Fauna). Mlekopitayushchie, 2, pp. 367—368; Satunin, K. A. Opredelitel' mlekopitayushchikh Rossiiskoi imperii (Key to Mammals of the Russian Empire). pp. 126—127, Tiflis. 1914.

1914. Mustela sacana. Thomas, O. On Small Mammals from Djarkent.— Ann. Mag. Nat. Hist., 13, Ser. 8, pp. 566—567 (near Przhevalsk).

1944. Mustela (Mustela) sibirica. Bobrinskii, N. A. III. Otryad Khishchnye. Ordo Carnivora (Ordo Carnivores (Ordo Carnivora)).— In: Opredelitel' mlekopitayushchikh SSSR, edited by Prof. N. A. Bobrinskii, p. 128, Moskva.

1956. Mustela (Kolonocus) altaica. Novikov, G. A. Khishchnye mlekopitayushchie fauny SSSR (Carnivorous Mammals of the Fauna of the USSR). p. 144. Moskva-Leningrad, Izdatel'stvo AN SSSR.

Type and type locality. The type specimen has not been preserved. Described from a specimen from the Ridder mine (Altai).

Diagnosis. Whitish or whitish straw-yellow color of lips and chin not clearly delineated, gradually diffuses and merges with general russet dull color of entire head. Frontal area of skull markedly humplike, convex. Postorbital constriction short, usually with well-marked constriction ("waist") and with lateral edges diverging posteriorly. Tympanic bullae with more or less parallel inner sides: distance between jugular foramina less than one half length of longitudinal axis of bullae. Choanal incisure extends posteriorly beyond level of posterior ends of molars by a distance which is less than width of bony palate between these teeth. Condylobasal length of skull in males no more than 53 mm, in females, 48 mm.

Measurements. Length of body with head (from 13 males and 16 females): males 235 — 287 mm, females 217 — 249 mm; length of tail: males 108 — 145 mm, females 90 — 117 mm; length of hind paw: males 40 — 47 mm, females 33 — 44 mm; height of ear: males 16.0 — 21.0 mm, females 14.0 — 20.2 mm. Weight: males up to 350 g, and females 220 g.

Skull measurements (from 14 males and 17 females). Condylobasal length: males 46.3 — 52.8 mm, females 40.0 — 47.1 mm; zygomatic width: males 23.1 — 27.6 mm, females 19.0 — 24.2 mm; interorbital width: males 8.8 — 12.2 mm, females 7.7 — 9.5 mm; mastoid width: males 20.2 — 24.0 mm, females 17.7 — 22.2 mm; maximum diameter of infraorbital foramina: males 1.7 — 2.6 mm; length of braincase: males 28.1 — 32.5 mm, females 27.1 — 30.3 mm; facial length: males 10.8 — 13.0 mm, females 8.8 — 11.0 mm; length of upper tooth row: males 13.2 — 15.6 mm, females 11.6 — 14.3 mm.

Description. In general structure resembles the Siberian weasel, but is smaller, with shorter fur and with less luxuriant tail (Figure 133).

Winter fur pale, dorsally yellowish brown but ventrally markedly lighter, varying there from yellowish straw-yellow to whitish straw-yellow. Upper part of head somewhat darker than back, brownish with slight coffee tinge. Area around lips, chin and upper part of throat whitish, with occasional light straw-yellow tinge. Tail somewhat more russet than back. Vibrissae grayish brown-whitish.

Summer fur grayish brown to gray with light yellowish and occasionally brown tinges. Head markedly darker than back.

Os penis similar in general traits to that of Siberian weasel but differs in greater curvature of hamate bend at distal end. Length of bone is 25.0 — 26.1 mm and width at base is 1.1 — 1.3 mm; height at base is 2.7 — 2.9 mm (Figure 134).

Skull (Figure 135) quite similar in general form to that of Siberian weasel differing in smaller size (see measurements), proportions, and in some structural peculiarities. Facial length of skull is 21.5 — 24.6%, in length of braincase 50.7 — 65.0% of condylobasal length (respective figures in the Siberian weasel are 22.7 — 24.5% and 55.0 — 58.2%).

Frontal area humplike, bulging, and elevated in relief above occipital section and above abruptly lowered nose. Length of braincase 58 — 66% of condylobasal length of skull (in the Siberian weasel, 55 — 60%). Mastoid width appreciably less than distance from basion to palation. Height of braincase in area of tympanic bullae is 80—87% of width of skull between mastoid processes. Area of postorbital constriction shorter than that of Siberian weasel, and constriction usually clearly marked ("waist"); lateral edges lie not parallel to longitudinal skull axis but diverge behind at an angle. Occipital crest, and even more so sagittal crest, relatively slightly developed. Infraorbital foramina small, ovally elongated; longitudinal diameter of foramina is up to as long as longitudinal diameter of alveolus of upper canine. Choanal incisure lacks reverse protrusions, has strongly turned-in sides and markedly narrow ends. Posterior edge of bony palate extends back beyond level of posterior ends of molars by a distance which is $\frac{1}{4}-\frac{1}{3}$ less than width of palate between molars. Hamulary process has slightly externally-divergent tip which however does not form hamate curvature. Tympanic bullae elongated and almost rectangular, with inner sides lying more or less parallel to each other; width of bullae, and distance between jugular foramina, are about half length of longitudinal axis [of bullae]. Teeth relatively large.

FIGURE 133. The Altai weasel, Mustela altaica Pallas. Photo by B.S. Yudin

Systematic notes. The Altai weasel is divided into a number of subspecies, distinctly differentiated by fur color. Comparison of series material from various parts of the range shows a definite pattern of change in fur color. The Altai, and probably the Sayans, are inhabited by the relatively dark and dull-colored nominate form. In the southerly direction the color is observed to lighten. The mountains of Central Asia are inhabited by very pale-colored individuals, e.g., the Pamir Altai weasel, M.a.birulai Ognev. On the other hand, in the southeasterly direction the color becomes more intense and bright. The Transbaikalian animal M.a.raddei Ognev has a more colorful and saturated reddish russet color than the nominate subspecies. Forms inhabiting southeast Asia (the north Indian M.a.longstaffi Wroughton, the Sikkim M.a.temon Hodgson and the Chinese M.a.astutus Milne-Edwards) have an even more saturated and vivid color.

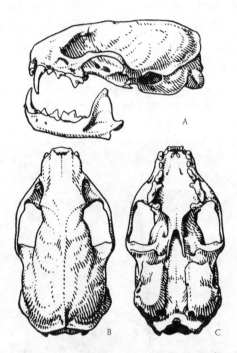

FIGURE 134. Os penis of the Altai weasel, Mustela altaica Pallas (after S.I. Ognev 1931)

FIGURE 135. Skull of the Altai weasel, Mustela altaica Pallas (original):

A — lateral view; B — dorsal view; C — ventral view.

Geographical distribution. The mountains of Asia, northwards to the mountains of the southern periphery of Siberia and southwards to north India and China, inclusively.

In the Soviet Union the Altai weasel is encountered in the mountains of Soviet Central Asia, of Kazakhstan, and of Southern Siberia (Map XVII).

It was first noted in the Altai by P.S. Pallas (1811). Hebler (1823) found it in the vicinity of the Ridder mines. Pavel Romanov, the taxidermi of Prof. E.A. Eversmann, collected the animal in 1843 in the area of the Upper Uimen (coll. Zool. Inst. Acad. Sciences USSR). N.F. Kashchenko

(1899) considered this carnivore one of the most common representatives of its genus on the Altai. A. P. Razorenova (1939) collected it in the Khankhara River valley. According to her the species is also known in Ongudai, Koop-Chingen, Kotanda, Uimen and Elikmonar. A. A. Nasimovich (1949) reported it for the Ust-Koksa area of the Gorno-Altai Autonomous Region. According to A. M. Kolosov (1939), it was encountered on the Chuya Alps and the Sailyugem Range, where the animal is extremely rare. Only 11 pelts reached the Kosh-Agach fur depots in 1935. The animal was not encountered by P. B. Yurgenson (1938) in the territory of the former Altai reserve.

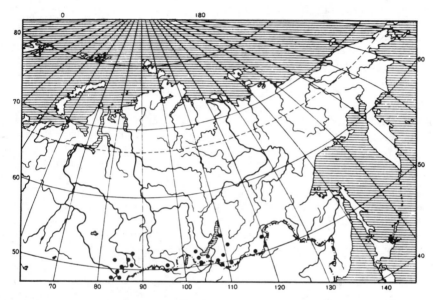

MAP XVII. Geographical distribution of the Altai weasel, Mustela altaica Pallas, in Siberia

In the southern Altai the Altai weasel occurs in the Kurchun, Katon-Karagai, Ust'-Kamenogorsk, Kirovsk and other districts of the East Kazakhstan Region, entering the low mountains of the Beskaragaiskii area of the Pavlodar Region. It is encountered in the Kalka Altai (Kuznetsov, 1948) and on the Mongolian Altai (Bannikov, 1954).

The animal's presence in the Sayans and in the Tuva Mountains is not validated by any concrete data in the literature (Tugarinov, 1916; Solov'ev, 1920; Polikevich, 1923; Shukhov, 1925; Yanushevich and Yurolov, 1949; Yanushevich, 1952, and others). V. N. Nadeev, who spent many years hunting animals in the Western Sayan, asserts that it is absent there. Judging by all the data, the animal is either extremely rare in these mountain countries or absent altogether, except at the eastern tip where, according to S. I. Ognev (1931), it is found in the Tunkinskie Gol'tsy. V. Ch. Dorogostaiskii obtained the Altai weasel near the village of Semenovshchina in the Irkutsk Region (coll. Zool. Mus. Moscow University).

According to I. P. Kopylov (1948), V. V. Timofeev (1949), and other sources, it occurs in the Khaman-Daban Mountains, where it was found in the Slyudyanka area. V. N. Skalon collected the animal in the Temnik River valley and in the area of Lake Gusinoe on the Monostoi Range. Collections are present from the upper Orongoi River, the Chikoi River valley, and Lake Zun-Torei (coll. Zool. Mus. Moscow University). It occurs in the Kyakhta area. P. S. Mikhno collected it near Kyakhta city and some 70 — 75 km away — at the villages Kiret and Tamir, as well as on the Chikoi River, some 16 km south of Savichi village (coll. Zool. Inst. Acad. Sciences USSR and Zool. Mus. Moscow University; see also Ognev, 1931). On the eastern shore of the Baikal it has been found in the vicinity of Barguzin (Ognev) and in the Barguzin reserve (coll. Zool. Mus. Moscow University).

In eastern Transbaikalia, according to B. A. Kuznetsov (1929), it inhabits the entire area, occurring with equal frequency in the steppes and in the taiga. This author has found the animal near the villages of Kyker, Zyulzikan, Kalinin, Staryi Chindant and Kulusutai, as well as near Lake Tsagan-Nor. On the upper Chita River it is a common animal (Pavlov, 1948). In the Chita River valley, near the village Smolenskii, it was obtained by I. A. Velinskii in 1938. On the Zhembarki River, the Altai weasel was obtained in 1940 by S. P. Kovalev (coll. of the Chita Regional Museum). It was collected in the Barguzin District by Timofeev (coll. Zool. Mus. Moscow University). Radde (1862) collected it in the Daurian Steppes near the village Kulusutai and in the area of the lower reaches of the Argun River.

According to K. Plyater-Plokhotskii (1936), it occurs in the western part of the Amur Region, and was obtained on the Amur in the vicinity of Blagoveshchensk (coll. Zool. Mus. Moscow University).

Survey of the subspecies. About 6 subspecies have been described, three or four inhabiting the Soviet Union and 2 of these in Siberia.

22a. **Mustela (Kolonocus) altaica altaica** Pallas (1811).
Altai weasel

1811. M u s t e l a   a l t a i c a. Pallas, P. S. Zoographia Rosso-Asiatica, 1, pp. 98 — 99, Petropoli.
1931. K o l o n o c u s   a l p i n u s   a l p i n u s. Ognev, S. I. Zveri Vostochnoi Evropy i Severnoi Azii (Animals of Eastern Europe and Northern Asia). Vol. 2, pp. 728 — 734, Moskva-Leningrad.

Type and type locality. See description of the species.
Diagnosis. Characterized by relatively dull and pale color. Winter fur pale yellowish brown dorsally and yellowish straw-yellow with cream tinge ventrally. Summer fur is darker — grayish brown to gray. Top and sides of head a more saturated grayish brown.
Measurements. Length of body with head (from 7 males and 5 females) males 235 — 260 mm (av. 241 mm), females 217 — 227 mm (av. 223 mm); length of tail: males 110 — 145 mm (av. 129 mm), females 104 — 113 mm (av. 108 mm); length of hind paw: males 41.0 — 47.0 mm (av. 44.1 mm), females 35.5 — 38.4 mm (av. 37.2 mm); length of ear: males 20.0 — 21.6 mm (av. 20.8 mm), females 15.7 — 18.2 mm (av. 16.8 mm).

Skull measurements (7 males and 5 females). Condylobasal length: males 51.2—53.0 mm (av. 52.5 mm), females 46.8 — 49.5 mm (av. 47.3 mm); zygomatic width: males 26.2—28.4 mm (av. 27.2 mm), females 23.2— 25.7 mm (av. 24.4 mm); interorbital width: males 10.3—12.6 mm (av. 11.3 mm), females 9.3 — 10.2 mm (av. 9.6 mm); mastoid width: males 22.8—24.0 mm (av. 23.3 mm), females 22.0—23.2 mm (av. 22.4 mm); length of braincase: males 28.0—31.3 mm (av. 29.6 mm), females 27.0—29.0 mm (av. 27.9 mm); facial length: males 11.0—13.0 mm (av. 12.2 mm), females 10.8—11.2 mm (av. 11.0 mm); length of upper tooth row: males 15.0—15.6 mm (av. 15.3 mm), females 13.8—14.3 mm (av. 14.1 mm).

Systematic notes. A well-differentiated subspecies characterized by rather dull and relatively dark winter fur; readily distinguished at first sight by this feature from the Transbaikalian Altai weasel M. s. r a d d e i Ognev and from the Semirech'e representatives of the species.

Geographical distribution. Mountains of southwestern Siberia eastwards to Lake Baikal.

Material studied. The Altai — 12 specimens; Semirech'e [Dzhery Su] — 3 specimens. Total — 15 specimens.

22b. Mustela (Kolonocus) altaica subsp. Semirech'e weasel

Type and type locality. No. 4566 in the S. U. Stroganov collections; female adult, 28 May 1953, from the collections of A. P. Lesnyak. Balkhash, the lower Ili River.

Diagnosis. Characterized by vivid color of summer fur. General tone of body's dorsal part and of tail brownish ocher with olive yellow tinge. Head brownish with slight coffee tinge. Ventral parts pure golden yellow. Lips and chin snow white, clearly marked off from intense golden color of throat and of forepart of chest.

Measurements. According to A. A. Sludskii (1953), the animals from the lower Ili River have the following measurements. Length of body with head: males 224—282 mm, females 218—230 mm; length of tail: males 116—132 mm, females 90—114 mm; length of hind paw: males 39—46 mm, females 34—35 mm; length of ear: males 16—20 mm, females 14 mm. Weight (from January to March): males 217—255 g, females 122—135 g.

Skull measurements (3 females). Condylobasal length: 42.6 — 44.2 mm; zygomatic width: 24.1—25.4 mm; interorbital width: 8.3—9.1 mm; postorbital width: 8.7 — 9.6 mm; mastoid width: 19.5—20.2 mm; length of upper tooth row: 12.0—12.8 mm.

Systematic notes. The subspecific status is as yet unclear. Thomas (1914), on the basis of two specimens from the vicinity of Przhevalsk, described a M u s t e l a s a c a n a. The principal feature differentiating s a c a n a from the Altai weasel M. a l t a i c a was given as the monotonous color of the chin and the throat. This feature is, however, variable and also frequently occurs in the Altai weasel in various areas of its range. Of the craniological features, Thomas can show only an insignificant variation in the structure of the tympanic bullae, a trait he himself did not consider essential.

Ognev (1931) reduced M. sacana, making the name synonymous with Mustela altaica Pallas (1811). The place of this form in the system of M. altaica subspecies is as yet unclear.

Only three specimens, from the area around Lake Balkhash, were examined by me. All were in their summer fur. In systematic features they are very peculiar, and are undoubtedly differentiated from the nominate subspecies in color, at least in color of summer fur.

The matter of the nomenclature of the Semirech'e Altai weasels from the Balkhash area should be left open until its relationship with M. A. sacana Thomas has been cleared up. If they prove not to be subspecifically identical, then a distinct name for the Balkhash area Altai weasel will be justified.

The diagnosis presented above should be considered a preliminary one.

Geographical distribution. The southern side of Lake Balkhash. According to A. A. Sludskii, it abounds on the lower reaches of the rivers Lepsa, Aksu, and Ili, several thousand pelts being processed on the lower Ili each year (Afanas'ev, Bazhanov, et al. 1953).

Material studied. A total of 3 specimens, from the lower Ili River.

22c. Mustela (Kolonocus) altaica raddei Ognev (1928).
Transbaikalian Altai weasel

1928. Kolonocus alpinus raddei. Ognev, S. I. Novye dannye po sistematike i geograficheskomu rasprostraneniyu nekotorykh vidov semeistva Mustelidae (New Data on the Systematics and Geographical Distribution of Some Species of Mustelidae Family).— Memuary Zoologicheskogo Otdeleniya Obshchestva Lyubitelei Estestvoznaniya, No. 2, p. 9; Auct. cit. Zveri Vostochnoi Evropy i Severnoi Azii (Animals of Eastern Europe and Northern Asia). Vol. 2, pp. 734—735, Moskva-Leningrad. 1931.

1951. Mustela altaica raddei. Ellerman, J. R. and T. C. S. Morrison-Scott. Checklist of Palaearctic and Indian Mammals, p. 259, London; Bannikov, A. G. Mlekopitayushchie Mongol'skoi Narodnoi Respubliki (Mammals of the Mongolian People's Republic). p. 95. Moskva, Izdatel'stvo AN SSSR. 1954.

Type and type locality. No. 3416 in the collection of the Zoological Institute of the Academy of Sciences of the USSR, male adult, 1 April 1956 from G. I. Radde's collections. Kulusutaev Post, near Lake Zun-torei (Torei-nor), Transbaikalia.

Diagnosis. Differentiated from nominate subspecies by more colorful and vivid general tone of winter fur, with development of yellowish ocher-russet tinges. Summer fur darker, with general rusty russet tone. Skull dimensions smaller (see below).

Measurements. Length of body with head (from 6 males and 7 females): males 249—280 mm (av. 265 mm), females 222—226 mm (av. 224 mm); length of tail: males 108—144 mm (av. 129 mm), females 110—117 mm (av. 106 mm); length of hind paw: males 40.8—44.2 mm (av. 42.3 mm), females 33.2—43.8 mm (av. 36.9 mm); length of ear: males 17.4—26.6 mm (av. 18.3 mm), females 16.0—20.2 mm (av. 17.3 mm).

Skull measurements (6 males and 5 females). Condylobasal length: males 49.5 — 52.3 mm (av. 50.5 mm), females 43.0 — 46.2 mm (av. 44.2 mm); zygomatic width: males 25.7 — 27.3 mm (av. 26.6 mm), females 20.0 — 24.5 mm (av. 22.6 mm); interorbital width: males 9.3 — 11.8 mm (av. 10.3 mm), females 8.1 — 10.0 mm (av. 9.2 mm); mastoid width: males 20.2 — 23.8 mm (av. 22.5 mm), females 18.7 — 19.4 mm (av. 19.0 mm); length of braincase: males 28.0 — 31.4 mm (av. 30.4 mm), females 26.6 — 27.8 mm (av. 27.3 mm); facial length: males 10.6 — 12.4 mm (av. 11.8 mm), females 9.2 — 10.0 mm (av. 9.7 mm); length of upper tooth row: males 13.0 — 15.3 mm (av. 14.5 mm), females 12.0 — 13.3 mm (av. 12.9 mm).

Systematic notes. This is a readily differentiated subspecies, recognized at first sight by its vivid and colorful fur. Systematically this subspecies should be placed closer to the nominate form than to the animal ranging in China, which latter Ognev (1931) took to be M. A. a s t a t u s Milne-Edwards (1870), described from materials from Muten (China). The latter has an even more vivid and intense color, and a peculiar coloration of the underparts (white with light straw-yellow or yellowish tinge on the belly; the white fied covering the lips and the chin extends to the throat and contrasts with the yellowish straw background of the chest; the intense brown of the outsides of the legs and the white color of the paws are also characteristic).

The systematic status of the animal occasionally encountered in southern areas of the Maritime Territory is as yet unsettled, since there are no collected materials from this area.

Materials studied. Transbaikalia — 14 specimens; the Amur Region - 1 specimen. Total — 15 specimens.

Biology. The habitat of the Altai weasel includes various biotopes, from the plain and mountain steppes of Transbaikalia and the reed thickets and tugai forest of the Semirech'e, to the high mountain landscapes of Southern Siberia and Central Asia, where it climbs as high as 3,500 m or more above sea level.

In Transbaikalia, according to A. A. Cherkasov (1867) and B. A. Kuznetsov (1929), this predator is encountered with equal frequency both in the steppes and in the taiga, and usually lives near human habitations. In villages it sometimes inhabits barns, sheds, and cellars. It occurs much more rarely far from human habitation, according to Kuznetsov. In the steppe it usually keeps close to colonies of the Daurian suslik (C i t e l l u s d a u r i c u s Brandt) and of Brandt's vole (M i c r o t u s brandti Radde). In the taiga belt Kuznetsov encountered it occasionally along river valleys.

On the Altai, the Sayans, the mountains near Lake Baikal, and the Yablonovyi Range, it lives chiefly in the taiga along riverain slopes and river valleys. It may also live above the timberline on alpine meadows and balds (Figure 136).

The nest is constructed in rodent burrows in cliff fissures, in cavities among stones, in tree roots, and in other natural shelters.

The Altai weasel moves quickly and adroitly, and has a brave and courageous nature, being fearless in its attack. It is notorious for its greediness, and if the occasion arises may kill more animals than it is able to eat.

FIGURE 136. Scrub thickets along mountain slopes in the northwestern Altai. Krasnoshchekov District, vicinity of Ust'-Pustynka. Biotope of the Altai weasel. Photo by B. S. Yudin

It is chiefly a nocturnal and crepuscular animal, but may occasionally hunt during the day.

The diet of the Semirech'e Altai weasel is generally similar to that of the Siberian weasel, the ermine, and other small carnivores; it feeds chiefly on Muridae, small birds, and other small animals. In Transbaikalia, according to A. S. Fetisov (1937), who examined the contents of 92 stomachs collected between November and January, the following percentages of various items were encountered: pikas and susliks — 35.3 %, Muridae— 37.1 %; small birds — 22.7%; fish — 1%. Of the birds, mostly small species occurred: pine buntings, common tits, bullfinches, meadow pipits, nuthatches, Daurian ptarmigan, etc.

Similar results were obtained in Transbaikalia by I. P. Brom. The 11 stomachs he examined showed the following percentages: rodents—99.1%, birds — 0.9%. The relationship between the rodent species was the following: Daurian pika — 27.2%; Daurian hamster — 9.1%; social vole — 36.5%; and Brandt's vole — 37.2%.

The Semirech'e weasel occasionally attacks hares, muskrats, gerbils, geese, pheasants and other animals (Sludskii, 1953).

Observations on reproduction are scanty. In Kazakhstan the rut occurs in February—March. At the end of March, large embryos are seen in the female obtained (Sludskii). On the Altai and the Western Sayan, according to my data, rut occurs in late February and March. The gestation period is apparently 40 days. The litter size is 2—8. The young grow and develop rapidly. At the age of two months, at the end of the

350

lactation period, they begin to lead an independent life. Young of the same litter stay together until autumn.

The animals' numbers, according to A. A. Sludskii (1953), undergo sharp variations, probably due to mass mortality from diseases and forest fires. The animal's fertility also probably varies with availability of food sources.

Molt occurs twice annually. The spring molt on the Altai and the Western Sayan occurs in March and terminates by May. Molt begins from the head and legs, extends to the neck, back and flanks, and then involves the croup and tail.

The complete replacement of the summer coat by winter fur occurs in the autumn [beginning], in September, and terminates about the first half of November. The autumn molt begins on the posterior part of the body, extends along the back, and gradually involves the head, flanks, underparts and limbs.

Practical importance. The animal's contribution to the fur trade is insignificant. It was seldom caught at all before the Revolution. Trade in the animal began to develop in 1920, and in the prewar years some 50,000 pelts were obtained. S. P. Naumov and N. P. Lavrov (1948) think that the animal remains unexploited almost throughout its range.

Pelts of the Altai weasel are not classified according to grades. The fur is usually dyed.

In agricultural areas the animal is beneficial, as it exterminates noxious Muridae.

15. Genus PUTORIUS Cuvier (1817). Polecats and minks

1817. Putorius. Cuvier, F. Regne Animal, 1, p. 147; Ognev, S. I. Zveri Vostochnoi Evropy i Severnoi Azii (Animals of Eastern Europe and Northern Asia). 2, pp. 666—668, Moskva. 1931; Stroganov, S. U. Opredelitel' mlekopitayushchikh Karelii (Key to Mammals of Karelia). p. 86, Petrozavodsk. 1949.

1840. Foetorius. Keyserling, A. and J. H. Blasius. Die Wirbelthiere Europas, p. 66 (type Mustela putorius L.).

1877. Cynomionax. Coues, E. Fur-bearing Animals. A Monograph of North American Mustelidae, p. 99.

Type species. Mustela putorius Linnaeus (1758).
Diagnosis. Similar in general to other true mustelids. Body build is slender and low. Length of body 290—562 mm, of tail 85—183 mm. Head relatively flat, with blunt muzzle and small ears, somewhat ovally blunted above. Fur fluffy, with dense light underfur and sparse, somewhat darker guard hair. Fur either uniformly colored throughout body or darker on ventral than on dorsal side. Head has clearly outlined "facial mask." Fur becomes more or less lighter for winter, but no complete whitening occurs.

Skull, in general form, is similar to that of mottled polecat Vormela, being differentiated from it only in a few structural details and odontological peculiarities. Skull is rather broad in occipital section, markedly narrow in postorbital area, and shorter in nasal part. Mastoid processes protrude conspicuously on either side. Hamular processes of pterygoid bones usually not joined with tympanic bullae by osseous bridges. Tympanic bullae rather large and weakly inflated with their width being approximately $\frac{3}{4}$ their length;

from above they are somewhat triangular — close anteriorly and markedly displaced posteriorly. Auditory tubes (meati) not developed. Paroccipital processes rudimentary. Distance between jugular foramina greater than one half length of tympanic bullae. Nasal bones expanded anteriorly and markedly tapering posteriorly in terminal part, wedging by their posterior ends between frontal bones. Only posterior parts of intermaxillaries are adjacent to the nasals.

Dental formula: $I\frac{3}{3}$; $C\frac{1}{1}$; $Pm\frac{3}{3}$; $M\frac{1}{2}$ = 34 teeth.

Lower carnassial tooth does not bear additional denticle on internal aspect of middle cusp. Talon of upper carnassial tooth bears sharp cusp. Upper molar broadened towards outside and bears a deep central constriction which imparts to crown a biscuit shape.

Geographical distribution. Europe, Asia (except for the southern part), North Africa, and North America. In the Soviet Union the range of the genus is the entire country except for the northern half of Siberia.

Systematic notes. The taxonomic position of the polecat and minks within family Mustelidae remains indefinite even at present, and has been treated differently by various students. Earlier works, such as Keyserling and Blasius (1840) and Blasius (1857) have justly, in my opinion, connected the polecats and minks with the true polecats, combining them in a single genus Foetorius Keys. and Blas. (1840). At the same time the minks were isolated by J. Wagner, also correctly in my opinion, in the distinct subgenus Lutreola Wagner (1841). This conception has been shared by later students, for instance by Trouessart (1898, 1910).

Subsequent authors have most often included the polecats and minks with the weasels and ermines (Mustela) or united them with the Siberian weasel Kolonocus.

D. Miller (1912) has combined the subgenera Putorius (s. str.) and Lutreola with Mustela s. str. in a single genus Mustela s. lato. A contemporary Soviet authority sharing this point of view is B. A. Kuznetsov (1944). K. A. Satunin (1914) also includes the Siberian weasels in Mustela s. lato, isolating them in the subgenus Kolonocus Satunin (1911). Miller's system, as corrected by Satunin, is accepted by the contemporary Soviet authority G. A. Novikov (1956). Ognev (1931) includes the polecats, minks, and Siberian weasels as individual subgenera within the single genus Putorius, while treating the weasels and ermines as members of genus Mustela.

Ellerman and Morrison-Scott (1951) include within genus Mustela s. lato (minks) the subgenus Mustela s. str., while isolating the polecats proper in a monotypical genus Putorius.

Anatomico-morphological studies show a great similarity between the above-mentioned members of this subfamily of Mustelidae, and point to the close kinship among them. At the same time, the species of this complex form differentiated homogeneous groups which reach a greater variety of degree of taxonomic differentiation than that provided for by the fixed taxonomic categories of subgenus and genus. The disagreements pertain only to evaluation of the rank of isolated groups.

After studying the extensive material available, I have come to the following conclusions as to the systematics of these animals. It should be noted above all that from form of the body, nature of the fur, and other external features, species can occasionally only be differentiated in combination with other morphological features.

The structure of the dental apparatus has no specific validity and is characteristic of many species which are distinctly differentiated by other features.

Skull structure is a reliable basis for isolation and creation of supraspecific systematic groups. By their craniological features, the above-mentioned subgenera are naturally grouped into two genera: Putorius, including the true polecat (Putorius s. str.) and the minks (Lutreola), and Mustela, including the weasels and ermines (Mustela s. str.) and the Siberian weasel Kolonocus.

The most essential craniological differences between the genera Putorius and Mustela, within the scope accepted in the present work, consist of structural peculiarities of the braincase and of the tympanic bullae.

The members of genus Putorius have relatively flat skulls, expanded in the occipital section, with powerfully developed and projecting mastoid processes; the tympanic bullae are triangular in plane and pyramidal in general form. The members of genus Mustela have skulls inflated in the cranial section and narrow in the occipital section, with rudimentary mastoid processes and with ovally elongated tympanic bullae, the latter lenticular in general form.

Extinct members of genus Putorius are known from the European Pliocene.

The number of species in genus Putorius is not as yet established. The fauna of the Soviet Union, including Siberia, contains four species, of which one, the American mink, is an introduced one set free in hopes of acclimatizing it.

Key to Subgenera and Species of Genus Putorius
Occurring in Siberia

1 (4). Color of fur not uniform; light underfur seen through dark tips of guard hair. Muzzle whitish, with characteristic "mask" in circumorbital area. Distance from choanal incisure to lower edge of foramen magnum appreciably less than mastoid width. . . . .
. . . . Subgenus Putorius s. str. (p. 355)

2 (3). Basal half of tail straw or rusty whitish, tip of tail black. Belly light yellowish-whitish. Postorbital part of skull relatively short, markedly tapered posteriorly (Figure 137, d). "Waist" (maximum constriction of postorbital area), when jaws are closed, seen in dorsal examination of skull to lie in front of line joining distal tips of coronary processes of lower jaws. . . . .
. . . . The Siberian polecat - Putorius eversmanni (p. 359)

3 (2). Tail black throughout length. Belly blackish. Postorbital part of skull relatively elongated, and slightly tapered posteriorly

(Figure 137, c). "Waist," when jaws are closed, seen in dorsal examination of skull to lie behind line joining distal ends of coronary processes of lower jaws . . . .
. . . . .The European or black polecat-**Putorius putorius** (p. 355)

4 (1).   Fur uniform in color (except for white lips and occasional white patches on throat, chest and belly); underfur black. Facial "mask" lacking. Hair of uniform length all over back. Distance from choanal incisure to lower edge of foramen magnum equal to mastoid width or slightly smaller. . . . . Subgenus **Lutreola** (p. 394)

5 (6).   Second upper premolar (Pm^2) adjacent only to anterior edge of the carnassial tooth (Figure 138, 2). External surface of upper jaw above carnassial tooth smooth . . . .
. . . . .The European mink - **P. (Lutreola) lutreola** (p. 395)

6 (5).   Second upper premolar (Pm^2) wedges into incisure between anterior and internal lobes of carnassial tooth (Figure 138, 1). External surface of upper jaw above anterior edge of carnassial tooth inflated in form of torulus, forming appreciable protrusion on lower edge of infraorbital foramen . . . .
. . . . The American mink **P. (Lutreola) vison** (p. 399)

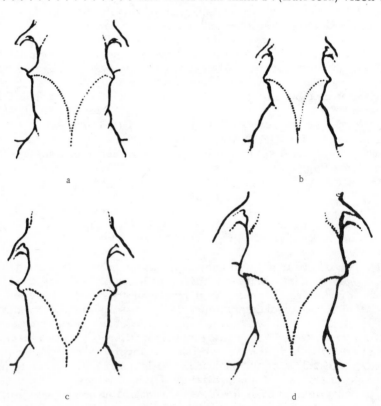

a

b

c

d

FIGURE 137. Region of postorbital skull constriction:

a — Siberian weasel, Mustela sibirica Pallas; b — Altai weasel, Mustela altaica Pallas; c — European or black polecat, Putorius putorius L.; d — Siberian polecat, Putorius eversmanni Lesson (after A. G. Novikov, 1956).

1. Subgenus P u t o r i u s s. str. True polecats

Synonymy: See the description of the genus.

Type species of the subgenus. M u s t e l a p u t o r i u s Linnaeus (1758).

Diagnosis. Dimensions relatively large. Length of body with head up to 562 mm, tail approximately one third as long. Head relatively slightly flattened and muzzle somewhat blunted. Heel pads hidden by fur in winter. Hair markedly longer on rear part of back than on mid-back. Fur color not monotonous: lighter color of underfur seen through dark tips of guard hair. Edges of ears have light fringe. Skull bulky, expanded in area of baincase, and elevated in frontal region. Postorbital processes well developed. Distance from choanal incisure to lower edge of foramen magnum appreciably less than mastoid width of skull. Width between external edges of occipital condyles equal to or almost equal to width of rostrum above canines. Mastoid width of skull more than one half its condylobasal length.

FIGURE 138. Structure of skull in area of upper carnassial tooth and infraorbital foramina of minks:

1 — the American mink, P u t o r i u s v i s o n Gray; 2 — the European mink, P u t o r i u s l u t r e o l a L.; arrow shows ridge on the upper jaw (after S. U. Stroganov, 1949).

Os penis thicker and more massive than in sable. Base of bone laterally compressed and tip hamately bent. Distal part of ventral aspect has a groove, which continues onto the hamate curvature.

The mode of life is terrestrial.

Geographical distribution. The range of the subgenus coincides with that of the genus. Fauna of the Soviet Union contains two species, which also occur in Siberia.

23. **Putorius (s. str.) putorius** Linnaeus (1758).
Black or European polecat

1758. M u s t e l a p u t o r i u s. Linnaeus, C. Systema Naturae, ed. X, 1, p. 46.
1785. M u s t e l a i l t i s. Boddaert. Elenchus Animalium, 1, p. 87, Quadrupeda.
1798. V i v e r a f o e t e n s. Thunberg. Beskrifning pa Sevenske Djur, p. 15.
1811. M u s t e l a p u t o r i u s. Pallas, P. S. — Zoographia Rosso-Asiatica, 1, p. 87, Petropoli. (partim); Ellerman, J. R.
T. C. S. Morrison-Scott. Checklist of Palaearctic and Indian Mammals, pp. 215—321, London. 1951.
1827. P. (u t o r i u s) v u l g a r i s. Griffiths. Cuvier's Animal Kingdom, 5, p. 120.

1843. Putorius foetidus. Gray, J. List of Species Mamm.
Brit. Mus., p. 64; Greve, K. Die Geograph. Verbreit. der jetzt lebend.
Raubthiere, pp. 180—183.

1850. Putorius verus. Simashko, Yu. Russkaya fauna (Russian
Fauna). 2, p. 357, Sankt-Peterburg.

1857. Putorius putorius. Blasius. Säugethiere Deutschlands,
p. 222; Barret-Hamilton.— Ann. Mag. Nat. Hist., Ser. 7, 13, p. 389;
Trouessart. Faune Mamm. d'Europe, p. 76, 1910; Satunin, K. A. Opredelit€
mlekopitayushchikh Rossiiskoi imperii (Key to Mammals of the Russian
Empire). p. 115, Tiflis. 1914.

1944. Mustela (Putorius) putorius. Bobrinskii, N. A. Otryad
khishchnye (Order Carnivores).— In: Opredelitel' mlekopitayushchikh SSSI
edited by N. A. Bobrinskii, p. 125, Moskva; Novikov, G. A. Khishchnye
mlekopitayushchie fauny SSSR (Carnivorous Mammals of the Fauna of the
USSR). pp. 147—158, Moskva-Leningrad. 1956.

1949. Putorius (s. str.) putorius. Stroganov, S. U. Opredelitel'
mlekopitayushchikh Karelii (Key to Mammals of Karelia). pp. 87 — 89,
Petrozavodsk.

Type and type locality. Uppsala, Sweden.

Diagnosis. Tail black or brownish black throughout its length.
Underparts blackish and not divided by broad light field. Skull, behind
postorbital processes, tapers very weakly posteriorly, not forming
conspicuous "waist." With jaws closed, maximum constriction of postorbit€
area lies behind tip of coronary processes of lower jaw.

Measurements. Length of body with head: males 350—460 mm, female
290—340 mm; length of tail: males 115—150 mm, females 85—123 mm;
length of hind paw: males 42.5—60.0 mm, females 33.0—47.0 mm; height o
ear: males 23.0—30.0 mm, females 20.0—25.0 mm. Weight: males up to
1,070 g, females 1,360 g.

Condylobasal lenght of skull: males 59.0—70.0 mm, females
51.3—60.0 mm; zygomatic width: males 35.0—41.8 mm, females
30.0—34.5 mm; interorbital width: males 16.0 — 19.4 mm, females
12.6—16.2 mm; width behind supraorbital processes: males 14.6—17.8 mr
females 13.3—15.2 mm; width of rostrum above canines: males
14.0—17.4 mm, females 11.5—15.2 mm; height in area of tympanic bullae:
males 23.0—27.0 mm, females 20.0—22.0 mm; length of upper tooth row:
males 18.3—21.2 mm; females 15.7—18.2 mm.

Description. Only slightly smaller than the Siberian polecat
(see measurements). Body build strong, body muscular but slender, legs
short.

Winter fur very long and luxuriant. Upper part glossy blackish brown.
Guard hairs have light bases and dark black-brown tips. Underfur dense,
light straw yellow-rusty and readily seen through the long and relatively spars€
guard hair. Lips and chin pure white. Area between eyes and ears, as wel
as ears' edges, silvery white. Tail completely black-brown. Belly
blackish.

Summer fur markedly shorter and sparser than winter fur, with grayer
color, lacking the gloss characteristic of winter fur.

Young about one year old have monotonous gray to grayish brown tone. In fall they acquire color of adults.

Length of adult os penis 36.0 — 40.3 mm.

Skull (Figure 139) bulky and very large, low, moderately expanded in occipital portion, slightly constricted in postorbital area, and shortened in rostral part. Frontal area markedly inflated and forms hump above braincase. Sagittal and occipital crests very conspicuous in adults, particularly in males. Postorbital processes relatively small. Mastoid processes massive and large. Skull moderately constricted in postorbital area, the narrowest places in this area, the so-called "waist," being (with jaws closed) found behind tips of coronary processes and not anterior to them as in Siberian polecat; this is the principal craniological difference between the European polecat and its nearest relative, the Siberian polecat Putorius eversmanni. Nasal bones expanded anteriorly, and sharply and markedly tapering to rear with posterior part wedged between frontal bones. Nasal aperture compressed laterally, with height markedly greater than width. Infraorbital foramina ovally elongated and lying somewhat obliquely. Tympanic bullae elevated in posterior half. Carotid foramen lies nearer to anterior edge of bullae. Antero-internal corners of auditory bullae show no processes connecting with ends of hamular processes. Hamular processes highly recurved externally, forming peculiar hooks. Paroccipital processes rudimentary.

Sexual dimorphism manifested in body size and weight and in size of skull (see measurements). Male skull characterized by rough and angular outlines and more developed crests.

Systematic notes. The systematic relationship between the black polecat and P. eversmanni is dealt with below in the description of P. eversmanni.

The intraspecific systematic differentiation of P. putorius must be left unsettled, due to paucity of material. I will note only that several subspecies have been described for Western Europe, these differing chiefly in dimensions and in fur color.

From the steppe areas of the Ukraine a subspecies P. p. orientalis Brauner (1929) has been described, this being distinguished, according to its author, by a lighter color.

The Transural area is probably penetrated by the nominate subspecies, which is characterized by relatively small size and by less luxuriant but relatively lighter winter fur.

Geographical distribution. Occupies almost all of Europe east to the Siberian slopes of the Central Urals, inclusively. In the last few decades the species has extended its range to the north and east. The movement of the European polecat in this direction follows changes in the landscape due to extension of agriculture in forest and steppe areas.

Data on distribution in the Siberian Transurals are scanty. L. P. Sabaneev (1874) recorded the northern boundary in the former Perm Province as 58°N lat. According to I. Ya. Slovtsov (1892) the species is encountered in the southern part of the former Tobolsk Province in the Tyumen, Ishim, and other districts. It is more or less established that at present the animal occurs occasionally on the eastern side of the Urals; in the

Sverdlovsk Region it reaches Irbit, from which its eastern boundary descends along the slope of the Urals almost to Orsk, where it turns west (Kuznetsov, 1944).

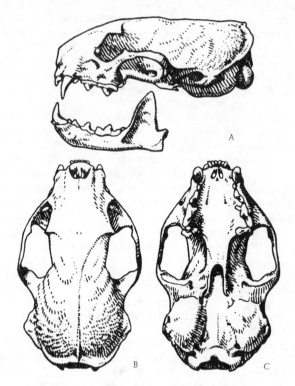

FIGURE 139. Skull of European polecat, Putorius putorius L. (original):

A — lateral view; B — dorsal view; C — ventral view.

The data presented, however, need corroboration. S. V. Kirikov (1952) mentions that he has no information on the distribution of the black polecat on the southern tip of the Urals. V. N. Pavlinin (in litt.) told me that the European polecat is at present nonexistent in the Transurals, according to data collected by him; the eastern boundary of its range extends west of Sverdlovsk.

Biology. The European polecat is a denizen of open forests, copses, meadows, and fields. It occurs in a variety of forest biotopes, especially on clearings, forest margins, among wooded glades, and in copses, river floodplains, fields, etc. It does not avoid human habitation and often lives in mills, barns, barnyards, grain and hay stacks, cellars and even attics of inhabited houses. It is occasionally encountered on the outskirts of large cities.

In the winter it often concentrates among unthreshed grain stacks or haystacks, being attracted by the abundance of Muridae. It is often encountered on the shores of nonfreezing rivers, where it catches frogs and dead fish.

The animal's diet has been relatively well studied only from the point of view of food objects and seasonal changes in them. The food of the polecat is variegated and consists of small animals. The first place in the diet is occupied by Muridae, followed by amphibians (toads and frogs) and birds.

Rut occurs only once annually, from late March till early May. The gestation period is about 40 days. The litter size is 2—12, but more often 4—6. The young open their eyes at the age of one month. The brood stays together with the mother till the autumn and occasionally even as late as the beginning of the next spring. For its daily rest and for nests, the animal uses various natural shelters, only rarely digging a burrow itself. It will make its home in the most variegated places, such as in heaps of stones or brushwood, under stumps, hollows, under bridges, cellars, in discarded badger or fox burrows, etc. The nest is lined with fur, down, feathers, moss, dry grass, leaves and other soft materials.

The animal's population dynamics are not sufficiently studied. Cases are known of a sharp rise and fall in the population, but the causes are as yet unknown.

Molt occurs twice annually: in spring and fall. The beginning of spring molt is March. By November the winter fur is complete.

The polecat is a nocturnal animal. Its senses are as well developed as those of its nearest relative.

Practical importance. The fur is considered good and valuable. The harm inflicted on game and domestic fowl is markedly smaller than the benefit received from the animal's being a fur-bearing animal and from its destruction of large numbers of noxious murine rodents.

Material studied. Central regions of the European USSR — 26 specimens, the Urals — 2 specimens. Total — 28 specimens.

24. **Putorius**(s. str.) **eversmanni** Lesson (1827).
Siberian or white polecat (Map XVIII)

1811. M u s t e l a p u t o r i u s. Pallas, P. S. Zoographia Rosso-Asiatica, 1, pp. 87 — 89 (partim).
1827. M u s t e l a e v e r s m a n n i. Lesson, R. Manuel de Mammologie ou histoire naturelle de Mammifères, p. 144, Paris.
1862. M u s t e l a p u t o r i u s. Radde, G. Reisen im Süden von Ost-Sibirien in den Jahren 1855 — 59. — Säugethierefauna, Bd. 1, pp. 39 — 45, St. Petersburg.
1913. M u s t e l a l i n e i v e n t e r. Hollister, N. — Proc. Biol. Soc. Washington, 26, p. 2. (Chagan Burgazy, the Altai).
1914. P u t o r i u s e v e r s m a n n i. Satunin, K. A. Opredelitel' mlekopitayushchikh Rossiiskoi imperii (Key to Mammals of the Russian Empire). p. 116, Tiflis; Bannikov, A. G. Mlekopitayushchie Mongol'skoi Narodnoi Respubliki (Mammals of the Mongolian People's Republic). pp. 87 — 91, Moskva. 1954.

1944. M u s t e l a (P u t o r i u s) e v e r s m a n n i. Bobrinskii, N. A. Otryad khishchnye (Order Carnivores).— In: Opredelitel' mlekopitayushchikh SSSR, edited by Prof. N. A. Bobrinskii, p. 126, Moskva; Novikov, G. A. Khishchnye mlekopitayushchie fauny SSSR (Carnivorous Mammals of the Fauna of the USSR). pp. 152—157, Moskva-Leningrad.

Type and type locality. The species has been described from a specimen collected in the steppe "between Orenburg and Bukhara." Details are given in the description of the nominate subspecies.

Diagnosis. Tail straw or rusty whitish in basal half and dark or black on tip. Belly light yellowish-whitish. Skull more or less sharply compressed behind postorbital processes (Figure 137). "Waist" (maximum constriction of postorbital area) lies, with jaws closed, at level of tips of coronary processes.

Measurements. Length of body with head: males 370 — 562 mm, females 295 — 520 mm; length of tail: males 80—183 mm, females 95—180 mm; length of hind paw: males 40—80 mm, females 43—72 mm; height of ear: males 23—26 mm, females 20—23 mm. Weight: males up to 2,050 g, females up to 1,350 g.

Condylobasal length of skull: males 61.7—82.2 mm, females 52.4—76.6 mm; zygomatic width: males 30.0— 58.9 mm, females 30.0—76.7 mm; interorbital width: males 15.9—24.2 mm, females 14.0—19.5 mm; width behind supraorbital processes: males 12.0—17.2 mm, females 11.3—15.3 mm; width of rostrum above canines: males 15.3—21.1 mm, females 13.2—17.4 mm; height in area of auditory capsules: males 23.0—33.5 mm, females 22.0—27.6 mm; length of upper tooth row: males 19.0—25.5 mm, females 18.0—24.2 mm.

Description. Somewhat larger than the European polecat (see measurements). Body build more slender and light.

Winter fur relatively long and soft, with dense underfur and sparse guard fur. Fur relatively pale, varying individually and geographically from straw yellow-whitish to rusty yellowish and rusty ocher of varying intensity, with sparse brown-black gloss formed by dark colored tips of guard hair. General tone on middle and posterior area of back darker than on anterior back and on flanks. Belly light straw yellow. Head shows facial area characteristic pattern of more or less marked coffee to gray brown "mask"; lips, chin, tips of ears, and sometimes forehead whitish or silvery white; occipital part same shade as facial "mask," but less intense; diffusely outlined patches lying anteriorly at base of ears are of same color (Figure 140). Head color becomes paler with age of animal, then disappears completely and entire head becomes silvery white. The chest, limbs and groin area are black-brown. Tip of tail is brownish black.

Summer fur shorter than winter fur, coarser, and with markedly more developed yellowish russet tinge.

Length of adult os penis 37.0—46.0 mm.

Skull (Figure 141) larger than that of European polecat, more bulky, particularly in occipital area, and usually markedly compressed in postorbital area. Frontal area with various degrees of inflation, but always flatter than in P u t o r i u s p u t o r i u s. Sagittal and occipital crests mostly well developed, particularly in adults and old males. Postorbital processes usually massive and very large but sometimes rudimentary, particularly in

aberrant individuals with weakly marked constriction of postorbital area.
Mastoid processes massive, large, and diverge markedly to either side.
Skull usually markedly tapered posteriorly in postorbital area (Figure 137).
Narrowest place in this area (so-called "waist"), in dorsal examination
of skull with jaws closed, seen to lie anterior to line joining upper ends of
coronary processes (compression of postorbital area ("waist") in
Putorius putorius, on the contrary, lies behind this line). This
feature is valid even in those relatively rare cases in which the "waist"
is very poorly developed (as in the European polecat).

FIGURE 140. Siberian or white polecat, Putorius eversmanni Lesson. Photo by B.S. Yudin

Nasals relatively broad anteriorly and taper gradually posteriorly,
wedging between frontal bones. Infraorbital foramina ovally elongated
and obliquely situated.
Tympanic bullae less expanded in posterior half than in European
polecat. Carotid foramen lies approximately in middle of inner side of
bulla. Paroccipital processes rudimentary. As a rule, no bony
processes extend from anterior angle of tympanic bullae, but this may
occur exceptionally; a single case is known to me when these processes
fused with the hamular processes of the pterygoid bones as in members
of genus Vormela (the mottled polecat). Tips of hamular processes
usually not bent out in form of distinctly marked hooks.
Sexual dimorphism manifested, as in European polecat, in dimensions
of body and skull: males are markedly larger than females (see
measurements). In the females the skull crests are less pronounced,
giving the skull a smoother outline.

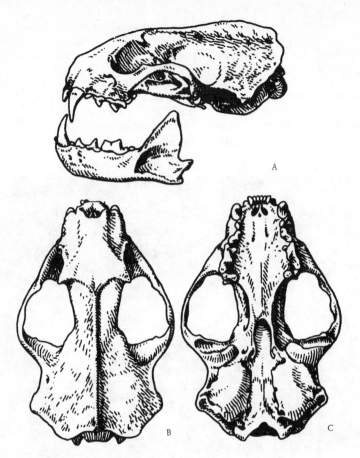

FIGURE 141. Skull of the Siberian of white polecat, P u t o r i u s
e v e r s m a n n i Lesson (original):

A — lateral view; B — dorsal view; C — ventral view.

Systematic notes. P. e v e r s m a n n i is taxonomically very close to
P. p u t o r i u s, being related by a number of features characteristic of
subgenus P u t o r i u s s. str. and presented in the description of the
latter. These are: the principal habitus-traits of the two polecats, the
structure of the os penis, craniological features, and some other organiza-
tional peculiarities. These peculiarities of the two polecat species have
given rise to a fundamental difference of opinion among numerous
zoologists concerning the systematic relationship between them; some
combine them in a single species, while others separate them in two.

The Siberian or white polecat P. e v e r s m a n n i was for a long time
after its original description treated as a variety of the European polecat
P. p u t o r i u s (for instance, in the works of E. Eversmann (1850), G. Radde
(1862), and V. Blasius (1884) among others).

J. Gray (1869) was the first to correctly define the systematic position
of the Siberian polecat, endowing it with the rank of independent species

on the basis of the characteristic craniological properties of P. eversmanni, namely, the appreciable constriction ("waist") of the postorbital
area of the skull. The specific nature of this feature was also confirmed
by Hensel (1881) in his study of skulls of the species of genus Putorius.

The specific autonomy of P. putorius and P. eversmanni has
been firmly established by such authorities as Miller (1912), Satunin
(1907, 1914), and Ognev (1931), along with a number of other mammologists.

It has been demonstrated from accumulated collection material that the
structure of the postorbital area of the P. eversmanni skull shows a
variation, occasionally skull specimens being found which distinctly lack
the marked constriction of the postorbital area (i. e., lack the so-called
"waist"). This serves for some authors as grounds for combining these
polecat species into one species and including the name P. eversmanni
in the synonymy of P. putorius, the difference between these polecats
being assigned only subspecific rank. Pocock's paper (1936) and the new
monograph by J. R. Ellerman and T. C. S. Morrison-Scott (1951) treat the
systematics of the polecat in such a manner.

The above-mentioned conception is not supported by the facts, and
indeed contradicts clearly established facts. These authors probably
lacked the material which would have given them a proper orientation in
the problem.

Those, who along with Pocock classify the Siberian and the European
polecats as a single species, are essentially given to the false assumption
of the existence of supposed transitional individuals and of a supposed
geographical variability. However, the presence in nature of such
"transitionals" has yet to be proved for polecats. Now, only individuals
which cannot reliably be included in a definite species can really be
called transitional. The collections of the Zoological Institute of the
Academy of Sciences of the USSR, of the Zoological Museum of Moscow
University, and of other Soviet scientific museums contain not a single
adult polecat specimen which could not be diagnosed from the totality of
systematic features.

The published data on transitional individuals are either bald statements
of the existence of the phenomenon, lacking any indication of how it is
manifested, or are references to a single variational property. Thus,
for instance, Ognev (1931) writes, "transitional forms (perhaps hybrids)
occur near the distribution boundary between the Siberian and the
European (light and dark) polecat ranges." Similar statements are made
by E. V. Sharleman (1915), P. A. Sviridenko (1935) and some other authors.
It is quite clear that these data present nothing which would permit
taxonomic evaluation of the alleged "transitional forms."

On the other hand, individuals which distinctly deviate in some feature
are taken as transitional forms. These are most often specimens of
P. eversmanni either lacking or having only poorly developed the
compression ("waist") in the area of the postorbital skull constriction.
Such individual skull variations are usually found in specimens which
in their other systematic features (structure of hair, color, craniological
details, etc.) without any doubt belong to P. eversmanni. They occur
extremely rarely and are probably not localized geographically. Pocock
(1936) bases his merging of the European and Siberian polecats into a
single species on such material, but such material only indicates

a deviation and as such has no systematic validity — it only makes diagnosis of the polecats difficult.

As shown above in the species diagnosis and description, the differences between the Siberian and European polecats are not confined to the form of the skull compression in the postorbital area and to the formation of the "waist," but are also based on other features.

The following principal features are specific for diagnosis of the polecat species:

1. The tail of P. putorius is black throughout its entire length; in P. eversmanni only the terminal third of the tail is black, while the basal half is light straw yellow.

2. The ventral side of the body of P. putorius is completely dark brown; in P. eversmanni the dark color is divided by a broad light field on the belly, with an occasional dark band extending along it.

3. The dorsal side of P. putorius is dark glossy black-brown; in P. eversmanni it is light rusty yellowish with an occasional diluted blackish brown tinge.

4. The postorbital area of the skull of P. putorius is moderately compressed, not forming a conspicuous "waist"; in P. eversmanni there is usually a clearly marked "waist."

5. The narrowest place in the skull's (with jaws closed) postorbital area is in dorsal view as follows: at a level behind the line joining the tips of the coronary processes in P. putorius, and in front of this line in P. eversmanni.

Zoogeographical data point to the specific validity of the animals examined. Their ranges overlap in an extensive area of the southern European USSR as well as in a number of localities in western Europe. Almost one half of the range of P. putorius lies within the distribution area of P. eversmanni.

The overlapping ranges of the Siberian and the European polecats is itself enough to rule out the idea of their being taxonomically identical.

Each of the polecats occupies its own characteristic habitat. P. putorius is a denizen of open forests, copses, meadows and fields, and gravitates to human habitation. In contrast to this, P. eversmanni avoids both the presence of man and woody biotopes, preferring open landscapes — steppes and semi-deserts. However, this does not exclude contact between the two species, and occasionally, under special conditions, they may inhabit the same habitat. Nevertheless, if hybrids between them do occur it is only under exceptional conditions. At any rate, reliable known finds of hybrids are extremely rare and this indicates sexual isolation — a quality which is extremely characteristic of species difference.

We should note that geographical variation is also differently manifested in the two polecats. In P. eversmanni the range of geographical variation is broad and includes overall dimensions of body and skull, hair structure, hair color, claw structure, and other features. Some 17 subspecies of P. eversmanni have been described so far, more or less differing on the basis of the above-mentioned features. In P. putorius, on the contrary, geographical variation is weak and only 2—3 subspecies, slightly differing in size and color, are known.

Geographical variation is also manifested in a peculiar way in these polecats. Thus in the eastern part of the P.putorius range a lightening of fur color is observed, while P.eversmanni in the same localities, on the contrary, has darker fur; this feature is observed for instance in the Ukraine and was noted in 1923 by A. A. Brauner.

Thus the morphological, biological and zoogeographical data can in no way be taken as grounds for a combination of the Siberian and European polecats into a single species but, on the contrary, point categorically to the species distinction between these different though related species.

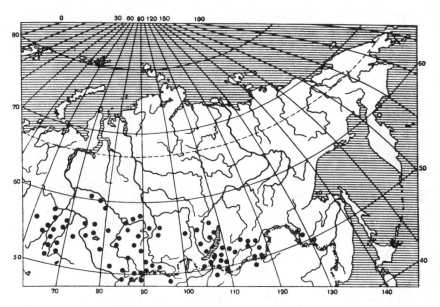

MAP XVIII. Geographical distribution of the Siberian polecat, Putorius eversmanni Lesson, in Siberia

From South Asia a number of polecats have been described whose systematic position is so far not clear to me; I have not encountered them in the field and the scanty literature on these animals is of little use taxonomically. These are: P.larvatus Hodgson (1849), inhabiting Tibet and Kashmir; P.tibetanus Horsfield (1851), described from southern Tibet; P. tiarata Hollister (1913), described from material from Kansu; and "Mustela putorius admirata" Pocock (1936), from Northeast China. It is possible that these polecats are subspecies of the Siberian polecat. Ellerman and Morrison-Scott include them with the "European polecat" as subspecies. The question is as yet unsolved.

Geographical distribution. The Siberian or light polecat ranges through the steppe and forest steppe zones of Eurasia from Hungary and Yugoslavia to the Amur steppes of Siberia, and south to the steppe areas of Central Asia, of Mongolia, and of Northeast China.

In the Soviet Union it occurs in forest steppe and steppe areas of the European part and of Siberia, in the Crimea, the Caucasus, Kazakhstan, and in the Central Asian republics.

In Siberia it ranges from the southern part of the Urals in the west to the valley of the lower Bureya in the east (Map XVIII). We present below some details on the polecat's distribution in Siberia.

On the eastern side of the Central Urals it was collected in July 1917 by N. Volchanetskii in the area of Lake Sinara, south of the city of Sverdlovsk, at about 56°10'N lat. (coll. Zool. Mus. Moscow University). In the northeastern direction, according to V. N. Pavlinin (in litt.) the Siberian polecat ranges up to Irbit (57°30'N lat.), and apparently further approximately to the city of Tobolsk. S. A. Kuklin (1937) reports the northern boundary in the Urals to be the upper Sosva River. Unfortunately, however, this author did not substantiate this boundary. In the northeastern part of the Sverdlovsk Region there have been catches in the Zaikovo, Baikalovo, Krasnopolyanskoe, Irbitsk and Turinskaya Slaboda districts. In the Ivdel, Gari and Tabory areas of the same region the polecat does not occur at present.

In Siberia, the northern boundary generally coincides with the southern boundary of the taiga, extending into the taiga only in some unwooded cropland areas.

According to information collected by Telegin (in litt.) the polecat has been obtained in the area of Tobolsk and also in the Dubrovnoe area (Laptev, 1958). In the former Tyumen County it was collected near Zharkovo in 1900 by D. Wardropper (coll. Zool. Inst. Acad. Sciences USSR). In the Tyumen District, according to statistics of recent years collected by F. D. Shaposhnikov (in litt.), it occurs no further north than the Velizhany, Vagai, and Yarkovo areas. Further east it was collected in 1909 by V. Ushakov near the city of Tara, on the right shore of the Irtysh (coll. Zool. Mus. Moscow University). According to P. Stepanov, it ranges in the valley of the middle Oni and Tara rivers. From here the northern boundary of the range, following the southern fringe of the taiga zone in the Novosibrisk Region, climbs north along the Ob River valley and enters the Tomsk Region.

The range in the Tomsk Region is scantily described. The old data from N. F. Kashchenko (1900) on its distribution within the Tomsk territory are simply not correct. Within the present boundaries of the Tomsk Region it is encountered only in the south. I. P. Laptev (1953) reports the boundary to extend along the Teterenka River to the village of Bakchar and from there to Minaevka village (between the mouths of the Ulu-Yul and Chichka-Yul), and further southeastwards along the right bank of the Chulym River. G. E. Ioganzen (1923) considers it a common species on the Chulym. On the Chulym the boundary passes somewhat north of Krasnoyarsk and runs on to the northern shore of the Baikal, skirts the lake, and then extends from Ust-Barguzin to the valley of the lower Bureya. Yudin collected the polecat near the city of Tomsk and the village of Kozhevnikovo.

The following data describe the polecat distribution south of the above-mentioned boundary.

According to Shaposhnikov's data (in litt.), within the Tyumen Region the polecat is obtained in large numbers in the Tyumen, Isevskoe,

Yurginskoe, Golyshmanovo, Uporovsk, Ishimsk and Berdyuzhsk areas, and is encountered, but in low numbers, in the Novo-Zaimka, Armizonskoe, Aromashevsko, and Vikulovsko areas.

In Kurgan, Omsk and Novosibirsk, according to available data, the Siberian polecat is widely distributed, inhabiting appropriate biotopes with maximal density.

FIGURE 142. The Ukok Plateau, Southern Altai. Biotope of the Siberian polecat. Photo by K. T. Yurlov

In the former Omsk District it was collected in 1928 by S. S. Turov. Collections exist from the area between Omsk and Petropavlovsk (coll. Zool. Mus. Moscow University), from the Baraba Steppe, and particularly from the vicinity of Lake Chany and the city of Novosibirsk (coll. S. U. Stroganov). M. D. Zverev (1931) reports that according to fur trade statistics for the years 1928—1929 polecats are particularly abundant, and that in the steppe areas of Western Siberia and in the Minusinsk Steppes the polecat was abundant in the 1930s in the Kiprinskoe area (between Barnaul and Kamen' na Obi) were a reserve then existed. K. A. Satunin obtained a polecat in 1900 in the vicinity of Ubinskoe (coll. Zool. Mus. Moscow University).

The polecat was obtained in the Kulunda Steppe in 1909 by Ioganzen (near the village of Pylkovo), and was collected in 1949 by Telegin and Yurlov south of Lake Chana and west of the village of Pankrushikha and by Yudin in the Pavlovsk area. It was collected near Zmeinogorsk in 1910 by a local amateur zoologist, the precentor A. I. Lavrov, near the villages of Novenskoe (coll. Zool. Mus. Moscow University) and of Lokot (coll. Zool. Inst. Acad. Sciences USSR). According to V. N. Savinov (1953) it occurs in all districts of the Altai Territory. G. N. Likhachev writes (1930) that it is encountered in the upper Ob pine forest.

On the Altai it is widely distributed, and the well-known explorer P. K. Kozlov collected it in 1899 near Altaiskoe village in the southern Altai and in 1900 near Lake Tan-Gul-Nor in the eastern Altai (coll. Zool. Inst. Acad. Sciences USSR) (Figure 142). Kashchenko (1899, 1902) mentioned specimens of the animal obtained in Cherga, Rybnushka Mako and at Shabalin village, as well as near Lake Chebok-Kol on the upper reaches of the Ulagan River. A. P. Razorenova (1939) collected it on the Bukhtarma River at the village of Sennoe and near the village of Khankhara. In the area of Uimen on the upper Katun River the polecat was obtained in 1847 by P. Romanov, taxidermist to Prof. E. A. Eversmann (coll. Zool. Inst. Acad. Sciences USSR). In the Ust'-Koksa area, according to A. A. Nasimovich (1949), fur trade statistics show that on the average, over the years, the Siberian polecat occupies second place (after the ermine). In the southeastern Altai, according to A. M. Kolosov (1939), the steppe polecat can be considered a rather common species and inhabits both the level part of the Chuya Steppe proper and the mountain ranges surrounding it. In the valley of the Chagan-Burgazy River the Siberian polecat was reported by Hollister (1913), who described the — in his opinion — new species Putorius lineiventer. Judging by all available data, this is nothing but our Putorius eversmanni Lesson. V. I. Osmolovskaya obtained the Siberian polecat in the alpine zone along the River Sarzhemata (A. M. Kolosov, 1939), and B. S. Yudin noted it many times in 1958 in the Chuya Steppe — along the Yustyd River and in the vicinity of Tashanta; according to his observations it abounds in the two localities.

According to K. T. Yurlov (personal communication), it is widely distributed on the Ukok Plateau, and this author observed the polecat in 1959 in the valleys of the Ak-Alakh and Ak-Kol (near lakes Kaldzhin Kul and Zerlyu-Kul), on the Bugyumyz and Ogyuz-Simas passes, and at the sources of the Dzhumala River; it was also obtained near Lake Muzdy-Bulak (coll. S. U. Stroganov),

It was obtained in the Kemerovo Region by V. N. Skalon (coll. Zool. Mus. Moscow University), and in the Gornaya Shoriya Gol'tsmaier writes (1935) that it is common in the steppe and on cropland and extremely rare in the taiga section (Figure 143).

It was encountered near Krasnoyarsk by A. Ya. Tugarinov in 1912 — close to the village of Ladeika some 7 km from the city (coll. Zool. Inst. Acad. Sciences USSR). V. Torgashev caught it in 1946 at Zamyatino village (coll. Zool. Mus. Moscow University). Near Shivera village on the Yenisei River, some 60 km below Krasnoyarsk, it was obtained in 1931 by K. A. Yudin (coll. Zool. Mus. Moscow University). In the former Kansk District, according to V. N. Troitskii (1930), it was obtained in areas adjacent to the Abakan, Taseevo and Shitka steppes.

In Khakasiya, the polecat is the most common species of mammal on the Abakan and Minusinsk steppes, from which collections made by F. F. Shilinger (coll. Zool. Mus. Moscow University) are available (see also P. Polikevich, 1923). O. Thomas (1912) reported that the Siberian polecat inhabits the valley of the Kemchik in the Tannu-Ola along with neighboring areas of Mongolia (Lake Achit-Nur). According to A. I. Yanushkevich (1952) it is encountered everywhere in Tuva except for the east Tuva highland, and on the Tannu-Ola Range is obtained along the upper reaches of the Elegest River. O. I. Gavrilov presented us with a specimen obtained in the vicinity of Chaa-Khol, which lies near the mouth of the Chaa-Khol River to the west of the city of Kyzyl.

FIGURE 143. A pine forest in Kulunda. Biotope of the Siberian polecat. Photo by K. T. Yurlov

According to G. Radde (1862) it occurs in the Sayans and on the Baikal Range. On the Eastern Sayan it was obtained near Mondy village, some 25 km from Lake Kosogol (coll. S. I. Ognev).

It is relatively rare in the Irkutsk Region. The northern boundary of its range here, according to I. P. Kopylov (1940) and other authors, runs through the southern parts of the Shitka and Bratsk areas and the northern part of the Ust'-Uda area. It is encountered, though more rarely, on the upper reaches of the Lena River in the Kachug area and the southern part of the Zhigalovo area. South of the above-mentioned localities the greatest density occurs in forest steppe areas and in areas adjacent to the railroad in the Baikal country.

In the Baikal country the region of Bayandai, Ust'-Ordynsk, and the Alarsk Steppe provided Skalon with specimens (coll. Zool. Mus. Moscow University). It occurs throughout the Sayan area, but chiefly in the eastern part.

In Transbaikalia the distribution area includes the vast forest steppe and steppe belt. Details of the northern and eastern boundaries of the range here are, however, incomplete.

On the eastern shore of the Baikal it extends north probably no further than the mouth of the Barguzin River.

Radde (1862) noted the polecat in the valley of the Uda River, in the Yablonovyi Range, and on the lower reaches of the Zeya, but his data concerning polecat distribution in the Bureya Mountains have not been confirmed by subsequent studies. A. Cherkasov (1867) mentions it in his list of animals occurring in the southwestern part of Transbaikalia. Kashchenko (1910, 1912) examined collections obtained around Troitskosavsk (now Kyakhta) and in the Aginsk Steppe. Skalon collected the species over a number of years in the Dzhida River valley, the delta of the Selenga River, on the Selenga's right tributary the Uda, and on its left tributary the Orongoi, near the city of Kyakhta, near Sharagol village on the right bank of the Chikoi River, in the area of the village Okino-Klyuchi on the left bank of the Khilok River, and on the Tsagan Daban Range (coll. Zool. Mus. Moscow University). B. A. Kuznetsov (1929) found the animal on the Yablonovyi Range, (Kyker village) and in its foothills (Zyuizikan village), in the forest steppe along the Nercha River (the city of Nerchinsk), on the Udinskii Range (Kalinino village), along the Onon River (the village of Staryi Chindant) and in the Daurian Steppes (Kulusutai village). In the Borzya area it was collected by Yu. Popov and P. B. Yurgenson (coll. Zool. Mus. Moscow University). According to E. I. Pavlov (1948) it occurs on the upper reaches of the Chita, but in insignificant numbers.

South of the Amur Region it was discovered in 1931 by Naidenov in the vicinity of Poyarkovo Station , near the village of Chesnokovo (coll. S. I. Ognev).

Survey of subspecies. The Siberian polecat shows more geographical variation than the European polecat, this being manifested in changes in fur structure and in dimension of body, skull and claws.

At present, 17 subspecies of the Siberian polecat have been described, 8 of these from Siberia.

24a. **Putorius**(s. str). **eversmanni eversmanni** Lesson (1827). Orenburg steppe Siberian polecat

1827. M u s t e l a e v e r s m a n n i. Lesson, R. Manuel de Mamm. etc., p. 144, Paris.

1931. P u t o r i u s e v e r s m a n n i e v e r s m a n n i. Ognev, S. I. Zveri Vostochnoi Evropy i Severnoi Azii (Animals of Eastern Europe and Northern Asia). 2, pp. 683 — 697, Moskva; Stroganov, S. U. Obzor podvidov stepnogo khorya (P u t o r i u s e v e r s m a n n i Lesson) Sibirskoi fauny (Survey of the Subspecies of the Steppe Polecat (P u t o r i u s e v e r s m a n n i Lesson) in the Siberian Fauna). — Izvestiya Sibirskogo Otdeleniya AN SSSR, No. 11, p. 149. 1958.

1936. P u t o r i u s p u t o r i u s e v e r s m a n n i. Pocock, R. I. The Polecats of the Genera P u t o r i u s and V o r m e l a in the British Museum. — Proc. Zool. Soc. London, pp. 703 — 705.

1951. M u s t e l a p u t o r i u s e v e r s m a n n i. Ellerman, J. R. and T. C. S. Morrison-Scott. Checklist of Palaearctic and Indian Mammals, p. 265, London.

1956. M. (P).e. e v e r s m a n n i. Novikov, G. A. **Khishchnye mleko-**
pitayushchie fauny SSSR (Carnivorous Mammals of the Fauna of the USSR).
pp. 156—157, Moskva-Leningrad.

Type and type locality. Ognev (1931) proposed that the "southern part of
the Orenburg Province" be taken as terra typica for the nominate subspecies
since the area designated in the first description of the species as the
type locality (the steppes "between Orenburg and Bukhara") contains two
subspecies of the steppe polecat. This corresponds to the valley of the
middle reaches of the Ilek River, in the area where its chief left tributary,
the River Bolshaya Khobda, empties into it, and this is the area we shall
take as the type locality for the subspecies.

Diagnosis. Winter fur moderately long, dense and soft. General tone
of color pale, straw yellow-whitish, often with ocher tinge. Underfur
white, tips of guard hairs on hindpart of back dark brown with brown tinge.
Length of guard hair 35—38mm. Tail in basal part like back, and black-
brown on tip; length of dark tip approximately one third length of entire tail.
Summer fur shorter and coarser, and russet with ocher tinges.

Measurements. Length of body with head: males 340—420 mm (av.
390 mm), females 290—380 mm (av. 320mm); length of tail: males
80—150mm (av. 120mm), females 80—130mm (av. 110mm); length of
hind paw: males 40—60mm (av. 50mm), females 30—40mm (av. 35mm).

Condylobasal length of skull: males 64.2—71.3mm (av. 67.0 mm),
females 56.7—61.3mm (av. 58.0 mm); zygomatic width: males
39.9 — 49.7mm (av. 45.5mm), females 33.0—40.0mm (av. 35.7mm);
height of skull: males 24.0—26.9mm (av. 25.2mm), females
23.0—24.8mm (av. 24.0mm); interorbital width: males 17.3—20.2mm
(av. 18.0 mm), females 14.1—17.2mm (av. 15.2mm); postorbital width:
males 12.0—14.6mm (av. 13.3mm), females 11.3—15.2mm (av. 13.0mm);
length of upper tooth row: males 20.0 — 22.5mm (av. 21.7mm), females
18.0—20.0mm (av. 18.9mm).

Systematic notes. This subspecies differs in series with the features
which were reported in the diagnosis. In the systematic respect it is
nearest to P.e.nobilis, which is described below.

Geographical distribution. West Kazakhstan, Aktyubinsk, Orenburg
and Sverdlovsk regions, and southern part of Bashkiria.

Material studied. Orenburg Region — 12 specimens ; West
Kazakhstan and Aktyubinsk regions — 26 specimens; Sverdlovsk Region.—
8 specimens; Bashkiria — 2 specimens. Total — 48 specimens.

24b. **Putorius eversmanni nobilis** Stroganov (1958).
North Kazakhstan Siberian polecat (**Figure 144, a**)

1958. P u t o r i u s e v e r s m a n n i n o b i l i s. Stroganov, S. U. Obzor
podvidov stepnogo khorya (P u t o r i u s e v e r s m a n n i Lesson) Sibirskoi
fauny (Survey of the Subspecies of the Steppe Polecat (P u t o r i u s
e v e r s m a n n i Lesson) in the Siberian Fauna).— Izvestiya Sibirskogo
Otdeleniya AN SSSR, No. 11, p. 150.

Type and type locality. No. 4404 in the collection of S. U. Stroganov, adult male, 18 March 1958, from the author's collections. Vicinity of the city of Kokchetav.

Diagnosis. Close to nominate subspecies, differing from it in the greater development of melanistic tone in hind part of back. Tips of guard hair on spine tar black, lacking brown tinges. Underfur pure white. Length of guard hair 35—38 mm. Tail relatively thinly covered with fur. Terminal part of tail glossy black, occupying about one third entire length of tail. Summer fur somewhat more russet than in nominate subspecies. Claws powerful, length on middle toes of forelimbs being 14.2—16.4 mm (Figure 144, a).

Measurements. Length of body with head: males 420—443 mm (av. 430 mm), females 300—410 mm (av. 340 mm); length of tail: males 120—160 mm (av. 140 mm), females 90—140 mm (av. 110 mm); length of hind paw: males 53—59 mm (av. 56 mm), females 45—54 mm (av. 49 mm).

Condylobasal length of skull: males 61.7—70.7 mm (av. 66.8 mm), females 52.4—58.0 mm (av. 56.7 mm); zygomatic width: males 38.9—44.9 mm (av. 42.5 mm), females 32.4—35.0 mm (av. 33.2 mm); heigh of skull: males 24.1—26.8 mm (av. 25.4 mm), females 24.1—26.8 mm (av. 24.0 mm); mastoid width: males 36.2—39.0 mm (av. 37.5 mm), females 30.0—34.3 mm (av. 31.7 mm); interorbital width: males 16.8—18.4 mm (av. 16.7 mm), females 14.0—15.7 mm (av. 15.0 mm); postorbital width: males 12.9—14.5 mm (av. 13.7 mm), females 12.0—14.2 mm (av. 13.0 mm); width between anteorbital foramina: males 17.9—20.2 mm (av. 19.0 mm), females 15.2—17.5 mm (av. 16.0 mm); length of upper tooth row: males 19.7—22.0 mm (av. 20.6 mm), females 17.0—18.3 mm (av. 17.7 mm).

Systematic notes. This subspecies is taxonomically close to the nominate subspecies and to P. e. pallidus. In contrast to these, the tips of the guard hairs on the spine are dense black without any brown or cinnamon brown hues. Although this feature seems small, it is characteristic and imparts a distinctive appearance to the animal, which also differs from P. e. pallidus by a denser winter fur.

The subspecies has very high quality fur, which in the fur trade is classified separately as "Petropavlovsk."

Geographical distribution. Range includes the southern peripheral districts of Western Siberia eastwards approximately to Lake Chany and the neighboring regions of Kazakhstan: i.e., North Kazakhstan, Kokchetav, Akmolinsk, Kustanai and the northern part of the Karaganda Region.

Material studied. Western Siberia — 140 specimens; North Kazakhstan— 56 specimens. Total — 196 specimens.

24c. **Putorius eversmanni pallidus** Stroganov (1958).
West Siberian polecat (Figure 144, b)

1958. Putorius eversmanni pallidus. Stroganov, S. U. Obzor podvidov stepnogo khorya (Putorius eversmanni Lesson) Sibirskoi fauny (Survey of Subspecies of the Steppe Polecat (Putorius eversmanni Lesson) in the Siberian Fauna). — Izvestiya Sibirskogo Otdeleniya AN SSSR, No. 11, pp. 150—151.

Type and type locality. No. 4356 in the Stroganov collection, adult female, 4 March 1958, collected by the author. Novosibrisk Region, vicinity of Kargat village.

Diagnosis. Differs from P. eversmanni nobilis in quality of winter fur. Hair somewhat longer and sparser than in nobilis and ligher in color; underfur white or straw yellow. Tips of guard hairs on hind part of back brown. Length of guard hairs 32—35 mm. Tail rather thinly furred, length of its dark brown part about one third length of tail. Summer fur lighter than that of North Kazakhstan subspecies. Claws are relatively weak, with length on middle toes of forelimbs 12,4—13.3 mm (Figure 144, b).

Measurements. Length of body with head: males 320—460 mm (av. 390 mm), females 290—410 mm (av. 340 mm); length of tail: males 90 —160 mm (av. 120 mm), females 70—140 mm (av. 110 mm); length of hind paw: males 40—70 mm (av. 54 mm), females 35—54 mm (av. 40 mm).

Condylobasal length of skull: males 65.2—70 8 mm (av. 67.2 mm), females 54.6—59.7 mm (av. 57.3 mm); zygomatic width: males 36.8—41.9 mm (av. 39.6 mm), females 33.6—35.7 mm (av. 34.2 mm); mastoid width: males 35.7—40.0 mm (av. 37.6 mm), females 30.8 — 35.2 mm (av. 32.5 mm); interorbital width: males 17.5—18.5 mm (av. 17.8 mm), females 14.8—16.0 mm (av. 15.2 mm); postorbital width: males 14.2—16.6 mm (av. 15.6 mm), females 12.4—13.2 mm (av. 12.7 mm); width between anteorbital foramina: males 19.0—21.2 mm (av. 20.0 mm), females 15.8 — 18.0 mm (av. 16.6 mm); length of upper tooth row: males 20.2—22.0 mm (av. 20.8 mm), females 17.2—18.2 mm (av. 17.7 mm).

Systematic notes. Polecats of this subspecies are readily differentiated in series from P. e. nobilis. They show a lighter coloration than the latter, due to weakening of the color intensity on the tips of the guard hair in the hind part of the back. In addition, the winter fur is shorter. The Siberian polecats encountered on the northeastern Altai (upper reaches of the Ulagan River) and the Uimen Steppe belong to this subspecies. Pelts of the West Siberian polecat are also classified as a distinct trade variety.

Geographical distribution. The steppes of the Altai area, the eastern part of the Novosibirsk Region (east of Lake Chany), the Kemerovo Region, and the steppes of the Krasnoyarsk territory and Irkutsk Region.

Material studied. Novosibirsk Region — 26 specimens; Altai territory— 18 specimens; Kemerovo Region — 4 specimens; Krasnoyarsk territory — 10 specimens. Total — 58 specimens.

24d. **Putorius eversmanni heptapotamicus** Stroganov (1960). Semirech'e Siberian polecat

1960. Putorius eversmanni heptapotamicus. Stroganov, S. U. Novye formy khishchnykh mlekopitayushchikh (Carnivora, Mammalia) palearktiki (New Forms of Carnivorous Mammals (Carnivora, Mammalia) of the Palaearctic).— Trudy Biologicheskogo Instituta Sibirskogo Otdeleniya AN SSSR, No. 6. Voprosy sistematiki i ekologii zhivotnykh.

Type and type locality. No. 4524 in the Stroganov collection, adult male, 4 January 1958 from the collections of A. P. Lesnyak. Area south of Lake Balkhash (Ili River).

Diagnosis. Distinguished from rest of subspecies by characteristic russet color (with ocher tinge) of winter fur. Underfur light yellow. Guard hair on hind part of back brownish-grayish brown. Length of guard hair 32—35 mm. Terminal third (approximately) of tail is dark brown. Summer fur shorter, sparser and coarser, with duller color.

Measurements. Length of body with head: males 350—420 mm (av. 385 mm), females 280—370 mm (av. 325 mm); length of tail: males 110—150 mm (av. 120 mm), females 110—120 mm (av. 115 mm); length of hind paw: males 50—60 mm (av. 56 mm), females 33—48 mm (av. 40 mm).

Condylobasal length of skull: males 64.0—69.0 mm (av. 65.4 mm), females 53.0—59.0 mm (av. 55.0 mm); zygomatic width: males 30.0—47.0 mm (av. 40.0 mm), females 30.0—40.0 mm (av. 33.6 mm); length of upper tooth row: males 19.6—20.8 mm (av. 20.2 mm), females 17.0—18.4 mm (av. 17.4 mm).

Systematic notes. The Siberian polecat inhabiting the Balkhash area and the neighboring low areas of the Semirech'e is noteworthy for the extremely characteristic peculiarity of its winter fur, this being almost indistinguishable from the summer fur in color, though when compared with the latter seemingly more colorfully russet ocher.

This subspecies is closest taxonomically to the North Kazakhstan polecat P. e. nobilis, but is rather sharply distinguished from it by the lesser silkiness and the peculiar color of the winter fur, which has a developement of russet ocher tone and has a less melanistic tone in the hind back. This subspecies has similar relationships with the other lowland forms of the Siberian polecat (i. e., with P. e. eversmanni and P. e. pallidus).

It is more clearly differentiated from the mountain forms (P. e. talassicus, P. e. lineiventer, P. e. tuvinicus, etc.), as it has shorter fur and lacks the characteristic contrast in fur color between the black tips of the guard hairs and their underlying pale whitish general background.

Geographical distribution. Altai steppes, Pavlodar, Semipalatinsk, East Kazakhstan and Karaganda regions.

Materials studied. Total of 17 specimens from the above-mentioned regions.

24e. **Putorius eversmanni lineiventer** Hollister (1913).
Altai Mountain Siberian polecat (Figure 144, c)

1913. Mustela lineiventer. Hollister.— Proc. Biol. Soc. Washington, 26, p. 2.

1931. Putorius eversmanni michnoi. Ognev, S. I. Zveri Vostochnoi Evropy i Severnoi Azii (Animals of Eastern Europe and Northern Asia). Vol. 2, pp. 697—702, Moskva-Leningrad (partim).

1951. Putorius putorius michnoi. Ellerman, J. R. and T. C. S. Morrison-Scott. Checklist of Palaearctic and Indian Mammals. p. 265, London (partim).

1958. Putorius eversmanni lineiventer. Stroganov, S. U.
Obzor podvidov stepnogo khorya (Putorius eversmanni Lesson)
Sibirskoi fauny (Survey of Subspecies of the Steppe Polecat (Putorius
eversmanni Lesson) in the Siberian Fauna). — Izvestiya Sibirskogo
Otdeleniya AN SSSR, No. 11, pp. 151 — 152 (lapsus calami).

Type and type locality. Oirotiya. Valley of the Chagan-Burgazy River.

Diagnosis. Characterized by extremely large size (condylobasal length
of skull is on average 74.0 mm) and peculiarities of hair. Winter fur
extremely long and coarse and somewhat shaggy. Length of guard hair
64 — 68 mm. Fur pale whitish with extremely slight yellowish hues. On
back, particularly on neck, shoulders and basal part of tail a yellowish
brown tinge is seen. Tips of guard hairs on hind part of back black, as is
terminal third of tail. A light gray-brown belt extends along belly connecting
dark-colored area of groin and chest. Underfur whitish. Claws powerful
and very long (Figure 144, c).

Measurements. Length of body with head: males 492 — 562 mm (av.
517 mm), females 430 — 520 mm (av. 475 mm); length of tail: males
156 — 183 mm (av. 168 mm), females 155 — 173 mm (av. 163 mm); length of
hind paw: males 66 — 80 mm (av. 71 mm), females 58 — 72 mm (av. 63 mm).

Condylobasal length of skull: males 75.6 — 82.2 mm (av. 80.0 mm),
females 68.4 — 76.7 mm (av. 71.8 mm); zygomatic width: males
52.2 — 58.9 mm (av. 54.0 mm), females 43.4 — 48.7 mm (av. 45.6 mm);
mastoid width: males 42.5 — 47.9 mm (av. 45.5 mm), females 37.4 — 43.2 mm
(av. 40.6 mm); height of skull: males 27.2 — 33.5 mm (av. 30.7 mm),
females 24.4 — 27.6 mm (av. 26.6 mm); interorbital width: males
20.2 — 24.2 mm (av. 23.3 mm), females 18.1 — 19.4 mm (av. 18.7 mm);
postorbital width: males 14.9 — 17.0 mm (av. 15.6 mm), females
13.0 — 15.0 mm (av. 14.0 mm); width between anteorbital foramina: males
22.0 — 25.2 mm (av. 23.9 mm), females 20.3 — 22.0 mm (av. 20.8 mm); length
of upper tooth row: males 22.3 — 25.5 mm (av. 24.0 mm), females
20.8 — 24.0 mm (av. 22.2 mm).

Systematic notes. The subspecies was described by Hollister (1913)
from a specimen from the Chagan-Burgazy (Sailyugen Range), as the
species Mustela lineiventer. Ognev (1931) has, and justly so,
reduced it, and thought it "to be expedient to temporarily consider
P. lineiventer as a synonym for P. e. michnoi until the problem is
elucidated on more extensive material." Ognev had no material from
terra typica of lineiventer, and the attempt to diagnose its subspecific
status was made on the basis of comparison of features of the typical
P. e. michnoi and of seven specimens "which, according to their
distribution, could have been considered P. e. lineiventer, or extremely
close to this (the Mongolian Altai, the Uryankhai territory, Semirech'e and
the Tien Shan)."

Examination of this and of newly collected material shows that the areas
enumerated are inhabited by taxonomically different forms. Thus, the
Uryankhai territory (today Tuva) and probably also the Mongolian Altai are
inhabited by P. e. tuvinicus while the Semirech'e is inhabited by P. e.
heptapotamicus; only the subspecific status of the polecat occurring
on the Tien Shan still remains unclarified. In the light of the data presented,

the identification of P. e. lineiventer with P. e. michnoi becomes
unnecessary. As a result of examination of extensive material from the
typical habitat of P. e. lineiventer, I have concluded that this form is a
distinct subspecies characterized by permanent morphological features
(which have been presented in its diagnosis).

Geographical distribution. Inhabits the southeastern areas of the Altai
and is particularly abundant in the Chuya Steppe and neighboring ranges,
where it climbs to heights of 3,000 m above sea level.

Material studied. Ten specimens from the Chuya Steppe and 30 pelts
processed in the Gorno Altai Region. Total—40 specimens.

24f. **Putorius eversmanni tuvinicus** Stroganov (1958).
Tuva Siberian polecat (Figure 144, d)

1958. Putorius eversmanni tuvinicus. Stroganov, S. U. Obzor
podvidov stepnogo khorya (Putorius eversmanni Lesson) Sibirskoi
fauny (Survey of Subspecies of the Steppe Polecat (Putorius
eversmanni Lesson) in the Siberian Fauna). — Izvestiya Sibirskogo
Otdeleniya AN SSSR, No. 11, pp. 152—153.

Type and type locality. No. 4403 in the Stroganov collection, adult
female, 20 April 1958 from O. I. Gavrilov's collection, Tuva, from village of
Chaa-Khol (west of the city of Kyzyl).

Diagnosis. Distinguished from P. e. lineiventer by small size and by
nature of fur. Condylobasal length of skull is about 65 mm (against 76 mm in
P. e. lineiventer). Hair longer (length of guard hair 60—62 mm), dense
and more fluffy. General background of winter fur is yellowish white with
tinge of ocher on flanks and particularly on back and light portion of tail;
hind part of back conspicuously blackened by intensive dark brown speckles of
guard hair through which yellowish underfur is readily seen. Tail
pronouncedly bushy with coarse hair; terminal third of tail dark brown.
Belly completely light with cream tinge. Summer fur has yellowish russet
general tone in area of shoulders and on flanks and is yellowish white on belly.
Back, particularly posterior part, more densely blackened by long, pure black
tips of guard hairs through which yellowish color is almost unseen. Claws
relatively weak and length on middle toes of forepaws is 14—15 mm
(Figure 144, d).

Measurements. Length of female body with head is 405 mm, length of
tail 135 mm, and length of the hind paw 55 mm. Weight of adult female
is 610 g.

Condylobasal length of skull: males 64.9 mm, females 64.6 mm;
zygomatic width: males 37.3 mm, females 38.2 mm; height of skull: males
24.7 mm, females 23.8 mm; mastoid width: males 35.7 mm, females
35.3 mm; interorbital width: males 16.2 mm, females 16.6 mm; postorbital
width: males 15.6 mm, females 18.0 mm; width between anteorbital
foramina: males 18.7 mm, females 18.1 mm; length of upper tooth row:
males 20.3 mm, females 19.6 mm.

Systematic notes. The subspecies is extremely peculiar, being differentiated
from P. e. lineiventer by presence of conspicuously marked vivid
yellowish russet tinge in winter fur. On the basis of its totality of systematic

features, P.e.lineiventer is closest to P.e.michnoi, whose diagnosis is presented below, being particularly approximated by the presence of an almost completely black-brown rear half of back and by the peculiar shagginess of the tail. In addition, P.e.tuvinicus probably has appreciably smaller body and skull dimensions than P.e.lineiventer and P.e.michnoi. Polecats from the Mongolian Altai characterized by development of russet in the winter fur probably belong to this subspecies.

Geographical distribution. Known from collections made near the village of Chaa-Khol, which lies near the mouth of the river of the same name (a left tributary of the upper Yenisei) to the west of the city of Kyzyl and the Tannu-Ola Range (the upper reaches of the Elegest River).

Material studied. Two specimens from Tuva and one from the Mongolian Altai. Total three specimens.

24g. Putorius eversmanni michnoi Kashchenko (1910).
South Transbaikalian Siberian polecat

1910. Putorius eversmanni var. michnoi. Kashchenko, N. F.— Ezhegodnik Zoologicheskogo Muzeya Akademii Nauk, Vol. 15, p. 271.

1914. Putorius larvatus michnoi. Satunin, K. A. Opredelitel' mlekopitayushchikh Rossiiskoi imperii (Key to Mammals of the Russian Empire). p. 116, Tiflis.

1931. Putorius eversmanni michnoi. Ognev, S. I. Zveri Vostochnoi Evropy i Severnoi Azii (Animals of Eastern Europe and Northern Asia). Vol. 2, pp. 697—702, Moskva-Leningrad (partim); Stroganov, S. U. Obzor podvidov stepnogo khorya (Putorius eversmanii Lesson) Sibirskoi fauny (Survey of Subspecies of the Steppe Polecat (Putorius eversmanni Lesson) in the Siberian Fauna).— Izvestiya Sibirskogo Otdeleniya AN SSSR, No. 11, pp. 153—154. 1958.

1951. Mustela putorius eversmanni. Ellerman, J. R. and T. C. S. Morrison-Scott. Checklist of Palaearctic and Indian Mammals, p. 265, London (partim).

Type and type locality. No. 2099 in the collection of the Zoological Institute of the Academy of Sciences of the USSR, pelt without skull, 23 August 1909. The Kiran River, some 20 km from Troitskosavsk, now Kyakhta.

Diagnosis. Characterized by large size (condylobasal length of skull averages 75 mm), high, relatively coarse fur with sparse underfur and long shaggy guard hair. Length of guard hair 80 mm. General tone of winter fur pale with whitish straw-yellow tinges, without russet hue. Tips of guard hair, particularly to rear of back, are glossy black, constrating with whitish lower fur layer. Tail very bushy. Summer fur has intense golden ocher-russet tone, with very well developed black tips of guard hairs, forming on back, and particularly in its posterior area a densely colored saddle without any yellow color showing through.

Measurements. Length of body with head: males 435—508 mm (av. 475 mm), females 392—477 mm (av. 440 mm); length of tail: males 159—185 mm (av. 175 mm), females 144—168 mm (av. 157 mm); length of hind paw: males 60—78 mm (av. 71 mm), females 57—68 mm (av. 62 mm); length of ear: males 24.4—26.4 mm (av. 25.3 mm), females 23.3—26.0 mm (av. 25.0 mm).

FIGURE 144. Subspecies of the Siberian (steppe) polecat, Putorius eversmanni Lesson:

a — Putorius eversmanni nobilis Stroganov
b — Putorius eversmanni pallidus Stroganov
c — P. eversmanni lineiventer Hollister

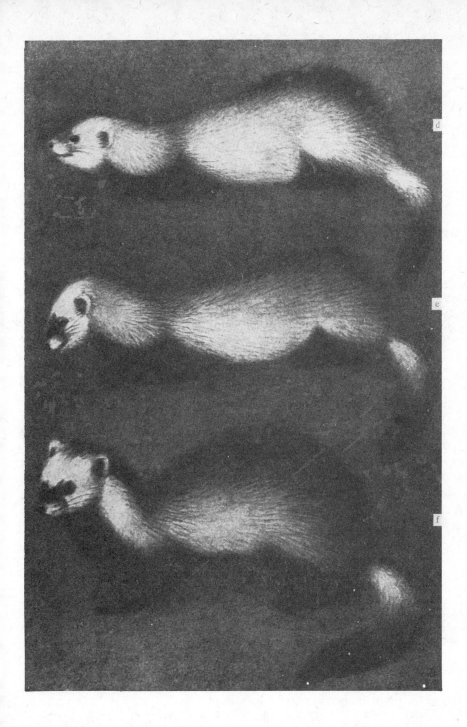

d — P.eversmanni tuvinicus Stroganov
e — P.eversmanni dauricus Stroganov
f — P.eversmanni amurensis Ognev

Condylobasal length of skull: males 69.2 — 78.0 mm (av. 75.0 mm), females 65.5 — 69.2 mm (av. 67.8 mm); zygomatic width: males 44.0 — 49.3 mm (av. 46.4 mm), females 40.0 — 44.9 mm (av. 42.2 mm); height of skull: males 25.6 — 28.7 mm (av. 27.0 mm), females 23.4 — 25.9 mm (av. 25.1 mm); mastoid width: males 37.0 — 42.3 mm (av. 40.6 mm), females 35.3 — 38.0 mm (av. 37.3 mm); interorbital width: males 18.3 — 20.5 mm (av. 19.1 mm), females 17.1 — 19.0 mm (av. 17.8 mm); postorbital width: males 12.0 — 16.9 mm (av. 14.4 mm), females 12.0 — 15.0 mm (av. 13.4 mm); width between anteorbital foramina: males 20.0 — 22.2 mm (av. 21.2 mm), females 18.9 — 20.8 mm (av. 19.9 mm); length of upper tooth row: males 20.3 — 23.4 mm (av. 22.1 mm), females 20.3 — 21.4 mm (av. 21.0 mm).

Systematic notes. Systematically extremely close to P. e. t u v i n i c u s, differing from it in larger size of body and skull (sea measurements) and in more conspicuous long fur, as well as in absence of russet in the winter fur.

More distinctly differentiated from P. e. d a u r i c u s, whose distribution is contiguous with this subspecies and which is characterized by a vivid yellowish russet color, an almost complete absence of black on the back, shorter guard hair, and smaller dimensions of the body and skull.

Geographical distribution. The southern and western Lake Baikal area and neighboring areas of Mongolia.

Material studied. The Tunkinskie Gol'tsy Range — 2 specimens; southwestern parts of the Baikal area — 30 specimens; Mongolia — 8 specimens. Total — 40 specimens.

24h. **Putorius eversmanni dauricus** Stroganov (1958).
East Transbaikalian Siberian polecat (**Figure 144, e**)

1958. P u t o r i u s   e v e r s m a n n i   d a u r i c u s. Stroganov, S. U. Obzor podvidov stepnogo khorya (P u t o r i u s   e v e r s m a n n i Lesson) Sibirskoi fauny (Survey of the Subspecies of the Steppe Polecat (P u t o r i u s e v e r s m a n n i Lesson) in the Siberian Fauna). — Izvestiya Sibirskogo Otdeleniya AN SSSR, No. 11, pp. 154—155.

Type and type locality. No. 4401 in the Stroganov collection, adult male, 12 January 1939, from I. A. Velinskii's collections. Found near the village of Smolenskoe in the vicinity of Chita.

Diagnosis. Winter fur characterized by vivid yellowish russet color of back, somewhat less saturated on the flanks and belly, and by light-colored part of tail. Towards rear of back color is markedly shaded by dark brown tips of guard hair. Dark brown terminal part of tail makes up about one quarter length of entire tail. Fur relatively high, with soft and dense underfur and extremely long guard hair; length of guard hair up to 45 mm. Summer fur distinguished by extremely vivid ocher-russet color; posterior part of back has more intense rusty-brown color.

Claws relatively weak: their length on middle toes of forelimbs is 12.4 — 13.0 mm (Figure 144, e).

Measurements. Length of body with head: males 400 — 460 mm (av. 445 mm), females 370 — 460 mm (av. 420 mm); length of tail: males

130 — 150 mm (av. 144 mm), females 124 — 146 mm (av. 138 mm); length of
hind paw: males 54 — 67 mm (av. 62 mm), females 48 — 62 mm (av. 57 mm);
condylobasal length of skull: males 64.6 — 68.0 mm (av. 65.0 mm),
females 63.0 — 64.5 mm (av. 63.8 mm); zygomatic width: males
37.3 — 42.0 mm (av. 39.2 mm), females 36.9 — 39.2 mm (av. 38.2 mm);
mastoid width: males 35.7 — 38.0 mm (av. 36.4 mm), females
35.3 — 37.2 mm (av. 36.0 mm); height of skull: males 24.7 — 26.0 mm (av.
25.2 mm), females 23.2 — 25.0 mm (av. 24.3 mm); length of upper tooth row:
males 20.3 — 23.4 mm (av. 22.1 mm), females 18.8 — 19.6 mm (av. 19.2 mm).

Systematic notes. This subspecies is one of the most vividly colored
forms, only the Amur polecat being more vivid. It stands closest
to P. e. a m u r e n s i s in its vivid rusty red color and in the reduction
of dark color on the guard-hair tips, but the characteristic long
fur and the particularly long guard hair align it more with
P. e. m i c h n o i. Systematically it occupies an intermediate position
between P. e. m i c h n o i and P. e. a m u r e n s i s.

Geographical distribution. Eastern Transbaikalia except for the
southern part.

Material studied. Northern part of Buryat- Mongol ASSR [now Buryatian
ASSR] — 5 specimens; Chita Region — 12 specimens. Total 17
specimens.

24i. **Putorius eversmanni amurensis** Ognev (1930).
Amur Siberian polecat (Figure 144, f)

1930. Putorius eversmanni amurensis. Ognev, S. I. Novyi
amurskii khor' (A New Amur Polecat). — Okhotnik, No. 11, p. 25;
Ognev, S. I. Zveri SSSR i prilezhashchikh stran (Animals of the USSR and
Adjacent Countries), Vol. 3, pp. 640 — 641, Leningrad. 1935; Stroganov, S. U.
Obzor podvidov stepnogo khorya (Putorius eversmanni Lesson)
Sibirskoi fauny (Survey of the Subspecies of the Siberian Polecat
(Putorius eversmanni Lesson) in the Siberian Fauna). — Izvestiya
Sibirskogo Otdeleniya AN SSSR, No. 11, p. 155. 1958.
1951. Mustela putorius amurensis. Ellerman, J. R. and
T. C. S. Morrison- Scott. Checklist of Palaearctic and Indian Mammals,
p. 266, London.

Type and type locality. No. M. 3433 in the Ognev collection,
winter, 1930. Valley of the middle Amur, area of the city of
Blagoveshchensk.

Diagnosis. A very distinctly differentiated subspecies of the
Siberian polecat, characterized by the peculiar structure of its coat.
Winter fur short and even throughout body, extremely dense and soft. Guard
hair short, slightly protruding above fur, and up to 20 mm long. General
tone of back a vivid russet-ocher, back toward rear being a brown russet
color and lacking the blackness characteristic of other Siberian subspecies.
Flanks pale ocher and belly whitish ocher. Tail weakly furred and almost
throughout its extent a vivid russet yellow, with a gray brown terminal part
reaching length of 32 — 36 mm; in other subspecies, dark end-part of tail
reaches at least 60 mm (Figure 144, f).

Systematic notes. This is one of the most distinctive and highly differentiated subspecies of the Siberian polecat. In fur color it somewhat resembles P. e. d a u r i c u s , but is distinctly differentiated from it by the extremely short and vividly colored winter fur.

Geographical distribution. The basin of the middle Amur. Found on the Yablonovyi Range, in the Uda River valley and and on lower Zeya River.

Material studied. Three specimens from the Amur Region.

Biology. The animal is characteristic of open landscapes. It lives in steppe, on the steppe portion of the forest steppe, and in semi-desert. In Central Asia it is locally encountered in the desert as well, but it avoids living in pure sand. In Siberia it penetrates only locally, in peripheral, logged-over areas containing large expanses of plowland, meadow, and pasture land, etc. It is encountered in the broad regions of the valleys of the Ob, Angara, and Lena, etc. In the Altai it climbs high into the mountains (Figure 145, 146); in the Chuya Alps it has been found at heights of about 3,000 m or more, going right up into the alpine meadows (Kolosov, 1939).

FIGURE 145. Virgin steppe, northwestern Altai. Biotope of the Siberian polecat. Photo by B. S. Yudin

An indispensable condition for a polecat biotope is an abundance of rodents (marmots, susliks, hamsters, etc.). In Western Siberia, according to observations by M. D. Zverev (1931), the polecat keeps to the open steppe. In the wooded steppe it prefers old fallow lands, pastures, large open fields, virgin land within fields, solonets soils, i. e., highest places of concentration of suslik, great jerboa, and hamster, as well as river valleys, lakes and marshes where the water vole abounds. It is also encountered on flooded meadows in the Ob River floodland, where it lives on the so-called "crests" — high sand hills sometimes covered with pine forests. These places are also inhabited by susliks and hamsters, and even by jerboas. In the Tomsk Region, according to B. S. Yudin, it lives on flooded meadows among concentrations of water vole. It avoids small insular birch forests, and copses, and dense shrub thickets.

FIGURE 146. Northwestern Altai, vicinity of Ust'-Pustynka in the Krasnoshchekovo area. Biotope of the Siberian polecat. Photo by B. S. Yudin

In Transbaikalia, according to A. A. Cherkasov (1867), it rarely lives in the forests, preferring open places in meadows and steppes, though it may occasionally live near human habitations.

According to observations by I. P. Brom (1954), in the forest steppe zone of Transbaikalia the polecat lives on the unwooded southern slopes of mountains and river valleys. Nearer the taiga, with the appearance of more birch—aspen and small insular larch forests the number of polecats decreases and the number of Siberian weasels increases. In the open steppe the polecat is ubiquitous, and is encountered with equal frequency in the valleys and on the stony summits of mountain ranges (Figure 147). In the southeastern parts of the Altai it inhabits both the plain and the Chuya Steppe proper, as well as the neighboring mountain ranges (Kolosov, 1939).

The Siberian polecat, according to observations in Western Siberia, lives in different biotopes at various seasons, this being a function of changes in feeding conditions. According to M. D. Zverev (1931), in the fall, when the lakes become frozen, the polecats often visit the lake shores, where they catch wounded ducks and other birds which for some reason were unable to fly south. In the first half of winter the polecat is rather frequently encountered on meadows, but its tracks cease there by the end of the winter. Winter tracks are encountered in reed thickets along rivers, lakes and marshes, and also among small birches and (occasionally) in strips of pine forest. Polecat tracks are common near hare nesting-places, as well as on sites where black grouse and willow ptarmigan pass the night. In winter the Siberian polecat, like the European polecat, is attracted to inhabited places, invading sheds, haystacks, grain stacks near farmsteads, barn floors, etc., all places where Muridae accumulate.

It lives in both temporary and permanent burrows, using the temporary ones only for short stretches and occasionally only for rests between foraging trips. It may occasionally use other abodes: hollows in trees and among stones, etc. In Transbaikalia, according to Cherkasov (1876), it occasionally lives in old wooden buildings, granaries, and sheds, and even under inhabited buildings. The animal sets up permanent burrows for prolonged stays, but these it rarely digs itself, instead generally occupying the burrows of susliks, marmots, hamsters, jerboas, and zokors (M y o s p a l a x), and even occasionally the discarded burrows of badgers, foxes and corsac foxes.

FIGURE 147. Northen forest steppe in the Kuibyshev area, Novosibirsk Region. Biotope of the Siberian polecat. Photo by B. S. Yudin

The burrows the animal builds itself are shallow, consisting of a more or less inclined gallery one meter long terminating in a moderately expanded chamber. The diameter of the entry is usually 7—12 cm. The earth dug out from the burrows is heaped up near the entry.

In the burrows of susliks and other large rodents the polecat broadens the narrow passages, sometimes extends them, and builds additional chambers and ramifications and new exit holes.

The burrows of females with broods are usually more complicated, having up to 14 passages and ramifications, these lying at a slant both horizontally and vertically, with an ampler nest chamber and additional chambers in which undevoured prey is stored. Two to three adjacent rodent burrows are usually adapted for this purpose and, at the exit holes which may number more than ten, there are heaps of earth. The nest chamber is occasionally lined with some dry material (Figure 148).

FIGURE 148. Young polecats in a burrow. Photo by B. S. Yudin

Two family burrows examined by Brom (1954) in Transbaikalia had been dug by the animals themselves at the bases of Mongolian bobak burrows. These burrows had (respectively) two and three round exits, 6—9 cm diameter; one exit was dug in such a manner that it communicated with the Mongolian bobak burrow. The soil near the entries was completely dug up and devoid of vegetation.

Inhabited burrows can be identified by the more or less freshly dug earth near the entrance, as well as by remnants of food and excrement, and occasionally by the pungent specific odor emanating from within.

The Siberian polecat may use a permanent burrow for a very long time, even for several successive seasons. M. D. Zverev (1931) reports a case where a female used a small abandoned hut several years in succession for raising her young, refusing to abandon it even after four of her young had been captured.

In winter the polecat usually goes on using its summer burrows, in which case no heaps of excavated earth are seen near the burrows. Snow near the winter burrow is trampled by the animal. When occupying an alien burrow the animal casts lumps of earth up onto the surface as in summer. Its tracks are similar to those of the Siberian weasel but are markedly larger. It moves in leaps ranging up to a meter in length. Claw prints may be seen on soft ground or snow.

The Siberian polecat is a dexterous, agile and bloodthirsty carnivore which hunts incessantly, attacking any animal it can overcome.

FIGURE 149. Tracks of a Siberian polecat hunting a water vole. Iskitim area in the Novosibirsk Region. Photo by V. I. Telegin

The senses, particularly hearing and smell, are very keen, and quite up to the level of its kin.

In winter the polecat may have to cover as much as 18 km a night in its search for food, making it hard for the animal to return to the same burrow for rest. It will therefore make use of several temporary or more or less permanent burrows. Generally, when sufficient food is available near a burrow the Siberian polecat will not wander very far.

Migrations from one locality to another are known, caused by depletion of the food base or by changes in feeding conditions in a given area. Thus a mass migration of the Siberian polecat up the River Ob was observed in the autumn of 1928 in the former Kamensk District by G. A. Velizhanin (1931). A similar phenomenon was also reported by local hunters.

Autumn migrations of the Siberian polecat in Western Siberia coincide with the time when susliks, hamsters and jerboas begin hibernating in their deep "plugged" burrows, which latter protect their denizens and thus cause a sharp decrease in the food resources of the polecat.

In winter the polecat migrates from areas covered with deep snow into those with less snow. Such a migration was recorded in December 1929 in the forest steppe on the right bank of the Irtysh River, where the polecat, after a heavy snowfall, shifted to the left, less snow-covered riverbank (Zverev, 1931). The Siberian polecat is a typical zoophagous animal, feeding exclusively on flesh (Figure 149). Plant materials (grain, grass, moss, pieces of wood, etc.) are occasionally swallowed, but these pass through the digestive tract without change. The daily ration, according to P. A. Sviridenko (1935), is about 150 — 160 g of flesh. In captivity a polecat starved to death on a daily ration of 70 g within 4 — 5 days, showing symptoms of severe dystrophy. The food consists mainly of rodents and more rarely of insectivores, birds, and other animals.

TABLE 10. Occurrence of various foods in stomachs of Siberian polecats in the forest steppes of Western Siberia (after M. D. Zverev, 1931)

Type of food	Number of stomachs containing the given food type	Percentage of total number of stomachs examined
1. Mammals	1,238	96.0
1. Suslik Citellus erythrogenys	20	1.5
2. Voles, unspecified	422	31.1
3. Water vole	143	10.7
4. Common redbacked vole	4	0.3
5. Mice, unspecified	9	0.7
6. Field mouse	64	4.8
7. Common hamster	314	23.3
8. Striped hairy-footed hamster	132	9.8
9. Jerboa	33	2.5
10. Blue hare	5	0.4
11. Large rodents, unspecified	44	3.3
12. Small rodents, unspecified	29	2.2
13. Weasel	1	0.1
14. Shrew	16	1.2
II. Birds	28	2.1
1. Black grouse	6	0.5
2. Hungarian partridge	2	0.2
3. Willow ptarmigan	5	0.4
4. Duck	2	0.2
5. Large birds, unspecified	3	0.5
6. Small birds, unspecified	6	0.5
7. Eggs of birds	4	0.3
III. Fish	3	0.23
IV. Amphibians (frogs)	1	0.1
V. Reptiles (snakes)	3	0.23
VI. Carrion	13	1.0
Total	1,348	100

Composition of the winter diet of the polecat in Western Siberia and Transbaikalia has been extensively studied.

M. D. Zverev (1931) reported results of a study made by Yu. N. Klimov of the contents of 1,348 stomachs collected by hunters in the winter of 1928 — 1929 in the forest steppe of Western Siberia — in the former Omsk district and to some extent in the Baraba, Novosibirsk, Slavgorod and Biisk areas.

The data are presented in Table 10, which shows that mammals, chiefly rodents, predominate in the polecat's diet and that the most important are the Muridae and such large species as the hamster, jerboa and others. Shrews were encountered in insignificant quantities and a carnivore (weasel) appeared only once. The amount of susliks is relatively low (1.5%), which Zverev (1931) explains as due to the rarity of this rodent in the area in which the stomachs were collected. My data, however, indicate that it may also be explained by the fact that in the winter it is extremely difficult for the polecat to dig out the burrows of hibernating susliks, so that by necessity it has to switch to other types of food. This is also confirmed by observations carried out in Kazakhstan. According to A. A. Sludskii, burrows of small susliks dug out by the polecat were found in November 1942 in the area of Aktyubinsk, but later, in December, the polecat mainly hunted voles.

Birds, chiefly Galliformes, were encountered in small numbers. Other animals (fish, amphibians and reptiles) were encountered in extremely small amounts.

Somewhat different percentages of food types were obtained by G. A. Velizhanin (1931) from coprological analysis. This author examined undigested food remnants found in excrements of the animal collected during March—December 1930 in the Kiprino District of the Altai territory; the results are presented in the following table (Table 11).

TABLE 11. Remnants of animals discovered in Siberian-polecat excrements collected from March to December 1930 in the Altai Territory (64 specimens)

Type of food	Number of stomachs containing the given food type	Percentage of total number of stomachs examined
1. Red-cheeked suslik Citellus erythrogenys	24	37.5
2. Daurian hamster	32	50.0
3. Dzhungarian ...... hamster	2	3.1
4. Common hamster	1	1.5
5. Voles	5	7.8
6. Southern birch mouse.	1	1.5
7. Willow ptarmigan ..	1	1.5
8. Unspecified birds ..	1	1.5
9. Tiger and ground beetles	1	1.5

The predominance of striped (Daurian) hamster remnants is explained by the fact that mass outbreaks of this rodent were observed at that time.

According to Velizhanin (1931), the percentage of suslik in the polecat's diet is markedly higher in summer than in winter, when the rodents hibernate and are hard to catch. The earliest find of remnants of suslik in the polecat's excrement was noted on 25 March, and the last on 29 September. These dates, according to observations, coincide with the times of spring awakening and of commencement of autumn hibernation for the suslik in the locality investigated.

In the complex steppe and desert zone of Kazakhstan the staple food resources of the Siberian polecat are various species of suslik (small, russet and sand suslik); their percentage in 38 stomachs reached 76.3% (Afanas'ev et al., 1953).

In the Chuya Steppe the polecat attacks marmots, probably young ones. According to A. M. Kolosov (1939) the proliferation of polecats here is connected with the presence of marmot, whose burrows the polecat appropriates. In stomachs of polecats obtained in the Chuya Alps remnants of marmots were discovered. According to local hunters, in winter the polecat occasionally enters the poorly made burrows and strangles the sleeping marmots. According to a report by E. M. Korzinkina (1935), ". . . a polecat was caught jumping out of a marmot burrow. When the burrow was investigated, a fresh marmot carcass with a torn thoracic cavity and with its liver and other organs devoured was discovered." B. S. Yudin caught a polecat in a marmot's burrow in 1950 near the city of Tomsk.

Yudin found remnants of a marmot eaten by a polecat in the Chuya Steppe, where in February 1958 he observed polecats living in colonies of marmots. By studying tracks he established that the polecat, moving from burrow to burrow, had traveled some 6 km and, digging through snow accumulations, had penetrated 32 burrows; during this itinerary only once did the animal distract itself from the marmot burrows (by entering a fissure between stones). It used marmot burrows for its daytime resting places, the same burrow sheltering the animal for several days in succession.

Data from A. A. Fetisov (1942), presented in Table 12, illustrate the diet of the Siberian polecat in Transbaikalia.

TABLE 12. Occurrence of food types in polecat stomachs in winter, Transbaikalia

Type of food	Number of stomachs containing the given food type	Percentage of total number of stomachs examined
Pika	584	76.2
Hare	1	0.1
Susliks	8	1.0
Siberian marmot	2	0.3
Jerboa	2	0.3
Hamsters	33	4.3
Common field-mice	29	3.8
Reed vole	12	1.6
Narrow-skulled vole	55	7.2
Root vole	1	0.1
Large-toothed redbacked vole	2	0.3
Rodents, unspecified	6	0.9
Shrew	1	0.1
Small birds, unspecified	7	0.9
Daurian partridge	23	3.0

The data of Table 12 show that the polecat's winter diet consists chiefly of small rodents, with a predominance of Daurian pika and as everywhere, small Muridae. The bird component is slight, with the main bird element being made up of partridge, i.e., of a more or less large bird whose terrestrial mode of life makes it most available to the polecat.

Data from Brom (1954) and B.I. Peshkov (1954) are available on the polecat; diet over the period from spring to autumn. These authors collected material (stomachs) in the Daurian Steppe, Brom examining the contents of 61, and Peshkov of 29 stomachs. The results are presented in Table 13.

TABLE 13. Occurrence of food types in the polecat's stomach in the spring—autumn period on the Daurian Steppe (after Brom and Peshkov)

Type of food	Brom, 61 specimens		Peshkov, 29 specimens	
	number of occurrences	percentage of occurrences	number of occurrences	percentage of occurrences
Siberian marmot	29	47.5	4	16.6
Daurian suslik	7	11.5	6	20.8
Daurian pika	12	19.7	2	8.4
Jerboa	2	3.3	—	—
Daurian hamster	2	3.3	—	—
Narrow-skulled vole	1	1.6	1	4.2
Mongolian vole	1	1.6	2	8.4
Daurian hedgehog	1	1.6	2	2
Birds, unspecified	2	3.3	—	—
Insects, unspecified	12	19.7	—	—
Plants	11	18.0	2	8.4

A comparison of Table 13 with Table 12 shows that the summer diet does not differ much from the winter diet, except for an increase in large rodents — the Siberian marmot and the Daurian suslik.

According to Brom's observations, in summer the polecat destroys young Siberian marmots, since he cannot manage adults and usually does not attack them. In winter the polecat digs out burrows of sleeping Siberian marmots in order to kill them.

The polecat occasionally eats carrion. Forty-five polecat stomachs collected on the steppes of the southeastern part of Transbaikalia show the following food percentages: rodents — 48.4; carnivores — 4.4; mammals, undiagnosed — 17.6; birds — 2.2; insects — 13.2. The carnivore (corsac foxes and polecats) remains were carrion.

The data presented in the table show that the predominance of various food-types in a given area depends on the composition of the local fauna and on the degree of availability of the animals eaten by the polecat in a given season.

The summer diets show a predominance of larger rodent: susliks, hamsters, etc. Birds, judging by all data, are an occasional catch. In captivity the polecat prefers rodents to birds (Sviridenko, 1935).

The polecat obtains the relatively large rodents (susliks, hamsters, etc.) by entering their burrows, but may occasionally catch them on the surface. Young polecats and females readily penetrate the burrows of susliks, hamsters, jerboas, zokor and other rodents. Adult males have to dig out a burrow and widen its passages before they can reach its inhabitant. When hunting on the surface, the polecat characteristically presses itself close to the ground and, hiding carefully, steals cat-like up to the suslik and swiftly attacks and strangles its prey.

Small rodents inhabiting shallow burrows are usually obtained from dug out nests. In winter these are caught under the snow; when the snow is deep the polecat makes a passage through the snow to the rodent burrows, returning to the surface via the same entry hole ("dive") by which it "dived" under the snow-surface. Black grouse and willow ptarmigan are obtained in the snow ("holes") in which they pass the night. Places where black grouse and willow ptarmigan pass the night on the outskirts of small birch or alder forests often show the tracks of polecats which have examined the "holes" of these birds.

Occasionally the polecat catches and kills more rodents or other animals than it can manage to devour in a given moment; it then, rather than eating the rodents completely, eats only the most palatable parts— mostly the innards minus the intestines.

A tendency to collect and store killed animals is characteristic of the animal and such stores are frequent in polecat burrows. According to a report of Zverev's (1931), 12 young susliks of half adult size were found in a dug out burrow on the Kuznetsk Steppe. The remnants of an already eaten suslik were also found there. Near the Zima post in the Irkutsk Region remnants of 13 susliks were found in a polecat burrow. According to P. A. Sviridenko (1935), polecat family burrows in the northern Caucasus always contained 5 to 20—30 or more strangled susliks. On the Lower Volga some 50 susliks were found in one polecat burrow.

In Western Siberia hamsters and other rodents, including remnants of a hare, were found in polecat burrows, in addition to the susliks. Birds, particularly grouse, were also found.

In Siberia the Siberian polecat is an animal with little marked rhythm of daily activity, being encountered at any time of day. However, it is most active at dawn and dusk and during the night. In cloudy weather it may often roam throughout the day. In hot summer weather it usually sleeps in its burrow at noon.

During violent snow storms and ground winds in winter it occasionally lies down for a long time in its burrow, not emerging for several days in succession. In warm weather, even when the temperature is lower than 30°C, fresh polecat tracks are encountered, but in lesser numbers than usual for the given locality (Zverev, 1931).

In summer, when rodents abound, the Siberian polecat hunts within a relatively small territory. In winter, when the conditions for obtaining food worsen, the animal is compelled to cover itineraries of 10—12 or as much as 18 km in search of food. While hunting, the polecat does not follow a straight line, but instead constantly changes direction, circling over a small area, turning back and pressing on, circling round the small birch groves encountered, and so on. It leaves nothing uninspected: a burrow, a layer of dry grass, a hollow in the snow or in the soil, a tussock, a hayrick, hollows of black grouse and willow ptarmigan, lairs of hares and trails of small animals, etc. In winter it likes to roam along small rivers, making trails under their steep banks. It also burrows into air holes in the ice and collects the fish remaining there.

The above is well illustrated by a map of a daily polecat itinerary in early winter, compiled by Zverev (1931). "The polecat after emerging from the burrow made a circle of some 12 km and returned to the same burrow. Its route is represented on the diagram by a dotted line which shows that on emerging from its burrow it at first passed through virgin land, examining stacks of hay and straw, then made some dives into the snow and dug out a hamster's burrow. Emerging onto stubble field and empty areas, the polecat dove vigorously into the snow, dug out burrows, and examined haystacks and hare- and grouse-lairs. After browsing in the empty areas the polecat returned to the burrow from which it had emerged, all the while meticulously avoiding entry into the forest" (Zverev, 1931).

The following data are available on the reproduction of the Siberian polecat in Siberia. According to observations of Zverev's (1931), the beginning of rut in the West Siberian polecat in captivity is the first third of March. Polecats obtained at this time in nature show signs of the beginning of rut. In the neighboring areas of North Kazakhstan rut begins in the first half of March, at which time the polecats are more mobile than usual. The males search for females and on meeting each other they will begin to fight (Afanes'ev et al., 1953).

In Transbaikalia, according to Cherkasov (1867), rut occurs in the second half of February and first half of March. "Several males will chase a female and will often fight fiercely, producing a shrill chirping or twitter."

The male mounts the female at short intervals, often of several minutes length. The coitus is extremely lengthy and a case is known of its lasting 2 hours and 55 minutes (Sviridenko, 1935).

The gestation time is 38—41 days. The young are born in the second half of April and in May. Blind young of the polecat have been discovered on the Kuznetsk Steppe in early May, and on 21 May young, aged 2—3 weeks, were found in the Kamensk area. Blind young polecats were found in May in the area of Zima Post in the Irkutsk Region. In early June young "the size of a brown rat" were found (Zverev, 1931). In the southeastern part of Transbaikalia, according to Brom (1954), the earliest encounter with a gravid female was recorded on 24 April and the latest on 14 July.

A second rut may occur in the female if the young die, and she mates again, giving birth to a second litter. This explains the existence of late polecat broods. Zverev (1931) reported that nine young polecats of half adult size were obtained in the Kamensk area on 15 November. On the Daurian Steppe Brom (1954) obtained a nursing female on 12 August, and an autopsy showed nine placental spots in the uterus, corresponding to the number of the young she had borne.

The litter size is 4—14 and the average is 8—9. However, data have been published pointing to larger litters in some females. Thus, according to Sviridenko (1935), in the northern Caucasus and the lower Volga area, where litter size is 8—10, females may bear as many as 15—18 young. Zverev (1931) heard hunters of Western Siberia tell of 15 young in a single brood.

The young are born small, weighing about 4—6 g. Dimensions, according to Sviridenko (1935), are as follows: length of body 65—70 mm, length of tail 14 mm, length of hind paw 8.5 mm.

The male does not take part in raising the brood, though cases are known in which male and female were found together in a nest with young. Such a situation probably arises when the male is being chased and has no other place to hide. In captivity "the males actively help the mothers to lick their abundant progeny" (Manteifel', 1948). The young grow very rapidly and at the age of three days sparse white hair becomes visible on the body. By the age of about ten days their size has grown twofold and their weight sixfold. At the same age, approximately, the milk teeth protrude and darkening of the limbs, back and forehead occurs. On the 20th day the color becomes darker and the facial "mask" becomes conspicuous. Eyes open at the age of one month; the teeth are already quite visible, and the young begin to crawl freely and frolic and play with each other, and with their mother. Lactation continues for about one and a half months, but from the age of approximately two months the young begin to suck the blood of rodents killed by their mother.

From the age of $1\frac{1}{2}$—2 months the entire brood joins the mother in hunting rodents. The young live in their mother's nest for about $2\frac{1}{2}$—3 months and occasionally longer. In Transbaikalia, undispersed broods of the animal have been seen in September (Brom, 1954), but these were late broods.

The young usually begin to lead an independent life in late summer.

Polecats become sexually mature at about the age of nine months.

The Siberian polecat, according to observations in Siberia, is mainly nocturnal, and can be encountered during the day only in extremely rare cases when, being bothered, it emerges from its abode. It is caught in snares only at night. In winter, particularly during severe frosts and snow storms, the animal's activity decreases markedly, and for long periods it will not emerge from its burrow — occasionally for several days in succession.

The polecat population is subject to marked changes at various times, due to many causes. Decrease in numbers is caused by famine, by steppe fires, by flooding of burrows with meltwater, and by epizootics. The Siberian polecat is subject to hemorrhagic septicemia.

Numerous species of lice and tick parasites live on the animal. Among internal parasites, the following helminths have been found: Ascaris columnaris, Capillaria putorii, Skrjabingylus nasicola.

Autumn molt begins in late September and terminates in late October and early November; it begins at the rear of the back, passing to the nape and flanks, and gradually shifting to the underparts. Summer molt occurs from February to April, beginning from the head and limbs and gradually including the back, belly, and tail.

Practical importance. The Siberian polecat is of twofold significance: as an exterminator of rodents harmful to agriculture and health, and as an object of the fur trade. It undoubtedly does a great deal of good exterminating noxious rodents, and it has been established that its daily diet is 150—160 g of flesh, which is equivalent to one suslik or to 10—20 small murine rodents. It actually exterminates more rodents than it can eat.

The fur is of lower quality than that of the European polecat, but its commercial significance may be greater, since it occupies a wider range. Hunting the animal in Siberia is today prohibited by law.

2. Subgenus Lutreola Wagner (1841). Minks

1841. Lutreola. Wagner, J. A. In: Schreber, J. Ch. Naturgesch. der Säugethiere, suppl. II, p. 239; Miller, G. S. Catalogue of the Mammals of Western Europe, p. 415, London. 1912; Satunin, K. A. Opredelitel' mlekopitayushchikh Rossiiskoi imperii (Key to Mammals of the Russian Empire), p. 113, Tiflis. 1914; Ognev, S. I. Zveri Vostochnoi Evropy i Severnoi Azii (Animals of Eastern Europe and Northern Asia), Vol. 2, pp. 747—749, Moskva. 1931; Novikov, G. A. Evropeiskaya norka (The European Mink), pp. 7—12. Leningrad, Izdatel'stvo Leningradskogo Gosudarstvennogo Universita, 1938; Stroganov, S. U. Opredelitel' mlekopitayushchikh Karelii (Key to Karelian Mammals). Karelo-Finskii Gosudarstvennyi Universitet, pp. 89—90, Petrozavodsk. 1949.

1843. Vison. Gray, J. List of Specimens of Mammals in the Collection of the British Museum, p. 64.

1871. Hydromustela. Bogdanov, M. N. Ptitsy i zveri chernozemnoi polosy Povolzh'ya (Birds and Animals of the Chernozem Belt of the Volga Area).— Trudy Obshchestva Estestvoispytatelei Kazanskogo Universiteta, 1, p. 167.

Type of the subgenus. Viverra lutreola Linnaeus (1761).

Diagnosis. Smaller than the polecat. Length of body up to 540 mm, length of tail about one half this. Head, particularly muzzle, somewhat flattened dorsally. Heel pads bare throughout year. Hair cover distributed evenly over body. Fur a monotone dark brown; underfur dark. Ears lack light fringe. Fur on lips pure white. Throat, chest, and belly occasionally with white patches. Skull relatively less expanded in cranial region than in polecats, and only slightly elevated in frontal area. Postorbital processes weakly developed. Distance from choanal incisure to lower edge of foramen magnum approximately equal to mastoid width of skull, at most only slightly smaller. Mastoid width approximately one half condylobasal length of skull. Width between external edges of occipital condyles greater than width of rostrum above canines.

Os penis differs from that of polecat. Groove on distal part of ventral aspect broader than in polecats. Tip spatularly expanded and curved ventrally.

Biology. Semiaquatic.

Geographical distribution. Europe, North Caucasus, Western Siberia (eastwards as far as Irtysh and Tobol) and North America.

Two species are known at present in the Soviet fauna: one of these, the American mink, was introduced from abroad. Its distribution began in 1933 at numerous points in the Soviet Union, including Siberia.

25. Putorius (Lutreola) **lutreola** Linnaeus (1761).
European mink

1761. Viverra lutreola. Linnaeus, C. Fauna Suecica, p. 5;
Pallas, P. S. Zoographica Rosso-Asiatica, 1, pp. 80—81, Petropoli. 1811.
1766. (Mustela) lutreola. Linnaeus, C. Syst. Nat., 1, 12 ed.,
p. 66.
1777. (Lutra) minor. Erxleben. J. Syst. Regni Anim., 1, p. 451.
1800. Lutra lutreola. Shaw. General Zoology, p. 443.
1827. Putorius lutreola Griffith. Animal Kingdom, by the Baron
Cuvier, 5, p. 122.
1840. Foetorius lutreola. Keyserling, A. and J. Blasius.
Wirbelthiere Europas, p. 69; Blasius, J. Säugethiere Deutschlands, p. 234.
1857.
1843. Vison lutreola. Gray. List. Mamm. Brit. Mus., p. 64
(partim).
1843. M. (artes) lutreola. Smith, C. H. Mammalia, p. 188.
1871. Hydromustela lutreola. Bogdanov, M. N. Ptitsy i zveri
chernozemnoi polosy Povolzh'ya (Birds and Animals of the Chernozem Belt
of the Volga Area). — Trudy Obshchestva Estestvoispytatelei Kazanskogo
Universiteta, 1, p. 167.
1879. Lutreola europaea. Homeyer. — Zool. Garten, 26, p. 184.
1910. Putorius (Lutreola) lutreola. Trouessart, E. L. Faune
Mamm. d. Europe, p. 75; Stroganov, S. U. Opredelitel' mlekopitayushchikh
Karelii (Key to Karelian Mammals), pp. 90 — 92, Petrozavodsk. 1949.
1912. Mustela lutreola. Miller, G. S. Catal. Mamm. West.
Europe, pp. 415 — 418, London.
1914. Mustela lutreola. Satunin, K. A. Opredelitel'
mlekopitayuschikh Rossiiskoi imperii (Key to Mammals of the Russian
Empire), pp. 112 — 144, Tiflis; Ognev, S. I. Zveri Vostochnoi Evropy i
Severnoi Azii (Animals of Eastern Europe and Northern Asia), Vol. 2,
pp. 749 — 769, Moskva. 1931; Novikov, G. A. Evropeiskaya norka (The
European Mink), pp. 1—173, Leningrad. 1939.
1944. Mustela (Lutreola) lutreola. Bobrinskii, N. A. Otryad
khishchnye (Carnivora). — In: Opredelitel' mlekopitayushchikh SSSR, edited
by N. A. Bobrinskii, p. 127, Moskva; Novikov, G. A. Khishchnye
mlekopitayushchie fauny SSSR (Carnivorous Mammals of the USSR Fauna),
pp. 157—162, Leningrad. 1956.

Type and type locality. The species was described from a specimen
from Finland.
Diagnosis. Posterior portion of second upper premolar (Pm^2) does not
wedge into bifurcation between anterior edge and talon of carnassial tooth.
External surface of upper jaw above carnassial tooth is even. Lower edge of
infraorbital foramina round.
Measurements. Length of body with head: males 380—430 mm, females
320—400 mm; length of tail: males 124—190 mm, females 120—180 mm;
length of hind paw: males 54.0—64.0 mm, females 49.0—56.0 mm. Weight:
males up to 739 g, females up to 440 g.
Condylobasal length of skull: males 56.4—68.0 mm, females 52.8—65.7 mm;
zygomatic width: males 30.8—40.0 mm, females 28.9—37.0 mm;

interorbital width: males 11.0—15.0 mm, females 10.7—14.0 mm;
postorbital width: males 11.2—15.0 mm, females 10.8—14.0 mm; width of
rostrum above canines: males 12.5—15.3 mm, females 11.3—14.7 mm;
mastoid width: males 27.0 — 34.9 mm, females 26.5—31.7 mm; height in
area of auditory capsules: males 19.0—27.0 mm, females 18.0—25.6 mm;
length of upper tooth row: males 15.6—20.0 mm, females 14.7—18.0 mm.

Description. Size relatively small, generally somewhat smaller
than that of American mink (see measurements). Head rather flattened
dorsally with blunt broad muzzle. Eyes small and long. Ears round and
short, barely protruding from fur. Neck thick, of approximately same thickness
as head. Body somewhat thickened posteriorly. Toes connected by web
covered with short hair. Tail weakly furred, its length about one third
length of body or somewhat longer. Fur relatively short, very dense and
flat on the body. Color of winter fur on the back varies from
relatively light russet brown to intense dark brown; color becomes
somewhat lighter on flanks and belly. Tail and feet brownish black, darker
than body. Underfur light gray or grayish brown. Lips, and usually chin
as well, surrounded by white fringe. Chest and throat often with one, two
or occasionally more white patches of different sizes and shapes. Summer
fur differs little in quality from winter fur. Hair of summer fur only
slightly shorter and coarser than that of winter fur. Difference in density
of underfur not significant. Color shows a development of rusty brown
tones, chiefly on flanks and belly.

Fur of the young dull, consisting of short and soft underfur through which
guard hair is seen

Length of adult os penis is 34.8—37.3 mm; terminal spatulum turned right.

Skull (Figure 150) less massive than that of American mink, relatively
broader in postorbital area but narrower in occipital section. Line of
profile in skulls of same age and sex is similar in the two species, but in
the plane, in dorsal examination, these differ essentially. In European
mink, rostrum relatively broader, zygomatic arches longer (though more
narrowly parted), postorbital region moderately narrowed: postorbital width
(distance) equal to or greater than width between orbits; mastoid processes
much less conspicuously developed. Sagittal crest rudimentary, being
more or less well-marked in posterior part only. Occipital crest
well developed but less so than in American mink. Anteorbital
foramina small, ovally long and obliquely set; their longitudinal axis is no
greater than that of canine alveolus. Lower edge of infraorbital
foramina lacks protrusion formed by torulislike expansion of upper jaw
above carnassial, and this expansion is absent. Tympanic bullae narrower
and longer proportional to skull sizes, and antero-internal angle more
acute than in American mink. Carotid foramina lie approximately in
middle of internal aspect of capsule. Stylomastoid foramina lie on
convexity of bullae.

Second upper premolar (Pm^2) only adjacent to anterior aspect of
carnassial tooth, not wedged into the bifurcation between anterior
edge and talon of carnassial.

Sexual dimorphism of European mink manifested in size and weight of
body, size of skull and other features. Males larger than females (see
measurements). Males characterized by better developed crests on skull
and by less smooth skull outlines.

Systematic notes. The European mink is readily differentiated craniologically from the American mink by the features presented above in the diagnosis and description of the species. External features are of only secondary significance in distinguishing between these species.

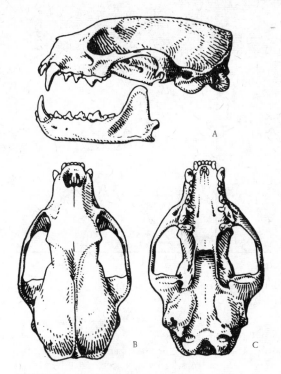

FIGURE 150. Skull of the European mink, Putorius lutreola L. (original):

A — lateral view; B — dorsal view; C — ventral view.

Geographical variations are slight in the European mink. Nevertheless various authors do recognize the existence of a number of subspecies; thus G. A. Novikov (1939), who studied this problem in detail, notes that the European mink throughout its range is divided into six subspecies, differing in size, in nature of fur, and in peculiarities of fur coloration.

The subspecific status of the European minks occurring in Western Siberia remains unclear due to paucity of collection material.

Geographical distribution. Occupies Europe from Switzerland and Western France east to the Urals, inclusively; also in the North Caucasus and in Transuralia.

In the Soviet Union it is distributed throughout the European part except for the Kola Peninsula, the tundra zone, and the Crimea. It occurs in the North Caucasus and in Transuralia.

In Siberia it is encountered in the pre-Ural parts of the Tyumen Region and east as far as the Irtysh (Map XIX).

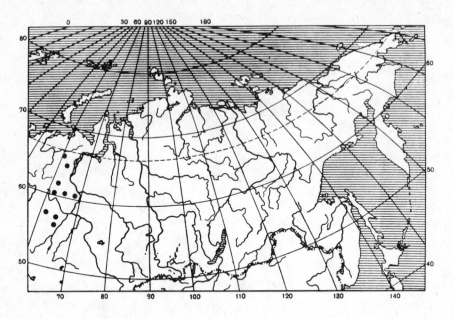

MAP XIX. Geographical distribution of the European mink, Putorius lutreola L., in Siberia

It was reported for the first time on the eastern slopes of the Urals by L. P. Sabaneev (1874), as a species gradually extending its range eastwards. On the Bogoslovskii [now Karpinsk] Urals (in the Pavda woods), on the Sosva, and apparently on the Lozva, it occurs "in rather large numbers and first appeared a long time ago." K. K. Flerov (1933), quoting local hunters, reports that it sometimes occurs on the Lyapin. It was obtained in 1926 near the village of Saranpaul'. On the Lyapin River it was reported as a rare species by Skalon and Raevskii (in litt. 1940). According to these authors, it was encountered further south on the upper reaches of the Lozva, Sosva and Tura rivers. According to E. S. Zhbanov, it was found on the Konda River in 1935. In the former Irbit County (eastern part of the present Sverdlovsk Region), N. P. Bulychev (1878) reported it as rare. I. Ya. Slovtsov (1892) mentions a mink obtained in 1886 on the Tura River in the area above Zhukovskaya. According to S. A. Kuklin (1937) it occurs in extremely small numbers in Transuralia and reaches Yalutorovsk. The boundary of its range in Transuralia, according to this author, extends in the following manner: beginning in the northwest on the "upper reaches of the Konda, it runs to the point where the Lozva River crosses the 60th parallel, and from there to the city of Irbit, where it turns east, skirting the city of Tyumen from the north; it then again descends south, approaches Yalutorovsk, and then goes further south to the 56th parallel, from where it extends in a rather straight line southwest toward the city of Magnitogorsk. It is rarely encountered east of this boundary, though a few individuals are present even on the upper reaches of the Northern Sosva River."

Biology. The life of the European mink is closely connected to fresh water, as it lives along creeks, rivers, and lakes. It keeps very close to these water bodies and rarely goes more than 100 m from shore. The mink prefers shores overgrown with shrubs and forests, undercut banks of small rivers and streams, and oxbow and other small lakes. It avoids the sandy shores of open pools.

The mink's diet has been insufficiently studied. It probably eats all the small land animals and water-fauna of the water bodies in its habitat. A considerable percentage of its diet consists of fish, water voles, small Muridae, amphibians, mollusks, crabs, etc. In summer it occasionally attacks water birds and eats their eggs.

Rut occurs in March—April. The gestation period is 43—72 days. The great difference in the length of gravidity is probably explained by a latent period in development of the egg, occurring in some females. The young are born at approximately the following dates: in the central belt of the European USSR, in May; in the southern areas, in April or early May. The litter size is 2—7 but most often 4—5. The eyes open at the age of one month. The family lives together till autumn. Life span averages 7—10 years.

In contrast to many other mustelids, the European mink has a permanent burrow, either one it digs itself or one it takes over from a water vole and merely widens a bit. The burrow is deep, with one side-branch; the entry is often hidden in the water. In addition to the permanent burrow it uses temporary abodes. A female with brood spends the summer in a relatively short stretch of shore, about 2 km long. In late autumn the animal migrates along small forest streams. Once ice has formed on the rivers the mink stays close to shallow rapids, to air holes in the ice cover, and to unfrozen rivulets and rivers.

Molt, in the central zone, begins in March, proceeds extremely slowly, and terminates in November. Mink fur is highly valued.

Practical importance. The European mink has a valuable fur but its percentage of the fur trade in Siberia is insignificant due to its low numbers.

Material studied. European USSR — 27 specimens; the Transurals — 3 specimens. Total — 30 specimens.

26. **Putorius (Lutreola) vison** Schreber (1777).
American mink

1777. M u s t e l a v i s o n. Schreber, J. Die Säugethiere, 3, 25, pl. 127b.
1884. P u t o r i u s v i s o n. True. — Proc. U. S. Nat. Mus., Vol. 7 (App. Circ. 29), p. 609 (partim).
1944. M u s t e l a (L u t r e o l a) v i s o n. Bobrinskii, N. A. Otryad khishchnye (Carnivora). — In: Opredelitel' mlekopitayushchikh SSSR, edited by N. A. Bobrinskii, p. 128, Moskva; Novikov, G. A. Khishchnye mlekopitayushchie fauny SSSR (Carnivorous Mammals of the USSR Fauna). Moskva-Leningrad, Izdatel'stvo AN SSSR, pp. 162—166. 1956.

1949. Putorius (Lutreola) vison. Stroganov, S. U. Opredelitel' mlekopitayushchikh Karelii (Key to Krelian Mammals). Izd. Karelo-Finskogo Gosudarstvennogo Universiteta, pp. 92—93, Petrozavodsk.

1949. Mustela vison. Popov, V. A. Materialy po ekologii norki (Mustela vison Br.) i rezul'taty akklimatizatsii ee v Tatarskoi ASSR (Data on the Ecology of the Mink (Mustela vison Br.) and the Results of Its Acclimatization in the Tatar ASSR). — Trudy Kazanskogo Filiala AN SSSR, No. 2, pp. 3—139.

1958. Lutreola vison altaica. Ternovskii, D. V. Biologiya i akklimatizatsiya amerikanskoi norki (Lutreola vison Brisson) na Altae (The Biology and Acclimatization of the American Mink in the Altai), pp. 15—16, Novosibirsk.

Type and type locality. The species has been described from a specimen from Quebec, east Canada.

Diagnosis. Second upper premolar (Pm^2) wedges with posterior part of crown into incisures between anterior edge and talon of carnassial tooth. External surface of upper jaw above carnassial tooth expanded in form of torulus, forming very conspicuous protrusion on lower edge of infraorbital foramina.

Measurements. Length of body with head: males 340—540 mm, females 300—450 mm; length of tail: males 170—250 mm, females 140—220 mm; length of hind paw: males 58—75 mm, females 50—60 mm; height of ear: males 22—30 mm, females 20—26 mm. Weight: males up to 1,600 g, females up to 800 g.

Condylobasal length of skull: males 65.0—71.2 mm, females 59.5—63.2 mm; zygomatic width: males 36.2—41.5 mm, females 33.0—35.7 mm; interorbital width: males 13.0—17.4 mm, females 11.6—15.2 mm; postorbital width: males 12.0—15.2 mm, females 10.4—14.0 mm; width of rostrum above canines: males 14.0—16.0 mm, females 10.6—14.5 mm; mastoid width: males 33.0—36.4 mm, females 27.4—30.3 mm; height in area of tympanic bullae: males 22.0—25.0 mm, females 20.4—22.4 mm; length of upper tooth row: males 20.6—22.8 mm, females 18.0—21.2 mm.

Description. Build similar to European mink but somewhat larger (see measurements); has longer tail and darker color. Length of tail is about one half length of body (about 46% to be more exact). The fur is longer, softer, and fluffier.

Winter fur dense and glossy, its color changing from a rather light brownish russet to a dark brown or even brown-black, the dark color-type predominating. Tail markedly darker than body and occasionally glossy black terminally.

Lower lip, sometimes upper lip, and chin pure white. White patches of varying shapes and sizes occur often on throat and occasionally on chest, belly, and groin.

Os penis markedly larger than that of European mink, its length in adult males reaching 40.0—49.7 mm; terminal spatulum not turned to right but is in same plane with axis of baculum (Figure 151).

Skull (Figure 152) larger and markedly more bulky than that of European mink, less elongated and relatively narrower in postorbital area, but

broader in occipital portion. Skull in profile quite like that of European
mink, but differs essentially from it in dorsal view. Rostrum narrower
than that of P. lutreola; zygomatic arches thinner and more widely
separated; postorbital area conspicuously compressed and narrower
than width between orbits; mastoid processes highly developed. In the nature
of postorbital constriction and in the degree of development of mastoid
processes and occipital crest, skull of American mink resembles that of
Siberian polecat. Sagittal crest moderately developed, as in Siberian mink.
Occipital crest extremely powerful. Anteorbital foramina large, ovally
elongated and obliquely set, with longitudinal axis greater than that of
canine alveolus. External surface of upper jaw above anterior edge of
carnassial-tooth crown elevated in form of torulus reaching lower edge of
anteorbital foramina, so that a conspicuous protrusion is formed at this
edge. Tympanic bullae broader and relatively shorter, with their antero-
internal angle less acute than in European mink. Carotid foramina lie
nearer to anterior edge of tympanic bullae. Stylomastoid foramina lie
in groove near mastoid processes.

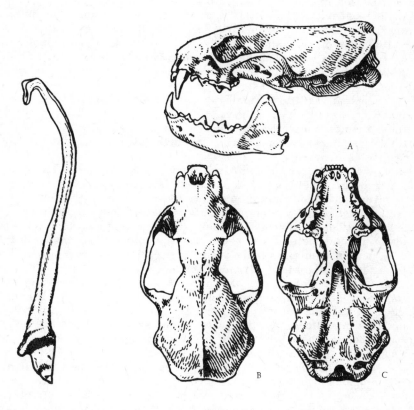

FIGURE 151. Os penis
of American mink,
Putorius vison
Gray (original)

FIGURE 152. Skull of American mink, Putorius vison
Gray (original):

A — lateral view; B — dorsal view; C — ventral view.

Second upper premolar (Pm²) wedges its posterior edge into bifurcation between anterior edge and talon of the carnassial tooth.

Sexual dimorphism is manifested as in European mink in body- and skull dimensions; males are larger than females and male skull crests are more conspicuous.

Systematic notes. Systematically the American mink is extremely close to the European, and in degree of taxonomic differentiation they have approximately the same relationship as the European and Siberian polecats, with the difference that their natural ranges lie on different continents.

The differences between the two mink species are rather clear and are presented in their descriptions.

P. (L.) v i s o n, according to American data, is subject to considerable intraspecific geographical variation. It is body- and skull-dimensions which chiefly vary, while color and other fur peculiarities vary less. Some 10 subspecies of mink are given for North America.

The American minks which have been distributed in Siberia for acclimatization originate from animals on breeding farms. Systematically this is heterogeneous material. I examined some 130 skulls and 300 pelts of American mink from various regions of the Soviet Union, as well as a great number of live animals on the Kola State Animal-Breeding Farm. The wide scope of individual variation in size and in fur quality and color, particularly the appearance of white spottiness on the underparts, is amazing.

Geographical variation, judging by the material studied, is as yet not manifested.

Thus, the newly formed American mink populations are as yet undifferentiated and systematically unconsolidated groups with unstable morphological features.

Mink acclimatization on the Altai is no exception. The attempt of D. V. Ternovskii (1958) to create a distinct subspecies L. v. a l t a i c a lacks justification and his description of this Altai "subspecies" is puzzling. The author dogmatically postulates differentiating features for the subspecies described but does not burden himself with argumentation or proof. He writes in the diagnosis: "The predominating color is brown and dark brown (90.1%), and in numerous individuals (36.4%) the appearance of a white patch on the upper lip is recorded. The hair cover is dense..."

Study of the original material shows the flimsiness of this diagnosis.

Fur color of the Altai minks in no way differs from specimens collected in Karelia and in the central areas of the USSR. Pelts with a glossy dark brown color predominate. Individual deviations are insignificant and are manifested in the degree of intensity of the background tone. Geographical color variations are not manifested.

The same holds true for fur density when studied by the usual method of pelt comparison. Ternovskii, by counting the number of hairs on four pelts, determined that the amount of hair per square centimeter of back surface in Altai minks varies from $22,664 - 37,100/cm^2$ and averages $29,458/cm^2$ (sic, no more, no less!). The author provides no corresponding data for other subspecies which, in this case, deprives the figures presented of any value and makes them unsuitable for systematic purposes.

As to the white patches and their localization on the body, Ternovskii indicates that 36.4% of the Altai population develop a white patch on the upper lip and 15.4% show white patches on the underparts. It is known that American mink bred in captivity often show various deviations in color, including numerous white spots. Clearly, this peculiarity is retained by some individuals when they are given freedom. It is hardly difficult to predict how persistent will be the white spots of the American mink on the Altai. However, even if the quantitative relationship of individuals with white spots reported by Ternovskii is retained, a subspecies cannot be established on the basis of this feature. It is well-established taxonomic practice that the creation of a subspecies is justified only if at least two thirds of the population are differentiated by a given feature or aggregate of features, and this condition is not fulfilled in the given case.

The author, in his systematic commentaries, indicates that the Altai mink differs in size from the mink acclimatized in the Tatar ASSR; actually, the Altai individuals coincide in size with the Tatar individuals.

The principal craniometric indexes for Altai minks (from measurements of 52 adult males) and Tatar minks (from measurements of 20 males, taken from the book by V. A. Popov) are as follows.

Condylobasal length of skull: in Altai minks 65.0 — 71.2 mm, in Tatar minks 65.0 — 71.5 mm; zygomatic width: respectively 36.0 — 41.5 mm and 36.5 — 42.4 mm; mastoid width: 33.0 — 36.4 mm and 31.6 — 37.4 mm; length of upper tooth row in both: 20.6 — 22.8 mm.

A similar picture is seen when craniometric data and body measurements for females are compared.

I thus conclude that L. v. altaica has no systematic validity and that its creation is not justified.

Geographical distribution. The homeland of P. vison is North America, where it occurs through the forest zone from the northern parts of Alaska and Canada south to New Mexico, Alabama and Florida.

The American mink was introduced into the Soviet Union for the first time in 1928 and was bred initially on Soviet state animal-breeding farms.

Efforts to acclimatize the mink in nature began in 1933, and it has been placed in a number of regions and republics. This work is still in progress today.

In Siberia the American mink has been introduced in the following localities.

In Western Siberia small groups of mink, 25 — 110 animals, were released on rivers and rivulets of the Ob system from 1934 on.

In the Khanty-Mansi National District, according to F. D. Shaposhnikov (in litt.) and local hunting institutions, American mink have been released in the following places.

In the Berezovo area, the mink was released in 1955 along the Lykhma and Amnya rivers, right tributaries of the Nadym [tr. note: Karym] River. Further south it was released in 1952 — 1954 in the Khanty-Mansi District along the Nazym River (near the village of Vershina) and along the Demyanka, north of the village of Kuim or Sipailovo, and along a tributary near the Eska post.

According to N.P. Lavrov (1946) the mink has been distributed in the following localities: in 1935 on the upper reaches of the Konda River and its tributary the River Ess; in 1937 on the Agan; and in 1941 on the Kantseyakh and Utersan rivers.

N.M. Berger (1954) relays reports from the hunter A.G. Golubev which indicate a relatively wide dispersal of the mink in 1950 in the valleys of the Agan and Trom"egan rivers (the right bank of the Ob River), where the mink "has settled the entire system of these rivers. Near the village of Mysovaya it has emerged onto the floodplain of the Ob River and it is continuing to spread along other tributaries. Very great concentration of the mink has been recorded along the Agan, Var"egan, Ambuta, Egut-Yakh, and Un-Yakh rivers."

In the Tomsk Region, according to Lavrov (1946), the mink has been introduced in the following districts: Vasyugan (the place of release being the Chebachya River, a right tributary of the Nyurolka River), the Tegul'de (released on the upper reaches of the Chichka-Yul, a tributary of the Chulym River), the Upper Ket (released on the Lisitsa River, a right tributary of the Ket River) and the Kargasok (released on the Naukha River, a tributary of the Nyurolka).

In a number of localities the mink has been acclimatized, is reproducing, and is widely distributed. But in most areas its numbers are small and it has not been locally acclimatized at all. Unfortunately, no research has been carried out on mink distribution, and even simple reconnaissance is lacking. The published data and the material obtained from hunters are contradictory. Thus, in a description of the fauna of the former Kondo-Sosva reserve, it is reported that the "mink has settled along the Konda River and has been acclimatized on the Nyurukh, Lezhya, Igotya, Zolotaya, A-akh rivers, in the Northern Sosva valley, tributaries of the Tapsui River, and at Lake Pontur."

On the Agan River, where some 100 minks were released in 1937, Golubev counted some 2,000 specimens in 1950, and according to him some 300 minks are caught in fish traps each summer. However, in the Khanty-Mansi National District, according to recent data by O. Levoshin (1959), all "releases proved unsuccessful except in the valley of the upper Agan River, and even there it occupies a small territory and has a low density."

According to I.P. Laptev (1958), in the taiga zone of Western Siberia "five isolated populations of the animal have been formed — in the valleys of the Agan, Yugan, Vasyugan, Ket, and Shudelka rivers, each 150 — 200 km from the next."

On the Altai, according to Lavrov (1946), the mink was released in 1940 in the valley of the Charysh River and also on the Belaya and its tributary the Zagrikha. In addition, minks were also released in 1937 in the valley of the Biya River and in a number of other localities.

At present, according to Berger (1954) and Ternovskii (1958), the mink is widely distributed on the Altai, being encountered in numerous districts of the Altai Territory. It is also encountered in the Gorno Altai near almost all large water bodies except those of the Kosh-Agach area. The contemporary range of the mink on the Altai has been formed both by release and by the natural dispersal of the animal.

Judging from all the data, the attempt at acclimatizing the American mink on the Altai has proved to be one of the most successful in Siberia.

On the Kuznetsk Ala-Tau, the mink has been found along the Antrop River, a tributary of the Kondoma (Berger, 1954).

In the Krasnoyarsk Territory, according to Lavrov (1946), large-scale attempts to acclimatize the animal were carried out and, according to this author, about 20% of the minks released in the Soviet Union are in this territory. According to G. D. Dul'keit and V. V. Kozlov (1948), the animal is occasionally encountered in the area of the "Stolby" reserve near Krasnoyarsk (in the valleys of the Mana and Bazaikha rivers).

In the Irkutsk Region mink distribution began in 1936, in the Slyudyanka, Ust'-Uda, Nizhneudinsk, Bratsk and Kachug districts. According to I. P. Kopylov (1948), the animals have not been acclimatized in the Slyudyanka area. The minks are multiplying in the Ust'-Uda and Nizhneudinsk districts.

According to Berger (1945), the minks released in the Kem River system have spread out and occupied most of the tributaries of this river. The highest density has been reached along the Zakem, Otnozhka, Belaya, Temnaya, Golchikha, and Tamanovka rivers. The mink is common near the villages of Kazachinsk and Bobrovka. The animal was released in 1951 along the Soya and Bren' rivers on the upper reaches of the Yenisei.

According to K. A. Vladimirov (1940), the mink has become widely distributed throughout the Ishim River system, a few individuals having been seen 400 — 500 km from the place of release. The animal is common along the Berezovka, Korda, Lis'ya, Gryaznukhae, Urktutnoi, Talaya, Elovaya, Porozhnyaya, Mostovaya, and Chara rivers. Reaching the area near the sources of the Ilim, the animal has penetrated from there into the tributaries of the Lena, Tilika, and Kikorei rivers.

Distribution of the mink in the Buryat-Mongol ASSR, according to Lavrov (1946), was carried out in 1939 on the Ona River (near Khorinsk village) and on the Saranzha — a left tributary of the Kulan — near the village of Mikhailovka. According to the hunting expert, Lavov, the animal has been acclimatized in the valleys of the above-mentioned rivers. It occurs on the Khudyku, Maldagan, Mailo-Gorkhon, Malyi Kul, Khoma, Ulyuta, Upper and Lower Khobyty rivers (Berger, 1954). According to A. G. Fetisov (1950) minks were settled in 1939 at the mouth of the Zhergokon River in the Selenga valley. The year following the distribution, minks were encountered along the Medvedkovaya, Chizhonga, and Chikoi rivers and at the mouth of the Buryat Spring, Shipovka, Lower Anaya, and Kharchaga.

A natural dispersal went on in the following years along the Chikoi, Chikokon and Zhergei. In the Chikoi valley the mink is common along the tributaries Exutai, Murgen, Kunalei, Asakan, Asy, Zagorliko, Shimbelinka, Shevin, Burecha, Yamnaya, Cheremukhovaya and Kanaleya. Along the Chikokon the mink has reached the source, occupying the Zakharovka, Shirokaya, and Glubokaya rivers, and along the Zhergei it has occupied the Khapchigir, Moloson, Burlukashikha, and Arei rivers and Lake Arei (Berger, 1954). Near Tanyurer, on the Anadyr, the mink and traces of its activities were observed in 1958 by B. S. Yudin.

The acclimatization of the American mink began in the Khabarovsk Territory in 1939 with distribution of the animal in the Nanai area, along the Anyui River and its tributaries the Aliu, Lari, Dike, and on the lower reaches of the Tormos, Alim, and Pak-Pu (Lavrov, 1946). The mink has been naturalized here and is continuing to spread into neighboring areas. According to the hunting expert, A. Vasenova (1957), the animal appeared in 1943 on the upper reaches of the Khor River, the Lazo District [Pereyaslavka], and in the Komsomolsk district in 1944 — along the Charmara and Khoso tributaries of the Khungari River.

A census carried out in 1945 showed that the mink stock along the Anyui included some 2,000 individuals. After 1948 the animal was caught for distribution in other areas of the territory. Beginning with 1950, the American mink began to be caught on the Khungari River as well, where its numbers have reached commerical density.

In 1952 the animal was introduced into the Magadan Region, where it has spread out along the Ola and Naekhan rivers. In 1958 it was released in the Ayan-Maya area.

The following data are available about distribution of the mink in the Maritime Territory. According to Lavrov (1946), the animal was released for the first time in 1936 on the Sita River, which is in the Sankhobe valley and lies within the Sikhote-Alin reserve; the animal rapidly acclimatized and began to multiply and disperse. According to G. F. Bromlei (1951), the mink, after settling the valleys of the rivers on the eastern side of the Sikhote-Alin, crossed over to the heads of the streams on the western slope.

According to Berger (1954), the animal was settled in 1951 on the Bikin River, where it exists to this day. It was rather widely distributed in the valley of the Iman, inhabiting the area all along this river and along the majority of its numerous tributaries (the Tatibe, Irma, Kolushta, Lower Sinancha, Vaku, etc.). The range of the mink on the Iman has, in some localities, joined its range along the Naitsukhem and Sankhoba rivers.

On the upper reaches of the Ussuri the mink was released along the Notto and Danants rivers, where it has become widespread and is an important object for the fur trade. In isolated parts of the Notto and Vakh-Notto rivers it is very densely distributed, and to the south it inhabits the Ulakhe, Lifudzin, Tibokhoze, Gudochou, Yaryadochkhu, Suchan, Maikhe, and Stebyashchukha rivers. In 1951 it was introduced south of Lake Khanka on the Lefu River.

On the shore of the Sea of Japan the animal has been introduced in the Sinkhoba River system, from which it has penetrated to the Selembe, Takema, Yamchu, Kema and Inutszin rivers.

Biology. The American mink has a mode of life similar to that of the European mink, being biotopically associated with various forest water bodies. In its homeland, North America, the animal often inhabits the seashore and marshes.

It prefers the shores of small rivers rich in fish. The most favorable areas for it are those cluttered with flotsam and broken wood, overgrown with trees and bushes, and abounding in nesting birds, murine rodents, and other animals. The hydrological regimen of the water body has a decisive importance for the mink, since the animal must have free access to water throughout the year. Thus the mink can live only on those water bodies which have areas remaining unfrozen in winter, or which have air holes in the ice and cavities under the ice (Figures 153, 154).

According to the observations of Ternovskii (1948), the winter density of minks on the Altai is directly proportional to the number of air holes in the ice on a given stretch of river. The smallest mink populations (1 — 2 per 10 km) were encountered where air holes were relatively rare (3 — 6 per 10 km), and the largest (5 — 7 animals per 10 km) in places where the number of air holes was correspondingly maximal (37 — 92 per 10 km).

Icing-over [of the water body] and disappearance of under-ice cavities are disastrous for the mink, depriving it of use of the water body. Observations are available which demonstrate that formation of ice layers compels the animal to migrate from a given locality. The minks will be completely absent from river stretches on which icing-over is frequent and involves large areas.

FIGURE 153. Floodplain of the Shuksha River, northeastern Altai. Biotope of the American mink. Photo by B. S. Yudin

Rivers with fish mortality in winter are unfavorable for the mink. In the West Siberian lowland many such rivers exist, and this is the chief hindrance to the mink's acclimatization in this area.

For shelter the animal uses hollows in trees and between roots, stones, etc., as well as earth burrows. On the Altai, according to Ternovskii (1958), of a total of 24 mink nests examined, 13 were in hollows in fallen trees, 8 were among roots and in hollows low on fallen and growing trees; one was in a tussock; one was dug in the ground, and one was in a hollow among stones.

The nests lay close to the river, at distances of 0.5 — 50 m [from it] most often 2 — 10 m from the water. The nests are usually constructed on unflooded places. When in danger the mink hides in the first available place: in niches under steep banks, under roots or uprooted trees, in accumulations of logs or flotsam, etc.

FIGURE 154. Sakhalin, area of Lake Tunaicha. Biotope of the American mink. Photo by N. A. Violovich

Ternovskii (1958) writes that "the nest chamber takes various forms, and in places where conditions permit the mink will widen the chamber, giving it a round-ellipsoid form. In burrows with hard walls which cannot be expanded by the animal, the chamber of course corresponds to the empty cavity... The size of the chambers varies. The smallest chamber of cylindrical form was 12 × 20 cm. The nest was in a hollow of a fallen willow..." The largest chamber of an ellipsoid form was situated among roots of a dry willow and was 20 × 29 cm. The average size of the 14 chambers examined was 16 × 24 cm. The nest chamber is situated in any part of the burrow: near the entry, in the middle, or at the end. In the 14 burrows examined the nests lay at distances of 30 cm to 2 m 40 cm from the exit, the commonest distance being 1 m.

The bottom of the chamber is lined with dry grass, moss, leaves, etc., and with some rodent fur and bird feathers. The burrows have from one to as many as five exits to the surface.

The external senses are well developed, hearing and scent being best and sight markedly poorer. The tactile sense and taste are well developed.

The mink is an adroit and agile animal, an excellent swimmer and diver, and easily catches fish in the water. It leads a chiefly crepuscular and nocturnal life, but in cloudy weather it may be active in the day as well. It is more active in spring and summer than in winter. The mink is a sedentary animal, and an individual will not leave the territory it has carved out for itself without necessity.

It feeds chiefly on Muridae and fish. The mink's diet has been fully studied on the Altai by Ternovskii (1958). Examination of stomach contents, food stores and food remnants, as well as of excrement (total of 1,719 data), enabled this author to work out the picture presented in the following table (Table 14).

TABLE 14. Diet composition of minks on Altai (after D. V. Temovskii. 1958)

Type of food	Number of occurrences	Percentage of total occurrences
Muridae	1,008	58.5
Rodents	927	53.8
Including:		
Murine	6	0.3
Voles	863	50.2
Birch mice (Sicistinae)	38	2.2
Russian flying squirrels		
(Pteromyidae)	5	0.3
Squirrels (Sciuridae) . .	7	0.4
Hares (Leporidae). . . .	4	0.2
Pikas (Ochotonidae) . .	4	0.2
Insectivores	81	4.7
Birds	58	3.3
Reptiles	17	1.0
Amphibians	95	5.8
Fish	945	54.9
Mollusks	1	0.05
Insects	441	25.6

As can be seen, mammals (58.5%) and fish (54.9%) occupy the first places.

Among mammals, the dominant position is occupied by voles, including all species of common red-backed voles and common voles occurring in the given locality. Fish are in second place. Twelve species of fish were found, including the following: grayling, salmon trout, Lenok trout, gudgeon, char, burbot, perch, the Amur ide, and others. The mink apparently hunts any fish available in the place it inhabits.

A considerable amount of insects was encountered, with aquatic forms predominating: caddis flies (Trichoptera), dragonflies and their larva (Odonata), water striders (Gerridae), haliplids (Halipidae), water beetles

(Dytiscidae), etc. As Ternovskii (1958) shows, minks very rarely eat insects. The high occurrence of insects (25.6%) in the diet must then be due to insects which enter the animal's digestive tract from the stomachs of fish it has eaten.

The mink's diet undergoes marked seasonal changes.

Table 15, presented below, shows the food items of the mink on the Altai according to seasons.

The seasonal variations in the mink's diet on the Altai relate to changes in conditions for obtaining food. In winter the deep snowfall makes hunting small Muridae difficult, and so the mink feeds chiefly on fish (88.6% of occurrences), with voles occupying second place (19.7%). In spring, with the disappearance of snow, the importance of rodents gradually increases, so that throughout the summer and autumn these animals occur at a high level (69.0% and 61.4%). The importance of fish drops (respectively 41.3% and 41.6%).

The diet also varies geographically, depending on the composition of the local fauna. Thus, according to K. A. Vladimirov (1940) the first place is occupied by water vole (30.1%), the second by small Muridae (20.5%), the third by birds (16.9%), and the fourth by fish (15.7%).

The mink, like many other animals, stores food when it is abundant. In the Tatar ASSR, according to V. A. Popov (1949), so-called larders of American mink have been found to contain 10 — 16 kg of fish. On the Altai, Ternovskii (1958) found the largest known American mink larder: 6 frogs, 3 water voles, 1 root vole, 1 viper, 9 minnows and a sculpin. In other cases too, mink stores have contained the most varied animals, including Russian flying squirrel, mole, water shrew, various shrews, frogs, lizards, and numerous species of fish, etc.

TABLE 15. Composition of mink food in various seasons (after D. V. Ternovskii, 1958)

Type of food	Winter, December to February, 370 items		Spring, March to May, 423 items		Summer, June to August, 310 items		Autumn, September to November, 616 items	
	quantity	%	quantity	%	quantity	%	quantity	%
Muridae	2	0.5	—	—	3	0.9	1	0.2
Voles	73	19.7	198	46.8	214	69.0	378	61.4
Sicistinae	—	—	7	1.6	6	1.9	25	4
Russian flying squirrel	—	—	3	0.7	—	—	—	—
Squirrel	1	0.2	—	—	—	—	—	—
Chipmunk	—	—	4	0.9	2	0.6	—	—
Hare	1	0.2	1	0.2	—	—	2	0.3
Pikas	—	—	—	—	1	0.3	3	0.5
Insectivores	9	2.4	12	2.8	18	5.8	42	6.8
Birds	14	3.8	6	1.4	11	3.5	27	4.4
Snakes	—	—	3	0.7	2	0.6	—	—
Lizards	—	—	3	0.7	5	1.6	4	0.6
Amphibians	2	0.5	53	12.5	31	10.0	9	1.5
Fishes	328	88.6	217	51.3	128	41.3	272	41.6
Insects	139	37.6	101	23.9	88	28.4	113	18.3

Reproduction of the American mink in nature is as yet insufficiently studied. The duration and dates of rut vary with the locality, the ecological conditions of the given year (condition of the foraging base, meteorological factors, etc.) and the state of the animal's health. Rut occurs in February — April. In the Tatar ASSR, according to Popov (1949), the height of rut is observed in the second or third week of March. In the Sverdlovsk Region, according to L. M. Tsetsevinskii (1939), the highest rut activity of minks observed was from 10—18 March. On the Altai, according to Ternovskii (1958), rut begins in late February and terminates in the first half of April. In the Irkutsk Region, according to K. A. Vladimirov (1940), rut occurs in late March and early April.

Duration of rut is about 30 — 45 days. For mink kept on breeding farms, according to M. D. Abramov (1951), duration of rut is no longer than 30 — 35 days. In Tataria, according to Popov (1949), it lasts some 30 days. On the Altai, according to Ternovskii (1958), duration of rut is about 45 days.

The gestation period is 36—75 days; this wide variation in length is associated with the presence of a latent phase, lasting 1 — 46 days, in the development of the fertilized egg.

Birth of the young has been observed as follows. On breeding farms, according to E. D. Il'ina (1952), the young are generally born around the same time, regardless of mating times. Most females give birth to young in the first third of May. In the Tatar ASSR, according to Popov (1949), the young appear in late April and early May. On the Altai, Ternovskii (1958) observed birth of young on 14—20 May. In the Irkutsk Region, the young appear in late May.

The litter size is 1—12 and in exceptional cases as large as 17. In the Tatar ASSR the average litter size over a period of six years was 3.5—5.8 (Popov, 1949). On the Altai, according to Ternovskii (1958), litters contained 2—7 (average 5) young. In the Irkutsk Region, the average number in the litter was 4 (Kopylov, 1948). The weight of the newborn young is 9—11 g, and the body length is 5—9 cm.

The young are born blind and toothless and their hair is weakly developed. They grow very rapidly, and in the first 40 days of life their size increases 15 — 20 times. The eyes open at the age of one month and teeth begin to appear after 22 — 26 days; at the same age the external auditory canal begins to open. The young mink, while still blind, are attracted by meat, reacting to its odor.

Minks kept in captivity swim willingly at two months and catch food from the water. At four months they almost reach adult size. By December — January it is difficult to tell the young from adults in external appearance.

The broods stay together until late summer. According to observations of Ternovskii (1958), young minks begin to be independent in late July or early August and more rarely in September.

The mink's enemies are all the large carnivores and birds of prey, primarily the wolf, fox, otter, eagle owl, Ural owl, golden eagle, etc. Food competitors of the mink are the Siberian weasel, ermine, weasel. local sable and Siberian polecat, as well as birds feeding on Muridae and fish (gray sea eagle, the osprey, etc.). Various species of ticks, fleas and helminths parasitize the mink. On the Altai, out of 65 minks examined by Ternovskii (1948), 47 were infected by the following helminths: Diphyllobotrium sp., Ascaris columnaris Leidy, Soboliphyme baturini Petrov, and others. The following fleas were found: Ceratophyllus rectangulatus and Ceratophyllus penicilliger. The tick Ixodes persulcatus was found.

Molt occurs biannually, in spring and autumn. Spring molt is markedly protracted, beginning in March and terminating in late June and in the first half of July. Autumn molt takes place from August to November, inclusively. The mink does not exhibit the sharp differences between winter and summer fur characteristic of other mustelids.

Practical importance. The American mink is a valuable fur-bearing species. Its fur is of higher quality than that of the European mink. The pelts are generally larger, the hair longer and softer and more darkly colored. It is bred on special breeding farms. New strains of distinctive color have been raised by animal breeders using zootechnical methods.

B. A. Kuznetsov (1952) gave the following description of new forms of American mink.

The silver mink. Characterized by a tinge of pure white guard hair among dark guard hairs of back and flanks. Degree of fur's silveriness corresponds to the number of these white covering hairs.

The platinum mink. General tone silvery gray (platinum) with varying degrees of darkness formed by mixture of black, white, and white-tipped-with-black guard hairs. The down is grayish.

Sable mink. Light brown with brown, and to some extent, white guard hair and dense grayish down.

"Pastel" mink. Characterized by light brown color and beige or light brown guard hairs. Underfur light blue-gray.

"Breath of spring" mink. Of a very light, pure silver bluish color.

"Cross" mink. White or light grayish color, usually with addition of black guard hair. Dark band extends along spine with crosslike pattern on shoulders.

White mink. Characterized by white color.

16. Genus VORMELA W. Blasius (1884). Mottled polecats

1884. Vormela. Blasius, W. Berichte der Naturforsch. Gesellsch. in Bamberg, 13, p. 9; Birulya, A. Ezhegodnik Zoologicheskogo Muzeya Akademii Nauk, 15, p. 327. 1910; Ognev, S. I. Zveri SSSR i prilezhashchikh stran (Animals of the USSR and Adjacent Countries), 3, p. 65. 1935; Ellerman, J. R. and T. C. S. Morrison-Scott. Checklist of Palaearctic and Indian Mammals, p. 250, London. 1951.

Type species. Mustela sarmatica Pallas (1771) = Mustela peregusna Gueldenstaedt (1770).

Diagnosis. Fur extremely spotty: dorsal parts in form of rusty yellow or dark coffee "shabrack" or saddle blanket, strewn with light yellowish spots; underparts black or with light spots; white band extends across head above eyes and occasionally showing a break on forehead; mouth surrounded by white ring; ears white. Front interior angle of tympanic bullae extended into thin process fused with hamulary process of pterygoid bone.

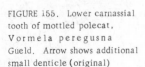

Dental formula: $I\frac{3}{3}$; $C\frac{1}{1}$; $Pm\frac{3}{3}$; $M\frac{1}{1}$ = 34.

Lower carnassial tooth with additional small denticle on lingual side of middle tubercle of crown (Figure 155).

Geographical distribution. Southern areas of Europe and Asia, from Rumania, Bulgaria and Asia Minor in the west to Mongolia and China in the east, and north to the Maritime, Lower Volga, Kazakhstan and Altai steppes, inclusively.

FIGURE 155. Lower carnassial tooth of mottled polecat, Vormela peregusna Gueld. Arrow shows additional small denticle (original)

Systematic notes. The genus is well-differentiated systematically. R. Hensel (1881) and A. Birulya (1910) approximate it with the African polecat genus Zorilla Oken (1816), and indeed the external appearance, color and craniological features (structure of auditory and occipital region, odontological features, and similar dental formation) do indicate kinship between these animals. The mottled polecat, on the other hand, is undoubtedly related to the true polecats (Putorius). This is shown not only by the pronounced craniological similarity, but also by the nature of individual species variation in some true polecats, particularly of Putorius eversmanni Lesson. Thus, my collection contains skulls of this species from the Kurgan Region and from Transbaikalia in which the hamulary processes of the pterygoid bone a e joined by a bony bridge with the tympanic bullae in the same manner as in the mottled polecat.

The genus is monotypic.

27. **Vormela peregusna** Gueldenstaedt (1770). Mottled polecat (Map XX)

1770. Mustela peregusna. Gueldenstaedt, A. L. — Nov. Comment. Acad. Sci. Imper. Ross. Petropolit., 14, p. 441.

1771. Mustela sarmatica. Pallas, P. S. Reise durch verschiedene Provinzen des Russischen Reiches, 1, p. 453 (Lower Volga area); Auct. cit. Spicilegia Zoologica, p. 79; Auct. cit. Zoographia Rosso-Asiatica, 1780, 1, p. 89. 1811—1831.

1851. Putorius sarmaticus. Simashko, Yu. Russkaya fauna (Russian Fauna). 2, p. 360; Bogdanov, M. N. Okhotnich'i i promyslovye zveri i ptitsy Evropeiskoi Rossii i Kavkazskogo kraya (Game and Hunting Animals and Birds of European Russia and the Caucasian Territory). — Zhurnal Okhoty i Konnozavodstva, Nos. 11—12, p. 232. 1873.

1910. Vormela koshewnikovi. Satunin, K. —Zoologisch. Anzeig., 36, p. 59 (Ashkhabad).

1910. Vormela tedshenica. Satunin, K. Loc. cit. p. 60 (Tedzhen Oasis).

1910. Vormela negans. Miller, G. S.— Proc. Unit. States National Mus., 38, pl. 17, p. 385 (Ordos Desert, China).

1912. Vormela peregusna. Miller, G. S. Catal. of the Mammals of Western Europe, p. 429, London; Pocock, R.— Fauna Brit. India, Mamm., 2, p. 384. 1941; Stroganov, S. U. Novye dannye po sistematike perevyazki (Vormela peregusna Gueldenstaedt) (New Data on the Taxonomy of the Mottled Polecat (Cormela peregusna Gueldenstaedt)).— Trudy Zoologicheskogo Instituta AN SSSR, 7, p. 129. 1948; Ellerman, J. R. and T. C. S. Morrison-Scott. Checklist of Palaearctic and Indian Mammals, p. 266, London. 1951.

Type and type locality. The species has been described from a specimen from the Don Steppes.

Diagnosis. The features of the species are identical with those of the genus and are given above in its description.

Measurements. Length of body with head: 290—347 mm; length of tail: 150—218 mm; length of hind paw: 39.4—45.4 mm; height of ear: 20.5—27.4 mm.

Weight 370 — 715 g.

Condylobasal length of skull: 51.0—62.0 mm; zygomatic width: 30.0—39.0 mm; height in area of tympanic bullae: 21.6—23.0 mm; interorbital width: 14.2—16.6 mm; width behind postorbital processes: 10.0—13.0 mm; width of rostrum above canines: 13.5—14.3 mm; length of upper tooth row: 16.7— 18.3 mm.

Description. Somewhat resembles polecat in build but is smaller in size; vivid spottiness of color conspicuous. Body thin and slender. Head relatively small, with blunted muzzle and large, almost triangular ears; ears conspicuously outlined due to white color. Tail very furry, its length greater than one half length of body with head. Webs between toes rudimentary. Claws sharp and recurved, length of claws on forelimbs 7.4 —16.7 mm.

Color extremely vivid and bright. Broad, pure white band extends across head in frontal area towards base of ears and is conspicuously outlined by dark brownish-black general background of top of head. White around mouth. Background color of back ("shabrack" (saddle blanket)) varies from straw yellow to dark coffee with scattering of more or less small, yellowish golden or rusty gray-brown spots of varying intensity. Number of light spots 25—60 or more. Underparts grayish black, sometimes strewn with rusty straw yellow or yellowish spots. Base of tail rusty brown; middle of tail straw yellow-whitish with rusty brown tinge; end of tail glossy black-brown. Summer fur coarser and stiffer, not differing much in color from winter fur.

Skull (Figure 156) similar in general structural traits to that of true polecats (subgenus Putorius), but smaller and with less elevated frontal area. Skull relatively short, moderately elongated in facial section, greatly compressed in postorbital part and broad in cranial region. Upper profile is gentle arch, slightly convex in postorbital area. Sagittal crest well developed in adult and old individuals. Mastoid processes protrude markedly to either side. Structure of nasals subject to variation: in some cases bones fork posteriorly and protrusion of anterior part of frontal bones wedges inside bifurcation, while in other cases nasals

414

lack this structural trait. Structure of maxillaries also varies. In a number of cases, protrusion extends from upper maxillary bone, which wedges between posterior parts of nasals and intermaxillaries, but in majority of cases intermaxillary bone apparently contiguous to nasal bone all along its inner side, as was noted long ago by A. Birulya (1910). Tympanic bullae rather large and swollen, are trapezoidal from above. Auditory tubes absent. External auditory canal covered above by edge of temporal bone. Distance between external edges of occipital condyles approximately equal to or slightly greater than width of rostrum above canines. Hamular processes (of the pterygoid bones) joined by a bony bridge with antero-internal angles of tympanic bullae. Infraorbital foramina barely one third of aveolus of upper canine. Talon of upper carnassial tooth flat, lacking denticle. Upper molar not expanded externally and has no middle constrictions. Lower carnassial tooth has additional small denticle lying on internal aspect of crown, at base of middle tubercle.

Os penis archlike, bent in terminal third, not forming hamate curve so characteristic for polecat; tip flattened and has lateral groove. Length of baculum 36.9 — 39.2 mm (Figure 157).

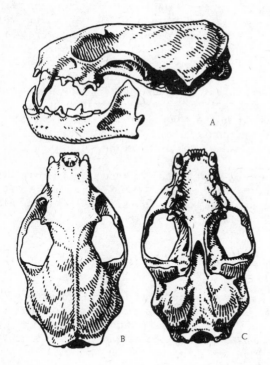

FIGURE 156. Skull of the sarmatier (mottled polecat), Vormela peregusna Gueld. (original):

A — lateral view; B — dorsal view; C — ventral view.

FIGURE 157. Os penis of mottled polecat, Vormela peregusna Gueld. (after S. I. Ognev, 1935)

Systematic notes. R. Pocock (1936), from a specimen supposedly collected by him in the vicinity of Lake Baikal, described a new "subspecies" V. p. ornata. Undoubtedly in his report the collection place of the type specimen was a clear mistake. The Baikal area has been thoroughly investigated for mammals and no student has ever found a mottled polecat there; nobody has even heard of one.

Geographical distribution. The range of the mottled polecat includes the southern area of Eastern Europe (including Rumania and Bulgaria) and South Asia to Mongolia, inclusively. In the Soviet Union it takes in the Black Sea steppes, Crimea, Lower Volga steppes, northern Caucasus, Transcaucasia, the desert and semidesert areas of Central Asia, Kazakhstan and the Altai steppes.

In Siberia the distribution is insufficiently studied and the various reports available are not corroborated by collection materials (Map XX).

E. A. Eversmann (1850) mentions a pelt of the mottled polecat which was sold in the village fair of Kundravakh, south of Lake Chebarkul on the east side of the Urals (about 55° 5' N lat.). To the south, the animal is known from the neighboring areas of Kazakhstan, for instance from the River Bolshoi Irgiz, on the left side of the Ural River in the Chkalov [Orenburg] Region (Afanas'ev et al. 1953).

The following published data are available with regard to the mottled polecat's distribution in the Altai and Altai steppes. According to S. I. Orlov and M. D. Zverev (1930) it is occasionally encountered in the former Rubtsovsk and Biisk districts (see also Zverev, 1932). According to A. V. Afanas'ev et al. (1953) a mottled polecat was obtained in 1927 near Semipalatinsk. Pelt processing statistics show that it has been obtained in the area of Ust'-Kamenogorsk. A. M. Kolosov (1939), quoting the director of the fur depot in Kosh-Agach, A. I. Mal'tsev, reports that the mottled polecat, though rare, is encountered in the Chuya Steppe. We examined two pelts obtained from there in the autumn of 1950 by I. D. Pronin. K. T. Yurlov was informed that a mottled polecat was obtained in the summer of 1957 near Lake Tarkhatinskoe.

Survey of subspecies. Six subspecies are known at present, differing chiefly in color and in distribution of color on the fur, in body- and skull-dimensions, and in form and length of the claws. The mottled polecat occurring in Siberia belongs to the light Semirech'e form.

27a. Vormela peregusna pallidior Stroganov (1948).
Semirech'e mottled polecat

1948. Vormela peregusna pallidior. Stroganov, S. U. Novye dannye po sistematike perevyazki (Vormela peregusna Gueldenstaedt) (New Data on the Taxonomy of the Mottled Polecat (Vormela peregusna Gueldenstaedt)). — Trudy Zoologicheskogo Instituta AN SSSR, 7, No. 3, pp. 129—131, Figures 1, 1a, 1c.

Type and type locality. No. 25701 in the collection of the Zoological Institute of the Academy of Sciences of the USSR, male, 1910, from

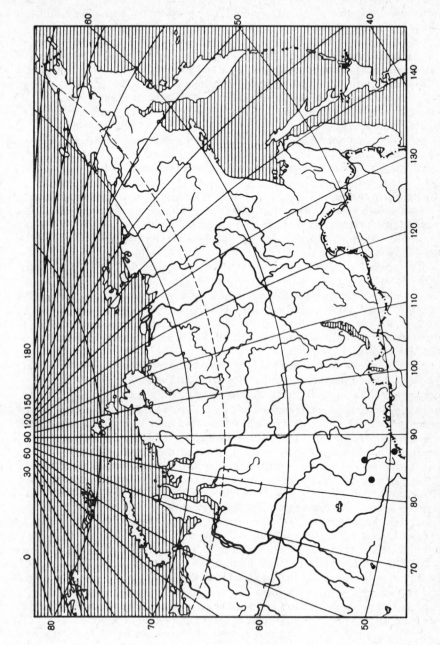

MAP XX. Geographical distribution of the mottled polecat, Vormela peregusna Gueld, in Siberia

417

collections of V. N. Shnitnikov. Semirech'e, Kopal County [now Taldy-Kurgan].

Diagnosis. Circumoral white ring includes chin, does not extend to throat and is not connected with frontal band. Frontal band usually without break on forehead, narrow bands occasionally extend from it to lower side of neck. Lateral occipital bands joined by broad "collar." Background color of shabrack (saddle blanket) straw yellow with scattered small rusty brown spots. Belly with numerous light spots. Claws very long, those on middle toes of forelimbs reaching 12.8 — 13.0 mm.

Measurements. Length of body with head: 290 — 320 mm (av. 315 mm); length of tail: 165 — 205 mm (av. 180 mm); length of hind paw: 39.5 — 43.3 mm (av. 41.6 mm); height of ear: 21.0 — 22.8 mm (av. 22.3 mm). Weight: males 610 — 715 g; females 450 — 600 g.

Condylobasal length of skull: 53.0 — 54.8 mm (av. 53.9 mm); zygomatic width: 32.5 — 35.5 mm (av. 33.9 mm); interorbital width: 11.6 — 13.0 mm (av. 12.3 mm); width of rostrum above canines: 13.5 — 14.0 mm (av. 13.7 mm); length of upper tooth row: 16.7 — 17.0 mm (av. 16.7 mm).

Systematic notes. V. p. pallidior is close to the Central Asian V. p. koshewnikovi Satunin, 1910 (= V. p. alpherakyi Birulya, 1910) but is readily differentiated from it by the considerable reduction of the dark coffee color on the shabrack and by the smaller (on the average) size and longer claws.

This subspecies differs more distinctly from the Ordos (China) subspecies V. p. negans Miller (1910), to which the mottled polecats occurring in Kazakhstan have sometimes erroneously been referred (Ognev, 1935, 1940; Shnitnikov, 1936; Bobrinskii, 1944). In contrast to V. p. negans, the fur of the underparts of V. p. pallidior is not completely black, having instead numerous light patches and in addition "collar" and scapular bands not as broad.

The differences of V. p. pallidior from the nominate subspecies and from V. p. obscura Stroganov (1948) of southern Tadzhikistan are more pronounced. It is distinctly differentiated from V. p. peregusna by the general color pattern and shorter claws (in V. p. peregusna the claws reach a length of 16.7 mm). V. p. obscura is smaller than V. p. pallidior, the claws are weaker and shorter (the length is no higher than 10 mm), the color is darker and the pattern shows a disjunction of the frontal band.

As I had the chance to mention earlier (Stroganov, 1948), the Zoological Institute of the Academy of Sciences of the USSR has a specimen of mottled polecat received from Dr. Pyasetskii with the word "China" on the tag, this specimen undoubtedly belonging to a distinct and still undescribed subspecies. This specimen is also mentioned by Ognev (1935), who considered it "a clearly marked V. p. negans"— though it is distinctly differentiated systematically both from V. p. negans and other subspecies. The principal difference is the fact that the ring from around the mouth not only includes the chin but also extends to the throat and joins in the infraorbital area with the frontal band.

I propose to name the above-mentioned subspecies Vormela peregusna chinensis subsp. n., taking as type specimen No. 1237 in the collection of the Zoological Institute of the Academy of Sciences of the USSR (coll. Dr. Pyasetskii). Terra typica for V. p. chinensis subsp. n. should be considered to be the valley of the lower Hwang Ho.

Geographical distribution. The range of V. p. pallidior extends from the eastern slopes of the Kara Tau to western Mongolia, inclusively, south apparently to the Turkestan and Altai ranges, and north to the Altai and Chuya steppes, inclusively.

Material studied. Southern areas of the European USSR — 12 specimens; Iran — 2 specimens; Turkmenia — 6 specimens; Uzbekistan — 6 specimens; Tadzhikistan — 14 specimens; Kazakhstan — 19 specimens; Chuya Steppe — 2 specimens; China — 1 specimen. Total — 62 specimens.

Biology. The mottled polecat is a characteristic animal of the open desert and semidesert. In [Soviet] Central Asia it occurs in oases and tugai [river-valley bottomland complexes of forest, scrub, and meadow]. It is reported in Siberia for the steppes of the western foothills of the Altai and for the Chuya Steppe. It feeds on small rodents, birds and other animals. The nest is made in a burrow. Gestation time is as yet undetermined. In Kazakhstan and Central Asia the young are born in February — March. A nursing female was obtained by me in the area of Tigrovaya Balka, on the lower reaches of the Vakhsh, on 14 March 1944. Litter size is 4 — 8. In Tadzhikistan I have encountered young already fending for themselves in May — June. Is active in twilight hours of both morning and evening. When alarmed it shows a characteristic aggressive posture — it rises up on its legs, arches its back, raises its tail and head, and gives vent to shrill and hoarse hisses.

Practical importance. Insignificant commercially since it is obtained only occasionally. In Soviet Central Asia the fur is used to make children's clothes. It is beneficial since it exterminates noxious Muridae.

IV.   Family **FELIDAE** Gray (1821).   Cats

1821.   Felidae.   Gray, J.   London Medical Repository, 15, p. 302. 1 April.

Description. The cat family comprises the most specialized of terrestrial carnivores, which vary in size from the small domestic cat to the enormous tiger. Build stocky but slender. Body supple, more or less elongate and muscular. Neck short and powerful. Head round, with short muzzle. Ears of moderate size, widely separated and often rounded at tips. Legs in most members of moderate length, with round paws. Forepaws bear five toes, hind paws four toes. Claws very sharp, and retractile (except in the cheetah). Digitigrade. Tail varies in length from very short (in lynx) to long, occasionally reaching no less than two thirds of body length. Tail evenly furred. Color highly variegated, but spotted or striped coats predominate. Sexual organ directed anteriorly only when erect. Usually urinate in a rearward-directed spurt.

Skull relatively short, high, and round. Upper line of skull profile extends from end of rostrum in even, more or less convex arch, does not show any fixed transition from muzzle to forehead. Jaws very short and powerful. Tympanic bullae usually highly inflated; internal cavity of each bulla divided by septum into two chambers of which anterior usually smaller than posterior.

Dental formula: $I\frac{3}{3}$; $C\frac{1}{1}$; $Pm\frac{2-3}{2}$; $M\frac{1}{1}$ = 28 or 30.

External incisors larger than internal. Canines large and sharp and in some species have sharp cutting keel along posterior side. Last upper premolar and first upper molar have been more pronouncedly differentiated as carnassial teeth than those of the rest of the Carnivora and form a perfect cutting apparatus; upper tooth has paracone and metastyle, and lower has paraconid and metaconid; heel is absent. Lower molars of sectorial type: highly compressed laterally, bearing sharp cutting cusps.

Systematic notes. Family Felidae originated from the Miacidae, primitive Paleocene carnivores. Extinct, highly specialized cats occur in deposits of Oligocene to Pleistocene age. Representatives of modern genera of Felidae are known beginning from the Upper Miocene of the Old and the New Worlds.

Family Felidae is usually divided into three subfamilies: Felinae — true cats; Pantherinae — snow leopards or panthers; and Acinonychinae — cheetahs. All are present in the USSR fauna, and members of the first two subfamilies occur in Siberia.

Thirty-five cat species are known in the modern fauna. Some 18 species are present in the Palaearctic fauna, and six of these 18 species occur in Siberia.

Geographical distribution. The cats are widely distributed in Europe, Asia, Africa, and America; they are absent from Australia, the Antilles and Madagascar.

Biology. In numerous respects the cats are the most specialized members of the order. In contrast to most carnivores, they are stenophagous animals, feeding exclusively on flesh, chiefly of warm-blooded animals. Cats in most cases do not run very well, and in catching prey the principal role is played not by pursuit, but rather by ambushing the prey. Cats display distinctive traits associated with their carnivorous mode of feeding and with their above-mentioned method of catching prey. They have a more supple skeleton than dogs, for instance, and extremely sharp and highly retractile claws. The claws do not touch the ground, since they are encased in special lobes of skin during walking, and thus do not become blunted. This also allows noiseless movement while stalking prey. At the moment of attack the claws emerge and are transformed into a deadly weapon. The powerful jaws are armed with strong teeth.

These specialized traits are extremely characteristic of the cats and serve both for attack and for active defense.

The premolars are of a peculiar structure. Aside from the carnassial tooth in the upper jaw, only one premolar similar to it functions. The upper molar is vestigial. No triturating surfaces have remained on the teeth. The dentition as a whole forms a scissorlike cutting apparatus which cuts food very effectively. The fleshy tongue is covered with numerous horny spines whose tips point backwards, making an effective grater for tearing meat from bones.

Most cats are stenotopic inhabiting a variety of places. They are distinguished by strength, agility, and rapidity of movement. Cats walk slowly, very cautiously, and noiselessly. They can make leaps several times longer than the length of their bodies. Most cats are able to climb trees.

They reproduce no more than once a year, and usually bear few young. Of the external senses hearing is the best developed, followed by sight. The sense of smell is much more weakly developed. Taste is well developed, cats having definite preferences among foods and loving blood and milk. Their intelligence is lower than that of dogs. They are easily tamed and accustomed to humans.

Practical importance. The cats are important as both commercial and sporting game. Numerous species damage stocks of useful animals and birds; they devour game and commercial animals. The harm to livestock breeding is of local significance.

Some large species (tigers and leopards) can occasionally be dangerous to humans.

Cats are of great value to zoological gardens and parks.

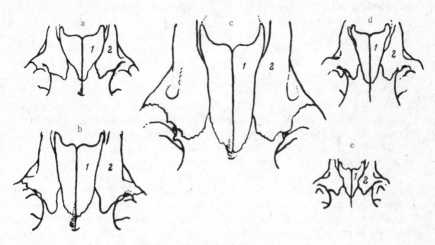

FIGURE 158. Nasal section (rostrum) of skull, dorsal view:

a – snow leopard or ounce, Felis uncia Schreb.; b – leopard, Felis pardus L.; c – tiger, Felis tigris L.; d – Lynx, Lynx lynx L.; e – manul cat, Felis manul Pallas; 1 – nasal bone; 2 – jawbone.

Key to Species of Cat Family (Felidae) Occurring in Siberia

1 (6). Suspension of hyoid bone not fully ossified, its lower part a tendinous cord. Larynx not pressed tightly to base of skull. Process of jugal bone falling far short of lacrymal foramen . . . . Subfamily **Pantherinae**-Panthers (p. 462)

2 (3). Size extremely large: length of body with head 160 – 300 cm, condylobasal length of skull 250 – 310 mm. Coat shows vivid transverse bands. Cheeks full, cheek hair long and forming cheek whiskers. Ears short and bluntly rounded. Nasal bones extend back markedly further than jawbones (Figure 158, c) . . . . **Panthera (Tigris) tigris**-Tiger (p. 477)

3 (2). Size large: length of body usually up to 160 cm, condylobasal length
of skull less than 230 mm. Fur lacks transverse bands, has scattered
black patches. Cheek whiskers absent. Ears triangular, with
rounded tips. Nasals extend backwards almost as far as jawbone
or even a bit further (Figure 158) 4
4 (5). General color yellow or russet. Back spots clearly delineated and
vividly colored; diameter of largest spots usually less than 5 cm.
Tail with relatively short hair; thickness of tail appreciably less than
thickness of middle part of foreleg. Condylobasal length of skull
180 — 223 mm. Frontal area slightly and gently convex, almost
flat, or with very slight longitudinal depression. Nasal bones
extend backwards somewhat beyond nasal processes of jawbones
(Figure 158, b). Tympanic bullae relatively narrow, moderately
inflated. Zygomatic process of squamosal closely approximated
to frontal process of zygomatic bone . . . .
. . . . Panthera s. str. pardus — Leopard (p. 462)
5 (4). General fur color grayish brown to gray without addition of yellow or
russet. Spots on back not clearly delineated, are diffuse and pale;
diameter of largest spots over 5 cm. Tail covered with long hair;
thickness of tail almost equal to that of middle part of foreleg.
Condylobasal length of skull 162 — 173 mm. Frontal area of skull
conspicuously convex with appreciable longitudinal medial depression.
Nasals do not extend backwards beyond line joining tips of nasal
processes of jawbones (Figure 158, a). Tympanic bullae relatively
flatter and broader. Zygomatic process of squamosal does not
reach frontal process of zygomatic bone . . . .
. . . . Panthera (Uncia) uncia — Snow leopard or ounce (p. 469)
6 (1). Hyomandibular cartilage of hyoid bone fully ossified. Larynx pressed
tightly to base of skull. Process of jugal bone extends beyond exterior
edge of lacrymal foramen (Figure 158, e) . . . .
. . . . Subfamily Felinae — True cats (p. 423)
7 (8). Tail short, being about as long as head and failing to reach paws
of extended hind limbs. Distal third of tail black. Ears long and
sharp, with tufts of hair on tips. Condylobasal length of adult skull
at least 120 mm . . . . Lynx lynx — Lynx (p. 441)
8 (7). Tail long, appreciably longer than head and going beyond paws of
extended hind limbs. Distal part of tail either without black or black
only at tip. Ears short and rounded, without tufts. Condylobasal
length of adult skull less than 120 mm 9
9 (10). Fur extremely long and luxuriant for cats. Posterior part of back
with sparse dark transverse bands. Chest lacks bands. Posterior
aspect of ear without white patch. No white bands extending from nose
upwards to top of head. Pattern of tail consists of dark rings; tip of
tail black. Anterior edge of tympanic bulla extends beyond anterior
side of postglenoid process. Postorbital distance (width) markedly
greater than distance between infraorbital foramina. Upper jaw lacks
first premolar. Upper carnassial with rudimentary talon . . . .
. . . . Felis (Otocolobus) manul — Manul cat (p. 432)
10 (9). Fur has length and luxuriance usual for cats. Coat spotty, lacking
transverse bands on back. Rusty bands extend across chest. Posterior

side of ear with large white patch. Two whitish bands extend from nose upwards towards forehead. Tail of spotted pattern and lacking black tip. Anterior edge of tympanic bulla fails to reach anterior side of postglenoid process. Postorbital width approximately equal to distance between infraorbital foramina. First premolar present in upper jaw, at least in young. Upper carnassial tooth with well-developed talon . . . .
. . . . **Felis (Prionailurus) bengalensis** — Leopard (p. 423)

1. Subfamily FELINAE. True cats

1917. Felinae. Pocock, R. J. The Classification of Existing Felidae.— Ann. Mag. Nat. Hist. (8), 20, pp. 329 — 350; Ognev, S. I. Zveri SSSR i prilezhashchikh stran (Animals of the USSR and Adjacent Countries), 3 pp. 114 — 115. 1935.

Description. * Small and medium-sized cats of extremely variegated external appearance and color, ranging from domestic cat to puma.

Hyomandibular cartilage normally ossified, holding larynx near base of skull and hampering its movement. Process of jugal bone extends beyond exterior edge of lacrymal foramen. Infraorbital foramen large, larger in diameter than upper external incisor (I^3).

Feet generally moderately long and massive. Ends of toes with individual skin lobes protecting their retractile claws at internal side of second and third digits and on external side of fourth and fifth digits. No mane on back of neck.

Geographical distribution. Coincides with that of the family.

Systematic notes. The subfamily includes 18 genera and subgenera, six of which are represented in the USSR. In Siberia the subfamily includes the following: F e l i s b e n g a l e n s i s Kerr, O t o c o l o b u s m a n u a l Pallas, and L y n x l y n x L.

17. Genus FELIS Linnaeus. True cats

28. **Felis (Prionailurus)** bengalensis Kerr (1792).
Leopard cat

1792. F e l i s b e n g a l e n s i s. Kerr, R. Animal Kingdom of Linnaeus, Vol. 1, p. 151. Mamm.

1837. F e l i s c h i n e n s i s. Gray, J. E.— Mag. Nat. Hist., ser. 2, Vol. 1, p. 577 (probably Canton, China).

1842. L e o p a r d u s e l l i o t i. Gray, J. E.— Ann. Mag. Nat. Hist., 10, p. 260 (Bombay).

1842. L e o p a r d u s h o r s f i e l d i i. Gray, J. E. Ibidem., p. 260 (Butan, N. India).

1843. L e o p a r d u s r e e v e s i i. Gray, J. E. List Mamm. Brit. Mus., p. 44 (China).

1844. F e l i s p a r d o c h r o u s. Hodgson, B. H.— Calcutta Journ. Nat. Hist., 4, p. 286 (Nepal).

---

* After R. I. Pocock (1907) and S. I. Ognev (1935).

1862. Felis undata. Radde, G. Reisen im Süden von Ost-Sibirien, Vol. 1, Säugethiere-Fauna, pp. 106—113, St. Petersburg. 1816. tab. 4, figs. 1—8 (nec Desmarest) (Amur River, 60 km below the mouth of the Zeya).

1867. Felis tenasserimensis. Gray, J. E. — Proc. Zool. Soc. p. 400, London (Tenasserim).

1867. Felis wagati. Gray, J. E. Ibidem, p. 400 (Tenasserim [Burma]).

1870. Felis scripta. Milne-Edwards, A. — Nouv. Arch. Mus., 7, Bull., p. 92, pls. 57—58, fig. 1 (Szechwan, China).

1871. Felis euptilura. Elliot, D. Remarks on Various Species of Felidae, etc. — Proc. Zool. Soc. London, p. 761, pl. 36 (instead of Felis undata Radde — nomen preoccupatum).

1868—1874. Felis microtis. Milne-Edwards, A. Recherches pour servir à l'Histoire Naturelle des Mammifères, p. 221, Paris. pl. 31 A, pl. 31 B, figs. 1—2 b (vicinity of Peking).

1868—1874. Felis decolorata. Milne-Edwards, A. Ibid., p. 223 (environs of Peking).

1883. Felis microtis. Elliot, D. G. Monograph Felidae, pl. 26 and text (Lapsus calami for Felis microtis).

1903. Felis ricketti. Bonhote, I. — Ann. Mag. Nat. Hist., 1, p. 374 (Foochow, S. China).

1903. Felis ingrami. Bonhote, I. Ibidem., p. 474 (northern Kweichow).

1905. Felis anastasiae. Satunin, K. Neue Katzenarten aus Central-Asien. — Ezhegodnik Zoologicheskogo Muzeya Imperatorskoi Akademii Nauk, 9, pp. 528—532, St. Petersburg. 1904 (Kam, E. Tibet).

1922. Felis manchurica. Mori, T. — Ann. Mag. Nat. Hist., pp. 609—610 (environs of Mukden [now Shenyang], Manchuria).

1930. Felis sinensis. Shih. — Bull. Dept. Biol. Sun. Yatsen Univers., No. 4. Canton (Chingsi [Tsingsi], Kwangsi).

Type and type locality. Type probably not preserved; described from a specimen from southern Bengal.

Diagnosis. Fur with density and length usual for cats. Ears short but protrude noticeably from fur, are rounded and lack tufts on tips. Coat spotted, without transverse band on back. Rusty bands extend across chest. Whitish band extends from nose upwards towards sinciput of head on each side. Back of ear shows large white patch. Tail has spotted pattern and black tip. Anterior edge of auditory bulla fails to reach anterior surface of postglenoid process. Postorbital width approximately equal to distance between infraorbital foramina. First upper premolar present at least during youth. Upper carnassial tooth with well-developed talon. Lower carnassial tooth has small third denticle on posterior edge.

Measurements. Length of body with head 44.5—83.0 cm; length of tail: 23.0—44.0 cm; length of hind paw: 11.5—14.0 cm; length of ear: 4.5—5.0 cm. Larger specimens reaching length of 107 cm are known.

Maximum length of skull: males 87.0—110.0 mm, females 77.0—91 mm; zygomatic width: males 57.0—72.3 mm, females 55.0—63.0 mm; length of upper tooth row: males 25.5—32.3 mm, females 25.4—30.0 mm.

Description. Resembles domestic cat in general build but is appreciably larger, has longer legs and somewhat shorter tail. Body build slender and compact. Head relatively small, not broad between ears, with rather short and narrow muzzle. Eyes small. Ears moderately long and protruding markedly from surrounding fur; upper edge of ears rounded and there are no tufts on ends. "Side whiskers" absent. Tail furry, length approximately one half that of body. Claws extremely sharp, highly recurved.

Pupil of eye vertically elliptical.

Coloration: two characteristic longitudinal whitish bands in frontal area, dense rusty brown spotty pattern on body, and transverse russet bands on chest.

Fur color subject to considerable individual variation. General tone on back goes from relatively pale grayish straw-yellow to dull grayish brown, usually with rusty tinges. Color becomes gradually lighter on flanks. Entire body irregularly sprinkled with longitudinal rusty yellow or brown spots, sometimes very blurred and diffuse. On spine patches fuse, forming three longitudinal dark brown bands. On dorsal surface of forepart of neck and on chest lie 4 — 5 transverse rusty or rusty brown bands. Dorsal side of ear with white patch at middle of internal margin. Vividly conspicuous whitish band extends from internal corners of eyes upwards along forehead. Chin and throat whitish. Belly yellowish white with dull rusty spots. Tail dorsally grayish or rusty grayish and ventrally lighter. Seven to nine indistinct dark rusty brown rings scattered along tail; tip of tail blackish.

Skull (Figure 159) longer, lower and narrower than in other small cats. Upper profile of skull slightly convex. Postorbital width of skull approximately equal to or less than width between infraorbital foramina. Frontal area narrow, gently convex, lacking longitudinal central depression. Sagittal crest very conspicuous in interparietal area. Occipital crest very well developed, with sharp upper edge; rather high. Rostrum rather short and thick in proportion to narrow form of skull. Zygomatic arches moderately broad. Antero-superior process of jugal bone extends beyond internal edge of lacrymal foramen. Orbits ovally elongated but markedly less so than in manul cats. Lower anterior edge of orbit very short, ovally blunted. Infraorbital foramina relatively small, vertically elongate; maximum axis of foramen greater than width of septum separating it from orbit. Nasal bones narrow in posterior area and distinctly broadened in anterior halves; do not extend posteriorly beyond level of back ends of mandibular processes. Hard palate longer than in manul cat, much longer than broad; extends beyond rear surfaces of molars by distance exceeding one half width of mesopterygoid fossa. Posterior palatine incisure lacks usual central protrusion. Pterygoid fossa very inconspicuous. Mesopterygoid fossa narrow in relation to proportions of skull. Presphenoid bone very narrow, with weakly marked lateral projections. Tympanic bullae rather large, greatly inflated, elongate, and anteriorly pointed; lie a bit back of mandibular articulation, anterior edges not reaching anterior side of postglenoid processes. Boundary between anterior and posterior chamber of bulla not clear. Distance between inner sides of bullae appreciably less than width of mesopterydoid fossa.   Longitudinal axis of anterior palatine foramina about one third shorter than longitudinal axis of alveolus of upper canine.   Posterior edge of angular process of lower jaw extends back beyond jaw articulation.

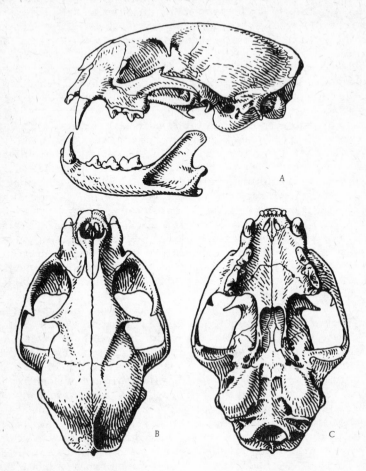

FIGURE 159.   Skull of leopard, F e l i s b e n g a l e n s i s Kerr (original):

A — lateral view; B — dorsal view; C — ventral view.

Dental formula: $I\frac{3}{3}$; $C\frac{1}{1}$; $Pm\frac{3}{2}$; $M\frac{1}{1}$ = 30.

Canines of moderate size: height of canine approximately $2-3$ mm greater than length of upper incisor row.   First upper premolars present at least in young individuals.   In adults this tooth usually disappears and its alveolus is covered up.   Thus, in our collection specimen No. 3278 from the Suputinka reserve has first premolars, while in specimen No. 4413 from the Kedrovaya Pad' reserve they are absent.   Out of 22 skulls from various parts of China, examined by Allen (1938), the first premolars were absent on one or both jaws in 8 specimens. Upper carnassial tooth has well-developed talon (talonum internum) bearing easily seen hypocone. Lower carnassial tooth with small hypoconid.

Systematic notes. The leopard cat has until recently been one of the taxonomically least studied species in family Felidae. As can be seen in the above list, the cat has about 20 species synonyms. The creation and description of "species" has been done chiefly on the basis of individual or geographical variations in fur color. As it happens, this cat is extremely polymorphic and on the vast territory of its range is subject to pronounced individual and geographical variation, particularly with respect to color. Let us consider, for example, the Amur leopard cat. Color variation is so considerable in this animal that, according to M. I. Zubarovskii (1939), even the same litter may contain cubs with different color details. According to N. A. Baikov (1915), two separate species of this animal occur in the Ussuri Territory: the large F e l i s e u p t i l u r a Elliot (body length 85 cm, tail 30 cm) and the small F e l i s u n d a t a Radde (body length 70 cm, tail 28 cm), distinguished by a more reddish principal fur tone and by smaller and whiter spottiness. Maak too, in his day (1861), wrote of two species of leopard cat in the Ussuri Territory. Nevertheless, examination of the material which has accumulated over the last 100 years shows that the Ussuri Territory is in fact inhabited by a single form of leopard cat, representing a well differentiated subspecies of the Asiatic leopard cat widely distributed in Southern Asia east of Kashmir and Baluchistan. There is no doubt that other authors as well have assigned definite taxonomic significance to color forms representing individual variation and have therefore created and described "species" without justification.

Modern authors (Allen, 1938; Pocock, 1939; Ellerman and Morrison-Scott, 1951) think that all the leopard cats of Southern Asia, along with F e l i s e u p t i l u r a, are from the identical species and combine them in the single species F e l i s b e n g a l e n s i s Kerr (1792), which latter was based on material from southern Bengal. This approach is in full agreement with the systematic material and is corroborated by study of the literature.

I have examined five specimens of leopard cat from Kansu, Szechwan, and eastern Tibet (Kam) collected by the expeditions of N. M. Przheval'skii, M. M. Berezovskii and P. K. Kozlov and kept in the collections of the Zoological Institute of the Academy of Sciences of the USSR. In fur color pattern and in specific cranial structure traits they are undoubtedly identical in the specific respect with the Soviet Amur leopard cat. The differences between them do not exceed the usual intraspecific systematic differences. They are treated accordingly by the above-mentioned modern scientists.

Allen (1938) has come to the conclusion that they are identical in the subspecific respect with the leopard cats inhabiting the rest of China except for Yunnan, where a related form (F e l i s b e n g a l e n s i s t e n a s s e r i m e n s i s Gray, 1867) occurs. Allen's conclusions are based on the study of 24 specimens collected in various parts of China.

The species identity of the Amur cat with F e l i s m i c r o t i s Milne-Edwards, 1868—74 (F e l i s b e n g a l e n s i s c h i n e n s i s Gray, 1837), described from a Peking specimen, was recognized as early as 1871, by D. G. Elliot. This interpretation of the systematic position of these cats has never been disputed. Elliot's monograph (1883) of family Felidae mentions a leopard-cat pelt in the collection of the British Museum from the vicinity of Shanghai which is indistinguishable from the type F. euptilura Elliot, 1871 (Felis bengalensis chinensis Gray).

As to the subspecific status of the Amur and Chinese leopard cats, they undoubtedly belong to different subspecies. They differ in size and winter fur color. The Chinese form is relatively small, more vividly colored, with distinctly marked spottiness and black patches on the belly. The nominate form is marked by even more intense color and a more vivid pattern. The Amur cat is thus an isolated subspecies, characterized by large size, duller color, different color pattern, and other features.

Geographical distribution. The Asiatic leopard cat occupies a vast area embracing South Asia from Beluchistan, India, and Kashmir east to the Pacific and the adjacent islands of Sumatra, Java, Borneo, Hainan, Taiwan (Formosa), Philippines, along with a number of smaller adjacent islands, and north to Northeast China and the Soviet Far East (inclusively).

In the Soviet Union it ranges over the Far East and north to about 51° N lat.

Maak (1861) mentions a specimen of this species presented to the Academy of Sciences from the vicinity of the city of Blagoveshchensk. According to Radde (1862), this cat was obtained on the Amur some 60 km below the mouth of the Zeya River. Przheval'skii (1870) writes that the animal occurs on the Amur in the southern part of its middle reaches, in the valley of the Ussuri and on the shore of the Sea of Japan between Olga Harbor and Pos'yet Bay. M. I. Yankovskii collected the species near Sidemi (coll. Zool. Inst. Acad. Sciences USSR). On Cape Gamov near Vladivostok, two specimens were obtained by A. D. Baturin in 1927 (coll. S. I. Ognev). According to V. K. Arsen'ev (1926), it ranges throughout the Ussuri Territory. V. S. Stakhanov provides the following description of the leopard cat's distribution: "In the Pos'yet area it inhabits the foothills of Gogo-Bo-Shan, reaching the sea at the Pallada roadstead and spreading north into the valley of the Uluncha River, along the Adimi, Sidemi, and Amba (Belaya) rivers, and onto the Gamov and Peschanyi peninsulas. It inhabits the Muravev-Amurskii Peninsula and the southern Maritime Territory in the valleys of the Maikhe, Steklyanukha, Tsemukha, Suchen, Sudzukhe, Pkhutsun and Tyutikhe rivers, and reaches the upper boundary of the Manchurian forest. The leopard cat ranges north along the shore of the Tatar Strait to the Samarga River, where it is already rare. This is probably its northern limit of distribution... In the Ussuri Territory it occurs along the Daubikha, Noto, Bikin and Khor rivers" (Ognev, 1935).

According to recent data from Zubarovskii (1939), the northern boundary of distribution on the left shore of the Amur extends from west to east at approximately 51° N lat., starting from the middle reaches of the Tom' River and from there crossing the Turanskii Range and the middle reaches of the Bureya River and running thence to the upper reaches of the Mutnaya River. Descending thereafter near the pass through the Lagar-Aul to 49° N. lat., it extends to the upper reaches of the Bidzhan River. In the

low-lying, damp localities of Birobidzhan, Smidovich, Kur-Urmi and
Khabarovsk districts, as well as long the entire Dabanda-Bolon lowlands,
the leopard cat is absent. The lower reaches of the Khungari, around
50° N lat., should be considered the animal's northern boundary on the
right bank of the Amur. It is known on the upper reaches of the Monoma
River (40° N lat.) where it is obtained near Slavyanka. From there the
boundary extends along the water divide of the Monoma, Anyui, and Khor
rivers, descending to the Mukhen' River. The cat is occasionally
encountered in the Gassinskaya Forest (around 48° N lat.) near Lake Pir
and in the area of the middle Piksa (also called Pikhtsa). Further east
the boundary, crossing the upper reaches of the Khor River, extends to
the Samarga River (47° N lat.) and the Sea of Japan.

The cat is very common in the following districts of the Maritime
Territory: Pos'yet, Vladivostok, Shkotovo, Suchan, Voroshilov [Ussuriisk],
Anuchino, Khanka and Grodekovo and in valleys of the rivers mentioned
above by Stakhanov in his description. My collection contains specimens
received from V. K. Timofeev which were obtained in the Kedrovaya Pad'
reserve, and specimens of Bromlei's from the Suputinka reserve. The
species is more than common on the water divide between the Daubikhe
and the Suchan. It inhabits Russkii Island. In the Amur Region the
population of this cat is markedly lower and only a few individuals are
obtained during the season.

Survey of subspecies. As said above, the leopard cat is variable over
its vast range and this is manifested in the isolation of geographic forms
of subspecific significance. Ellerman and Morrison-Scott (1951) report
seven subspecies. The differences between these lie in points of fur color
and, to some extent, in size as well.

One subspecies, the Amur leopard cat, occurs in Siberia.

28a. Felis (Prionailurus) bengalensis euptilura   Elliot
(1871). Far Eastern or Amur leopard cat

1862. Felis undata. Radde, G.   Reisen im Süden von Ost-Sibirien,
Vol. 1, Säugethier-Fauna, pp. 106—113, St. Petersburg. tab. 4, figs. 1—8.
(nec Desmarest, 1816); Przheval'skii, N. M.   Puteshestvie v Ussuriiskom
krae (Journey through the Ussuri Territory), pp. 242—243, Sankt-Peterburg.
1870 (biology).

1871. Felis euptilura.   Elliot, D.   Remarks on Various Species of
Felidae, etc.— Proc. Zool. Soc. London, p. 761, pl. 76 (nomen novum pro
Felis undata Radde, 1862, nec Desmarest, 1816).

1904. Oncoides bengalensis raddei.   Trouessart, E. L.
Catalogus Mammalium, Supplement, p. 271.

1914. Oncoides euptilura microtis.   Satunin, K. A.
Opredelitel' mlekopitayushchikh Rossiiskoi imperii (Key to Mammals of the
Russian Empire), p. 167, Tiflis.

1922. Felis manchurica.   Mori, T.— Ann. Mag. Nat. Hist., 10,
p. 609 (vicinity of Mukden [Shenyang], Manchuria).

1935. Felis (Prionailurus) euptilura microtis. Ognev, S. I.
Zveri SSSR i prilezhashchikh stran (Animals of the USSR and Adjacent

Countries), Vol 3, pp. 150—157, Moskva-Leningrad, figs. 68—75; Zubarovskii, M. I. Dal'nevostochnyi lesnoi kot (The Far Eastern Leopard Cat).— Byulleten' MOIP, Vol. 48, Nos. 2—3, pp. 57—81, Moskva. 1939.

1936. Felis euptilura microtis. Zolotarev, N. T. Mlekopitayushchie basseina r. Imana (Mammals of the Iman River Basin), pp. 96—97, Moskva-Leningrad.

1951. Felis bengalensis euptilura. Ellerman, J. R. and T. C. S. Morrison-Scott. Checklist of Palaearctic and Indian Mammals, p. 313, London.

1956. Felis (Prionailurus) euptilura. Novikov, G. A. Khishchnye mlekopitayushchie fauny SSSR (Carnivorous Mammals of the USSR Fauna), pp. 246—248, Moskva-Leningrad. fig. 166—167.

Type and type locality. The type has apparently not been preserved. Described from a specimen collected on the Amur some 60 km below the mouth of the Zeya River.

Diagnosis. Distinguished from F. b. chinensis Gray by lighter and duller color of fur. Maximum length of male skull 98.6—110.0 mm, against 80.0—94.6 mm for Chinese leopard cat. Fur paler and with less conspicuous spotty pattern on body and tail and less rusty-colored belly spots.

Measurements. Length of body with head: males 65—83 cm, females 61—77 cm (a few particularly large specimens may reach length of 107 cm); length of tail: 35—44 cm; length of ear: 4.5—5.0 cm. Weight 4.2—6.8 kg.

Condylobasal length of skull: males 89.5—93.9 mm, females 82.3—85.9 mm; zygomatic width: males 60.7—65.4 mm, females 57.0—60.0 mm; interorbital width: males 14.4—15.9 mm, females 14.0—15.5 mm; postorbital width: males 27.0—28.8 mm, females 26.0—28.0 mm; width between infraorbital foramina: males 27.5—29.0 mm, females 25.7—27.3 mm; length of upper tooth row: males 31.0—32.3 mm, females 27.8—30.0 mm.

Systematic notes. The systematic relationship of the Amur leopard cats with the Chinese and the nominate forms has been treated above.

The nomenclature for the Amur cat should be made more precise. Satunin (1904, 1914), Ognev (1935) and other authors have designated it by the name microtis, given by A. Milne-Edwards (1868—1874) to the leopard cats of the Peking vicinity.* It is impossible to agree with these designations since they contradict the priority rules.

Ognev (1935) thinks that terra typica for F. euptilura Elliot is the vicinity of Shanghai. However, this opinion is groundless, since the argument that Elliot (1883) in his monograph on the Felidae mentions a specimen found in the vicinity of Shanghai which was indistinguishable from the type euptilura will not support an arbitrary treatment of the matter. All that can be concluded from what Elliot reports is that the Peking and Shanghai cats belong to the same species. Elliot's work contains a description of species — not of subspecies — of cats, among them being F. euptilura, to which he quite rightly linked F. microtis Milne-Edwards (1868—1874) as a synonym; but it in no way follows from this that the Amur cat euptilura and the Peking cat microtis are one and the same subspecies.

---

* Felis microtis Milne-Edwards (1868—1874) is a synonym of F. chinensis Gray (1837), described from a specimen collected by J. R. Reeves in southern China, apparently near Canton.

G. Allen (1938) and other modern authors regard F. microtis as one of the numerous synonyms of F. b. chinensis Gray.

It should be evident from the data presented that the only valid name for the Amur leopard cat can be the term euptilura, which Elliot (1871) gave it in place of the name undata Radde which had proven to be a nomen preoccupatum (Felis undata Desmarest, 1816). Thus the terra typica of F. euptilura is the River Amur some 60 km below the mouth of the Zeya River, where the type specimen was collected.

The Mukden cat Felis manchurica Mori (1922), described on the basis of one pelt (without skull) and collected in northeast China near Mukden, probably belongs to the same subspecies. According to the description of T. Mori (1922), it is characterized by an extremely light grayish general type of fur color. The author approximates this cat with euptilura.

The description of the coloration presented in the species description was made on the basis of the Soviet Far Eastern materials.

Geographical distribution. The Far East, where it occurs along the shore of the Sea of Japan, on some offshore islands (Russkii Island), in the valley of the Ussuri and the Amur, and north approximately to 51° N lat. In the relatively recent past it was encountered westwards up to the area of the city of Blagoveshchensk. It is particularly abundant in the southern part of the Ussuri Basin.

Material studied. Maritime Territory — 12 specimens; the Amur River valley — 4 specimens; China — 5 specimens. Total — 21 specimens.

Biology. Chiefly inhabits the Siberian stone pine types of Manchurian taiga, where it keeps to the more open areas having fallen trees, trees with hollows, and a rich fauna of Muridae and small birds. In the winter it is encountered in river-valley scrub and sometimes approaches inhabited places. The Amur cat can often be encountered near nonfreezing streams and in creek ravines.

Its food consists of various small animals, chiefly rodents and birds. It is not adverse to eating fish and reptiles and may also hunt squirrels, chipmunks and hares. Przheval'skii (1870) reported that this cat attacks roe-deer fauns. When living near villages in winter it may occasionally attack domestic fowl.

It mates in March and at this time is active throughout the day, displaying very ferocious behavior, the males on meeting another of their kind engaging in fierce battles. Gestation period is about two months. The young are born in the middle and second half of May. The litter size is 1—3, most often 2.

The Amur cat lives a very secluded life, passing the day in its den and becoming active at dawn and at night, when it hunts its prey, and so on. Its dens are in cliff fissures, in hollows under stones and among roots of trees, and in tree hollows.

It leads a solitary life except during the nuptial period, when several males may chase one female. It climbs trees well. In escaping from danger, for instance from attacking hounds, the cat will quickly attempt to climb into the trees.

Its tracks and footprints are similar to those of the domestic cat but are somewhat larger. Prints of the digits are thicker and longer.

Practical importance. Occupies an insignificant position in the fur trade, some 1—1.5 thousand pelts being processed yearly. It is obtained occasionally during hunting for other animals. The harm it inflicts on hunting and on poultry breeding is barely felt, due to its extremely low population and narrow range.

29.   **Felis (Otocolobus) manul** Pallas (1776).   Manul
cat   (Map XXI)

1776. **Felis manul**. Pallas, P. S.   Reise durch verschiedene Provinzen des Russischen Reichs, Vol. 3, p. 692, Anhang; Pallas, P. S. **Felis manul**, nova species asiatica.— Acta Petropolitana pro anno 1781, pars prior, p. 278 (233), tab. 7; Pallas, P. S.   Zoographia Rosso-Asiatica, 1, pp. 20—23, Petropoli. 1811—1831; Eversmann, E.   Estestvennaya istoriya mlekopitayushchikh zhivotnykh Orenburgskogo kraya (Natural History of the Mammals of the Orenburg Territory). pp. 12—14, Kazan. 1850; Radde, G.   Reisen im Süden von Ost-Sibirien, Vol. 1, Die Säugethierfauna, pp. 104—106, St. Petersburg. 1862; Milne-Edwards, A.   Recherches pour servir à l'Histoire Naturelle des Mammifères, p. 225. 1868—1874 (1872) pl. 31 C; Ellerman, J. R. and T. C. S. Morrison-Scott.   Checklist of Palaearctic and Indian Mammals, p. 308, London. 1951; Bannikov, A. G. Mlekopitayushchie Mongol'skoi Narodnoi Respubliki (Mammals of the Mongolian People's Republic). pp. 143—146, Moskva. 1954.

1841. **Felis (Otocolobus) manul**. Brandt, F.   Observations sur le Manoul (**Felis manul** Pallas) — Bull. Scient. publié par l'Acad. Imp. des Sc. de St. Petersburg. Vol. 9, p. 37; Bobrinskii, N. A.   Otryad khishchnye (Carnivora).— In: Opredelitel' mlekopitayushchikh SSSR, edited by N. A. Bobrinskii, pp. 160 — 161, Moskva, 1944; Novikov, G. A. Khishchnye mlekopitayushchie fauny SSSR (Carnivorous Mammals of the USSR Fauna), pp. 260 — 263, Moskva-Leningrad.   1956.

1842. **Felis nigripectus**. Hodgson, B. H. Report on the Mammals of Tibet with Description and Plates of Some New Species.— Journ. Asiat. Soc. Bengal, Vol. 11, p. 276.

1850. **Lynx manul**. Simashko, Yu. Russkaya fauna (Russian Fauna), p. 557, Sankt-Peterburg. plate 16, fig. 1.

1905. **Trichaelurus manul**. Satunin, K. **Trichaelurus** eine neue Feliden Gattung.— Ezhegodnik Zoologicheskogo Muzeya Imperatorskoi Akademii Nauk, Vol. 9, p. 496. 1904; Zur Systematik der Familie Felidae.— Izvestiya Kavkazskogo Muzeya, Vol. 4, p. 251, Tiflis. 1910.

1913. **Otocolobus manul**. Birulya, A. K sinonimike **Otocolobus manul** (Pallas) (Contribution to the Synonymy of **Otocolobus manul** (Pallas)).— Ezhegodnik Zoologicheskogo Muzeya Imperatorskoi Akademii Nauk, Vol. 18; Birulya, A.   Materialy po sistematike i geograficheskomu rasprostraneniyu mlekopitayushchikh (Data on the Taxonomy and Geographical Distribution of Mammals).— Ibidem, Vol. 21, pp. 130—162. 1916. plates 17—19; Flerov, K. K. Khishchnye zveri (Fissipedia) Tadzhikistana (Carnivorous Animals (Fissipedia) of Tadzhikistan).— In: B. S. Vinogradov, E. N. Pavlovskii and K. K. Flerov. Zveri Tadzhikistana, ikh zhizn' i znachenie dlya cheloveka, pp. 196 — 200, Moskva-Leningrad. 1935. fig. 70.

Type and type locality. The type was described by Pallas from a specimen lacking a precise designation of the terra typica. In the survey of its geographical distribution, the Tatar-Mongolian deserts are the first localities mentioned.

Diagnosis. Fur extremely long and dense for cats. Ears only slightly protruding from surrounding fur, short, bluntly rounded, without distal tufts. Color pattern on head spotty black and in form of transverse bands on back, particularly in posterior half. Tail with pattern of dark rings; tip of tail black. Anterior edge of auditory bullae extends beyond anterior side of postglenoid process. Postorbital width markedly greater than distance between infraorbital foramina. First upper premolars absent. Upper carnassial tooth with rudimentary talon. Lower carnassial tooth does not have third small denticle on its posterior edge.

Measurements. Length of body with head: 50—62 cm; length of tail: 23—31 cm; height of ear: 4—5 cm. Weight 2.5—3.5 kg.

Condylobasal length of skull: males 73.8 — 83.0 mm, females 72.0—78.2 mm; zygomatic width: males 66.0—74.0 mm, females 66.0—67.7 mm; infraorbital width: males 18.0—20.0 mm, females 17.0—19.5 mm; postorbital width: males 37.0 — 39.8 mm, females 36.8—38.6 mm; width between infraorbital foramina: males 27.0—29.0 mm, females 26.4—28.0 mm; length of upper tooth row: males 28.2 — 29.5 mm, females 26.7—28.8 mm.

Description. A relatively small cat, its size being somewhat larger than that of the domestic cat. Body is massive and legs are short and thick. Muzzle extremely broad and blunt. Eyes enormous and directed straight ahead. Ears extremely short and broad, bluntly rounded, lacking tufts and protruding relatively slightly from surrounding fur. Small "cheek whiskers" descend from ears. Tail thick and about one half as long as body. Claws rather thin and highly recurved.

Fur silky and very dense, and long and luxuriant as in no other cat. General color on back varies from russet (in the Turkestan manul cat) to yellowish gray with grizzly hair and blackish tinge (in the nominate form). Underfur in middle back extremely dark. Underparts brownish and groin whitish. Limbs russet. Pattern of color specific, being expressed on head by black spottiness and on back, particularly in posterior part, in form of transverse bands. "Side whiskers" gray, with two blackish bands extending backwards from cheeks. Antero-superior part of nose, lips, chin and throat white. Tail with transverse brown or black ring pattern; tip of tail blackish.

Skull (Figure 160) round, very broad, short and high. Upper line of profile steep convex arch. Postorbital width markedly greater than distance between infraorbital foramina. Frontal area broad, flat or slightly concave, lacking longitudinal depression. Sagittal crest very weakly expressed and barely extending beyond anterior edge of interparietal bone. Occipital crest more conspicuous. Rostrum extremely short and very broad. Zygomatic arches widely parted. Antero-superior process of jugal bone long and thin, extending beyond internal edge of lacrymal foramen. Orbits large and almost round, more rarely slightly elongated, and directed markedly frontwards. Lower anterior edge of orbit not thick, but thin and sharp. Infraorbital foramen small, roundedly oval, almost perpendicular, its maximum axis smaller than width of septum separating the foramen from orbit. Nasals mostly taper evenly, and extend back only slightly beyond level of rear ends of maxillary processes; in Tibet manul cat they are somewhat narrowed in middle. Hard palate short, broader than long and extends somewhat beyond posterior edges of molars. Posterior palatine incisure without protrusion formed in area of palatine suture by postero-internal corners of palatine bones. Pterygoid fossa absent. Hamular process of pterygoid usually absent, more rarely present in form of small denticle. Presphenoid bone narrow, with rhomboidal expansion in center, size of expansion varying from barely visible in Tibet manul cat to very broad in Mongolian and Turkmenian manul cats. Tympanic bullae large, greatly inflated, ellipsoidal, and rounded anteriorly; protrude anteriorly in such a manner that their anterior edges extend beyond anterior aspect of postglenoid processes. Anterior chamber of bulla (pars ecto-tympanica) approximately same size as posterior (pars entotympanica). More or less conspicuous groove extends between these. Distance between tympanic bullae appreciably greater than half width of mesopterygoid fossa. Longitudinal axis of anterior palatine foramina approximately one half of longitudinal axis of alveolus of upper canine. Angular process of lower jaw does not project back beyond jaw articulation.

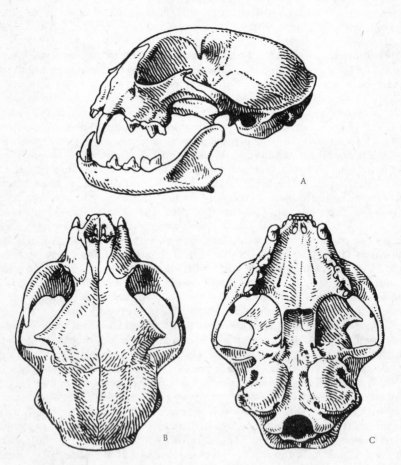

FIGURE 160. Skull of manul cat, Felis manul Pallas (original):

A — lateral view; B — dorsal view; C — ventral view.

Dental formula: $I\frac{3}{3}$; $C\frac{1}{1}$; $Pm\frac{2}{2}$; $M\frac{1}{1} = 28$.

Upper canines large: height of canine approximately 4 — 5 mm greater than length of upper incisor row. First upper premolars lacking. Upper carnassial tooth has rudimentary talon (talonum internum), on which is small denticle visible only in young. Lower carnassial lacks hypoconid.

Systematic notes. In the degree to which it expresses typical cat organization, the manul cat is one of the most specialized of all cats. This has been noted by previous students (Satunin, in litt.; Ognev, 1935; et al.). Birulya (1916), an acknowledged authority on this group, considered the manul-cat stock progressive in this respect. In manul cats, the teeth are maximally concentrated in the mouth corner. The first premolar disappears, the upper molar remaining in the form of an atrophied rudiment displaced lingually from the tooth row. The carnassial tooth has an elongated and narrow crown and a rudimentary talon. These modifications of the dental system, along with an increase in width of the zygomatic arches to make room for the massive musculus temporalis, intensify the cutting function of the dental apparatus as a whole; this is associated with the predominance of flesh in the diet.

On the basis of important systematic features, the manul cat is closest to the Turkestan sand cat Felis (Eremaelurus) thinobius Ognev. They are first of all approximated by similarity of general skull form, and in addition by the position of the auditory bullae (bullae tympani), whose anterior edges have shifted foreward past the postglenoid processes. This feature is also characteristic of the South Asiatic cat Pardofelis marmorata Martin (1837). The manul cat and the sand cat are also characterized by an another common trait — the presence of dark underfur on the middle back. In the light of these data, V. G. Heptner and G. P. Dement'ev (1937) quite correctly assigned them to the same genus, since there are more similarities than differences in the cranial structure of these cats.

Geographical variations in the manul cat consist chiefly of color changes. Three subspecies of manul cat are known at present: the nominate subspecies, inhabiting the northern part of the range and characterized in general by gray fur; the Central Asiatic F. m. ferrugineus Ognev (1928), characterized by russet fur; and the Tibetan F. m. nigripectus Hodgson (1842), characterized by a grayer fur color with presence of black bands on the body and tail and more vividly colored spots on the head, as well as by craniological differences.

Geographical distribution. Widely distributed in Asia, in north from the Astrakhan Steppes to the Altai and Transbaikalia and south to Iran, Baluchistan, the southern slopes of the Himalayas and the eastern districts of China proper.

In the Soviet Union it occurs in southern Transcaucasia and in Soviet Central Asia, Kazakhstan and South Siberia. In Siberia it occurs in the Altai, Tuva and Transbaikalia.

The following data (Map XXI) are available for the distribution of the animal in Siberia.

On the Altai it was noted for the first time by F. V. Gebler (1837), as a species entering via the Argut and Chuya (see also Brandt, 1841).

G. S. Karelin (1841, 1844) recorded the abundance of the animal on the southern Altai (on the Narym Range along the Kurchum River). Its distribution in the Kosh-Agach area, and particularly on the Argut, is also confirmed by data collected by A. P. Razorenova (1939).

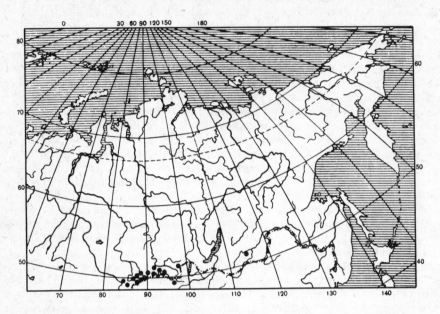

MAP XXI. Geographical distribution of the manul cat, Felix manul Pallas, in Siberia

According to recent data from A. M. Kolosov (1939) manuls are rather common on the Chuya Steppe, the yearly take of manul pelts reaching the Kosh-Agach fur depots being 100—150 pieces (in 1934, 133 pelts were obtained; and in 1935, 102). Kolosov reports this cat being obtained in the northern part of Chuya Steppe along the Chagan-Uzun River and further south along the Kokure River (at its frontier portion in the Tarkhatty area). According to questionnaires, it is also encountered in the Istyut area, east of Tashanta, along the Chagan-Burgazy River, and in the Beltyr area, and very rarely along the Kurai. It occasionally figures in the fur take from the territory of Dzhasatersk village. Kuznetsov (1948), quoting V. I. Datsenko, reports that manul cats are occasionally encountered on the southern Altai near the Mongolian frontier and in the area of Lake Marka-Kul,

In Tuva, according to A. Ya. Tugarinov (1916), it inhabits the upper and middle reaches of the Kemchik River, being more often encountered on southern slopes of the Tannu-Ola Range (see also Shukhov, 1925). According to A. I. Yanushevich (1952), it is rather common in the valley of the Tes-Khem, inhabits Mongun-Taiga, and is encountered, but more rarely, in the western part of the Tuva basin. Some 157 pelts were obtained in 1947, of which the Ubsa Nur basin yielded 98 pieces, the Mongun-Taiga 24, and the Tuva basin the rest.

Kashchenko (1910) mentions two specimens of the animal, obtained in the Yankhar site area on the Selenga and near the village of Shara-golskaya in the former Troitskosavsk County [now Kyakhta]. According to Radde (1862), it is not rare along the Onon River in the vicinity of the hamlets of Sokui and Abagatui, around Lake Tarei-Nor, and in the Aginskoe Steppe. It is encountered in the neighboring areas of Mongolia (Bannikov, 1954).

Survey of subspecies. As mentioned above, the manul cat is divided throughout its vast range into subspecies, of which three are known. The nominate subspecies ranges in Siberia.

29a. **Felis (Otocolobus) manul manul** Pallas (1776).
North Asiatic manul cat

1776. **Felis manul.** Pallas, P. S. Reise durch verschiedene Provinzen des Russischen Reichs, Vol. 3, p. 692. Anhang.

1905. **Trichaelurus manul mongolicus.** Satunin, K. Trichaelurus eine neue Felidegattung. — Ezhegodnik Zoologicheskogo Muzeya Imperatorskoi Akademii Nauk, Vol. 9, p. 501, Sankt-Peterburg. 1904 (Mongolia); Satunin, K. A. Opredelitel' mlekopitayushchikh Rossiiskoi imperii (Key to Mammals of the Russian Empire), p. 181, Tiflis. 1914 (East Siberia).

1907. **Otocolobus manul mongolicus.** Pocock, R. I. — Proc. Zool. Soc. London, 1, p. 302.

1914. **Trichaelurus manul manul.** Satunin, K. A. Loc. cit. pp. 179 — 181.

1916. **Otocolobus manul manul.** Birulya, A. Materialy po sistematike i geograficheskomu rasprostraneniyu mlekopitayushchikh (Data on Taxonomy and Geographical Distribution of Mammals). — Ezhegodnik Zoologicheskogo Muzeya Imperatorskoi Akademii Nauk, Vol. 21, pp. 151 — 152; Ognev, S. I. Zveri SSSR i prilezhashchikh stran (Animals of the USSR and Adjacent Countries), Vol. 3, pp. 177 — 186, Moskva-Leningrad. 1935.

1938. **Felis manul manul.** Allen, G. M. The Mammals of China and Mongolia, Part 1, pp. 453 — 457, New York; Ellerman, J. R. and T. C. S. Morrison-Scott. Checklist of Palaearctic and Indian Mammals, p. 308, London. 1951; Bannikov, A. G. Mlekopitayushchie Mongol'skoi Narodnoi Respubliki (Mammals of the Mongolian People's Republic), pp. 145 — 146, Moskva. 1954.

1956. **Felis (Otocolobus) manul manul.** Novikov, G. A. Khishchnye mlekopitayushchie fauny SSSR (Carnivora of the USSR Fauna), p. 263, Moskva-Leningrad.

Type and type locality. See above description of the species.

Diagnosis. Winter fur dorsally gray with general rusty-clay tone, silvery white tinge, and lightly streaked with black of a uniform tone or with indistinctly outlined bands. Belly grayish. Nasals evenly tapered to base and do not have central constriction. Presphenoid bone rhomboidally expanded in middle.

Systematic notes. The nominate subspecies has more structural traits in common with the Turkmenian manul cat, F. m. ferrugineus, Ognev described from material from Kopet Dagh. The material examined does not show craniological differences. In contrast to the nominate subspecies, the Turkmenian manul is characterized by uniformly vivid rusty russet fur and by replacement of black with more intensive reddish russet. Russet manul cats include individuals with color near to that of the nominate subspecies, though more saturated. Manuls colored thus are probably few in number and occur much more rarely than the russet ones.

The subspecies is distinctly differentiated from the Tibet manul cat, F. m. nigripectus Hodgson, both by color and cranial structure. In contrast to F. m. manul, the Tibetan subspecies is characterized by grayer tones and by presence of more vivid black spots on head, bands on body and ringlike pattern on tail. Nasals of Tibet manul have conspicuous median constriction. Presphenoid bone has no rhomboidal expansion in middle.

FIGURE 161. High mountain steppe at sources of the Chagan-Burgazy River in the southeastern Altai. Biotope of the manul cat. Photo by K. T. Yurlov

Geographical distribution. Given above in description of the species.

Material studied. The Altai — 4 skulls and 5 pelts; Kazakhstan — 1 skull and 2 pelts; Turkmenia — 1 skull and 5 pelts; Transbaikalia — 4 skulls and 8 pelts; Mongolia — 1 skull and 1 pelt; China — 2 skulls and 3 pelts. Total — 13 skulls and 24 pelts.

Biology. This is chiefly a mountain animal, living in foothills to altitudes of 3,000 m. In Siberia it occurs in the mountain steppes of the

Altai and in the Transbaikalian steppes (Figure 161). In the southeastern part of the Altai, according to A. M. Kolosov (1939), it roams chiefly on rock streams, called locally "kurumnik." In Transbaikalia, according to P. S. Pallas (1776), it prefers the stony sections of the steppes.

The data on its biology are extremely scanty and fragmentary. It occupies discarded burrows of marmots and other animals and lives in caves, cliff fissures, and under stone slabs. It leads an extremely secluded crepuscular and nocturnal life, but occasionally may also be active during the day. It feeds chiefly on small rodents. According to A. S. Fetisov (1937) who examined 502 items from the southwestern part of Transbaikalia, the percentages of various food types in the manul's diet were as follows: pikas — 89 %, Muridae — 44 %, susliks — 3 %, hares — 2 %, insectivores — 1 %, and birds — 2 %.

In Transbaikalia the young are born in late April and in May. The litter size is usually 5 — 6.

According to observations in captivity, the animal is wild and vicious. When irritated it does not hiss as do most other cats, but only gives vent to a shrill sound through almost closed lips. The louder voice of the manul cat is reminiscent to some extent of the barking of a small dog and to some extent of an owl's cry (Pocock, 1907).

Practical importance. Insignificant due to low population. Obtained occasionally, chiefly by trapping. The fur is of better quality than that of other small cats and is more highly valued. The animal apparently causes no harm to man or his economy.

18. Genus LYNX Kerr (1792). Lynxes

1792. L y n x. Kerr, R. Anim. Kingd., pp. 72 — 73.
1821. L y n c e u s. Gray, J. — London Med., 15, p. 302 (F e l i s l y n x Linnaeus).
1834. L y n h u s. Jardine, W. Naturalist's Library, Mamm., 2, p. 274 (F e l i s l y n x Linnaeus).
1857. L y n x. Blasius, J. H. Säugethiere Deutschlands, p. 161 (subgenus of the genus F e l i s); Miller, G. S. Catalogue of the Mammals of Western Europe, pp. 470 — 471, London. 1912 (F e l i s l y n x Linnaeus); Ognev, S. I. Zveri SSSR i prilezhashchikh stran (Animals of the USSR and Adjacent Countries), 3, pp. 196 — 198. 1935 (F e l i s l y n x Linnaeus).

Type species. F e l i s l y n x Linnaeus (1758).
Diagnosis. Cat of medium size (length of body up to 150 cm, of tail up to 31 cm), distinguished from its nearest kin by long legs, shortness of tail, development of ear tufts, and "cheek whiskers" and craniological and odontological features. Tail approximately equal to length of head and fails to reach paws of extended hind limbs. Ears extremely long and pointed, with long hairs on tips forming a tuft. Cheeks full, "cheek whiskers" well developed. Limbs long. Claws large. Digits connected by webs almost to distal phalanges. Spottiness consists of pattern of short bands and round spots. Occasionally spottiness extremely poorly expressed, particularly in winter fur, and disappears completely on body, but always

FIGURE 162. The lynx, L y n x l y n x L. After specimen No. 5611, Zoological Museum of Moscow University. Painted by V.A. Vatagin

remains on limbs. Distal third of tail black. Condylobasal length of adult skull at least 120 mm. Anterior edge of tympanic bulla does not reach jaw articulation. Postorbital width varies, sometimes greater, sometimes sometimes smaller than width between infraorbital foramina.

Dental formula: $I\frac{3}{3}$; $C\frac{1}{1}$; $Pm\frac{2}{2}$; $M\frac{1}{1}$ = 28.

Upper canines large: height of canine approximately ¾ length of entire upper row of molars and premolars. Upper carnassial tooth with well-developed talon. Lower carnassial tooth bears a conspicuous small third denticle on its posterior edge.

Geographical distribution. The boreal and temperate zones of the Northern Hemisphere. In Europe south to the Mediterranean coast; in Asia to the western Himalayas; in North America as far as Mexico.

Systematic notes. The lynx genus is systematically distinct. It represents an aberrant branch of subfamily Felinae characterized by its peculiar appearance and by the craniological and odontological traits reported in the diagnosis.

The genus contains five species, three of which occur in North America.

One species, also occurring in Siberia, is present in the Soviet Union.

30. **Lynx lynx** Linnaeus (1758). Lynx
(Figure 162, Map XXII)

1758. Felis lynx. Linnaeus, C. Syst. Nat., ed. 10, 1, p. 43.

1792. Lynx vulgaris. Kerr, R. Anim. Kingd., Syst. Cat. No. 294, p. 157.

1798. Felis borealis. Thunberg, S. P. Beskrifning pa Svenska Djur., Mamm., p. 14 (North Sweden).

1798. Felis kattlo. Schrenk, F. Fauna Boica. Durchgedachte Gesch. der in Bayern einheim. Thiere, 1, p. 52 (Bohemia).

1820. Felis lyncula. Nilsson, S. Skand. Fauna, I, p. 14 (Scandinavia).

1824. Felis pardina. Temminck. Loc. cit., p. 116 (near Lisbon, Portugal).

1824. Felis cervaria. Temminck. Monogr. Mamm. p. 106 (Asia).

1825. Felis lupulinus. Thunberg, C. P. Denkschr. K. Akad. Wissensch., 9, p. 189. München (North Scandinavia).

1825. Felis vulpinus. Thunberg, C. P. Loc. cit., p. 192 (near Uppsala, Sweden).

1829. Felis virgata. Nilsson, S. Illuminerade Figurer till Skandinaviens Fauna, Lund, pls. 3, 4 (Sweden).

1847. Felis isabellina. Blyth, E. — Journ. Asiat. Soc. Bengal, 16, p. 1178 (Tibet).

1907. Lynx pardella. Miller, G. S. — Ann. Mag. Nat. Hist., 20, p. 398 (Spain).

1908. Lynx sardiniae. Mola. — Boll. Soc. Zool. Ital. Roma, 9, p. 48 (Sardinia).

1912. Lynx lynx. Miller, G. S. Catalogue of the Mammals of Western Europe, p. 471, London.

1915. Lynx dinniki. Satunin, K. A. Mlekopitayushchie Kavkazskogo kraya (Mammals of the Caucasian Territory), 1, p. 391, Tiflis (conjectural name for the North Caucasian lynx).

Type and type locality. The species was described from a specimen found near Uppsala, Sweden.

Diagnosis. Features of the species fully coincide with those of the genus and are given in the diagnosis of the latter.

Measurements. Length of body with head (from 6 males and 3 females): males 87.0 — 104.0 cm, females 82.0 — 91.0 cm; length of tail: males 18.0 — 24.0 cm, females 20.0 — 31.0 cm; length of hind paw: males 23.2 — 26.0 cm, females 23.0 — 26.0 cm; length of ear: males 7.5 — 9.6 cm, females 8.0 — 9.9 cm. Weight: 16 — 32 kg.

Measurements of skull (from 57 males and 32 females): Overall length of skull: males 142.0 — 167.0 mm, females 131.0 — 152.0 mm; condylobasal length of skull: males 128.0 — 153.0 mm, females 120.0 — 140.0 mm; zygomatic width: males 91.0 — 122.0 mm, females 91.0 — 116.0 mm; maximum width: males 60.0 — 71.3 mm, females 59.0 — 66.0 mm; height in area of tympanic bullae: males 59.0 — 67.0 mm, females 58.2 — 64.0 mm; interorbital width: males 32.0 — 38.2 mm, females 27.0 — 33.2 mm; postorbital width: males 36.2 — 42.3 mm, females 36.0 — 41.2 mm; width between infraorbital foramina: males 42.0 — 49.2 mm, females 40.5 — 44.0 mm; length of upper tooth row: males 46.5 — 60.6 mm, females 45.0 — 52.0 mm.

Description. Doglike build, with long legs, short tail, and well-developed "side whiskers" and ear tufts. Head relatively small, round with short muzzle. Ears extremely long, expanded at base and pointed at tip, crowned by long hairs in form of characteristic tuft. Cheeks with luxuriant "side whiskers" extending from ears to throat and surrounding facial part of head posteriorly. Legs massive with large paws; digits connected by webs almost to distal phalanges. Tail extremely short (approximately as long as head), truncated; fails to reach paws of hind limbs when extended.

Pupils vertically elliptical.

Fur very soft, dense and long. Color of fur varies widely. Background color of winter fur from light ashen gray with bluish tinge to vivid reddish russet. Color pattern formed by short bands and by spots on back and flanks. Pattern occasionally weakly marked or completely absent on body, but always remains on legs. Color of spots varies from brown-gray to dark brown and blackish. Lips and edging around eyes white. Underparts and groin whitish and usually spattered with indistinct spots. Ear tufts black. Tail with pattern of dark transverse rings; distal third of tail black.

Summer fur shorter and coarser. Principal [background] color more saturated, with pronounced reddish to dark reddish brown hue. Pattern more conspicuous (Figure 162).

Skull (Figure 163) markedly convex, short, broad and high. Upper profile in form of very steep arch, highest in frontal area and descending very abruptly anteriorly and more gently towards back of head. Skull expanded in area of braincase and markedly compressed rostrally. Postorbital processes massive and very long, directed to either side, backwards, and downwards; tips are rather close to well-developed frontal processes of zygomatic arches. Frontal area broad and either convex or with median longitudinal depression; latter most clearly expressed in Altai lynxes. Sagittal crest conspicuously developed, particularly near occipital area. Occipital crest very pronounced, with short "rib" at apex. Zygomatic arches very widely parted; zygomatic width about 70% of condylobasal length of skull. Orbits ovally rounded, set at oblique angles to frontal area of skull. Anterosuperior process of jugal bone extends to anterior upper margin of lacrymal foramen or even beyond it. Lower anterior margin of orbit thick and ovally blunted. Infraorbital foramina oval, vertically elongated, their maximum foramen axis almost two thirds of width of septum dividing foramen from orbit. Nasals broad, lanceolately narrowed, and wedged into frontal area by broad tip. Anterior lateral process of nasals narrow, extending markedly forward and overhanging nasal opening. Frontal processes of nasals extend posteriorly approximately to same level as back ends of maxillary processes or somewhat further. Bony palate short, its length only 20% greater than width. Choanal incisure ovally concave anteriorly, lacking reverse projections in middle. Pterygoid fossa rudimentary. Presphenoid bone with broad base, usually conical, with serrated sides on basal part and markedly narrow tip wedging into vomer. Tympanic bullae (bullae tympani) high, markedly inflated, long, and (seen from above) pointed in front; lie somewhat behind jaw articulation, with anterior edge falling short of anterior side of postglenoid processes. Boundary between anterior and posterior chamber readily visible and extending in form of arch directed on a slant anteriorly from stylomastoid foramen to foramen of eustachian tubes. Distance between tympanic bullae approximately equal to width of mesopterygoid fossa. Lateral paroccipital processes project weakly in form of broad plates above surface of posterior part of tympanic bullae. Longitudinal axis of anterior palatine foramina less than longitudinal axis of upper canine. Coronoid process of lower jaw has markedly outwardly-arched superior margin.

Dental formula: $I\frac{3}{3}$; $C\frac{1}{1}$; $Pm\frac{2-3}{2}$; $M\frac{1}{1}$ = 28 (30).

Upper incisors form straight line. Upper canines large: height of canine approximately 75% of length of entire row of upper molars and premolars. First upper premolars usually absent but occasionally present on one or both sides; alveoli usually conspicuous when these teeth have been lost early in life. Upper carnassial tooth large, with one denticle on anterior margin. Second lower molars very rarely retained. Lower carnassial tooth with additional small denticle on posterior margin, this lacking in members of genus Felis s. str.

Systematic notes. The lynx is characterized by a broad scope of individual variation, particularly in fur color, which makes establishment of subspecies difficult. Due to insufficient material, it is impossible at present to carry out a full systematic survey of intraspecific forms of the lynx, and only the most differentiated subspecies can be characterized, i. e., those whose systematic identity engenders no particular doubts. These include the lynxes occurring in the mountains on the southern periphery of Siberia, in the Far East, and in northeastern Siberia. They usually differ in peculiarities of fur color, in size and in craniological details. A survey of the Siberian subspecies of the lynx is presented below.

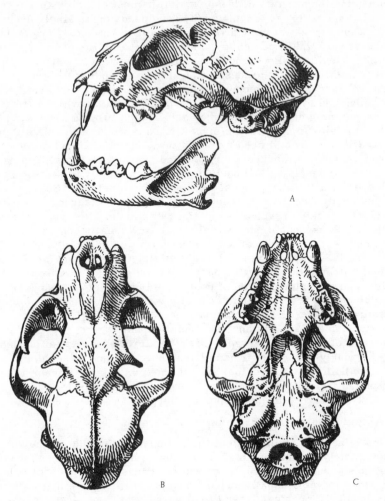

FIGURE 163. Skull of Lynx lynx L. (original):

A — lateral view; B — dorsal view; C — ventral view.

Geographical distribution. The range of the lynx includes the wooded and mountainous areas of Europe, Asia as far south as the Himalayas and North America.

In the Soviet Union it is encountered in the forest belt, the Caucasus and the mountain areas of Soviet Central Asia.

It is widely distributed throughout Siberia except for the steppe zone and Kamchatka (Map XXII).

In the Northern Urals, according to Flerov (1933), the lynx is encountered only in the Lyapin Basin and does not venture further north. On the Synya it is encountered only exceptionally. However, according to S. A. Kuklin (1937), it is more abundant in the Northern Urals than in other areas; there it is encountered rather frequently and occurs even in "large forest steppes and steppe pine forests, e.g., in the Sinara and Uglich forests." According to A. N. Dubrovskii (1940) the lynx is caught in the upper reaches of the Kharampur River near Lake Voden-To.

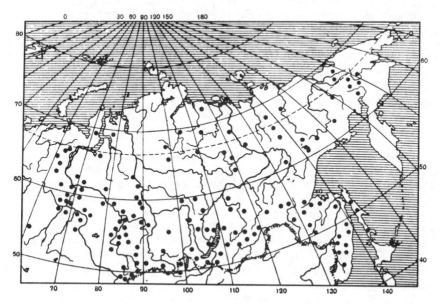

MAP XXII.   Geographical distribution of the lynx, L y n x   l y n x   L., in Siberia

The lynx is a common form in the Surgut taiga, according to S. Shvetsov (1888), I. Ya. Slovtsov (1892) and other authors, S. M. Chugunov (1951) reported it for the Yugan River. According to Slovtsov (ibidem), the lynx occurs in southern areas of the former Turinsk District, but only occasionally enters the northern part or the Pelym area. It was obtained by V. N. Skalon (coll. Zool. Mus. Moscow University) in the former Konda-Sosva Reserve.

According to N. P. Bulychev (1878), the lynx is fairly common in the northwestern part of the former Irbit County.

According to hunters' reports collected by Shaposhnikov (personal communication), it never occurs in large numbers anywhere in the Tyumen Region, though it is encountered rather often in a number of districts. It is much more abundant in the Khanty-Mansi National District and in the areas of Tobolsk, Tyumen, Abatskii, Baikolovo, Berdyuzh'e, Golyshmanovo, Dubrovinoe, Novo-Zaimka, Omutinskii, Polnovatskii and Uporovo.

In the Omsk Region the lynx is rare, being encountered only in the northern, taiga-covered areas. In the valley of the Irtysh it was collected by I. S. Polyakov (coll. Zool. Inst. Acad. Sciences USSR).

In the Tomsk Region it occurs throughout the vast expanses of taiga. In the Narym Territory, according to V. P. Anikin (1902), it is a fairly common form and is caught in great numbers. According to my data, the lynx is common in the Verkhneketskii [upper Ket], Kolpashevo, Shegarka and Bakchar areas. According to observations of G. E. Ioganzen (1923), it is rather common along the Chulym River, particularly along its tributaries. B. S. Yudin told me that the lynx occurs in the Kozhevnikovo area, where it is quite abundant near Simanskii canal and on some islands in the Ob River.

In the Novosibirsk Region it is generally rare, usually occurring in the Severnoe and Pikhtovka areas and the northern parts of the Kolyvan', Oyash and Bolotnoe areas. According to B. S. Yudin, it occurs year-round in the Oesh River valley. M. D. Zverev (1932) reports the lynx as a common species along the northern part of the Turksib [railroad] (the former Novosibirsk and Barnaul districts). In recent years it has been obtained in the Karakanskii pine forest and in a number of forest steppe districts of the Novosibirsk Region on the right bank of the Ob.

In the Altai Territory, according to V. N. Savinov (1953), the lynx occurs throughout the taiga zone and also in the ribbonlike strips of pine forests. * According to G. N. Likhachev (1930), it ranges throughout the territory of the Upper Ob forest tract, but in small numbers. It is common in the pine forests and floodplain deciduous-forest strips near the villages of Pavlovsk and Shelabolikha, where it was collected in the winter of 1958 by B.S. Yudin. Five lynxes were obtained in the ribbonlike strips of pine forests in the steppes near the Altai in the Egorevskii area during the hunting season of 1951—1952, and an additional five or six lynxes still inhabited the area (V. I. Telegin, personal communication).

In the Altai, according to A. P. Razorenova (1939), the lynx is rather common in wooded areas, particularly in the Maiminsk, Ongudai, Ulagan and Uimen' areas.

Yudin gave me a lynx skull obtained in 1952 in the Turochak area.

In the Ust'-Koksa area of the Gorno Altai Autonomous Region, according to Nasimovich (1949), the lynx is "periodically encountered throughout the area and is common in some places, e.g., in the vicinity of Sakhsabai, along the Malyi Sugat River, etc. It does not live along the upper Katun in winter, but migrates together with the roe deer."

In the southeastern Altai, according to A. M. Kolosov (1939), it occurs rather rarely, with no more than a few dozen pelts reaching the fur depots at Kosh-Agach. It is encountered on the bare cliffs of the Chuya Alps (Kuraiskii and Sailyugemskii ranges). K. T. Yurlov encountered the animal in 1959 in the treeless valley of the Dzhazator River, but it is very rare there.

It was reported by N. I. Yablonskii (1904) for the Bukhtarma River area, where it was obtained in 1882 by V. Plotnikov near the village of Chernovaya (coll. Zool. Inst. Acad. Sciences USSR).

In the former Altai Reserve, according to P. B. Yurgenson (1938), the lynx is rare, but its tracks have been observed in winter on the upper reaches of the Kobukhu River, on the "saddle" of the Chichilgan Range, above Okporok,

* [Belts of pine forest (from 5 to 10 km) on sandy deposits in ancient valleys of glacial streams.]

446

in the lower reaches of the Kyga and Koksha rivers, near the mouth of the Konui and on the Bolshoi Abakan, almost to the mouth of the Kairu River. It was obtained in 1935 on the western shore of Lake Teletskoe, in the area of Mt. Kuporosnaya.

It is common in the taiga districts of the Kemerovo Region. N. A. Korotkevich collected it in 1906 in the valley of the Mras-Su River, near the village of Sosnovaya Gora and on the Salair Range, in the valley of the Kondoma River, near the village of Talei (Chugunov, 1915).

In the Gornaya Shoria, according to Gol'tsmaier (1936), the lynx is rare and for this reason is not hunted. In the area of Krasnoyarsk the animal was collected by M. E. Kobort in 1891—1892, on the Karakush and Slizneva rivers (coll. Zool. Inst. Acad. Sciences USSR). According to P. Polikevich (1923), it inhabits the taiga areas of the Kakhass Autonomous Region and the upper part of the valley of the Greater and Lesser Yenisei, and is rare in the taiga zone of the Western Sayan (Yanushevich and Yurlov, 1949). D. K. Solov'ev (1920) reported that it ranges throughout the taiga zone of the Sayans up to the alpine zone. L. and I. Kozhanchikov (1924) reported the animal from the Kazyr and Kizyr rivers as well as in the taiga along the Yenisei's course through the Sayans. K. I. Gromov (1951) reported the lynx among the animals in the Sayan Reserve. Yurlov frequently encountered lynx tracks in the taiga along the Agul River in 1952.

In the Irkutsk Region, according to I. P. Kopylov, A. V. Dubrovol'skii and I. A. Shergin (1940), the lynx is encountered everywhere, but in small numbers. It occurs on the upper reaches of the Lower Tunguska and in the Angara area, most often along the upper reaches of the Vikhoreva River (a left tributary of the Angara). It also inhabits the taiga near the Sayans, the valley of the Lena, and the northwestern Baikal area, particularly along the Notai, Nazimi, Birilei and Kirenga rivers. In eastern and northwestern Baikalia it is widespread. It is also common in the valley of the Vitim, according to A. A. Pogudin (1930), and, similarly, in the former Kirensk District. I. S. Polyakov (1873) reported the lynx in the Upper Lena and Baguldeika. According to G. Radde (1862) it is encountered in the Baikal Mountains in the valley of the Oka River. It is found in small numbers in the Chuna-Angara area of the former Kansk District (Troitskii, 1930).

G. Tel' (1880) reported catching a lynx near Yeniseisk. Occasionally it is encountered in the valley of the Elogui, more rarely on the Baikhu; it inhabits the Kolches and Galaktionikha rivers and the upper valley of the Syma River (Podarevskii, 1936). On the Stony Tunguska the lynx is more abundant in the eastern half of the valley, where it is obtained near the trading posts Verkhnaya Kontora (Tatura River), Vana-Vary, and Oskoba (Oskoba and Soba rivers); it becomes more abundant further south (Naumov, 1934).

Along the northern Yenisei, according to N. P. Naumov (ibidem), the lynx is extremely rare. No more than an average of 10 pelts are obtained each year in the Turukhansk territory. On the left bank of the Yenisei, according to E. O. Yakovlev (1930), the lynx reaches north only to 60° N lat. On the mountainous right bank of the Yenisei the lynx is abundant and ventures further north, to the Kheta River, where it has been obtained on the left tributary — the Ayakli River (about 60° 30' N lat.). As reported by Naumov (ibidem), the lynx is common here in the eastern areas, along the upper reaches of both the Upper and Lower Tunguska rivers; a record exists of its capture on the Lower Tunguska in the area of the Kochechuma River (about 64°—64° 30' N. lat.). Middendorf (1867) encountered lynx along the Yenisei north to the timberline.

It is extremely rare on the lower Khatanga — Lena watershed, according to Romanov (1941). The northern boundary coincides here with the northern forest boundary. It only very rarely ventures out onto the tundra. Romanov mentions two cases of entry onto the tundra: in the western part of the Lena delta around 72° 45' N lat., and on the shore of the Laptev Sea in the southern part of the Bykovskii Peninsula [Trusi Bay] around 71° 40' N lat. It is also extremely rare south of the Lena—Khatanga area. Romanov, while traveling from the village of Saskylakh (on the Anabar River) to the Vilyui River in the spring of 1935, saw tracks of isolated individuals at the following places: on the upper Luchikan River (a right tributary of the Malaya Kuonamka), on the Olenek River some 30 km below the mouth of the Dolgokhan River, on the Baty-Sala River (a left tributary of the Chemidyakyan River), and on the Tyung River above the mouth of the Chemidyakyan.

Maak (1858, 1886), on the basis of questionnaires, reported the lynx to be very rare throughout the area between the Lena and the Vilyui, on the northern tributaries of the Vilyui, and along the middle reaches of the Olenek River (about 68° N lat.); he knew of extremely rare cases when single specimens were obtained on the Chona, in the area of Suntar, and below the city of Zhigansk on the Menkere River.

In the valley of the Indigirka, according to N. M. Mikhel' (1938), the lynx occurs throughout the forest zone almost up to the village of Allaikha, but mostly in the Oimyakon and Moma areas. According to V. I. Belyk (1953), it ranges throughout the taiga areas of Yakutia, but chiefly east of the Lena, being very rare west of this river.

On the Verkhoyansk Range it is occasionally encountered south of Verkhoyansk (Buturlin, 1913). On the Adycha River near the village of Adychinskaya it was collected in 1925 by M. I. Tkachenko (coll. Zool. Inst. Acad. Sciences USSR). It occurs on the upper reaches of the Kolyma River (Ognev, 1926).

On the Omolon E. I. Shmidt obtained it some 150 km from the river's mouth (coll. S. I. Ognev), and it has also been taken on the Bolshoi and Malyi Anyui (Portenko, 1941).

On the Anadyr the lynx was encountered for the first time by L. Belopol'skii (1937) on the upper reaches of the river. Portenko (1941) reported that "it penetrates the western parts of the Anadyr Territory extremely rarely, apparently either just accidentally or due to an occasional increase in its population in the Kolyma forests." Portenko mentioned the following points where the lynx has been observed or obtained: on streams between the Anadyr and Main, near the village of Oselkino, west of the city of Markovo, near the village of Eropol, and on the upper Penzhina River. B. S. Yudin reports that it occurs extremely rarely in the Telviem area.

The lynx is not found on Kamchatka. It undoubtedly ranges on the Okhotsk shore of Siberia, but we have no concrete data about its distribution there.

N. T. Zolotarev (1934) observed that in the valley of the Ud River and the upper reaches of the Selemdzha its distribution is wide but its numbers small.

In Transbaikalia the lynx is widely distributed in the wooded areas and was reported for the northeastern shore of the Baikal by S. S. Turov (1924, 1936), although in small numbers. It is common in the valley of the Vitim River and is encountered in the taiga of the Khamar-Daban and in the Tunkinskie Belko Mountains (Kopylov, Dobrovol'skii, Shergin, 1940). A. S. Fetisov (1950) mentioned specimens which he examined that came from the Khamar-Daban, Selenginsk (Barun-Burinkhan), Ivolginsk and Kyakhta districts of Buryat-Mongolia.

On the upper Chita River, according to E. Pavlov (1948), the species is very rare and of importance for the fur trade in this area.

In eastern Transbaikalia, according to information collected by V. A. Kuznetsov (1929), it inhabits the mountain taiga districts, being encountered in the Yablonovyi Range and its foothills (the villages Kyker and Zyulzikan) and in the Undinskie Mountains (the villages Kalinino and Shivki). Radde (1862) reported the lynx in the Nerchinsk Range.

In the valley of the Gilyui and Oldoi, according to G. N. Gassovskii (1927), it is encountered extremely rarely; he saw signs of the animal near the Lagunai River and encountered it on the Yankinsk and Tukuringra ranges.

According to Maak (1861), it inhabits the entire valley of the Ussuri, living in the Khekhtsyr Mountains and the mountains near Aua, in the ranges of Tankhe and Akuli, and in the Situkha Mountains near the Daubikhe and Sandukhu rivers. Przheval'skii (1870) was of the opinion that the lynx is fairly rare throughout the Ussuri Territory. It is generally encountered in the dense coniferous forest of the main range of the Sikhote-Alin, being rather abundant along the upper reaches of the Bikin River and encountered extremely rarely on the western shore of Lake Khanka.

In the valley of the Iman, according to Zolotarev (1936), the lynx is rare and its distribution is chiefly associated with the upper reaches of this river and its tributaries. It has been obtained in the vicinity of the city of Khabarovsk, and on the Samarga and Kolumbe rivers, as well as near Sidemi (coll. Zool. Inst. Acad. Sciences USSR).

Ognev (1935) reported the following survey of lynx distribution (based on work done by V. S. Stakhanov): "In the Far East the lynx is a typical inhabitant of the Ayan-Okhotsk forest flora, which to a certain degree determines the boundary of its distribution in the region. The lynx is quite common in the taiga from the Uda to the Tugur River as far as the forests of Nikolaevsk on the Amur. It is found throughout the Amgun district, along the Bureya and Zeya rivers, and on the Mikhvach Range, avoiding open marshy spaces, e.g., the extensive Dabanda-Bolon and Evoron marshes. It is common in the northern parts of the Sikhote-Alin Range and reaches far south along a narrow belt of mountains within the boundaries of the taiga. In the forests along the Khungari River, where a Manchurian flora occupies the area on the river's lower reaches, the lynx's range extends from the boundary of Siberian stone pine upwards into the region where larch—birch forests predominate.

On the Sikhote-Alin Range the lynx descends south as far as the upper Iman and possibly to the Vaku River. It is very rarely found on the upper reaches of the Noto and Suchan rivers." Lynx was collected by G. F. Bromlei in the Suputinka Reserve (coll. S. U. Stroganov), where it keeps close to the sources of the Kamenka River and of the Anikin (Bromlei and Gutnikova, 1955). On the Spuk River in the Ternei area the lynx was obtained by Yu. Salmin (coll. Zool. Mus. Moscow University).

On Sakhalin the lynx has been known from time immemorial, and it was reported as far back as 1858 by L. Schrenck from the upper reaches of the Tym River. According to A. M. Nikol'skii (1889) it lives in the heavily wooded inner parts of the island. Shmidt (1862) observed the lynx along the mountain ranges, by which it descends to the southern tip of the island (where it is, however, rarely encountered).

Ognev (1935) reports the following data after N. R. Obrekht (from a 1933 manuscript) concerning lynx distribution on Sakhalin. According to these data, the animal is extremely rare on the island, particularly in the northern part. Questioning traders and hunters, he "found it to be rare in the Onarka and Poronai river valleys and in the mountain taiga of the Poronai woods in the Pil'vo forests. It is probably more common in southern Sakhalin, e. g., near the Korsakov military post. It is of no commerical value."

Survey of subspecies. The number of lynx subspecies is not yet established. No less than eight subspecies have been described for the Palaearctic. Six subspecies occur in the USSR, five of these in Siberia.

30a. **Lynx lynx lynx** Linnaeus (1758). Common lynx

1758. F e l i x l y n x. Linnaeus, C. Systema Naturae, ed. X, 1, p. 43.
1914. L y n x l y n x l y n x. Satunin, K. A. Opredelitel' mleko-pitayushchikh Rossiiskoi imperii (Key to Mammals of the Russian Empire). p. 172, Tiflis; Ognev, S. I. Zveri SSSR i prilezhashchikh stran (Animals of the USSR and Adjacent Countries), 3, p. 198. 1935.
1914. L y n x l y n x b o r e a l i s. Satunin, K. A. Loc. cit., p. 175.

Type and type locality. See above description of the species.
Diagnosis. Chiefly characterized by relatively small size (condylobasal length of skull averages 134.3 mm) and by craniological details. Frontal area of skull convex, lacking median longitudinal depression. Color highly variable, with vividly spotted individuals predominating.
Measurements (males 23 specimens, females 17 specimens). Overall length of skull: males 141.7 — 153.0 mm (av. 147.4 mm), females 131.6 — 143.2 mm (av. 138.0 mm); condylobasal length: males 128.0 — 141.0 mm (av. 134.3 mm), females 120.0 — 135.8 mm (av. 131.4 mm); zygomatic width: males 95.0 — 106.2 mm (av. 102.6 mm), females 91.0 — 100.0 mm (av. 96.7 mm); mastoid width: males 60.0 — 67.0 mm (av. 61.7 mm), females 59.0 — 63.0 mm (av. 61.3 mm); height in area of tympanic bullae: males 55.0 — 66.2 mm (av. 58.0 mm), females 54.0 — 61.0 mm (av. 57.2 mm); interorbital width: males 32.0 — 35.9 mm (av. 33.4 mm), females 27.0 — 33.2 mm (av. 30.0 mm); postorbital width: males 39.2 — 42.3 mm (av. 40.3 mm), females 39.0 — 41.2 mm (av. 40.0 mm); width between infraorbital foramina: males 42.0 — 46.9 mm

(av. 44.0 mm), females 40.5 — 44.0 mm (av. 42.2 mm); width of rostrum
above canines: males 38.0—41.0 mm (av. 39.5 mm), females 36.5—39.2 mm
(av. 38.7 mm); length of upper tooth row: males 46.5 — 51.6 mm
(av. 49.0 mm), females 45.7 — 51.0 mm (av. 48.6 mm).

Systematic notes. The nominate subspecies is quite clearly
differentiated systematically and is recognized when series material is
compared. It is characterized by the skull's small size and distinct
sculpturing. In comparison with skulls of other subspecies the skull of
L. l. lynx is very round, with a more distinctly convex upper profile and
with a somewhat inflated frontal area lacking a longitudinal depression.

The wide scope of color variation makes this feature unsuitable for
diagnostic use. The widest color variation of the lynx may occur in the same
locality, but for general characterization of the subspecies we may note that
vividly spotted specimens predominate.

Geographical distribution. Europe, West Siberian lowland, and the valley
of the Yenisei.

Material examined. European USSR — 36 specimens; Western Siberia
(valley of the Irtysh and the Ob)— 7 specimens; Central Siberia (valley of
the Yenisei) — 1 specimen. Total — 44 specimens.

30b. **Lynx lynx wardi** Lydekker (1904). Altai lynx

1904. F e l i x   l y n x   w a r d i. Lydekker, R. The Coloration of the
Lynxes.— The Field, Vol. 104, p. 576.

Type and type locality. The subspecies was described from a specimen
collected in the Altai.

Diagnosis. Larger than the nominate subspecies (condylobasal length of
skull averages 147.0 mm). Frontal area of skull not convex, has distinctly
marked longitudinal depression in middle. Individuals with weakly marked
spots predominate.

Measurements. (males 13 specimens, females 6 specimens). Overall
length of skull: males 154.5—164.7 mm (av. 160.0 mm), females
150.0—153.2 mm (av. 152.0 mm); condylobasal length: males
145.0—149.5 mm (av. 147.0 mm), females 136.0 —142.0 mm (av. 139.0 mm);
zygomatic width: males 113.0—115.0 mm (av. 112.8 mm), females
112.0—114.0 mm (av. 112.8 mm); mastoid width: males 66.0 — 69.5 mm
(av. 67.6 mm), females 59.0 — 62.8 mm (av. 60.4 mm); height of skull in
area of tympanic bullae: males 60.7—67.0 mm (av. 64.2 mm), females
58.2—60.6 mm (av. 59.3 mm); interorbital width: males 33.9— 36.8 mm
(av. 35.2 mm), females 30.8— 33.2 mm (av. 32.4 mm); postorbital width:
males 37.0— 40.5 mm (av. 37.7 mm), females 37.0 —40.0 mm (av. 37.4 mm);
width between infraorbital foramina: males 44.4—48.7 mm (av. 45.2 mm),
females 44.3—45.4 mm (av. 45.0 mm); width of rostrum above canines:
males 41.3—45.0 mm (av. 42.5 mm), females 40.0—41.5 mm (av. 40.7 mm);
length of upper tooth row: males 51.8—60.6 mm (av. 53.4 mm), females
48.7—50.6 mm (av. 49.6 mm).

Systematic notes. The Altai lynx was described by R. Lydekker (1904)
from a single pelt from the Altai. According to Lydekker's observations,
this specimen is characterized by its extremely light color. The back is pale

reddish brown ("pale rufous fawn"), the flanks pinkish white, the underparts pure white; pale brown spots are scattered over the legs alone.

K. A. Satunin (1914), on acquainting himself with the diagnosis of L. l. w a r d i, wrote: "I find nothing in Lydekker's description which might distinguish the Altai lynx from the common lynx, L. l. l y n x, in its winter coat."

Ognev (1935), who examined two lynx pelts from the Altai, found that they were to some extent similar in color to the pale-colored L. l. i s a b e l l i n a Blyth (1874) described from Tibet; but on the other hand, he wrote that series of pelts from the central and northern parts of the RSFSR "may contain specimens which are difficult to distinguish from the Altai individuals." According to Ognev, "it is difficult to decide where to refer the Altai lynx without access to craniological material"; and there he left the problem.

I examined 17 lynx skulls collected in different areas of the Altai and 10 pelts at a fur post. The Altai lynx appeared to be completely distinguishable from other forms thanks to features of cranial structure and the skull's relatively large size. It is characterized by a pronounced flatness of the skull's frontal area, which bears a conspicuous longitudinal depression. The upper skull profile is less convex than in the nominate subspecies. On the basis of skull size, the Altai lynx occupies an intermediate position between the small L. l. l y n x and the large East Siberian L. l. w r a n g e l i.

The Altai lynx is generally pale, varying from grayish with a cream tinge to smoky gray with more or less strong russet tones. The degree of spottiness varies, with a muted spotty pattern predominating.

The Altai lynx is undoubtedly a well-differentiated subspecies.

Geographical distribution. Altai. I had materials collected in the following areas of the Altai: Turochak, Lake Teletskoe, Bukhtarma, Ongudai, Uimon, and Oirotiya. I relate the form distributed in the Khakass Autonomous Region to the same subspecies.

Material examined. Altai — 17 skulls and 10 pelts; Khakassiya — 2 skulls. Total — 19 skulls and 10 pelts.

30c. **Lynx lynx kozlovi** Fetisov (1950).
Baikalian lynx

1922. F e l i x l y n x var. b a i c a l e n s i s. Dybowski. — Arch. Tow. Nauk, 1, p. 351, Lvov (nom. nud.).

1950. L y n x l y n x k o z l o v i. Fetisov, A. S. — Izvestiya Biologo-Geograficheskogo Nauchno-Issledovatel'skogo Instituta pri Irkutskom Gosudarstvennom Universitete, 12, No. 1, pp. 21—22.

Type and type locality. No. 80 in the collections of the Zoological Museum of Irkutsk University, male, adult, 12 January 1942. The Buryat ASSR, Salenga District, Barun-Burinkhan.

Diagnosis. Smaller than the Altai lynx (condylobasal length of male skull averages 142 mm). Frontal area of skull more or less flat. Color highly variable regarding degree of spottiness.

Measurements (males 23 specimens, females 7 specimens). Overall length of skull: males 152.0 — 157.0 mm (av. 155.0 mm), females

146.0 — 152.0 mm (av. 149.0 mm); condylobasal length: males
139.0—144.2 mm (av. 142.0 mm), females 134.0 — 139.0 mm (av. 136.0 mm);
zygomatic width: males 106.0— 111.5 mm (av. 109.2 mm), females
101.0—110.2 mm (av. 104.2 mm); mastoid width: males 66.8 — 71.3 mm
(av. 67.3 mm), females 61.7—65.9 mm (av. 64.1 mm); height in area of
tympanic bullae: males 58.2—62.8 mm (av. 61.4 mm), females
59.0 — 62.5 mm (av. 60.5 mm); interorbital width: males 32.8—36.0 mm
(av. 34.2 mm), females 33.0—38.0 mm (av. 34.9 mm); postorbital width:
males 40.0—44.3 mm (av. 41.9 mm), females 40.6— 45.0 mm (av. 42.4 mm);
width between infraorbital foramina: males 44.2—46.8 mm (av. 45.7 mm),
females 43.0—47.6 mm (av. 44.1 mm); width of rostrum above canines:
males 39.9 — 43.0 mm (av. 41.5 mm), females 39.3—42.0 mm (av. 39.5 mm);
length of upper tooth row: males 49.9 — 51.6 mm (av. 50.7 mm), females
48.0 — 51.8 mm (av. 49.1 mm).

Systematic notes. The subspecies is characterized by average
craniometric data on material in series.

It is systematically close to the Altai lynx, but smaller than it. The
frontal area of the skull has a sharper configuration.

Geographical distribution. The southern areas of Central Siberia, from
Khakassiya east approximately to the Selenga. A. S. Fetisov (1950)
reported it for the following districts of Baikalia: Irkutsk, Usolsk,
Cheremkhovsk, Nizhne-Udinsk, Tofalyaria [the Tuva Karagass tribal
lands] and southwestern Transbaikalia, where it was found on the
Khamar-Daban.

Material examined. 24 skulls and 5 pelts.

30d. **Lynx lynx wrangeli** Ognev (1928).
East Siberian lynx

1928. L y n x   l y n x   w r a n g e l i. Ognev, S. I. Rysi (The Lynxes).—
Okhotnik, Nos. 5—6, pp. 22—23; Auct. cit. Zveri SSSR i prilezhashchikh
stran (Animals of the USSR and Adjacent Countries). 3, pp. 232—235. 1935;
Ellerman, J. R. and T. C. S. Morrison-Scott. Checklist of Palaearctic and
Indian Mammals, p. 309, London. 1951.

Type and type locality. No. 12692 in the collection of the Zoological
Institute of the Academy of Sciences of the USSR, male, adult, winter 1925,
from the collections of M. I. Tkachenko. Valley of the Adycha River near
the village of Adychinskaya in Khotan-Khaya, Verkhoyansk area.

Diagnosis. Differs from other Siberian subspecies in large skull dimensions (condylobasal length of male skull averages 152 mm, with zygomata
more widely separated). Frontal area of skull flat, lacking longitudinal
depression. Individuals with reduced spotty pattern predominate. General
tone of winter fur very light smoke-gray, with occasional straw-yellow tinge.

Measurements (8 males and 6 females). Overall length of skull:
males 162.0 —167.0 mm (av. 165.0 mm), females 144.0—150.0 mm (av.
148.0 mm); condylobasal length: males 147.0—155.0 mm (av. 152.0 mm),
females 130.2—133.5 mm (av. 132.0 mm); zygomatic width: males
118.1—121.1 mm (av. 120.0 mm), females 106.0—116.0 mm (av. 114.0 mm);

mastoid width: males 71.1−72.3 mm (av. 71.4 mm), females
62.9−65.0 mm (av. 63.0 mm); height of skull in area of tympanic bullae:
males 65.0 − 67.0 mm (av. 66.2 mm), females 61.0−64.6 mm (av. 62.3 mm);
interorbital width: males 38.0 − 38.6 mm (av. 38.2 mm), females
32.0−35.0 mm (av. 33.0 mm); postorbital width: males 39.0 − 42.0 mm
(av. 40.7 mm), females 37.0−41.2 mm (av. 39.7 mm); width between
infraorbital foramina: males 48.0 − 49.2 mm (av. 48.7 mm), females
44.2 − 46.3 mm (av. 45.4 mm); width of rostrum above canines: males
42.2−46.4 mm (av. 44.3 mm), females 39.2−41.7 mm (av. 40.4 mm);
length of upper tooth row: males 50.2−56.7 mm (av. 54.0 mm), females
48.5−50.4 mm (av. 49.6 mm).

Systematic notes. This is a paler form, with a large skull. It is
systematically nearest to the Altai L. l. w a r d i, but appreciably larger
than it.

The coat has been little studied. Uniformly gray specimens with weakly
spotted legs are encountered as well as others with a contrasting spotty
pattern.

Geographical distribution. Northeastern Siberia, west approximately to
the basin of the upper Vilyui and south to Barguzin and the Stanovoi Range.

Material examined. Yakutia − 6 skulls and 2 pelts; Chukchi Peninsula −
1 pelt. Total − 6 skulls and 3 pelts.

30e. **Lynx lynx neglectus** subsp. n. Far Eastern lynx

Type and type locality. Skull No. s-41310 in the collection of the
Zoological Museum of Moscow University, male, adult, January 1945, from
G. F. Bromlei's collection. Maritime Territory, Suputinka Reserve,
Glazkovka.

Diagnosis. Relatively large subspecies (condylobasal length of male
skull averages 145 mm). Frontal area more or less flat, without
conspicuous longitudinal depression. General tone dull grayish-reddish
brown, marked with indistinct small brownish black spots which are more
conspicuous on legs. Underparts white with blackish gray speckles.

Measurements (9 males and 6 females). Overall length of skull: males
157.0−167.0 mm (av. 162.0 mm), females 146.0− 158.0 mm (av. 150.6 mm);
condylobasal length: males 143.0−146.7 mm (av. 145.0 mm), females
132.0−139.6 mm (av. 137.2 mm); zygomatic width: males
110.7−113.2 mm (av. 112.0 mm), females 107.0−110.0 mm (av. 108.3 mm);
mastoid width: males 66.1−71.3 mm (av. 69.2 mm), females
63.0−64.9 mm (av. 64.2 mm); height in area of tympanic bullae: males
63.0−68.9 mm (av. 65.0 mm), females 60.0−62.0 mm (av. 61.2 mm);
interorbital width: males 37.4−39.0 mm (av. 38.1 mm), females
32.0−34.2 mm (av. 33.0 mm); width between infraorbital foramina: males
47.0 −48.5 mm (av. 48.0 mm), females 43.9 −45.8 mm (av. 44.6 mm); width
of rostrum above canines: males 44.0−45.8 mm (av. 45.0 mm), females
40.0 43.0 mm (av. 42.2 mm); length of upper tooth row: males
50.2−52.3 mm (av. 51.3 mm), females 47.0 −48.2 mm (av. 47.6 mm).

Systematic notes. The Far Eastern lynx is a well-differentiated
subspecies, characterized by the features presented in the diagnosis.

It can be systematically approximated with L. l. w r a n g e l i, it differs in having a smaller skull and less prominent cheekbones. The skull is larger and more massive than in the Baikalian lynx.

Geographical distribution. Maritime Territory and the Amur River area.

Material examined. Skulls — 12 specimens; pelts — 2 specimens; Total — 14 specimens.

Biology. The lynx is a typical forest-dweller, and is mainly found in secluded, sparsely populated forest areas, both in lowlands and hilly regions. It avoids open forests.

In the West Siberian lowland it lives in various types of taiga, preferring areas with a dense understory and overgrown old burns, where the blue (mountain) hare is abundant.

In the zone of the West Siberian forest steppe, the lynx lives in the most secluded areas of the Upper Ob pine forests. Along the Irtysh it inhabits the ribbonlike strips of pine forest (Figures 164, 165).

FIGURE 164. Fir taiga on the upper Tara River in the Novosibirsk Region. Lynx biotope. Photo by K. T. Yurlov

The lynx is the only Russian cat adapted to life in the snow-bound taiga; it has developed certain morphological adaptations for movement on loose snow. In the lynx the legs are longer and the paws broader than in other Russian cats. The paws are densely furry in winter, so that a kind of "snow ski" is formed, as in the blue (mountain) hare. This trait distributes the specific load* and,

* Load per unit area of supporting paws.

together with the long legs, facilitates the animal's movements on deep and loose snow (Formozov, 1946).

Nevertheless, whenever possible the lynx avoids areas with abundant snow.

On the Altai, according to G. D. Dul'keit (1953), the lynx keeps mainly to less snowy areas with highly dissected topography; it occurs very rarely above 1,800 m (Figure 166), i. e., [above] the timberline, being more common on rocks in sunny spots than on northern exposures or on gentle mountain-taiga slopes. The lynx is completely absent from the vast stretches of the high-mountain tundra. In dense forest tracts the lynx avoids areas with abundant snow and thus, in numerous places on the upper reaches of the Bolshoi Abakan, is absent in winter. The areas around Lake Teletskoe are very characteristic habitats. The right bank of the Chulyshman River is also a typical habitat, but the lynx is less abundant here, due to the numerous wolves.

In the southeastern Altai, according to information collected by A. M. Kolosov (1939), the lynx "keeps to the completely woodless biotopes along the rocky mountain ranges lining the Chuya Steppe (the Chuya Alps, Kurai and Sailyugem ranges)," and to similar localities in the northern Hangay, according to A. G. Bannikov (1954). In the Mongolian and Gobi Altai the lynx is a true rock-dweller, preferring localities where rocks alternate with shrubs.

In the Minusinsk taiga, according to L. and I. Kozhanchikov (1924), the lynx prefers the dense taiga, particularly places with musk deer.

FIGURE 165. Pine forest in the upper Ob area. Lynx biotope. Photo by K. T. Yurlov

In the Eastern Sayans the lynx, according to D. K. Solov'ev (1920), inhabits the entire taiga zone to the upper timberline. "It occurs in the most secluded and desolate areas of the taiga, far from villages, and prefers coniferous forest." It does not penetrate the alpine zone.

In the Irkutsk Region, according to I. P. Kopylov, A. V. Dobrovol'skii and A. I. Shergin (1940), the lynx habitats are the forest tracts of the northern and mountain-taiga parts of the region. The specific composition of the vegetation varies in the areas inhabited by the lynx, but the animal lingers more in forests with a dense understory and shrubs (near burns and stretches of taiga).

The habitats of the lynx in the southwestern areas of Transbaikalia, according to A. Cherkasov (1867), are dense secluded forests, high rocky mountains, wooded mountain cliffs with overhanging rocks, and rock streams. It is not encountered near populated areas.

In Yakutia it inhabits the taiga areas.

In the Maritime Territory and the regions around the River Amur it occupies various biotopes. In the valley of the upper Iman River and its tributaries, according to N. T. Zolotarev (1936), the lynx inhabits coniferous forests of the Okhotsk type. In the southern parts of the Maritime Territory, e. g., in the Suputinka Reserve, according to the observations of G. F. Bromlei, the lynx occurs in the most secluded places at the sources of the Kamenka River and the Anikin spring, where broadleaf-spruce forests predominate. Thence it makes extensive migrations in search of food into the rest of the wooded areas of the reserve.

FIGURE 166. Taiga in the area of Lake Teletskoe, Altai. Lynx biotope. Photo by V. I. Telegin

The lynx is a sedentary animal and its individual range in the West Siberian lowland is usually no more than $15-25\,km^2$. However, when food is scarce, it may go far beyond these bounds and roam quite widely, occasionally even going north into the forest tundra and south into the small insular birch groves of the forest steppe zone. In the taiga zone its search for food may sometimes lead it to concentrate in areas of extensive cropland, where the Murid population is higher than in the virgin taiga. Cases are known where the lynx has entered villages and even cities.

During the winter the lynx migrates from areas with deep and loose snow. In the Altai, according to G. D. Dul'keit (1953), "observation of two broods of lynxes, lasting for two winters, has shown that these lynxes stayed within an area of $20-30\,km$ along Lake Teletskoe. The denser the snow, the wider the hunting areas of the lynx became. When the ground is crusted over with frozen slush or with frozen snow, individual lynxes will migrate long distances. In February 1947 the itinerary of a lynx was traced overland above the timberline from the valley of Lake Teletskoe through the valley of Bolshoi Abakan ($36\,km$), and this was only a part of its path. The winter migrations of the lynx depend not only on the abundance of food but also on conditions of the snow cover. Deep or loose snow compels the lynx to temporarily occupy very narrow habitats, and in individual cases to suffer privation."

Lynx tracks are similar to those of the domestic cat, with the difference that in winter the soles of the lynx's paws are densely furred, so that the pads of the digits do not leave clear imprints. The tracks lie not in one line but somewhat to the side of the line of passage (Figure 167). The claws leave no marks. The prints of the hind paws completely coincide with those of the forepaws. No signs of "dragging" occur on the trails. The pace of the lynx is about $40\,cm$. The almost round footprints are about $8-12\,cm$ long and wide (Formozov, 1952).

The lynx usually moves at a regular pace, rarely by leaps. When moving, the lynx is always on the alert, its gait light and springy. A group of lynxes (usually a brood) travels in Indian file, the ones behind following exactly in the footsteps of those before. In case of danger, the lynx climbs trees on steep slopes. It easily swims rivers.

The voice of the lynx is rarely heard, except during the nuptial period. A. Cherkasov (1867) and N. I. Yablonskii (1904) described its voice as a loud purr and meowing which has a particularly shrill, though muted note at twilight. According to Cherkasov, the frantic cries of the lynx, particularly during oestrus, produce an uneasy feeling and strongly affect the hunter's nerves. "A man hearing these voices for the first time, particularly during the night and when the echo carries sounds in the lonely, limitless taiga, involuntarily shudders; his heart will beat more strongly and shivers will run through his body. I felt this myself on hearing these cries for the first time...."

The external senses of the lynx are very well developed except for the sense of smell, which is not sufficiently acute, as in numerous other cats. The lynx is a very alert animal. To find its bearings in its environment it primarily uses hearing and sight. The lynx has almost limitless patience. When hiding in ambush or in the crown of a tree, it may await the appearance of its prey for hours on end. It catches its prey in one or more leaps and tears it with claws and teeth. Cases are known in which a lynx has leaped from a tree onto passing deer, elk, or musk deer and then clung to its victim's back, inflicting fatal wounds. If it misses its prey, as happens occasionally, the lynx does not give up the hunt, but tenaciously follows its prey and at the appropriate moment ambushes it.

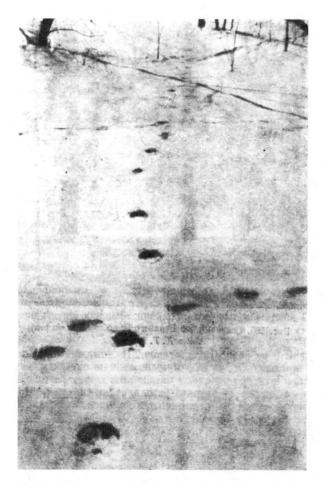

FIGURE 167. Lynx tracks. Tomsk Region. Photo by K. T. Yurlov

The lynx is a nocturnal animal. It sets out in search of prey at dusk and lies down to rest in its den at dawn; however, when hungry, it may also hunt during the day.

The lynx feeds on the flesh of various animals and birds. The staple food in most localities consists of blue hare, small rodents, and birds.

When there is a scarcity of fresh flesh, it may eat carrion. It attacks
roe deer, musk deer, reindeer, young elks and maral deer. In areas
where the hare population is low it lives chiefly on ungulates. In the
Altai, G.D.Dul'keit (1953) reported, the winter diet of the lynx consists
of the following (percentages of a total number of 56 observations made
along the animals' trails):

Maral deer	14.3%
Roe deer	58.9%
Musk deer	8.9%
Domestic sheep	3.5%
Blue hare	7.1%
Capercailzie	2.0%
Carrion	5.3%

A hunting brood often attacks maral deer, particularly in localities
with deep snow and at times when there is a frozen snow crust. Dul'keit
(1953) mentions the following case of lynxes hunting deer in the area of
Lake Teletskoe. "Two lynxes killed a young male maral in March on
Chiri Brook, and about two days later an adult female maral was killed
in the vicinity. On the upper reaches of the Koksha River, at a time
when snow depth was 90 cm, lynxes killed an adult male maral on the
solid frozen snow crust, and similar cases are not rare. The roe deer,
and more rarely the musk deer, are the staple winter diet of the lynxes
in our area... When fresh food is abundant, the lynx very rarely visits
remnants of alien food and carrion. When satiated, the lynx may leave
a large carcass partly uneaten or may disregard it completely."
P. B. Yurgenson (1938) mentions lynxes catching roe deer in the Altai
Reserve.
    The summer diet of the lynx is not so well known. Excrement collected
in summer by Dul'keit was found to contain remnants of small rodents —
Muridae, pikas, chipmunks, and various birds. Eight excrements
examined on the Altai in May—June by F. D. Shaposhnikov (1956) were found
to contain remains of adult musk deer and one fawn. Shaposhnikov saw
"tracks of a pair of lynxes hunting musk deer, one moving higher up on the
slope of the mountain and behind and the second lower down and in front.
The frightened prey had ended up between the two predators." The author
twice found musk deer killed by lynxes in the month of September.
Cherkasov (1867) observed lynx attacking roe deer and a fox in the
southwestern part of Transbaikalia.
    The mating period of the lynx in Siberia occurs from mid-February to
late March, though these dates can apparently differ in different
geographical areas and due to other factors. The lynx is a polygamous
animal and several males will pursue one female. Yablonskii (1904), who
observed the lynx on the Altai, communicates that 2 or 3 and occasionally
more males may court one female. "I chanced to see five and even six
males courting one female in the taiga. Fierce fights may occur among the
males for possession of the female..."
    Gestation time is 9—10 weeks, and the young are born in May—June.
The litter size is 2 or 3, more rarely 1, 4 or 5; the young are born blind

but grow and develop quite rapidly. The eyes open on the 8th—12th day. The mother nurses her young for 2—3 months. When the young have grown somewhat, they begin to hunt with their mother. The brood usually stays with the mother till the beginning of the next rut, when the old males chase the adult offspring away from the mother. The young cling together for a certain time after being left by the mother; then the brood gradually disbands. Sexual maturity sets in at the age of about 2 years. The life span is apparently 13—14 years (Krumbiegel, 1930).

The lynx population of a given area is not constant, instead undergoing marked fluctuations, probably associated with fluctuations in the populations of the animals which form its staple food supply. Thus, in periods when the blue hare population declines sharply a corresponding decrease is also observed in the lynx population — caused by its migration to another area. Cases are known in which young lynxes have died of starvation (Dul'keit, 1953). The lynx may suffer from coccidiosis and helminthiasis. The wolf and the glutton are its only serious food competitors. The competition of other carnivores and birds of prey is of much less significance for the lynx.

Molt occurs twice annually. In Siberia the spring molt takes place in April—May, and the autumn molt in November.

Practical importance. The lynx hurts commercial hunting and trapping by attacking such valuable game species as hares, ungulates, and birds. Its commercial value in the fur trade is small since the catch is low. The fur of the lynx has good commercial qualities and is used in the natural state and dyed, chiefly for collars and hats. Lynx pelts are graded according to size, season, color, and other features.

The fur standard divides lynx pelts into two strains: northern and Caucasian.

2. Subfamily PANTHERINAE. Leopards or panthers

1917. Pantherinae. Pocock, R. I. The Classification of Existing Felidae. — Ann. Mag. Nat. Hist. (8), 20, pp. 329—350.
1935. Pardinae. Ognev, S. I. Zveri SSSR i prilezhashchikh stran (Animals of the USSR and Adjacent Countries), 3, p. 235.

Description. * This subfamily includes the largest cats, from the snow leopard to the tiger and lion.

Hyomandibular suspension of hyoid bone incompletely ossified, its lower portion consisting of tendinous cord permitting greater mobility of larynx, which is not fused to base of skull.

Process of jugal bone falls far short of lacrymal foramen. Infraorbital foramen large, its diameter greater than that of upper external incisor (I^3).

Legs of moderate length and massive. Claws retractile. Hairs on upper part of neck for the most part not forming mane.

Geographical distribution. Most of Africa and Asia, plus South America from Columbia to Patagonia and Central America as far as Mazatlan and Sinaloa in Mexico.

* After R.I. Pocock (1917) and S.I. Ognev (1935).

Systematic notes. The subfamily contains five genera and subgenera, three of which occur in the USSR. The subfamily is represented in Siberia by the following: P a n t h e r a   t i g r i s L., P. p a r d u s L. and P. u n c i a Schreber.

19. Genus PANTHERA. Panthers (leopards)

31. **Panthera** (s.str.) **pardus** Linnaeus (1758).
Panther (leopard). Russian name — "Bars" (leopard) *
(Map XXIII)

1758. F e l i s   p a r d u s. Linnaeus, C. Systema Naturae, 1, 10 ed., p. 41.
1777. F e l i s   p a n t h e r a. Schreber, C. L. Säugethiere, 3, p. 384 (Algeria).
1794. F e l i s   f u s c a. Meyer. — Zool. Annalen for 1793, Vol. 1, p. 394 (Bengal).
1816. P a n t h e r a   v u l g a r i s. Oken. — Lehrb. Nat., 3, 2, p. 1058 (unavailable).
1832. F e l i s   p a l e a r i a. Cuvier. Hist. Nat. Mamm. pl. 121, text (Algeria).
1833. F e l i s n i m e r. Hemprich and Ehrenberg. — Symb. Phys. Mamm., 2, pl. 17 (Arabia).
1856. F e l i s   t u l l i a n a. Valenciennes, M. A. — Comt. Rendus Acad. Sci., 42, pp. 1035 — 1039. (Smyrna).
1857. F e l i s   o r i e n t a l i s. Schlegel, H. Handleiding tot de oefening der Dierkunde, 1, p. 23. pl. 2, fig. 13 (Korea).
1858. F e l i s   i r b i s. Schrenck, L. Reisen und Forschungen im Amur Lande, p. 96 (nec. Ehrenberg. 1930).
1862. L e o p a r d u s   j a p o n e n s i s. Gray, E. C. — Proc. Zool. Soc., p. 262, London (Japan).
1863. L e o p a r d u s   p e r n i g e r. Gray, J. E. Catal. Hodgson's Coll. Brit. Mus., 2, ed., p. 3 (Sikkim).
1867. L e o p a r d u s   c h i n e n s i s. Gray, E. J. — Proc. Zool. Soc., p. 264, London. (nec. F e l i s   c h i n e n s i s Gray. 1837) (mountains west of Peking).
1867. F e l i s   f o n t a n i e r i i. Milne-Edwards, A. — Ann. Sci. Nat. Zool., 8, p. 375(Peking district).
1868. P a n t h e r a   a n t i q u o r u m. Fitzinger, L. — Sitzungsberichte Akad. Wissensch., 58, p. 466, Wien (nec. Gray. 1827).
1878. F e l i s   l e o p a r d u s. Sclater, W. L. — Proc. Zool. Soc., London, London. p. 289, (nec Schreber. 1775, terra typica probably Iran).
1903. F e l i s   v i l l o s a. Bonhote, J. — Ann. Mag. Nat. Hist., 11, p. 475 (shore of Amur Bay).
1907. P a n t h e r a   h a n e n s i s. Matschie, P. — Wissenschaftl. Ergebn. Expd. Filchner in China, 10, p. 198 (Hingan-fu).

---

* The correct Russian name for this species is "bars." The term "leopard" is bookish and unnatural. The occasional attempts at introducing it into the Russian literature have no scientific basis and lead to an inadmissible confusion in nomenclature, to say nothing of cluttering up the language. The term "bars" is used by S. I. Ognev, K. A. Satunin, N. M. Przheval'skii and all the most competent Russian zoologists ([Russian] editor's note).

1951. Panthera pardus. Ellerman, J. R. and T. C. S. Morrison-Scott. Checklist of Palaearctic and Indian Mammals, pp. 316 — 317. London.

1956. Felis (Pardus) pardus. Novikov, G. A. Khishchnye mlekopitayushchie fauny SSSR (Carnivorous Mammals of the Fauna of the USSR), pp. 270—274, Moskva-Leningrad. figs. 185—186.

Type and type locality. The species was described for the first time from a specimen from Egypt.

Diagnosis. Overall color yellow or reddish brown. Spotted black pattern with sharply outlined and intensely colored spots, diameter of largest spots usually less than 5 cm. Tail covered with short hairs; tail much thinner than middle part of foreleg. Frontal area of skull weakly and gently convex, almost flat, or with very slight median depression. Nasals extend posteriorly somewhat beyond nasal processes of jawbones (Figure 168). Tympanic bullae relatively narrow, moderately inflated. Jugal process of temporal bone comes quite close to postorbital processes of jugular bone.

Measurements. Length of body with head: males 120 — 160 cm; length of tail: 75 — 110 cm; length of hind paw: 24 — 26 cm; height at shoulders: 50 — 78 cm. Weight up to 75 kg. Females smaller. Isolated large specimens encountered reaching lengths of 180 cm. G. Allen (1938) mentions a male obtained in Hopeh (China) with a body length of 208 cm and a tail 85 cm long.

Maximum skull length: males 193 — 256 mm, females 180 — 218 mm; condylobasal length: males 186 — 223 mm, females 176 — 188 mm; zygomatic width: males 123 — 172 mm, females 116 — 135 mm; interorbital width: males 38 — 50 mm, females 32 — 49 mm; postorbital width: males 38 — 50 mm, females 36 — 42 mm; mastoid width: males 84 — 95 mm, females 77 — 89 mm; height in area of tympanic bullae: males 75 — 81 mm, females 68 — 77 mm; width of rostrum above canines: males 53 — 65 mm, females 50 — 53 mm; length of upper tooth row: males 65 — 75 mm, females 60 — 68 mm.

Description. A large, slender and powerful cat with a long tail. Body long, muscular and agile, with relatively short legs. Head relatively small, with very convex forehead, posteriorly sloping parietal area and moderately blunted muzzle. Ears short and triangular, with rounded tips and without tufts. "Side whiskers" and mane not developed. Tail long, reaching about two thirds of length of body with head, and covered with relatively short hair; tail appreciably thinner than middle part of foreleg.

Pupil round. Fur short, rough, and dense. Length of hair on back about 25 mm. Color of fur highly variable, both individually and geographically. General background of winter fur varies dorsally from very dull light yellow to glossy yellowish-reddish brown with golden tinge, gradually becoming lighter on flanks and on lower limbs and eventually turning white on underparts. Spotted pattern with clearly delineated dense rosettelike black spots scattered all over body, legs, and tail. Diameter of largest spots usually less than 5 cm. Patches in some cases merge into bands on flanks and in posterior back. Spots on tail often form transverse rings.

Summer fur shorter and sparser than winter fur, with general color somewhat more intense. Young are more lightly colored, the background tone being grayish yellow and occasionally dirty white.

Skull (Figure 168) large, relatively long, moderately broad and low. Upper profile forms a gentle arch smoothly descending posteriorly, while in front profile is slightly convex. Frontal area slightly convex, almost flat or with very slight longitudinal depression. Sagittal crest highly developed, high, and extends forward to posterior corner of frontal area. Occipital crest large, pointing upwards and backwards; protrudes above occipital condyles. Rostrum moderately broad, its width above canines markedly (almost one third) greater than postorbital width of skull. Zygomatic arches massive and relatively narrow dorsally. Zygomatic process of squamosal comes close to postorbital (frontal) process of zygomatic bone. Antero-superior process of zygomatic bone falls far short of lacrymal foramen. Orbits ovally elongated. Lower anterior edge of orbit slightly thickened and roundly blunted above. Infraorbital foramina rather large and ovally rounded. Maximum axis of infraorbital foramen almost one-and-a-half times wider than septum separating it from orbit. Nasals very long and moderately broad, smoothly tapering posteriorly. Posterior ends of nasals extend for short distance beyond level of posterior parts of nasal processes of maxillaries. Hard palate elongated, its width 35—50% less than its length; extends back beyond end of molars by distance approximately equal to width of mesopterygoid fossa. Posterior part of hard palate (at edge of choanal incisure) has two longitudinal keels on either side. Choanal incisure with median projection. Presphenoid relatively narrow and long, with lateral appendages of pterygoid form slanting posteriorly. Tympanic bullae relatively narrow, thick-walled and moderately inflated; situated far behind jaw articulation, their anterior edges falling far short of posterior wall of glenoid fossa articulations (by a distance equal to more than one half the width of the mesopterygoid fossa). Anterior chambers (pars ectotympanica) of bullae inflated and not flattened as in tiger. Boundary between anterior and posterior auditory chambers (pars ecto- and endotympanica) inconspicuous and slightly bent inward; runs from stylo-mastoid foramen to anterior edge of foramen of eustachian tubes. Distance between tympanic bullae markedly (by $\frac{1}{3}-\frac{1}{5}$) greater than width of mesopterygoid fossa. Width of external auditory meatus $\frac{1}{2}-\frac{2}{3}$ size of alveolus of upper canine. Paroccipital processes massive, not rising higher than level of tympanic bullae. Jugular foramina rather large and markedly ovally elongated. Coronoid process tapers slightly.

Canines relatively thin, but very high and sharp; height of upper canine about two thirds of length of upper tooth row (premolars + molar). First upper premolar (Pm^1) oval in cross section. Second upper premolar (Pm^2) extended posteriorly; maximal width of tooth not greater (usually less) than one half its length. Anterior third cusp developed to various degrees. Upper carnassial tooth (Pm^3) lacks additional fifth cusp on anterior outer corner; posterior cusp of posterior lobe smaller than anterior one. Upper molar (M^1) small, elongated, somewhat longer than first premolar (Pm^1). First lower premolar (Pm_1) broadened posteriorly. Second lower premolar (Pm_2) markedly broadened posteriorly; longitudinal axis of crown equal to or slightly shorter than that of lower carnassial tooth. Lower carnassial tooth (M_1) two-cusped, with protoconid and paraconid of almost equal size; rudiment of talonid present only on posterior edge of crown.

464

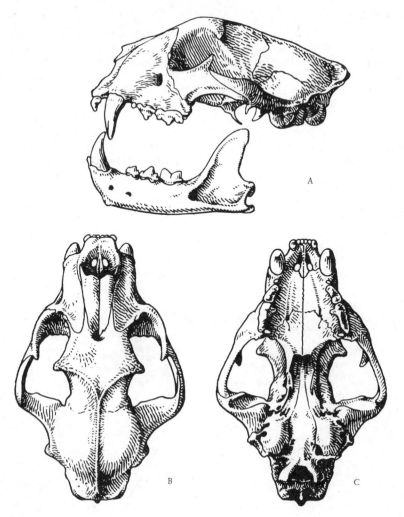

FIGURE 168. Skull of panther (leopard), P a n t h e r a p a r d u s (original):

A — lateral view; B — dorsal view; C — ventral view.

Systematic notes. This animal displays notably wide intraspecific
systematic differentiation, expressed in the isolation of numerous
subspecies differing in fur color, dimensions of body and skull, and
details of cranial structure. Ellerman and Morrison-Scott (1951) include
14 subspecies of the animal in their list. The systematic relationships
among these, the diagnostics, and the geographical distribution are as
yet not sufficiently elucidated.

Geographical distribution. Occupies a very wide range, including
Africa and South Asia northwards to the Caucasus, the Amur area and
Japan, inclusive.

In the Soviet Union it ranges over the Caucasus, the southern parts of Turkmenia, the mountains of southwest Tadzhikistan (the Gissar Range), and the Amur River area, where it extends north to about 50° N lat. (Map XXIII). The following reports are available on the distribution of the animal in the Soviet Far East.

According to Maak (1861), it inhabits the entire valley of the Ussuri River, from mouth to upper reaches, extending further south to the area near its sources. It is encountered in the area of Lake Khanka. Radde (1862) gave the northern limit of its distribution as the Bureya Range, and Middendorf (1867) as the Tyrma River, while N. A. Baikov (1927) gave the valley of the Kumara [Huma Ho] River (about 52° N lat.). According to Przheval'skii (1870), it inhabits the entire Ussuri Territory but is encountered there much more rarely than the tiger, being most often seen in the southern parts of the Maritime Territory. Noack (1891) reported the animal from Korea to Sidemi and Suifun. According to M. I. Yankovskii (1882) it is encountered as often as the tiger in the area of the frontier village of Tizenkhe. According to observations made by V. K. Arsen'ev (1926), it occurs in the Suifun, Poset and Barabash areas of the Maritime Territory.

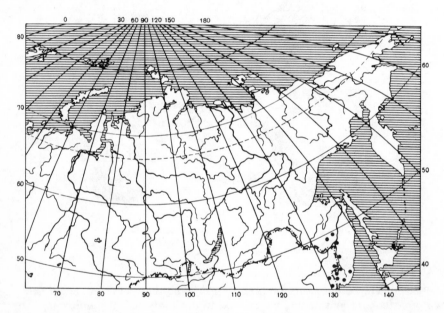

MAP XXIII. Geographical distribution of the panther (leopard) Panthera pardus L. in Siberia

The animal was collected on Cape Gamov, near Vladivostok, by S. N. Konrad in 1923 and by A. A. Bogoyavlenskii in 1927, and has been bagged on the shore of Astaf'ev Bay by A. Baturin (coll. S. I. Ognev). G. F. Bromlei (1951) mentioned the animal as being present in the Sudzukhe Reserve, and himself collected it in the Suputinka Reserve (coll. S. U. Stroganov). Ognev (1935) mentioned the animal from the area of Olga Bay and from Sidemi (Pos'yet Bay). F. D. Pleske once had a skull specimen obtained in 1882 in the vicinity of Konstantinovskii, near the village of Poltavka. N. Smirnov obtained the animal's skull near Pogranichnaya Station (coll. Zool. Inst. Acad. Sciences USSR).

It is known (though rarely) to penetrate far north of its usual range. Thus, according to observations of N. A. Baikov (1927), it occasionally reaches southern Transbaikalia.

It was reported for Sakhalin as far back as 1858 by L. I. Schrenck, and later by A. M. Nikol'skii (1889), but this has not been confirmed by further studies (P. I. Suprunenko, 1890, and other authors).

Survey of subspecies. As mentioned above, taxonomists distinguish 14 subspecies of the animal, including 3 occurring in the Soviet Union. One subspecies occurs in Siberia.

31a. **Panthera** (s.str.) **pardus orientalis** Schlegel (1857).
Amur or Korean (East Siberian) leopard

1857. Felis orientalis. Schlegel, H. Handleiding tot de oefening der Dierkunde, 1, p. 23, pl. 2, fig. 13.

1858. Felis irbis. Schrenck, L. Reisen und Forschungen im Amur Lande, p. 96, St. Petersburg. (nec Ehrenberg. 1830); Maak, R. Puteshestvie na Amur (Voyage to the Amur). Sankt-Peterburg. 1859; Auct. cit. Puteshestvie po doline reki Ussuri (Voyage through the Valley of the Ussuri River). Vol. 1, Sankt-Peterburg. 1861; Radde, G. Reisen im Süden von Ost-Sibirien, p. 104, St. Petersburg. 1862.

1903. Felis villosa. Bonhote, J. — Ann. Mag. Nat. Hist. 11, p. 475 (Shore of Amur Bay).

1914. Leopardus pardus orientalis. Satunin, K. A. Opredelitel' mlekopitayushchikh Rossiiskoi imperii (Key to Mammals of the Russian Empire), p. 160, Tiflis.

1935. Pardus pardus orientalis. Ognev, S. I. Zveri SSSR i prilezhashchikh stran (Animals of the USSR and Adjacent Countries), 3, pp. 244—250. figs. 111—113, tabl. 5.

Type and type locality. The first description of the subspecies was made from a specimen from Korea.

Diagnosis. Characterized by rather soft and long fur (30 — 50 mm on back and 70 mm on underparts), relatively vivid color, and some craniological features. Background of winter fur glossy, varying from light cream to more saturated yellowish-reddish brown with golden tones; color becomes lighter on flanks and outer side of legs, white on belly and inner side of legs. Spotty pattern more dense than in Caucasian leopard and consists of deep black spots. Summer fur with more saturated colors. Skull markedly compressed interorbitally; ratio between interorbital width and condylobasal length of skull averages 19.5%, as against 22.6% in Caucasian leopard.

Measurements (from 6 male specimens). Length of body with head: 107—136 cm (av. 125 cm); tail: 82—90 cm (av. 86 cm); length of hind paw: 24—27 cm (av. 25 cm); height at shoulders: 64—78 cm (av. 72 cm). Weight 32—40 kg.

Maximum length of skull: 204.0—232.0 mm (av. 213 mm); condylobasal length: 186.0—200.0 mm (av. 189.0 mm); zygomatic width: 129.0—144.0 mm (av. 138.0 mm); interorbital width: 34.3—39.9 mm (av. 37.8 mm); postorbital width: 36.8—45.0 mm (av. 40.2 mm); mastoid width: 86.8—95.0 mm (av. 89.5 mm); height of skull in area of tympanic bullae: 76.8—81.5 mm (av. 79.4 mm); length of upper tooth row: 67.8—68.7 mm (av. 68.0 mm).

Systematic notes. The Amur or Korea (East Siberian) leopard is a well-consolidated subspecies characterized by consistent morphological features such as fur quality and cranial structure. According to these features, the subspecies is nearest to the Chinese Panthera pardus chinensis Gray, 1867 (= fontanierii Milne-Edwards, 1867), described from material from the mountain forests west of Peking. Judging by features of specimens from Eastern Tibet and Kansu kept in the Zoological Institute of the Academy of Sciences of the USSR (the leopard of these areas is identified by G. Allen (1938) with the Peking form), the Chinese leopard is characterized by a greater vividness of general background color, with a more intensely black spotty pattern. There are apparently no craniological differences from the Amur leopard.

The Caucasian leopard, in comparison with the Amur form, is of a dull and pale color; the spotted black pattern has a brownish tinge and a generally plain appearance. Its fur, even in winter, consists of short, rough hairs.

Geographical distribution. See description of geographical distribution of the species. How far to the southwest the range of this form extends is as yet unknown. The subspecies occurs in northeastern China.

Material examined. Caucasus — 10 skulls and pelts; Soviet Central Asia — 2 skulls and 16 pelts; Maritime Territory and Amur Region — 12 skulls and 6 pelts; China — 4 skulls and 5 pelts. Total — 28 skulls and 32 pelts.

Biology. Occupies various biotopes, chiefly mountains. In the Far East it inhabits hilly wooded areas, but somewhat more to the south, in Manchuria, it penetrates true mountains.

The den is located in the most secluded thickets of the forest, in inaccessible sections cluttered up with fallen timber, in shrub thickets, in woods on steep ravines, etc.

The leopard chiefly eats large ungulates, but does not disdain smaller prey — rodents, birds, and other animals. Occasionally it may also attack wolves and foxes, as well as livestock and domestic dogs. It captures large animals by stealing up on them or by waiting in ambush.

The annual life cycle of the leopard except for the reproduction period is to a large extent associated with changes in its feeding conditions. It leads an essentially nomadic life, following herds of ungulates, in summer following them high into the mountains and in winter descending to the lower zones, into the foothills.

In the Far East rut occurs in January—February. Gestation lasts for about three months. The young are born in April and May and the litter size is 2—5, usually 2 or 3. The eyes open at the age of ten days. The brood stays with the mother till late autumn or winter.

The leopard is mainly nocturnal, being most often encountered at dawn or twilight, only rarely during the day. The external senses are well developed. It climbs trees and cliffs well and can make enormous leaps when necessity arises. The animal is characterized by rapidity, agility and daring of movement, and in this respect can be recognized as one of the most perfect of cats. It can overtake roe deer and musk deer within a short distance. The animal's voice is a loud growl. Molt occurs twice a year — in the spring and autumn. The times and succession of the molt on the different parts of the body have not been traced in nature.

Practical importance. Occupies a rather insignificant place in the fur trade since it is obtained only occasionally and accidentally, and always in small number. The pelts are used for carpets and more rarely to make cloth. The pelts are not standardized according to varieties but are sorted according to size and fur quality. Young leopards are occasionally caught alive and kept in zoological gardens and parks.

The harm inflicted to the hunting trade is insignificant due to the leopard's low numbers. It can, however, hinder the breeding of deer for "pantys" [non-ossified deer antlers] when deer are kept in large enclosures.

It attacks humans only in extreme cases of self-defense when wounded.

32. **Panthera uncia uncia** Schreber (1776). Snow leopard or ounce (Figure 169, Map XXIV)

1776. Felis uncia. Schreber, C. L. Säugethiere, 3, tabl. 100, 1776; text, p. 386. 1777.

1811. Felis pardus. Pallas, P. S. Zoographia Rosso-Asiatica, 1, pp. 17—18 (nec Linnaeus. 1758).

1830. Felis irbis. Ehrenberg, C. G. Observations et nouvelles sur le Tigre du nord et la Panthère du nord, recueillies dans le voyage de Sibèrie fait par M. A. de Humboldt.— Ann. des Sc. Nat., pp. 394—413. Paris (Altai); Simashko, Yu. Russkaya fauna (Russian Fauna). p. 568, Sankt-Peterburg. 1851. tabl. XIX A, fig. 2.

1855. Felis uncioides. Horsfield.— Ann. Mag. Nat. Hist. Ser. 2, Vol. 16, p. 105 (Nepal).

1858. Uncia irbis. Severtzow, N. Notice sur la classification multisèriale des Carnivores.— Revue et Mag. de Zool., 10, p. 386.

1894. Felis irbis. Greve, C. Die geographische Verbreitung der Raubthiere, pp. 70 —72, Halle.

1914. Leopardus unica. Satunin, K. A. Opredelitel' mleko-pitayushchikh Rossiiskoi imperii (Key to Mammals of the Russian Empire). pp. 161—162. Tiflis.

1935. Uncia uncia. Ognev, S. I. Zveri SSSR i prilezhashchikh stran (Animals of the USSR and Adjacent Countries). Vol. 3, pp. 263—270, Moskva-Leningrad. figs. 115 —120, tabl. 6.

1951. Panthera uncia. Ellerman, J. R. and T. C. S. Morrison-Scott. Checklist of Palaearctic and Indian Mammals, p. 320, London; Bannikov, A. G. Mlekopitayushchie Mongol'skoi Narodnoi Respubliki (Mammals of the Mongolian People's Republic). pp. 136—138, Moskva. 1954.

1956. Felis (uncia) uncia. Novikov, G. A. Khishchnye mleko-pitayushchie fauny SSSR (Carnivorous Mammals of the Fauna of the USSR). pp. 274—277, Moskva-Leningrad. figs. 187—189.

Type and type locality. Buffon (1761) was the first to mention and provide a drawing of the animal under the name "once," adding that the "once" lives in Persia and is trained for hunting. Its first binominal name, Felis uncia, it received from Schreber [Die Säugethiere, III, Plate 100 (1777)]. Schreber based himself on Buffon's data, which had described a specimen of the animal from Persia (today Iran). That country should therefore be taken as terra typica. There is no need for greater accuracy about the type locality at present.

Diagnosis. General background color of fur is grayish to brown-gray, without tinges of yellow or russet. Spotty pattern pale, spots diffuse. Diameter of largest spots over 5 cm. Tail covered with long hair, and is almost as thick as middle part of foreleg. Frontal area of skull markedly convex, with appreciable median depression. Nasal bones do not extend posteriorly beyond nasal processes of jaw bones (Figure 158). Tympanic bullae flatter and broader than those of leopard. Jugal process of the temporal bone falls far short of postorbital process of jugal bone.

Measurements. Length of body with head: 107—130 cm; length of tail: 90—96 cm; height at shoulders about 60 cm. Weight 25—40 kg.

Male skull dimensions: maximum length: 180—190 mm; condylobasal length: 165—173 mm; zygomatic width: 122—134 mm; interorbital width: 43—47 mm; postorbital width: 50—52 mm; mastoid width: 79—84 mm; height in area of tympanic bullae: 71—76 mm; width of rostrum above canines: 48—53 mm; length of upper tooth row: 58—63 mm.

Diagnosis. Resembles leopard in general appearance, but is more stocky and long-tailed; is readily recognized by extremely long fur with indistinct pattern in form of large dark patches and rosettes. Head relatively small, frontally rounder than in leopard, with short, bluntly rounded ears lacking distal tufts. Mane not developed and cheeks not full (no "side whiskers"). Tail long — longer than $3/4$ length of body — and covered with long hair, thus seeming very thick; thickness almost equal to that of foreleg (Figure 169).

The pupil is round.

Fur rather long, dense and soft; length of hair on back 55 mm. General background color smoky grayish, with light yellowish tinge. Flanks become ligher below and show more developed yellowness. Belly whitish. Spotty pattern consists of large, diffuse, indistinctly outlined ringlike dark gray or blackish spots, some compact small spots being scattered among them. Diameter of large spots over 5 cm. Head bears only the smaller, compact spots. Proximal third of tail bears less vividly-colored rosettes than do rest of distal parts, where large, distinctly outlined black spots are present in form of rings (not always marked). In hind part of back the spots occasionally concentrate into three longitudinal dark stripes.

With age the spotty pattern becomes even more diffuse and unclear.

Spotty pattern more conspicuous in young individuals, in which color of spots is more intense than in adults.

FIGURE 169. The snow leopard (ounce), P a n t h e r a   u n c i a Schreb. After specimen in the Zoological Museum of Moscow State University. Painted by V. A. Vatagin

Skull (Figure 170) is somewhat smaller than that of leopard, being markedly shorter and greatly broadened in cranial section. This is expressed in the fact that postorbital width is 30% of condylobasal length, and mastoid width 48%; in leopard respective indexes are 21% and 44%. Upper profile of skull strongly convex, descending rather steeply back in area of postorbital processes and appreciably concave in anterior part, forming saddle in area of tips of nasals. Frontal area markedly elevated and bears rather deep median depression. Skull crests, both sagittal and occipital, conspicuous. Rostrum broad, its width above canine approximately equal to postorbital width of skull. Zygomatic arches very massive and widely parted. Zygomatic process of temporal bone does not reach frontal process of zygomatic bone. Antero-superior process of jugal bone not reaching lacrymal foramen. Orbits slightly elongated and oval. Lower anterior margin of orbit not thickened at all. Infraorbital foramina ovally elongated. Maximum diameter of infraorbital foramen almost equal to or slightly larger than distance between foramen and orbit. Nasal bones short and broad, evenly tapering posteriorly. Posterior ends of nasals do not extend back beyond line joining posterior ends of nasal processes of maxillaries (Figure 170). Hard palate short, width being 80% of its length, and extends beyond end of molars by a distance markedly less than width of mesopterygoid fossa. Choanal incisure has two conspicuous median protrusions. Presphenoid bone broad and short, with large pterygoid appendages on either side. Tympanic bullae relatively broad, thick-walled, and flat, and lie near jaw articulation; anterior margins fall short of glenoid fossa (fossa glenoidea — articularis) by distance approximately equal to one half width of mesopterygoid fossa. Boundary between anterior and posterior auditory chambers greater than in leopard and sloped forward, beginning internally at stylomastoid foramen and terminating some distance internally from margin of eustachian tube foramen. Distance between bullae approximately equal to width of mesopterygoid fossa. Width of external auditory meatus about two thirds of upper canine alveolus. Paroccipital processes protrude conspicuously above surface of bullae, and have their tips pointed and hooked forward. Jugular foramina relatively small and round. Coronoid process narrower than in leopard.

Canines large, high and sharp; cusp of upper canine approximately one third shorter than length of upper tooth row (premolars + molar). First upper premolar (Pm^1) is in cross section an approximately equilateral triangle, the inner rear angle being rounder. Second upper premolar (Pm^2) short and broad, not broadened posteriorly, maximum width of its crown being greater than one half its length; anterior third cusp rudimentary. Upper carnassial tooth (Pm^3) lacks additional fifth cusp on anterior external corner; two halves of posterior lobes almost equal in size and height. Upper molar (M^1) small, low, and rather broad, being smaller and shorter than first premolar (Pm^1). First lower premolar (Pm_1) not broadened posteriorly. Second lower premolar (Pm_2) barely broadened posteriorly, with longitudinal axis of its crown appreciably shorter than that of lower carnassial tooth. Lower carnassial tooth (M_1) tricuspidate, posterior margin of crown bearing additional cusp in form of small denticle (talonid); protoconid appreciably larger than paraconid.

Systematic notes. The snow leopard, or ounce, is a distinctly differentiated species. Though systematically close to the leopard, the two species are nevertheless distinctly different in their aggregate of characteristic structural traits, particularly in cardinal points of cranial structure. In contrast to the leopard, the snow leopard displays less variation and is thus more consolidated in this respect.

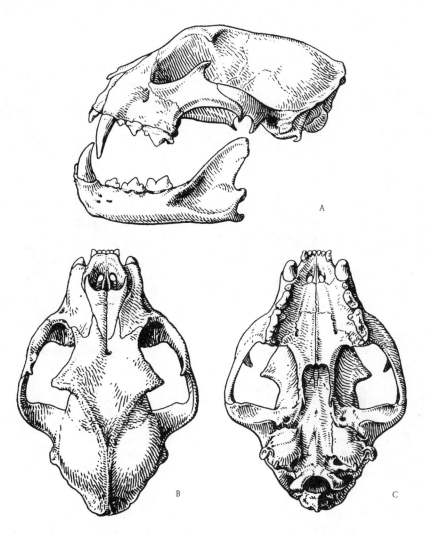

FIGURE 170. Skull of the snow leopard (ounce), Panthera uncia Schreb (original):

A — lateral view; B — dorsal view; C — ventral view.

Geographical distribution. Himalayas, Tibet, Szechwan, Kansu and Mongolia, and in the Soviet Union the mountains of Central Asia, of Kazakhstan, and of the southern periphery of Siberia.

In Siberia it occurs, though rarely, on the Altai and Sayans and in Tuvinia (Map XXIV). Data on its distribution here are extremely scanty. According to F. G. Gebler (1837) and A. M. Nikol'skii (1884) it is encountered in Dzhasater and Chuya. N. F. Kashchenko (1899, 1900) encountered the animal in the central Altai, namely on the upper reaches of the Argut and in the valley of the Proezdnaya River, a tributary of the Belaya Berel' (upper reaches of the Bukhtarma).

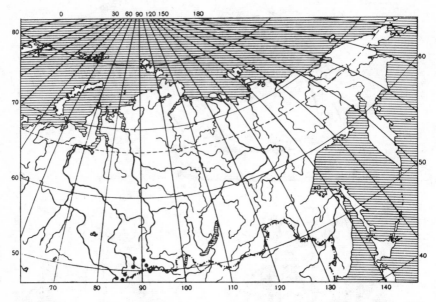

MAP XXIV. Geographical distribution of the snow leopard, P a n t h e r a   u n c i a Schreber, in Siberia

On the Argut it has been taken near the mouth of the Shavla River (Razorenova, 1939). According to A. Gorchakovskii (1912) "it lives in narrow valleys of the Chuya, Kara-Su, Sarkabu, Karai and Koron-gol." V. I. Vereshchagin (1908) reported its having been obtained in the Chuya Alps. In the mountain ranges surrounding the Chuya Steppe, according to A. M. Kolosov (1939), the snow leopard is permanently resident, and several specimens of the animal are obtained yearly. "Most often local hunters hunt the animal in the Kuikh-tanar, Il'dugem and Ayuty areas and, in addition, it is often obtained on the Kara-Alakha River. According to A. I. Mal'tsev, director of the fur trade establishment at Kosh-Agach, the animal is also encountered on the Bor-Burgazy and Bekemor rivers (beyond the Barguzin) and in the "belki" [snow-covered peak] mountains of the Mukhor-Tarkhatty area." K. T. Yurlov saw snow-leopard tracks in October 1959 in the mountains at the source of the Sarbertek River (a left tributary of the Ak-Alakha River some 40 km from its mouth), and has also reported that a snow leopard was obtained in 1957 near Kyzyl-Many in the Chuya Steppe.

The snow leopard was reported for the southern Altai by N. I. Yablonskii (1902) as being very rare. According to V. Selevin (1929), it occurs

more often on the upper reaches of the Bukhtarma and further east. In
1922—1927, local hunters encountered snow leopards or their tracks on
the upper Berel' and Archaty rivers, at the mouth of the Foma River, in
the Tarbagatai Range of the southern Altai, and near the village Archaty
on the Pronikha River. Tracks were also reported from Srednyaya
Bukhtarma and from near the village of Zyryanovsk. Kolosov (loc. cit.),
quoting V. V. Dmitriev, reported that the snow leopard "is encountered in
the upper Bashkaus and its tributaries (Kumurlu and Kalbakai)," Dmitrov
"in 1931 having seen a pelt at Ulagan which had been obtained in this area.
It undoubtedly occurs on rock streams lower down the course of the
Bashkaus, some 40 km from Ulagan."

The following data are available on the snow leopard's penetrations of
the former Altai reserve. Smirnov reports an entry into the southern
Lake Teletskoe area, in the valley of the Kyga River (Kolosov, 1939);
P. B. Yurgenson (1938), quoting observers in the Altai reserve, reported
repeated entries for many years in succession in the area of the Taulok
and Yuk-Pash mountains (on maps: Iik-Bazhi), which lies between the
Kyga River, the bay of the same name on Lake Teletskoe, and the Kairu
and Chulyshman rivers. Snow-leopard trails were traced at various times
along the upper Kyga River, extending from the upper Chul'cha over to
Mt. Taulok. The animal is also found on the upper Bashkaus River and
probably on Mt. Altyn-Tu.

According to G. E. Grum-Grzhimailo (1914), the snow leopard is
considered a rare species in the alpine zones of the Altai and the Sayans.
According to Radde, it occurs in the area of Lake Baikal and in the basin
of the Upper Yenisei.

In the Tuva Republic it was reported by A. Ya. Tugarinov (1916) from
the upper Kemchik River. I. N. Shukhov (1925) thought that it must be very
rare in Tuvinia. At a fur post Yanushevich (1952) saw three pelts which
had been taken by hunters in the Mongun-Taiga.

Survey of subspecies. Two subspecies differing in fur color
have been described. The nominate subspecies ranges in Siberia.

32a. **Panthera (Uncia) uncia uncia** Schreber (1776).
Snow leopard or ounce

The synonymy, the source of the first description, and the terra typica
are given above in the description of the species.

Diagnosis. Distinguished from Central Asian ounce by relatively
saturated general color of fur and more developed spotty pattern.

Measurements. See above in description of the species.

Systematic notes. The intraspecific taxonomic differentiation of the
snow leopard still remains almost completely unstudied, since museums
lack collections from numerous places in the animal's range. Central
Asia has been particularly poorly studied, with only a few specimens being
available from this area.

Only one subspecies other than the nominate has been described —
P. uncia unicoides Hogdson (1855), whose terra typica is Nepal.
The taxonomic significance of this description is difficult to judge at
present.

Ellerman and Morrison-Scott (1951) considered the snow leopard a monotypic species. However, judging by material available at the Zoological Institute of the Academy of Sciences of the USSR (originating from Tibet and the neighboring mountainous regions of Szechwan and Kansu, and collected by Przheval'skii and his associates), the animal is subject to geographic variation, in color at any rate. Central Asian specimens are marked by general lightening of the fur and also by reduction of the spotty pattern. They are clearly spotted in the fronto-parietal area, on the withers, limbs, and distal part of the tail, but the rest of the body is strewn with indistinct diffuse spots.

The Central (non-Soviet) Asian snow leopard is undoubtedly an isolated subspecies. Its relationship with the Nepal form remains unclear, since no material for comparison is available, so I shall refrain from attaching nomenclature.

Geographical distribution. Iran, Central Asia, Kazakhstan, Altai, Sayans, Tuva, Mongolia and mountains of northeast China.

Material studied. Siberia — 1 skull and 7 pelts; Soviet Central Asia — 2 skulls and 14 pelts; Central Asia — 2 skulls and 3 pelts. Total — 5 skulls and 24 pelts.

Biology. The ounce, or snow leopard, is a characteristic member of the fauna of high rocky mountains. Its habitat embraces biotopes lying within the zone between 1,500 and 4,000 m above sea level, where it keeps to alpine meadows and treeless rocks and can often be encountered in the nival zone. In a number of areas, however, the ounce always stays lower down, i. e., in the tree and scrub zone. Thus, on the Dzhungarian Ala-Tau it may be locally encountered at altitudes of 600—700 m, and on the Talass Ala-Tau at 1,200 m.

In winter, when the snow carpet is deep, the ounce moves down from the high mountains with their severe conditions into the area of the coniferous forest. These seasonal migrations, judging by observations in Central Asia, are rather regular and are probably caused by the seasonal migrations of the goats and sheep which are the stable winter food of the ounce. In famine years the ounce will search for prey near settlements and may occasionally attack domestic livestock. The den is constructed in caves and rock fissures. According to observations by E. P. Spangenberg and A. M. Sudilovskaya (1954), ounces in the Kirghiz Ala-Tau rest during the day in nests built by black vultures in thick but low juniper trees. Copious remnants of molting fur in the nests point to the fact that ounces pass a considerable part of their time there.

The diet of the ounce consists both of large animals (goats, sheep and deer) and smaller animals (various rodents and even birds, particularly snow cocks, etc.). Occasionally it attacks livestock grazing on mountain pastures. The prey is ambushed.

Data on reproduction are scanty. Rut occurs in late winter or in early spring. The gestation time is about three months. The litter size is usually 2 or 3, more rarely 4 or 5. The young are born in April—May. By the middle of summer the kittens accompany their mother on her hunting trips. The litter apparently stays together throughout the winter. The ounce is active not only at twilight and at night but occasionally even during the day. Like other cats, the ounce is agile and moves quickly and with great strength. It has a very cautious nature and can hide in any locality.

Practical importance. Obtained in insignificant quantities. The world ounce catch is no more than 1,000 per year. The pelts are not classified into categories and are used chiefly to produce carpets. The animal is captured for zoological gardens and parks.

Due to the low numbers of the animal and its association with localities with a low human population, harm to hunting and to livestock breeding is insignificant. The animal is dangerous to man only when wounded.

33. Panthera (Tigris) tigris Linnaeus (1758). Tiger

1758. Felis tigris. Linnaeus, C. Systema Naturae, 1, 10 ed., p. 41 (Bengal); Pallas, P. S. Zoographia Rosso-Asiatica, 1, pp. 15 — 17. 1811 — 1831.

1815. Felis virgata. Illiger. Uebersicht der Säugethiere nach ihrer Verbreitung über die Weltth. — Abh. Königl. Akad. Wissensch., p. 98, Berlin (Mazandaran, North Iran).

1842. Felis mongolica. Lesson, R. P. Tabl. Regn. Anim., p. 5010, (nomen nudum).

1858. Tigris striatus. Severtzov, N. Notice sur la classification multiseriale des Carnivores. — Revue et Mag. de Zool., 10, p. 386.

1867. Tigris regalis. Gray, J. — Proc. Zool. Soc., London, p. 263 (nomen novum pro tigris Linnaeus, 1758).

1868. Felis longipilis. Fitzinger, L. Sitzungsber. Kaiser. Akad. Wissensch. Wien, 58, p. 455 (Central Asia).

1905. Tigris septentrionalis. Satunin, K. A. Mlekopitayushchie Talysha i Mugani (Mammals of Talysh and Mugan). — Izvestiya Kavkazskogo Muzeya, 2, pp. 145 — 152, Tiflis (Talysh, Transcaucasia); Auct. cit. Opredelitel' mlekopitayushchikh Rossiiskoi imperii (Key to Mammals of the Russian Empire). pp. 156 — 157, Tiflis. 1914.

1907. Tigris amurensis. Satunin, K. Der Amur-Tiger. Neue Baltische Waldmannsblätter, No. 4, p. 73 (ex Dode. — Proc. Zool. Soc. London, p. 480, 1874).

1915. Tigris mikadoi. Satunin, K. A. Koreiskii tigr (Korean Tiger).—Nasha Okhota, No. 7, pp. 17 — 18 (nomen novum pro Tigris amurensis Satunin, 1907; nec Dode, 1874).

1951. Panthera tigris. Ellerman, J. R. and T. C. S. Morrison-Scott. Checklist of Palaearctic and Indian Mammals, pp. 318 — 319, London.

1956. Felis (Tigris) tigris. Novikov, G. A. Khishchnye mlekopitayushchie fauny SSSR (Carnivorous Mammals of the Fauna of the USSR). pp. 266 — 270, Moskva-Leningrad. figs. 182 — 184.

Type and type locality. The species was described for the first time from a specimen from Bengal.

Diagnosis. Dimensions extremely large: length of body no less than 150 cm, condylobasal length of skull 25 cm. Color of fur rufous fawn

FIGURE 171. Tiger, Panther tigris L. After specimen in the Moscow zoo. Painted by V. A. Vatagin

with black transverse belts. Hairs on cheeks long and form "side whiskers." Frontal ends of nasals extend posteriorly appreciably further than posterior margins of maxillaries (Figure 158). Tympanic bullae moderately and evenly convex, their anterior edge flat. Paroccipital processes higher than level of bullae, have flat tip, and are anteriorly hamate. Zygomatic process of squamosal externally reaches base of postorbital (frontal) process of zygomatic bone.

Measurements. Length of body with head: males 162—300 cm, females 160—270 cm; length of tail: males 85—110 cm, females 76—88 cm; length of hind paw: males 34—36 cm, females 32—35 cm; height of ear: males 9.5—10.8 cm, females 9.0 — 10.0 cm. Weight (after Baikov, 1925): males up to 320 kg, females up to 180 kg; V. P. Sysoev (1952) reported a male weighing 384 kg.

Maximum length of skull: males 304—362 mm,* females 197—300 mm; condylobasal length: males 274—324 mm, females 256—276 mm; zygomatic width: males 210—285 mm, females 190—215 mm; mastoid width: males 122—142 mm, females 103—122 mm; interorbital width: males 60—72 mm, females 56—62 mm; postorbital width: males 60—68 mm, females 56—66 mm; height of skull in area of tympanic bullae: males 106—122 mm, females 92—114 mm; length of upper tooth row: males 93—113 mm, females 72—98 mm.

Description. A very large and powerful cat of low, slender build. Body long and muscular, but agile. Head rounded, with somewhat convex forehead, with short, distally twisted ears lacking tufts on end, and with luxuriant "side whiskers," particularly in males. Legs of moderate length and bear broad paws armed with enormous, sharp, semilunar curved claws. Tail of moderate length, about one half length of body with head (Figure 171).

Pupil of eye round.

Fur dense, relatively short. Background of fur rufous fawn with conspicuous pattern of numerous black transverse stripes. Underparts white. Tail streaked with black rings. Background color varies from dull and pale yellowish ocher to vivid ocher-reddish rufous or orange. Striped pattern varies from intense dark brown to black-brown or black.

Summer fur characterized by even shorter and coarser hair and greater saturation of general color.

Skull (Figure 172) very large and massive, with widely parted zygomata, short and thick rostrum, narrow and relatively low braincase. Upper profile forms slightly convex arch descending back rather gently and but little lowered in facial region, with only barely visible saddle before nasal aperture. Frontal area with conspicuous longitudinal depression, particularly marked in old males. Sagittal and occipital crests conspicuous, posteriorly overhanging foramen magnum. Postorbital processes relatively short and broad. Zygomatic process of squamosal externally reaches base of frontal process of zygomatic zone. Antero-superior process of zygomatic bone falls short of lacrymal foramen. Orbits ovally elongated. Lower anterior edge of orbit slightly thickened and bluntly rounded above. Infra-orbital foramina of moderate size (one half or one third that of alveolus of upper canine) and ovally elongated vertically. Maximum diameter of

---

* N. A. Baikov (1925) reported a skull measuring 400 mm, but this is an extraordinarily aberrant specimen.

foramen markedly exceeds (by $\frac{1}{6}$ to $\frac{1}{2}$) width of septum separating it from orbit. Nasals moderately broad and long. Frontal ends of nasals extend posteriorly far beyond posterior edges of maxillaries. Hard palate elongated (its width being $35-50\%$ shorter than its length) and extends beyond posterior end of molars by distance greater than width of mesopterygoid fossa. Longitudinal keel present on either side of posterior part of hard palate near the choanal incisure. Presphenoid bone broad with lateral pterygoid appendages. Tympanic bullae small, thick-walled, and of elongated elliptical form, moderately and evenly convex; their anterior margins before eustachian tube foramen are highly flattened; they lie behind the jaw articulation, their anterior margins falling far short of posterior wall of glenoid fossa (by at least one half width of mesopterygoid fossa). Boundary between anterior and posterior auditory chambers extends from stylomastoid foramen, slanting arcuately inwards externally to eustachian tube foramen. Minimum distance between bullae approximately equal to width of mesopterygoid fossa. Width of external auditory meatus barely one third that of alveolus of upper canine. Paroccipital processes massive and project above level of tympanic bullae; tips are flat and anteriorly hamate. Jugular foramina large and round. Coronoid processes gently tapered.

Canines extremely large, height of upper canine reaching 65 mm. First upper premolar (Pm^1) broad and roundedly triangular in cross section; sometimes this tooth shows only as a minute rudiment or disappears completely on one or both jaws. Second upper premolar (Pm^2) elongated, with lingual side broadened posteriorly, its width being approximately one half its longitudinal axis; anteriorly there is a well-developed supplementary denticle. Upper carnassial tooth (Pm^3) sometimes has supplementary fifth cusp on anterior exterior corner. Upper molar (M^1) approximately same size as Pm^1, and elongated; is very often lost as animal ages. First lower premolar (Pm$_1$) somewhat extended posteriorly; longitudinal axis of crown more or less shorter than that of lower molar (carnassial). Carnassial two-cusped, the hypoconid higher, though somewhat shorter, than the protoconid.

Systematic notes. The tiger is sharply differentiated from the other panthers by the features given above. It is nearest craniologically to the lion, Panthera leo L., particularly in the structural similarity of the tympanic area and the dental apparatus.

The systematics of the various tiger subspecies, insofar as elaborated at present, is based on variation in the general size of the animal, the quality of its pelt, and to some extent on craniological details, including the dental structure. About two dozen tiger subspecies have been described, though there are actually far fewer. Study of this problem shows that in the case of the tiger, as in that of many other mammals, subspecies are frequently based on single specimens and sometimes only on published data. This has produced an absurd confusion in the intraspecific systematics of the tiger. The validity of numerous forms described is doubtful, and even the valid subspecies are, in most cases, inadequately described, their synonymy not in order, and their geographical distribution not very well known. It is difficult at present to make a more or less critical survey of tiger subspecies, since there is insufficient collected material available. The list of subspecies given by Ellerman and Morrison-Scott in their checklist of Palaearctic and Indian mammals (1951) is very useful, but cannot help us solve this problem.

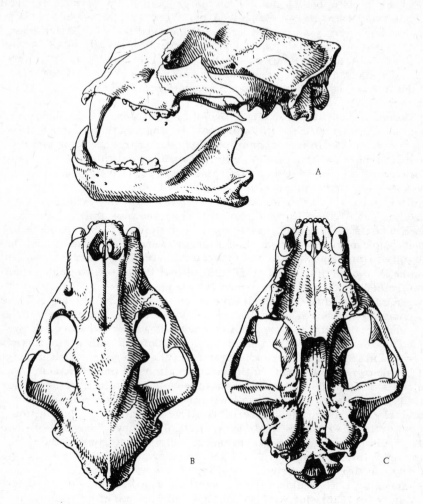

FIGURE 172. Skull of the tiger, P a n t h e r a t i g r i s L. (original):

A — lateral view; B — dorsal view; C — ventral view.

The foregoing also applies to the tigers ranging the Maritime Territory and the Amur area. This tiger was described, in terms of the lowest systematic unit ("variation"), by Dode (1871) under the name F e l i s t i g r i s var. a m u r e n s i s. According to Dode, the tiger of the Amur and Ussuri shows several features differentiating it from the Bengal tiger (the nominate subspecies); the hair is longer, the color less dark, and the black bands less pronounced ("Cette espèce féline, qui

481

habite sur les bords du fleuve Amour et du fleuve Oussouri, présente quelques différences avec le F e l i s t i g r i s b e n g a l e n s i s ; poils plus longs, couleur moins foncée, bandes noires moins prononcées."

Satunin (1907), basing himself on material from the Maritime Territory (Yankovskii Peninsula), redescribed the tiger as distinguished from the Caspian tiger by somewhat smaller size, and more vivid color (with development of a reddish tone), and by intensely black stripes. He named the tiger T i g r i s a m u r e n s i s Satunin (ex Dode). Satunin (1915) later separated the Maritime tiger from the Amur a m u r e n s i s Dode and named it T i g r i s m i k a d o i (nomen novum pro T i g r i s a m u r e n s i s Satunin, 1907; nec Dode, 1871).

Satunin's motivation for his taxonomic conclusions can be understood from an exchange (1915) with Smirnov,* in which Satunin treated the discrepancy between the description of the Amur tiger's color and the collection material from the Maritime Territory as follows: "According to Smirnov, the local hunters distinguish between two tiger breeds: the local one — a large form with a longer dull coat —, and another, smaller one with a shorter but more vivid coat; the latter the local inhabitants call the "Korean" breed. Smirnov was able to verify these reports for himself, having once seen the two tigers together in Vladivostok market. The paler and longer-haired tiger was almost one-and-a-half times as large as the other, more vividly colored one, although judging by the teeth it could be concluded that the latter was older than the former. This important piece of evidence completely clears up the matter. Dode and the others described the first tiger, which should bear the name T i g r i s a m u r e n s i s, while I described a completely different, still undescribed tiger, to which I erroneously gave the name used by Dode [for the other]." As mentioned above, Satunin named this tiger T i g r i s m i k a d o i. As can be seen from the foregoing, Satunin made his breakdown of Far Eastern tigers in an almost a priori manner, on the basis of comparing the diagnosis of Dode's essentially rather super- ficially characterized Amur tiger with the results of his own study of material collected in the southern Maritime Territory.** In addition, he was influenced by the local hunters' reports of two "breeds" of tiger, etc. Satunin has, by the way, unquestionably misinterpreted the facts reported to him by Smirnov. The local hunters of the Maritime Territory do indeed differentiate between two tiger "breeds," a distinction also mentioned by L. G. Kaplanov (1948) for the central Sikhote-Alin and by N. A. Baikov (1925), for N. E. China,† but examination of collection material shows that in reality these "breeds" are nothing but cases of the individual variation which occurs throughout the tiger's range — i. e.,

---

* Prof. N. A. Smirnov (1878 — 1942) — a famous zoologist who specialized in pinnipeds and cetaceans.
** Satunin never saw the tigers of the Amur in the field.
† Baikov's book (1925) gives a photograph of the hunter Charaev with two tigers he killed in 1912 near the Shihtowhotze post. The legend says: "Left — a female Amur tiger; right — a Korean tiger." No difference between the two tigers can be discerned in the picture. Baikov writes of the two breeds "Amur" and "Korea." Now, hunters are known to often take conspicuously marked types of individual deviation in numerous animal species for independent "breeds." Thus, hunters almost everywhere differentiate between two breeds of bear: the small "anteater" and the large "carrion eater."

are variants devoid of systematic significance. As to the tigers Smirnov saw
in the Vladivostok market, the information on them reported by Satunin is devoid
of any taxonomic value, since the place of collection and the sex of the specimens
are unknown.   These could have been extreme cases of individual variation
in color and size.   Even a single litter of tigers may contain large and small
and variously colored individuals (Baikov, 1925).

Nevertheless, Satunin's example led to the idea taking root that there
are two forms of tiger in the Far East: southern, Korean form and
northern, Amur one. According to Ognev (1935), the Korean tiger,
P. t. coreensis Brass, 1904 (mikadoi Satunin, 1915), is large, though
smaller than the Amur one (Ognev provides no measurements, due to absence
of reliable data), and has relatively shorter hair and a vivid, red-tinged ocher-
yellow ground color in the winter fur.   The stripes are conspicuous, but are
narrower and more widely separated than in the Caspian tiger, P. t. virgata Illiger, 1915.   The Amur tiger, P. t. longipilis Fitzinger, 1868
(amurensis Dode, 1871) is characterized by very large dimensions
(overall length of male skull reaches 400 mm), long hair, and by pale and
dull yellowish ocher ground color in the winter fur.   The striping is as in
the previous form.   Ognev's ideas (1935) about the systematics of the Far
Eastern tigers are highly speculative, and are not borne out by actual
material.   Ognev (1935) himself reported that not only is the zoogeographical
boundary of differentiation between the two Far Eastern forms of tiger
problematical, but that "it is so far impossible to express clearly, precisely,
and briefly the diagnoses and the differentiating taxonomic features."

The southern form was described by the above-mentioned scientists
mainly from a specimen in winter coat from Sidemi (No. 3029 in the
collection of the Zoological Institute of the Academy of Sciences of the USSR).
Ognev writes that he had occasion to see numerous pelts, as well as live
Maritime Territory tigers, which in general features were closer to the
southern form.

The northern form was described by the aforementioned author without
recourse to actual collection material.   The sole reference being to a
stuffed tiger kept in Moscow's Darwin Museum, without indication of the
place of collection.   According to Ognev (1935), this specimen is closest to
the Amur tiger, and in addition Ognev quotes F. D. Pleske as having told
him that he had seen two tigers from the Ussuri Territory in the Berlin
zoo.   "The animals were extremely powerful and massive, and were marked
by light color and by surprisingly long, almost bushy fur.   There is no
doubt that they belong to the northern race." And these are all the actual
data there are for establishing the northern form.   The measurements
Ognev gives for the Amur tiger are taken from hunting literature and
contradict the craniometric data.   Thus, the overall male skull length for
the Amur tiger is given by Baikov (1925) as up to 400 mm; the largest
Ussuri Territory male examined by Ognev (No. 2088 in the collection of the
Zoological Museum of Moscow University) had a skull 360.3 mm long.

I have examined extensive tiger material in the collections of the
Zoological Institute of the Academy of Sciences of the Zoological Museum of
Moscow State University, and of certain other establishments, as well as
a few specimens belonging to private persons, a total of about 20 pelts and

27 skulls of various ages and sexes, and in addition have examined numerous live tigers kept in the Moscow and Leningrad zoos. As a result, I have become convinced that all the tigers inhabiting the Soviet Far East are subspecifically identical. No systematic differences exist between the northern and southern Far Eastern tigers.

The subspecies* mentioned are nothing but cases of variation of the Soviet Far Eastern tiger, and are not associated with any definite biotope or geographical area. For example, let us take the color. The collection of the Zoological Museum of the Moscow State University contains two pelts of adult females, in winter fur, collected in 1939 on the lower Amur and on the Ussuri. These specimens can be considered topotypes of P. t. amurensis Dode. The color, far from being a pale, dull yellowish ocher, turns out on the contrary to be vivid, an intense rusty brown-ocher general tone with a noticeable reddish tinge. The transverse stripes are intensely black. These pelts are much more vivid than are many of the specimens from the southern parts of the Maritime Territory referred to P. t. coreensis Brass.

The coat is in general uniformly long and luxuriant in all Far Eastern tigers (the length of the male's winter fur reaching 53—58 mm on the back). Przheval'skii reported the length of the winter coat on a male pelt acquired by him from some Chinese as 70—75 mm on the withers and 50—55 mm on the back. As to measurements, the craniological material available does not permit differentiation between two types, a small and a large, localized geographically. And as to the tigers inhabiting northeastern China and northeastern Korea, judging by the descriptions in the literature (Baikov, 1925; Brass, 1904, 1911; Pocock, 1929) of their characteristic traits, it may be assumed with a high degree of reliability that they are identical with the Soviet P. t. amurensis.

Geographical distribution. The tiger is distributed widely over the southern parts of Asia, from the southeastern part of Transcaucasia and Iran in the west to Indochina, eastern China, Korea, northeast China and the Amur River area, inclusively. In the east it inhabits the islands of Sumatra, Java, Bali, and Taiwan (Formosa), and some smaller islands as well.

In the Soviet Union it ranges over southeastern Transcaucasia, over Central Asia (in the floodplain forests of the Syr Darya and Amu Darya and their tributaries and in the Balkhash basin), and over the Far East.

In Siberia, disregarding the extremely rare cases of individual visits, it ranges only in the Maritime Territory and the Amur River area (Map XXV).

The following data have been published on penetrations of the tiger into Western and Eastern Siberia.

According to F. Hebler (1840), the tiger has been taken many times within the Russian Altai. The predator was seen and killed in 1810 or 1811 near Bukhtarminsk. A second animal was killed in the same area in 1829. One tiger was killed in October 1839 near the village of Setovka, some 50 miles south of Biisk. According to reports of G. Spasskii (1815), a tiger entered the Alei River in 1813 and was killed at the Loktev plant near Zmeinogorsk. According to N. I. Yablonskii (1904), a tiger was bagged in

---

* The local hunters' two "breeds."

484

1814 near the village of Yamyshev. According to A. M. Nikol'skii (1883), a tiger was obtained near Zmeinogorsk in 1848. The above-mentioned entries of the tiger into the area of Zmeinogorsk, Biisk and Barnaul were probably recorded by Brandt back in 1856.

The animal enters Western Siberia, judging by all the data from Kazakhstan (where it occurs to the present day in the area of Lake Balkhash).

A number of authors mention entry of the tiger into East Siberia. N. A. Severtsov (1855) mentions a tiger obtained in 1828 in the area of Balagansk (on the Angara at about 52°30' N. lat.). Radde (1862) mentioned a tiger entry into Transbaikalia. According to him, the animal was killed in 1844 near the Nerchinskii plant.

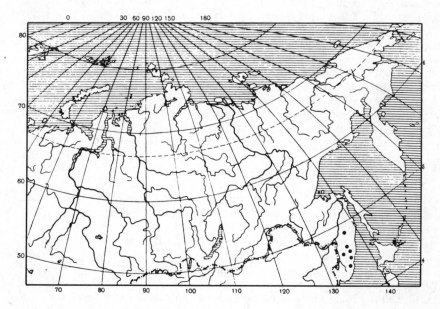

MAP XXV. Geographical distribution of the tiger, Panthera tigris L., in Siberia

R. Maak (1859), among other explorers, writes that tigers were seen and killed on the Argun and in Transbaikalia, in the mountains of the Stanovoi Range and even near the city of Yakutsk.

Mounted in the Yakutsk Museum is a tiger killed in November 1905 on the Aldan River some 80 km from Ust'-Maya. Tracks of another tiger were observed in the same area, the tigers probably having entered from the Amur River area (Tugarinov, Smirnov and Ivanov, 1934; see also Satunin, 1915; Ognev, 1935).

According to the newspaper "Komsomol'skaya Pravda" (of 14 January 1945), two tigers were obtained in winter in the Chita Region, one of them on the Gazimur River in the Ust'-Kara area (Novikov, 1956).

The distribution of the tiger in the Far East is as follows. Tigers were encountered here in earlier times east of the lower Bureya River and northwards to 50°N. lat., a few individuals reaching 52° or even further north.

Tigers were taken in the valley of the Bureya River and on the Amur in 1853 by Radde (collection Zool. Inst. Acad. Sciences USSR). Schrenck (1858) reported the tiger for the area of the mouth of the Amur, where, however, as along the course of the river, it is rare. According to Maak (1859, 1861) the tiger is often encountered in the valley of the middle Amur, from the Khingan Range to the area situated somewhat below the mouth of the Ussuri River, being oftenest encountered near the mouths of the Sungari and Ussuri. It inhabits the entire Ussuri valley, being common there, particularly in the vicinity of Lake Khanka.

Przheval'skii (1870) writes that the tiger is found throughout the Ussuri Territory and deep into the Amur area, being encountered here to about 52° N. lat. In the winter of 1868/69 tigers reached the mouth of the Goryun on the lower Amur and penetrated above the mouth of the Kumara on the upper Amur. Tigers may occasionally be encountered further north of this boundary, being found even in Transbaikalia and penetrating Sakhalin over the ice of the Tatar Strait (see also Schrenck, 1862; Nikol'skii, 1889). The animal is, however, far more common in the southern parts of the Maritime Territory than in the northern parts, being particularly abundant in the basin of Lake Khanka, in the region of the Upper Ussuri, and on the seashore between Olga and Pos'yet bays. On his winter expedition this famous explorer encountered tiger tracks every day, seeing the animal itself on the Suchan River. According to M. N. Yankovskii (1882), nine tigers were obtained in the area between Slavyansk Bay and the Arabella River in 1880/81. According to Baikov (1925), the tiger is locally fairly common in southern areas of the Maritime Territory.

The data from V.K. Arsen'ev which Ognev (1935) cites only add a few details to the foregoing picture of tiger distribution in the Maritime Territory.

At the present time the range in the Far East, due to the increase in settlement, the opening up of new croplands, and other new conditions, has ceased to be compact, and the animal is now encountered sporadically, in scattered patches in the most secluded localities of the Maritime Territory. Yu. A. Salmin (1940) describes the following tiger distribution for the 1930s. The northern boundary of the range extended from Voznesensk to Nizhne Tambovskoe on the Amur (valleys of the Goryun and Khungari rivers), where tiger tracks were observed twice during the preceding years. The tiger still had commecial value in the forests along the Khor, Podkhorenka and Bikin rivers and on the upper tributaries of the Iman. Only a few tigers remained along the Bidzhan, Kur, Urmi, and Tyrma and in the Pos'yet area. In the Sikhote-Alin reserve the tiger inhabited the upper Iman — along the Amu River, and particularly along this river's tributaries, the Nikula and Baizal, where it was common; it also frequented the upper reaches of the Kolumbe, Ankheza, Lyuchikheza and Tatibe rivers and the sources of the Iman proper. On the eastern slopes of the range, tiger tracks could be seen yearly within the reserve along the Sitsa River (a right tributary of the Sankhobe).

According to L. G. Kaplanov (1948), the northern limit of the tiger's range in the 1940s was the Anyui River (49° N. lat.). Occasional stragglers were reported up to lakes Kizi and Khadi near the mouth of the Amur, and north of the Birinzha River, a tributary of the Tyrma (basin of the Bureya River).*

---

* A.V. Afanas'ev mentions a straggler in the summer of 1931 on the upper Amgun' River.

By the 1940s the number of localities inhabited by the tiger had shrunk and the animal's population decreased. Kaplanov gives the following list of localities where tigers were killed by various persons between 1926 and 1940: the Budukhe and Tu-Nantse rivers; the Ta-Sinancha; the Yamagan (near Peshchernoe); the Tatibe River; the Sanchikheza vicinity; the Chichiveza River (below the Vakhumbe); the upper Ta-Sinancha and Syao-Sinancha rivers; the Ankheza and Lyuchikheza rivers; the ranges Tu-Nantsy, Talinguzy, Arlu and Beitsa; the Kolumbe (Sya-Nancha), the Iman (some 15 km above Sigatun), the Orochenka (a left tributary of the Iman); and Mount Vakhtumbe (near the Sanchikheza River). A lone tiger was recorded near Spassk, and a female with two young was observed in the Chernigovka woods, on the right side of the Lefu River. A tiger census which Kaplanov made in the central Sikhote-Alin, which took in the reserve and centered mainly on the valley of the upper Iman, showed only 10—12 tigers of various ages present on an area of about 30,000 km^2.

The tiger has been absent on the Bikin River for a number of years; it has not been found along the Khor or its tributary the Maitai, on the Podkhorenka, or on the Obor. Tigers were found in the following localities during the hunting season of 1939—1940: the upper reaches of the Anyui, the Suntar (upper reaches of the Bira), and the areas of Teplye Klyuchi and Birobidzhan. The largest unbroken area of tiger range is the valley of the Upper Iman and the Sikhote-Alin reserve, but even here the population density is about one individual per 2,000 km^2. Kaplanov gives the total number of tigers for the entire Soviet Far East as "a few dozen individuals, probably no more than 20—30 specimens."

The Sudzukhe reserve, according to G. F. Bromlei (1951), is permanently inhabited by tigers in its northern parts, along the rivers Vanchin and Yanmut'hovza. The tiger is encountered in the Suputinka reserve almost every year, but only in autumn, descending from the Dadyan-Shan' Range to the sources of the Kamenka and the Anikin (Bromlei and Gutnikova, 1955).

In the Khabarovsk Territory, according to V. R. Sysoev (1952), the tiger has survived in small numbers along the upper reaches of the rivers Mukhen, Nelta, Khor, Nemptu, Si and Suntara.

Bromlei (in litt.) has supplied us with up-to-date information on tiger distribution and population in the Far East.

In the Khabarovsk Territory, according to an investigation carried out by the hunting inspectorate, the tiger inhabits an area of 8,000 hectares (including 2,700 unexamined hectares for which there is no doubt that the tiger lives there). Twenty-three tigers were found on the above territory. The tiger population by administrative districts was as follows: the Obluch'e area of the Jewish Autonomous Region (along the tributaries of the Bidzhan River) showed six tigers; the Birobidzhan District — two; the Vyazemskii — one; the S. Lazo District — 12; the Nanai tribal lands — one; and the Komsomolsk — one. Tiger appearances have been reported for the Kur-Urma, Upper Bureya, and other districts of the Khabarovsk Territory, and for the Arkhara area of the Amur Region.

Tigers have been found in the following districts in the Maritime Territory according to Bromlei's report (in litt.): Vladivostok, Spassk, and Khasansk. Two tigers live there. The Kirovskii and Shmakovsk districts (valleys of the Shatukhe and Bolshaya Kabarga rivers) were found to contain two males and one female with two young. In the Kalininsk District tigers occur along the rivers Khanikhoza, Tudo-Vakhu, and Sebucharu. Two males and two females were found there, one of the latter with two young. In the Chuguevka District tigers live along the rivers Sandagou, Yanmut'havza, Sydagou, Chumatugou, Sinancha, Da-Nantsa, Noto, and the upper reaches of the Iman. Here seven tigers were recorded, including a female with two young. In the Krasnoarmeisk District tigers are encountered along the rivers Tatibe, Kolumbe (the Iman), and Bolshaya and Malaya Sipancha, where three tigers were recorded, including one female with a litter of three young. In the Lazo and Olga areas the tiger is encountered along the rivers Sudzukhe, Taukhe, Pfusung and Vantsin. Two tigers were recorded. On the Vantsin River a female with a litter of four young was discovered in 1957. In the Anuchino, Budenovsk and Ivanovka areas tigers occur along the Erldagou, on the upper reaches of the Suchan, along the Malaza and Tudagou, and on the upper reaches of the Lefu River. One female was recorded along the upper reaches of the Samazga, in the Ternei area.

The census thus turned up a total of 35 tigers in the Maritime Territory.

In northeast China the tiger has survived to the east of the Liaolin Range and, in smaller numbers, in the Alin and Lesser Khingan mountains (Baikov, 1914).

In North Korea the tiger is mainly associated with the areas bordering northeast China; in more southerly areas the tiger was bagged in the years 1920—1930. After 1953 tigers were caught for export in the districts of Musan, Hyensan, Onsong and Hoeryong, the 1956 take being ten tigers (G. F. Bromlei, in litt.).

Survey of subspecies. About two dozen tiger subspecies have been described, but in reality the number is markedly lower. About six subspecies are distinguished at present, and two of these extend into the Soviet Union.

One subspecies occurs in Siberia.

33a.   **Panthera (Tigris) tigris amurensis** Dode (1871).
Amur tiger

1871. Felis tigris var. amurensis. Dode.— Proc. Zool. Soc. London, p. 480.

1904. Felis tigris coreensis. Brass, E. Nutzbare Tiere Ostasiens, p. 4. (Korea).

1907. Tigris amurensis. Satunin, K.— Neue Balt. Waldm.-blätter, No. 4, p. 73; Satunin, K. A. Opredelitel' mlekopitayushchikh Rossiiskoi imperii (Key to the Mammals of the Russian Empire). p. 157, Tiflis. 1914.

1915. Tigris mikadoi. Satunin, K. A. Koreiskii tigr (The Korean Tiger).—Nasha Okhota, No. 7, pp. 17—18. (nomen novum pro Tigris amurensis Satunin. 1907; ex Dode, 1871).

1925. Felis tigris manchurica. Baikov, N. A. Man'chzhurskii tigr (The Manchurian Tiger). pp. 3—4.—Kharbin, Izd. Obshchestva izucheniya Man'chzhurskogo Kraya. (Manchuria).

1929. Panthera tigris amurensis. Pocock, R. — Journ. Bombay Nat. Hist. Soc., 33, p.527.

1935. Tigris tigris coreensis. Ognev, S. I. Zveri SSSR i prilezhashchikh stran (Animals of the USSR and Adjacent Countries). 3, pp.282—287, Moskva-Leningrad. figs. 127—131. (partim).

1935. Tigris tigris longipilis. Ognev, S. I. Loc. cit., p.287 and following pages (partim).

1938. Tigris tigris amurensis. Allen, G. M. — The Mammals of China and Mongolia, 1, pp.487—488, New York. (partim).

1951. Panthera tigris longipilis. Ellerman, J. R. and T. C. S. Morrison-Scott. Checklist of Palaearctic and Indian Mammals, p.318, London.

1951. Panthera tigris coreensis. Ellerman, J. R. and T. C. S. Morrison-Scott. Loc. cit. pp.318—319.

Type and type locality. Dode (1871) indicated in his paper that he was describing the tiger living along the banks of the Amur and Ussuri rivers. The terra typica of P. t. amurensis Dode should thus be the area where the Ussuri empties into the Amur, i. e., the vicinity of the city of Khabarovsk, where tigers occurred in the middle of the last century.

Diagnosis. Characterized by extremely luxuriant, dense and high fur with color less saturated than in South Asian tigers, and by odontological features. The general tone of the winter fur is ocher-yellowish, varying from relatively light and dull to vivid with more or less intense reddish tinge. The pattern of narrow but widely spaced mat or glossy black stripes is conspicuous. The upper carnassial tooth (Pm^3) lacks the additional fifth cusp on the anterior external corner.

Measurements. Length of body with head: males (6 specimens) 188—290 cm, females (3 specimens) 166—172 cm; length of tail: males 85—100 cm, females 82—88 cm; length of hind paw: males 34—36 cm, females 32—35 cm. Weight, according to Ognev (1935), is up to 320 kg.

Maximum length of skull: males 304—360 mm (av. 330 mm), females 204—300 mm (av. 250 mm); condylobasal length: males 274—324 mm (av. 290 mm), females 250—280 mm (av. 269 mm); zygomatic width: males 194—245 mm (av. 220 mm), females 190—203 mm (av. 198 mm); mastoid width: males 118—142 mm (av. 129 mm), females 114—122 mm (av. 118 mm); height in area of tympanic bullae: males 97—118 mm (av. 100 mm), females 92—97 mm (av. 95 mm); length of upper tooth row: males 94—113 mm (av. 102 mm), females 87—98 mm (av. 92 mm).

Systematic notes. The Amur tiger, as mentioned above, was originally described by Dode (1871) under the name amurensis. Ognev (1935), however, cited it under the name longipilis, on the basis of the fact that "the description of Tigris longipilis given by L. Fitzinger fits the northern race of tiger well," and proposed taking as terra typica the "area of the middle part of the former Amur Region." Obviously, this arbitrary treatment cannot be accepted. Fitzinger (1868) gave the following range for T. longipilis: "Mittel-Asien und südlicher Teil von Nord-Asien, wo diese Form bis zum 53. Grade Nordbreite hinaufreicht." According to established practice, where there is no direct indication of the type locality by the author of a new description, the terra typica is accepted to be the original locality mentioned in the area of the geographical distribution of the form described. Soviet Central Asia was the first region given for T. longipilis. In those days the concept "Central Asia" took in non-Soviet Central Asia, while what is now called Soviet Central Asia was then included in Western Asia (see V. Siver's "Aziya, Vsemirnaya geografiya" [Asia, a World Geography], St. Petersburg, 1909). As a result, one of the areas of contemporary Central Asia in which tigers occurred in those days should be taken as terra typica — in this case, the basin of the Tarim and the Lop Nor, where tigers survive to the present day.* Pocock (1929) treats this problem in a similar way, and I think that the name P. t. longipilis belongs, by the rule of priority, to the tiger inhabiting the valley of the Tarim and the Lop-Nor, whose later synonym is P. t. lecogi Schwarz (1916).

Geographical distribution. Maritime Territory and the Amur River area, northeast China and northeast Korea.

Material examined. Caucasus — 2 pelts and 8 skulls, Soviet Central Asia — 6 pelts and 9 skulls, China (Sinkiang) — 2 pelts and 3 skulls, Northeast China — 1 pelt, Maritime Territory and the Amur River area — 9 pelts and 7 skulls. Total — 20 pelts and 27 skulls.

Biology. The habitat of the Amur tiger consists mainly of wooded mountain biotopes. The tiger finds conditions best in mixed Siberian stone pine—broadleaf Manchurian type forest, and prefers uninhabited wooded expanses dissected by deep canyons, with outcrops of cliffs and rock streams, rich in ungulates, particularly wild boar.

On the central Sikhote-Alin, according to Kaplanov (1948), the most common tiger biotopes are the river valleys and Manchurian floodplain riverain forests; though the animals also roam the mountains, ascending ranges of up to 1,600 m, they nevertheless prefer localities with smoother relief. Kaplanov writes that "tigers move with ease in spruce forests and over open burns occupied by sparse forests or small growing oaks and filberts, being attracted there by the abundance of Manchurian wapiti and elks."

Baikov (1925), who hunted tiger for many years in Northeast China, says that though in search of food the tiger may occasionally descend into the foothill forests, it should nevertheless be considered a denizen of secluded mountain forests, noting that "in localities where the mountain ranges are inaccessible, where the slopes are steeper and more precipitous, where vast rock streams with perpendicular high cliffs, stony expanses, stones and caves are available, one can be sure to find tigers in permanent residence." However, not just the relief of the locality and the type of forest is important for the tiger, but the density and biotopical distribution of the animals on whose flesh it feeds, as well as the general wildness and untouched nature of the place.

The tiger keeps to localities sparsely populated by man, where wild boars, Manchurian wapiti and other ungulates are abundant and where the meteorological and other natural conditions facilitate its hunting in a given season.

---

* The tigers occurring here are characterized by light color and long fur, i.e., correspond to the diagnosis of T. longipilis Fitzinger.

The individual range of a tiger takes in a vast area — up to three or four thousand or more square kilometers. The tiger does not live in any one place but is continuously roaming in search of food or more favorable ecological conditions. In summer it lives in the mountains at or above 1,200 m, where relatively temperate microclimatic conditions prevail. In the autumn it moves lower down. Thus, in the Suputinka reserve, which lies in the Ussuriisk area of the Maritime Territory, the tiger is seen every year in the autumn, entering for a certain time by descending from the Dadyan-Shan Range to the sources of the Kamenka and the Anikin. Tiger tracks are not seen in the reserve at other times of year (Bromlei, and Gutnikova, 1955). In winter the tiger, following the ungulates, moves to areas with less snow.

According to Baikov's observations (1925), it the number of ungulates should decrease the tiger will set out on long migrations — sometimes of 100 km of more — but after a while will return to its starting point.

If rendered insecure through logging or frequent hunting, the tiger will move to a quieter place and not return. According to Yu. A. Salmin (1940), in localities where the wild boar is extensively hunted the tiger, molested by the hunters and hounds, may leave the wild-boar areas and move to the upper reaches of the rivers.

The tiger makes its den in wild secluded mountain localities — in caves, cliff fissures, under overhanging rocks, and in steep canyons. The den consists of a hollow or a flat area, occasionally lined with dried leaves or grass. The tiger uses the den for raising its young and as shelter from bad weather. The animal, however, will usually go to rest in the first suitable place it encounters, usually near some large animal it has killed.

The tiger is characterized by smooth, catlike movements; it has an easy and graceful gait and walks carefully and noiselessly. Though its usual gait is a broad-paced lope, it is capable of rapidly charging and can make enormous leaps. When walking it places the hind paw into the print of the forepaw. The length of the pace is 70 — 80 cm for an adult male, somewhat less for a female. It can make leaps of up to 4—5 m when running. In running down prey it may leap up to 7 m, and in the downward direction may even reach 10 m.

The male pawprint is larger and more elongated than that of the female, with the middle toes more clearly projecting forward.

The male pawprint is 15—16 cm long and 13—14 cm wide, the female 14—15 cm long and 11—13 cm wide. According to Baikov (1925), an experienced hunter can determine the sex, weight, age and degree of fatness of an animal from its pawprint. Thus, if the print has a diameter of 20 cm or more the animal is big, weighing up to 240 kg. Young tigers leave rather large tracks, since their paws are disproportionately large, but these tracks are shallow, due to the low weights of the young.

The indefatigability of the tiger, and its ability to travel for several days in succession over dozens and dozens of kilometers, are astounding. One day's travel may, according to Kaplanov (1948), be 20—50 km, and according to Baikov (1925), even as much as 100 km. The tiger is endowed with great strength, and can lift a wild boar or a wapiti and even drag an elk.

The animal does not avoid water, and swims well. On hot summer days it likes to bathe. It bears low temperatures very well and easily endures severe frost. Tree-climbing is done only by young tigers not older than two years and weighing no more than 60 kg.

Hearing is the best developed sense, the tiger being capable of picking up the slightest rustle. The sense of smell is apparently less developed, and sight is far poorer still.

The tiger is a taciturn animal. Its voice is rarely heard, even in places where it is always to be found. Only during rut do the males utter a muted growl. Baikov (1925) writes: "During fights for females the tiger's roar resembles that of a lion, but more muted, with hoarse bubbling overtones. . . . Usually the tiger utters a long, wailing sound, frequently and rapidly repeated, and ending in three or four short calls. Sometimes a low guttural call is heard, resembling a-oon or e-o-oon. When attacking prey or when angry, the tiger roars mutedly and utters a sound resmbling a cough. Usually the call of the tiger has a frightening effect in the great, wild, primeval forest. At night it inevitably arouses visions of the terrible strength of the colossal cat." According to P. A. Manteifel (1927), the tigress in heat utters a special snorting sound resembling that of the horse. The male roars like thunder, its powerful roar resembling a roaring cough or a sudden explosive shot, this being uttered when the predator is excited or annoyed. In fights over females the tiger's roar resembles that of a lion, but is more muted, with hoarse bubbling overtones. The tiger is among the most courageous, but at the same time secretive and sensitive of animals. It does not fear man but tries to avoid him. It is possible to live a long time in localities where tigers occur and not to see them at all. Only the ferocious roar heard in the thickets of the forest, and the numerous tracks, droppings, and discarded remnants of slaughtered animals will attest to the ferocious animal's presence.

Before seizing its prey the tiger keeps to the ground and then makes one or more enormous leaps. Its attacks are as quick as lightning. The tiger never pursues fleeing prey (Baikov, 1925). In stalking prey and in moving about, the tiger makes full use of all declivities in an area; its movements are soundless and hidden even in dense thickets of up to 0.5 m in height.

A clearly manifested trait of the tiger is that it follows trails and prints of wild boar, deer and other large animals. If it encounters human tracks it may follow these too. During an excursion in the Tigrovaya Balka in southern Tadzhikistan (along the lower reaches of the Vakhsh River), I was many times an object of the tiger's attention. Many times, going back along a road or trail some 5—10 minutes after having passed that way, I saw the characteristic footprints of the tiger crossing mine. Many cases arose which made my blood run cold, in which I became convinced that a tiger was following me like a ghost, as if stalking me. Early one morning in June 1944, some 15 minutes after having reached the "Tigrovaya Balka" reserve by car, I went for a walk along the road by which I had arrived. Some 50—60 m from the boundary of the reserve I saw fresh tiger tracks on my car's tire marks. Examination of the tracks showed that the tiger had followed the road, jumped aside at the approach of the car, lain in wait in the clumps of plumegrass (E r i a n t h u s) to let my car pass, and then gone back to the road and followed me for about a kilometer.

The tiger roams chiefly at dusk, before and after sunset, and during the night. The day is usually passed in sleeping in the den; the animal rises at approach of evening, goes to drink, and then roams in search of food. However, it may also be active during the day.

The tiger does not stay long in any one locality, but usually roams within its individual range from one locality to another. Females nursing young lead a more sedentary life.

According to observations of Kaplanov (1948), the winter life of the tiger "is an alternation of long trips lasting several days, of devouring the catch, and of resting near the catch some five — ten days, depending on the size of the catch." In the summer tigers probably lead a more sedentary life; large-scale migrations have nevertheless been observed even at that time of year.

The tiger feeds mainly on the flesh of various animals, principally wild boar, various deer, and other animals. It may sometimes even attack bears. Occasionally it catches birds or small animals. It will eat fish and insects, and should food be scarce is not above eating carrion. Occasionally, it will eat Siberian stone pine nuts together with the shell, plus various forest berries and fruits.

Kaplanov (1948) observed the tiger's methods of hunting wild boar, wapiti, elk and bear by following tracks. "The tiger follows the trails of the animal and waits on the lee side, where it lies in ambush awaiting the approach of its prey. It appears that the tiger hunts at night, when it is easier for it to remain unnoticed. Occasionally it frightens its prey on approach, in which case it makes leaps in pursuit, usually without result, giving up the chase after some 100 — 200 m. Whatever prey the tiger takes it kills almost instantaneously, by biting through the cervical vertebrae at the back of the head ... Only large bears cannot be killed immediately, due to their thick nape. The tiger will not follow the trails of its prey for a long time, the only exception being groups of wild boars ... In summer the tiger ambushes animals, particularly wapitis, in creeks where they come to browse and to drink water, particularly in solonetz areas."

According to Baikov (1925), large tigers can take on bears of almost their own weight. The tiger will stalk the bear, generally ambushing it on a cliff or burn from the lee side. The unsuspecting bear, unaware of danger, ambles slowly into the ambush and the tiger "attacks from above, sinking the claws of one paw into the chin and those of the other into the neck and biting through the cervical vertebrae."

On the Sikhote-Alin, Kaplanov (1948) on 15 February 1940 discovered the aftermath of the attack of a tigress on a female bear lying in its den. The tigress, probably having picked up the bear's scent, had deviated sharply from its course and stealthily crept up to the den by short steps, the den being constructed on the ground below a Siberian stone pine tree. "The tigress had dug a hole on the opposite side of the den and frightened the female bear into it, by jumping alternately to the entry of the den and to the hole. At an appropriate moment the female bear had been seized by one of its forepaws, and dragged outside, and the cervical vertebrae had been been bitten through at the back of the bear's head. The skin of the palm had been torn off one of the bear's forepaws and the digits ripped off. The tigress's clawmarks could be seen on the bark of the Siberian stone pine near the entrance to the den in some places, and there was a small trampled-down area with traces of blood around the tree. The bear had been dragged somewhat downward by the tigress and had been devoured completely during the course of a few days with only the head, fore- and hind legs with the long bones (the articular heads being gnawed away), and some remnants of fur remaining... The year-old young, weighing some 30 kg, had probably been killed in the den itself (the skulls were bitten through), since the walls and ceiling were spattered with blood; the young bears had been dragged down, still warm, for some 30 m where they had been lain and left untouched under a pine tree. No traces remained of the carcass, since the tigress had spent no less than eight days near the den," and after that had gone off its original direction.

Tigers sometimes attack livestock and dogs. They occasionally attack humans, but this occurs very rarely.

Kaplanov (1948) calculates that one adult tiger devours an average of 30 large animals, each of average weight 100 kg, or the same weight of other animals, each year.

Tiger reproduction has not yet been adequately studied in the field. According to Przheval'skii (1870), tiger rut in the Ussuri Territory occurs in January (old calendar). According to Baikov (1925), the time of rut and mating in Northeast China is late December and early January, and this may be some two weeks later in young individuals. According to P. A. Manteifel (1927), rut in Ussuri tigers in the Moscow Zoo occurred in 1927 in the last ten days of January. Kaplanov (1948) writes that tigers usually mate during the winter. According to V. P. Sysoev (1952), tigers in the Khabarovsk Territory mate in January. In the nuptial period, males in search of females roam widely and become less cautious. Several males may court one female, and then fierce fights occur between them. By the termination of the nuptial period the males and females have separated and are living individually. In zoological gardens, after the termination of the rutting period, the females become inimical to the males and fights may occur between them.

Gestation time, according to observations in the Moscow Zoo, is 95—107 days.

This means that the young should be born during the second half of April and in May. In the Khabarovsk Territory, according to Sysoev (1952), the birth of the young occurs in April, though young tiger cubs are found in the field at various times. Thus, according to Salmin (1940), "in December 1932, in the area of the Beitsukhe River, a right tributary of the Iman, a young tiger cub weighing 2.5 kg was caught alive. Four dead cubs weighing 4—6.2 kg were found in January 1933 on the Iman. An adult tigress obtained in May 1933 in the vicinity of the Sanchikhezy camp was found to contain five completely developed embryos. In the winter of 1937/38, three tiger cubs aged three—four months were found on upper tributaries of the Iman River."

Rut is apparently repeated in some of the females which have not been impregnated during the winter.

The litter size is usually 2—4, in rare cases 5. The newborn are the size of cats, weighing 785—1,500 g. The length of the body is 315—400 mm, of the tail 130—160 mm, and the ear height is 15—25 mm. The young are born blind and with closed ear apertures. Their color pattern is striped. The stripes are conspicuous, particularly on the head, tail and paws. The claws are unpigmented. Growth and development is relatively slow. The

eyes are definitely open by the age of 5—10 days. The milk teeth appear at
the age of two weeks. The juvenile molt takes place at the age of
3.5—5.5 months. According to Kaplanov (1948) young tiger cubs are
capable of following their mother at a very early age, at first for very short
distances and then for many kilometers, thus gradually expanding the area
of their habitat. Kaplanov writes: "Leaving the cubs, the mother goes to
hunt and having caught the prey, returns for the young and leads them after her
to the kill; the family remains there while it devours the prey. The mother
will not leave young cubs below age of six months alone for long periods,
but older cubs may be left for five—six days, and those two years old for
as long as two weeks. If the cubs are small the mother will not make
them follow her from place to place, but will bring the new kill to the site
of the previous one."

The young are nursed with the mother's milk for a period fo six months.
The litter does not disband upon termination of lactation, but continues to
live with the mother for two—three years, and hunts with her. According
to Kaplanov (1948), three-year-old tigers probably follow their mother on
all her hunting trips.

The female tiger is extremely attached to her progeny, and defends
them courageously. According to Baikov (1925) "the tigress is madly
courageous when protecting her young as she is cautious, cunning and
prudent in raising them. Despair and mother love will make her attack
hunters in mad fury and lose her usual caution."

The tiger attains sexual maturity in the fourth year of life. The full
development of physical strength and maturity is reached at the age of five
years. The life span is 40—50 years.

The tiger has practically no direct enemies, and only man can destroy
it. However, it has numerous food competitors — all the large carnivores
(bears, wolves, lynxes, gluttons, yellow-throated martens, etc.).

Molt occurs twice annually. The winter fur is replaced in the spring, in
March, by the shorter and sparser summer fur. First to be replaced is
the hair on the muzzle and legs and on the black stripes. The entire
molting process takes some two weeks. In autumn, in September, the
winter fur, denser and longer, with a well-developed underfur, begins to
grow. Replacement of the claws takes place in autumn.

Practical importance. The widely prevalent opinion, mentioned in the
hunting literature and shared by the population, that the tiger is unquestionably
harmful, is not always correct. In some cases it does undoubted good by
exterminating the excessive numbers of wild boars which inflict extensive
harm on agriculture and horticulture.

The harm inflicted on livestock breeding is strictly local. Salmin (1940)
has noted quite justly that "the harm the tiger does to livestock is often
exaggerated." The Ussuri tiger is completely different from tigers of
Soviet Central Asia, which do harm to livestock breeding. In the Soviet
Far East the tiger inhabits localities sparsely populated by man, were
livestock breeding is undeveloped. It attacks livestock extremely rarely
and the damage it does is insignificant. Salmin (1940) writes: "The tiger
attacks humans extremely rarely, except in cases of tigers wounded during
hunting or by traps. The tiger shrinks from man, and even more from
attacking him. Few cases of attack on humans are known, and the stories
of its bloodthirstiness towards humans are exaggerated." According to
Sysoev (1952), no cases of tigers attacking humans or livestock in the
Khabarovsk Territory have been reported for the last 25 years.

The tiger is an animal whose range and population is gradually and steadily decreasing, and it faces complete extermination. The question of its protection and preservation is now a major problem. The few specimens which have the habit of attacking livestock, not to speak about those which attack humans, should of course be exterminated.

The tiger's commercial significance as a fur-bearing animal is insignificant, despite the high price fetched by the skin, since only a few of them are processed. The pelt of the tiger is used chiefly for the preparation of carpets and for taxidermy. Hunting the Amur tiger is at present prohibited.

Young tigers are caught for zoos by special permit.

BIBLIOGRAPHY

Publications in Russian

Abramov, M. D.   Ob ispol'zovanii samtsov norki (On the Utilization of
    Male Minks (Pitorius)). — Karakulevodstvo i Zverovodstvo, 1, 1951.
Abramov, N. A.   Opisanie Berezovskogo kraya (Description of the
    Berezov Area). — Trudy Russkogo Geograficheskogo Obshchestva,
    Vol. 12, Sankt-Peterburg. 1857.
Adlerberg, G. P.   Khishchnye zveri (Carnivora, Fissipedia) Arktiki
    (Carnivorous Animals (Carnivora, Fissipedia) in the Arctic). — In:
    Zveri Arktiki edited by Prof. N. A.Smirnov, Leningrad, Izd.
    Glavsevmorputi. 1935.
Adol'f, T. A.   Rost i razvitie medvezhat po nablyudeniyam v Moskovskom
    zooparke v 1940 godu (Growth and Development of Bear Cubs Observed
    in the Moscow Zoological Garden in 1940). — Trudy Moskovskogo
    zooparka, Vol. 4. 1949.
Afanas'ev, A. V., V. S. Bazhanov, M. N. Karelov, A. A. Sludskii,
    and E. I. Strautman.   Zveri Kazakhstana (Animals of Kazakhstan),
    Alma-Ata. 1953.
Afanas'ev, A. V. and N. T. Zolotarev.   Novye dannye po sistematike i
    rasprostraneniyu krasnogo volka (New Data on the Systematics and
    Distribution of the Siberian Red Dog (Cuon alpinus hesperius
    Afanasiev et Zolotarev)). — Izvestiya AN SSSR, Ser. 7, No. 3. 1935.
Anikin, V. P.   Otchet o komandirovke v Narymskii krai letom 1900 goda
    (A Report on the Expedition to the Narym Area in Summer 1900).—
    Izvestiya Tomskogo Universiteta, Vol. 22, Tomsk. 1902.
Arsen'ev, V. K.   Komandorskie ostrova. Rybnye i pushnye promysla
    Dal'nego Vostoka (Commander Islands. Fisheries and Fur-Trades
    of the Far East). 1923.
Arsen'ev, V. K.   V debryakh Ussuriiskogo kraya (In the Jungles of the
    Ussuri Area), Vladivostok. 1926.
Arsen'ev, V. K.   Skvoz' taigu (Through the Taiga), Moskva. 1950.
Averin, Yu. V.   Nazemnye pozvonochnye Vostochnoi Kamchatki
    (Terrestrial Vertebrates of Eastern Kamchatka). — Trudy
    Kronotskogo Gosudarstvennogo Zapovednika, Moskva. 1948.
Baikov, N. A.   V gorakh i lesakh Man'chzhurii (In the Mountains and
    Forests of Manchuria).— Petrograd, Izd. Nasha okhota. 1914.
Baikov, N. A.   V lesakh i gorakh Man'chzhurii (In the Forests and
    Mountains of Manchuria), Moskva. 1915.
Baikov, N. A.   Man'chzhurskii tigr (The Manchurian Tiger). — Harbin,
    Izd. Obshchestva izucheniya Man'chzhurskogo kraya. 1925.
Baikov, N. A.   Zverovyi promysel v Man'chzhurii (Fur Trade in
    Manchuria). — Okhotnik, No. 2, Moskva. 1927.

Baikov, N. A.   Okhota na volkov i medvedei (Wolf and Bear Hunting),
    Tomsk. 1949.
Bannikov, A. G.   Mlekopitayushchie Mongol'skoi Narodnoi Respubliki
    (Mammals of the Mongolian People's Republic), Moskva. 1954.
Barabash-Nikiforov, I. I.   K faune zverei i ptits Tobol'skoi gubernii
    (On the Fauna of Animals and Birds in the Tobolsk Province). —
    Uchenye Zapiski SGU, Biologicheskaya Seriya, Vol. 14, No. 1. 1937.
Barabash-Nikiforov, I. I.   Kalan (Enhydra lutris L.), ego
    biologiya i voprosy khozyaistva (The Sea Otter (Enhydra
    lutris L.), its Biology, and Economic Problems). — In: Sbornik
    "Kalan," Glavnoe Upravlenie po zapovednikam, Moskva. 1947.
Belopol'skii, L.   Okhotnich'e-promyslovye bogatstva Chukotskogo i
    Anadyrskogo raionov (Hunting and Commercial Resources of the
    Chukchi and Anadyr Regions). — Boets-Okhotnik, No. 7. 1937.
Belousov, V.   K voprosu o medvede-shatune (The Problem of the Bear-
    Roamer). — Okhotnik i Pushnik Sibiri, No. 1. 1926.
Belyk, V. I.   Sostav i raspredelenie okhotopromyslovoi fauny mleko-
    pitayushchikh Yakutii (Composition and Distribution of the Hunting
    and Commercial Fauna of the Mammals of Yakutia). — In: Sbornik
    Promyslovaya fauna i okhotnich'e khozyaistvo Yakutii, No. 1, Yakutsk.
    1953.
Berger, N. M.   Promyslovye zveri Zapadnoi Sibiri (Commercial Animals
    of Western Siberia), Novosibirsk. 1946.
Berger, N. M.   Introduktsiya norki (Mustela vison Br.) v SSSR
    (Introduction of the Mink (Mustela vison Br.) to the USSR). —
    Uchenye Zapiski Novosibirskogo Gosudarstvennogo Pedagogicheskogo
    Instituta, No. 9. 1954.
Birulya, A.   O sistematicheskom polozhenii perevyazki (The Taxonomic
    Position of the Mottled Polecat (Putorius sarmatius)). —
    Ezhegodnik Zoologicheskogo Muzeya Akademii Nauk, Vol. 15. 1910.
Birulya, A.   Materialy po sistematike i geograficheskomu
    rasprostraneniyu mlekopitayushchikh. VI. O rasakh Otocolobus
    manul (Pallas) i o polozhenii ego v sisteme semeistva Felidae
    (Data on the Systematics and Geographical Distribution of Mammals.
    VI.   On the Races of Otocolobus manul (Pallas) and its Place
    in the System of Family Felidae). — Ezhegodnik Zoolo-
    gicheskogo Muzeya Akademii Nauk, 21. 1916.
Birulya, A. A.   K voprosu o geograficheskikh formakh belogo medvedya
    (Thalassarctos maritimus Phipps) (The Problem of
    Geographical Forms of the White Polar Bear (Thalassarctos
    maritimus Phipps)). — Trudy Zoologicheskogo Instituta AN SSSR
    1. 1932.
Blagoveshchenskii, S.   Medvezh'ya okhota (Bear Hunting). — Okhotnik,
    No. 2. 1928.
Bobrinskii, N. A.   Opredelitel' okhotnich'ikh i promyslovykh zverei SSSR
    (Key to Game and Commercial Animals of the USSR). — Moskva-
    Leningrad, KOIZ. 1928 (1932, 1935).
Bobrinskii, N. A.   Otryad khishchnye. Ordo Carnivora (Order
    Carnivora). — In: Opredelitel' mlekopitayushchikh SSSR, edited
    by Prof. N. A. Bobrinskii, Moskva. 1944.

Bogorodskii. Mediko-topograficheskoe opisanie Gizhiginskogo okruga (Medical and Topographic Description of the Gizhiga District). — Zhurnal Ministerstva Vnutrennikh Del, No. 2. 1853.

Brandt, I. F. Pozvonochnye zhivotnye severno-evropeiskoi Rossii i v osobennosti Severnogo Urala (Vertebrates of North European Russia and Particularly of the Northern Urals). Vol. 2, Sankt-Peterburg. 1856.

Brauner, A. A O khor'kakh (On Polecats (Mustela putorius L.)). — Ukrayins'ke Myslyvstvo ta Rybalka, Nos. 2 — 3. 1923.

Brom, I. P. Materialy po biologii Zabaikal'skogo khor'ka (Data on the Biology of the Transbaikalian Polecat). — Izvestiya Irkutskogo Gosudarstvennogo Nauchno-Issledovatel'skogo Protivochumnogo Instituta Sibiri i Dal'nego Vostoka, Vol. 12, Irkutsk. 1954.

Brom, I. P., Z. M. Vovchinskaya, and L. V. Fedorova. O roli khishchnykh mlekopitayushchikh v rasprostranenii blokh gryzunov (The Role of Carnivorous Mammals in Spreading Fleas from Rodents). — Zoologicheskii Zhurnal, Vol. 27, 2. 1948.

Bromlei, G. F. Sikhote-Alin'skii zapovednik (The Sikhote-Alin Reserve). — Zapovedniki SSSR, Vol. 2, Moskva, Geografgiz. 1951$_1$.

Bromlei, G. F. Sudzukhinskii zapovednik (The Sudzukha Reserve). — Zapovedniki SSSR, Vol. 2, Moskva. 1951$_2$.

Bromlei, G. F. Znachenie kharzy kak khishchnika i sposoby ee unichtozheniya v Primorskom krae (The Importance of Martes flavigula as a Carnivore and Means of its Extermination in the Maritime Territory). —In: Sbornik "Preobrazovanie fauny pozvonochnykh nashei strany," edited by A. A. Nasimovich, Moskva, Izd. MOIP. 1953.

Bromlei, G. F. and Z. I. Gutnikova. Suputinskii zapovednik (The Suputinka Reserve), Vladivostok. 1955.

Bromlei, G. F. Gimalaiskii medved' (Selenarctos thibetanus ussuricus Heude, 1901) (The Asiatic Black Bear (Selenarctos thibetanus ussuricus Heude, 1901)). — Zoologicheskii Zhurnal, Vol. 34, No. 1. 1956.

Brusnev, M. Otchet nachal'nika ekspeditsii na Novo-Sibirskie ostrova dlya okazaniya pomoshchi baronu Tollyu (A Report by the Head of the Expedition to the New Siberian Islands to Assist Baron Toll). — Izvestiya Akademii Nauk Otdeleniya Fiziko-Matematicheskikh Nauk, Vol. 20, Sankt-Peterburg. 1904.

Bryklin. Pis'ma s Sakhalina (Letters from Sakhalin). — Zapiski Sibirskogo Otdela Geograficheskogo Obshchestva, Irkutskii Otdel, No. 7. 1864.

Bulychev, N. P. Ocherk flory i fauny Irbitskogo uezda (A Survey of the Flora and Fauna of the Irbit County). — Zapiski Ural'skogo Obshchestva Lyubitelei Estestvoznaniya, Vol. 4. 1878.

Buturlin, S. A. Nablyudeniya nad mlekopitayushchimi, sdelannye vo vremya Kolymskoi ekspeditsii 1905 goda (Observations on Mammals Carried out during the Kolyma Expedition in 1905). — Dnevnik Zoologicheskogo Otdeleniya Obshchestva Lyubitelei Estestvoznaniya, Novaya Seriya, Vol. 1, No. 5, Moskva. 1913.

Buturlin, S. A. K voprosu ob altaiskom medvede (The
   Altai Bear). — Okhotnik Altaya, Nos. 9 — 10. 1924.
Byalynitskii-Birulya, A. Ocherki iz zhizni ptits polyarnogo
   poberezh'ya Sibiri (Essays on Bird Life of the Siberian Coast). —
   Zapiski Akademii Nauk, Seriya 8 po Fiziko-Matematicheskomu
   Otdeleniyu, Vol. 18, Sankt-Peterburg. 1907.
Chalikov, B. G. and K. P. Samko. Tobol'skii okrug. Kratkoe opisanie
   (The Tobol'sk District. A Brief Description). No. 1, Tobol'sk. 1926.
Chekanovskii, A. L. Svedeniya ob ekspeditsii na Nizhnyuyu Tungusku
   (Data on an Expedition to the Lower Tunguska). — Izvestiya RGO,
   Vol. 9, Otdel 2. 1873.
Cherkasov, A. Zapiski okhotnika Vostochnoi Sibiri (1856 — 1863)
   (Hunter's Reports from Eastern Siberia (1856 — 1863)), Sankt-
   Peterburg. 1867.
Chugunov, S. M. Mlekopitayushchie i ptitsy Surgutskogo uezda (Mammals
   and Birds of the Surgut County). — Ezhegodnik Tobol'skogo
   Gubernskogo Muzeya, Vol. 24. 1915.
Dement'ev, G. P. Volk (The Wolf). — Moskva-Leningrad, Vneshtorgizdat.
   1933.
Dinnik, N. Ya. Zveri Kavkaza, chast' 2. Khishchnye (Animals of the
   Caucasus, Part 2. Carnivora), Tiflis. 1914.
Ditmar , K. Posadki i prebyvanie na Kamchatke v 1851 — 1855, chast' 1
   (Settling and Staying in Kamchatka in 1851 — 1855, Part 1). —
   Istoricheskie otchety po putevym dnevnikam, Sankt-Peterburg. 1901.
Dobrotvorskii, N. P. Yuzhnaya chast' Sakhalina (The Southern Part of
   Sakhalin). — Izvestiya Sibirskogo Otdeleniya Russkogo
   Geograficheskogo Obshchestva, Vol. 1, Nos. 2 and 3. 1870.
Doppel'm aier, G. G. Sobolinyi promysel na severo-vostochnom
   poberezh'e Baikala (Sable Trade on the Northeastern Coast of the
   Baikal), Verkhneudinsk-Leningrad. 1926.
Dorogostaiskii, V. Ch. Novyi podvid korsaka iz Yuzhnogo Zabaikal'ya
   (A New Subspecies of the Corsac Fox (Vulpes corsac L.) from
   Southern Transbaikalia). — Izvestiya Irkutskogo Gosudarstvennogo
   Protivochumnogo Instituta Sibiri i Dal'nego Vostoka, Vol. 1. 1934.
Dubrovskii, A. N Pushnye zveri Yamal'skogo natsional'nogo okruga
   (Furry Animals of the Yamal Autonomous Region). — Trudy Nauchno-
   Issledovatel'skogo Instituta Polyarnogo Zemledeliya, Zhivotnovodstva
   i Promyslovogo Khozyaistva, No. 13. Pushnoi promysel Yamal'skogo
   natsional'nogo okruga, Leningrad, Izdatel'stvo Glavsevmorputi. 1940.
Dul'keit, G. D. Zametki o promyslovykh zhivotnykh Tuguro-
   Chumikanskogo raiona (Notes on the Commercial Animals of the
   Tugur-Chumikan District). — Okhotnik, No. 6. 1927.
Dul'keit, G. D. Materialy po izucheniyu biologii sobolya i sobolinogo
   khozyaistva ostrova Bol'shoi Shantar (Data on the Study of Sable
   Biology and Sable Economy on Bol'shoi Shantar Island). — Izd.
   Izvestii Tikhookeanskoi Nauchno-Promyslovoi stantsii, Vladivostok.
   1929.
Dul'keit, G. D. Novye mlekopitayushchie i ptitsy na beregakh Teletskogo
   ozera (New Mammals and Birds on the Shores of Lake Teletskoe). —
   Zametki po Faune i Flore Sibiri, No. 7. 1949.

Dul'keit, G. D. Znachenie rysi i rosomakhi kak khishchnikov v prirodnom komplekse Altaiskoi taiga (Importance of the Lynx (Felis lynx) and Gluton (Wolverine (Gulo) gulo L.) as Carnivores in the Natural Compound in the Altai Taiga). — In: Sbornik "Preobrazovanie fauny pozvonochnykh nashei strany," edited by A. A. Nasimovich. Moskva, Izd. MOIP. 1953.

Dul'keit, G. D. Raspredelenie i migratsii mlekopitayushchikh gornoi taigi Vostochnykh Sayan v zavisimosti ot rezhima snezhnogo pokrova (Distribution and Migration of Mammals from the Mountain Taiga of the East Sayans in Relation to the Snow Cover Regime). — Trudy Biologicheskogo Instituta, No. 5. 1959.

Dul'keit, G. D. and V. V. Kozlov. Materialy k faune mlekopitayushchikh zapovednika "Stolby" (Data on the Mammal Fauna of the "Stolby" Reserve). — Trudy Gosudarstvennogo Zapovednika "Stolby," Krasnoyarsk. 1958.

Dul'keit, G. D. and L. M. Shul'pin. Ptitsy Shantarskikh ostrovov (Birds of the Shantar Islands). — Trudy Biologicheskogo Nauchno-Issledovatel'skogo Instituta pri Tomskom Gosudarstvennom Universitete, Vol. 4, Tomsk. 1937.

Dunaeva, T. N. and V. V. Kucheruk. Materialy po ekologii nazemnykh pozvonochnykh tundry Yuzhnogo Yamala (Data on the Ecology of Terrestrial Vertebrates of the Southern Yamal Tundra). — In: Sbornik Materialy k poznaniyu fauny i flory SSSR, novaya seriya, otdel zoologicheskii, No. 4. 1941.

Dunin-Gorkavich, A. A. Sever Tobol'skoi gubernii (The North of the Tobol'sk Province). — Materialy k Poznaniyu Fauny i Flory Rossiiskoi Imperii, otdel zoologicheskii, No. 1, Moskva. 1892.

Dunin-Gorkavich, A. A. Tobol'skii Sever (The Tobol'sk North). Vol. 2. 1910.

Egorin, N. F. Podvidy pestsov SSSR i ikh rasprostranenie (Subspecies of Russian Arctic Foxes (Alopex lagopus L.) and their Distribution). — Trudy Tomskogo Gosudarstvennogo Universiteta, Vol. 90. 1935.

Egorov, N. N. K faune pozvonochnykh lentochnykh borov. Sbornik statei po lesnomu khozyaistvu, etc. (On the Fauna of Vertebrates of the Pine Forest Belt. Collection of articles on forestry, etc.). — Trudy Lebyazhinskoi ZONLAS, No. 1, Sverdlovsk-Moskva, Goslestekhizdat. 1934.

Eversmann, E. Estestvennaya istoriya mlekopitayushchikh zhivotnykh Orenburgskogo kraya (Natural History of Mammals of the Orenburg Area), Kazan. 1850.

Fedoseev, Gr. V tiskakh Dzhugdyra (In the Mountains of Dzhugdyr). — Novosibirsk, Knizhnoe izdatel'stvo. 1956.

Fetisov, A. S. Vrednye i poleznye mlekopitayushchie v sel'skom khozyaistve Zapadnogo Zabaikal'ya (Harmful and Useful Mammals in the Agriculture of Western Transbaikalia). — Izvestiya Irkutskogo Gosudarstvennogo Oblastnogo Muzeya, Vol. 2. 1937.

Fetisov, A. S. Zimnie kormovye ob"ekty kunitseobraznykh Zabaikal'ya (Winter Food Items of Family Mustelinae of Transbaikalia). — Izvestiya Biologo-Geograficheskogo Nauchno-Issledovatel'skogo Instituta pri Irkutskom Gosudarstvennom Universitete, Vol. 9, Nos. 3—4. 1942.

Fetisov, A. S. Novyi podvid rysi (Lynx lynx kozlovi subsp. n.) iz Vostochnoi Sibiri (A New Subspecies of the Lynx (Lynx lynx kozlovi subsp. n.) from Eastern Siberia). — Izvestiya Biologo-Geograficheskogo Nauchno-Issledovatel'skogo Instituta pri Irkutskom Gosudarstvennom Universitete, Vol. 12, No. 1, Irkutsk. 1950.

Fetisov, A. S. Amerikanskaya norka i rezul'taty ee akklimatizatsii v basseine Chikoya Chitinskoi oblasti (The Mink Mustela vison Schr. and Results of its Acclimatization in the Chikoi Basin of the Chita Region). — Izvestiya Biologo-Geograficheskogo Nauchno-Issledovatel'skogo Instituta pri Irkutskom Gosudarstvennom Universitete, Vol. 12, No. 2, Irkutsk. 1950.

Flerov, K. K. Ocherk zhizni burogo medvedya na Severnom Urale (An Essay on the Life of the European Brown Bear (Ursus arctos L.) in the Northern Urals). — Ezhegodnik Zoologicheskogo Muzeya AN SSSR. 1929.

Flerov, K. K. Ocherki po mlekopitayushchim Polarnogo Urala i Zapadnoi Sibiri (Essays on the Mammals of the Polar Urals and Western Siberia). — Izvestiya Akademii Nauk SSSR. 1933.

Formozov, A. N. Sputnik sledopyta (Guide for the Pathfinder), Moskva-Leningrad. 1936.

Formozov, A. N. Sputnik sledopyta (Guide for the Pathfinder), Moskva, Izd. MOIP. 1952.

Gassovskii, G. N. Gilyui-Ol'doiskii okhotnich'e-promyslovyi raion (The Gilyui-Ol'doi Hunting and Commercial District). — Trudy Pervoi Konferentsii po izucheniyu proizvoditel'nykh sil Dal'nego Vostoka, Vladivostok. 1927.

Geptner [Heptner], V. G. Medvedi (Bears).—Moskva-Leningrad, Vneshtorgizdat. 1933.

Geptner [Heptner], V. G. Materialy po mlekopitayushchim ostrova Diksona, prilezhashchei chasti Severo-Zapadnogo Taimyra i Karskogo morya (Data on the Mammals of Dickson Island, the Adjacent Part of Northwestern Taimyr and the Kara Sea). — Sbornik Trudov Gosudarstvennogo Zoologicheskogo Muzeya pri MGU, No. 3, Moskva. 1936.

Gerasimov, M. V. Sakhalinskie zapovedniki (The Sakhalin Reserves). — Zapovedniki SSSR, Vol. 2, Moskva, Geografgiz. 1951.

Glen, N. P. Otchet o puteshestvii po ostrovu Sakhalinu 1860—1862 gg. (Report on a Voyage to Sakhalin (1860—1862)). — Trudy Sibirskoi Ekspeditsii Russkogo Geograficheskogo Obshchestva, Vol. 1, Sankt-Peterburg. 1868.

Golovin, D. N. Zametki o medvezh'ikh berlogakh (Notes on Bear Lairs). — Okhotnik, No. 8. 1928.

Gol'tsmaier, G. V gornoi Shorii (In Gornaya Shoriya). — Boets-okhotnik, No. 3, Moskva. 1935.

Gorchakovskii, A. Zhivotnye Chuiskoi stepi (Animals of the Chuya Steppe). — Rybolov i Okhotnik, Nos. 9 — 10, Vyatka. 1912.

Gromov, K. I. Sayanskii zapovednik (Sayans Reserve). — Zapovedniki SSSR, Vol. 2, Moskva. 1951.

Grum-Grzhimailo, G. E. Opisanie Amurskoi oblasti (Description of the Amur Region), Sankt-Peterburg. 1894.

Grum-Grzhimailo, G. E. Zapadnaya Mongolia i Uryankhaiskii krai (Western Mongolia and the Uryankhai Area). Vol. 1. 1914.

Il'ina, E. D. Zverovodstvo (Fur Farming). Moskva, Zagotizdat. 1952.

Ioganzen [Iohansen], G. E. Po Chulymu, Otvet o zoologicheskikh ekskursiyakh, predprinyatykh v yanvare 1914 goda, letom i osen'yu 1915 goda v vostochnoi chasti Tomskoi gubernii (Through Chulym. A Report on Zoological Excursions Undertaken in January 1914 and in Summer and Autumn 1915 in the Eastern Part of the Tomsk Province). — Izvestiya Tomskogo Universiteta, Vol. 72. 1923.

Iokhel'son, V. I. Ocherk zveropromyshlennosti i torgovli mekhami v Kolymskom okruge (An Essay on Animal Industry and Fur Trade in the Kolyma District), Sankt-Peterburg. 1898.

Kalinnikov, N. F. Nash krainii severo-vostok (The Soviet Far North-East). Supplement to Issue No. 34. — Zapiski po Gidografii, Sankt-Peterburg. 1912.

Kaplanov, L. G. Biologiya i promysel losei v basseine reki Dem'yanki (Elk in the Dem'yanka River Basin: Biology and Trade). — In: Sbornik Los' i ego promysel, edited by P. B. Yurgenson, Moskva. 1935.

Kaplanov, L. G. Tigr, izyubr', los' (Tiger (Felix tigris), Manchurian Wapiti (Cervus elaphus xanthopygus), and Moose (Alces alces)). — Moskva, Izd. MOIP. 1948.

Kashchenko, N. F. Rezul'taty Altaiskoi zoologicheskoi ekspeditsii 1848 goda (Results of the Altai Zoological Expedition, 1848). — Pozvonochnye, Tomsk. 1899.

Kashchenko, N. F. Opredelitel' mlekopitayushchikh zhivotnykh Tomskogo kraya (Key to Mammals of the Tomsk Area), Tomsk. 1900.

Kashchenko, N. F. O peschanom barsuke i o sibirskikh rasakh barsuka (The Sand Badger and Races of the Siberian Badger). — Ezhegodnik Zoologicheskogo Muzeya Akademii Nauk, Vol. 6. 1901.

Kashchenko, N. F. Mlekopitayushchie, sobrannye Altaiskoi ekspeditsiei P. G. Ignatova v 1901 godu (Mammals Collected by the Altai Expedition of P. G. Ignatov in 1901). — Ezhegodnik Zoologicheskogo Muzeya Akademii Nauk, Vol. 7. 1902.

Kashchenko, N. F. O kollektsii mlekopitayushchikh iz Zabaikal'ya (Collection of Mammals from Transbaikalia). — Ezhegodnik Zoologicheskogo Muzeya Akademii Nauk, Vol. 15. 1910.

Kashchenko, N. F. Novye issledovaniya po mammologii Zabaikal'ya (New Studies on Mammalogy of Transbaikalia). — Ezhegodnik Zoologicheskogo Muzeya Akademii Nauk, Vol. 18, Nos. 3 and 4. 1912.

Kertselli, S. V. O migratsiyakh belogo medvedya (Migrations of the White Polar Bear (Thalarctos maritim us Phipps)). — Okhotnik, No. 12, Moskva. 1921.

Khodorin, N. — Okhota i Okhotnich'e Khozyaistvo, No. 1. 1959.

Khitrov. Opisanie Zhiganskogo ulusa (A Description of Zhigansk Village). — Zapiski Sibirskogo Otdeleniya Russkogo Geograficheskogo Obshchestva, 1. 1856.

Kirikov, S. V. Ptitsy i mlekopitayushchie v usloviyakh landshaftov yuzhnoi okonechnosti Urala (Birds and Mammals in the Landscape of

the Southernmost Part of the Urals).— Moskva, Izdatel'stvo AN
SSSR. 1952.

Kirikov, S.V. Istoricheskie izmeneniya zhivotnogo mira nashei strany
v XIII—XIV vekakh. Soobshchenie 4-e. Izmenenie arealov sobolya i
lesnoi kunitsy (Historical Changes in the Animal Kingdom of Russia in
the 13th—14th Centuries. Communication 4. Changes in the
Geographical Range of the Sable and the Pine Marten, M. martes L.).—
Izvestiya AN SSSR, Seriya Geograficheskaya, No. 1. 1958.

Kiris, I. D. Ekologiya sredneobskoi belki (Ecology of the Squirrel of the
Middle Ob).— In: Sbornik "Ekologiya belki," edited by N.A. Bobrinskii,
KOIZ. 1934.

Kirpichnikov, A. A. K biologii pestsa yugo-zapadnogo poberezh'ya
Taimyra (The Biology of the Arctic Fox (Alopex lagopus L.) of the
Southwestern Coast of Taimyr).— Byulleten' MOIP, otdel
biologicheskii, Vol. 46, No. 1. 1937.

Klimov, Yu. N. Materialy po biologii gornostaya (Data on the Biology of
the Ermine (Mustela erminea L.)).— Trudy Biologicheskogo
Nauchno-Issledovatel'skogo Instituta pri Tomskom Gosudarstvennom
Universitete, 7, Tomsk. 1940.

Kolosov, A. M. K biologii korsaka i stepnoi lisitsy (The Biology of the
Corsac Fox (Vulpes corsac L.) and the Afghan Fox (Vulpes
korsak)).— Byulleten' Moskovskogo Obshchestva Ispytatelei Prirody,
otdel biologicheskii, Vol. 44 (4). 1935.

Kolosov, A. M. Fauna mlekopitayushchikh Altaya i smezhnoi Mongolii
v svyazi s nekotorymi problemami zoogeografii (Mammal Fauna of
the Altai and Adjacent Mongolia in Relation to Problems of Zoogeography).— Zoologicheskii Zhurnal, Vol. 18, 2. 1939.

Kolyushev, I. I. Materialy po faune i promyslu zapadnogo ugla
Taimyrskogo poluostrova (Data on the Fauna and Trade of the Western
Part of the Taimyr Peninsula).— Materialy po Izucheniyu Sibiri,
Vol. 4, Tomsk. 1933.

Kolyushev, I. I. Mlekopitayushchie krainego severa Zapadnoi i Srednei
Sibiri (Mammals of the Extreme North, Western and Central Siberia).—
Trudy Biologicheskogo Nauchno-Issledovatel'skogo Instituta, Vol. 2,
Tomsk. 1936.

Komarov, L. V. Puteshestvie po Kamchatke v 1908—1909 godakh (A
Journey through Kamchatka in 1908—1909).— Botanicheskii Otdel
Ekspeditsii Russkogo Geograficheskogo Obshchestva, No. 1. 1912.

Komarov, V. L. Botanicheskii ocherk Kamchatki (Botanical Survey of
Kamchatka).— Kamchatskii sbornik, 1, Leningrad, Izdatel'stvo AN
SSSR. 1940.

Konstantinov, M. Pushnoi promysel i pushnaya torgovlya v Yakutskom
krae (Fur Trade and Fur Commerce in Yakut Territory), Irkutsk.
1921.

Kopylov, I. P. Okhotnich'e khozyaistvo Irkutskoi oblasti (Hunting in the
Irkutsk District), Irkutsk. 1948.

Kopylov, I. P., A. V. Dobrovol'skii and I. A. Shergin. Promyslovye
zveri Irkutskoi oblasti (Commercial Animals of the Irkutsk Region),
Irkutsk. 1940.

Koryakov, B. F.   Rasprostranenie i promyslovoe ispol'zovanie sobolya
na Urale (Distribution and Commercial Utilization of Sable in the
Urals).— Trudy Vsesoyuznogo Nauchno-Issledovatel'skogo Instituta
Okhotnich'ego Promysla, No. 8, Moskva, Zagotizdat. 1948.

Korzinkina, E. M.   Biologiya i ekologiya surka i surkovyi promysel v
Kosh-Agachskom aimake (Biology and Ecology of the Marmot and
Marmot Trade in Kosh-Agach Region). — In: Sbornik "Ekologiya
surka," Moskva, Vneshtorgizdat. 1935.

Kozhanchikov, L. and I.   Promyslovaya okhota i rybolovstvo v
Minusinskoi taige (Hunting and Fishing in the Minusinsk Taiga).
Ezhegodnik Gosudarstvennogo Muzeya im. Mart'yanova. 1924.

Krasheninnikov, S. P.   Opisanie zemli Kamchatki (Description of
Kamchatka).   8th ed.— Moskva-Leningrad, Izd. Glavsevmorputi.
1949.

Krivoshapkin, M. O.   Eniseiskii okrug i ego zhizn' (The Yenisei District
and its Life). 1865.

Kuklin, S.   Kratkii obzor okhoty v Surgutskom krae (A Brief Survey of
Hunting in the Surgut Area).— Nash Krai, Nos. 8 — 9, Tobol'sk. 1925.

Kuklin, S. A.   Zveri i ptitsy Urala i okhota na nikh (Animals and Birds of
the Urals and their Hunting), Sverdlovsk. 1937.

Kuznetsov, B. A.   Melkie pushnye vidy Vostochnogo Zabaikal'ya (Small Fur
Species of Eastern Transbaikalia).— Pushnoe Delo, No. 12. 1928.

Kuznetsov, B. A.   Zverovye promysly Vostochnogo Zabaikal'ya (Hunting
in Eastern Transbaikalia).—Trudy po Lesnomu Opytnomu Delu, No. 4,
Moskva. 1929.

Kuznetsov, B. A.   Geograficheskaya izmenchivost' sobolei i kunits
fauny SSSR (Sables and Martens of the Fauna of the USSR —
Geographical Changes). — Trudy Moskovskogo Zootekhnicheskogo
Instituta, 1, Moskva. 1941.

Kuznetsov, B. A.   Mlekopitayushchie Kazakhstana (Mammals of
Kazakhstan).— Izd. MOIP. 1948.

Kuznetsov, B. A.   Okhotnich'e-promyslovye zveri Kuril'skikh ostrovov
(Game and Commercial Animals of the Kuril Islands).— In: Sbornik
Pushnye bogatstva SSSR, Moskva, Gosudarstvennoe izd. tekhnicheskoi
i ekonomicheskoi literatury po voprosam zagotovok. 1949.

Kuznetsov, B. A.   Osnovy tovarovedeniya pushno-mekhovogo syr'ya
(Principles of Classifying Staple Commodities of Fur-Bearing and
Fur Resources).— Zagotizdat. 1952.

Laptev, I. P.   Mlekopitayushchie Aleksandrovskogo raiona Tomskoi
oblasti (Mammals of the Aleksandrovskoe District of the Tomsk
Region).— Zametki po Faune i Flore Sibiri, No. 17, Tomsk. 1953.

Laptev, I. P.   Okhotnich'e khozyaistvo Tomskoi oblasti i perspektivnoe
ego razvitie (Hunting in the Tomsk Region and its Anticipated
Development), Tomsk. 1953.

Laptev, I. P.   O rasprostranenii nekotorykh mlekopitayushchikh v
Zapadnoi Sibiri (The Distribution of Some Mammals in Western
Siberia).— Zametki po Faune i Flore Sibiri, No. 18, Tomsk. 1955.

Laptev, I. P.   Mlekopitayushchie taezhnoi zony Zapadnoi Sibiri (Mammals
of the Taiga Zone of Western Siberia).— Izd. Tomskogo Universiteta.
1958.

Lavrov, N. P. Materialy k biologii kolonka (Data on the Biology of Mustela sibirica).— Zoologicheskii Zhurnal, Vol. 16. 1937.

Lavrov, N. P. Akklimatizatsiya i reakklimatizatsiya pushnykh zverei v SSSR (Acclimatization and Reacclimatization of Fur-Bearing Animals in the USSR).— Moskva, Zagotizdat. 1946.

Lavrov, N. P. Akklimatizatsiya i reakklimatizatsiya pushnykh zverei v SSSR (Acclimatization and Reacclimatization of Fur-Bearing Animals in the USSR).— Moskva, Zagotizdat. 1949.

Levoshin, O. Obogashchenie fauny Khanty-Mansiiskogo natsional'nogo okruga (Expansion of the Fauna of the Khanty-Mansiiskii National District).— Okhota i Okhotnich'e Khozyaistvo, No. 5, Moskva. 1959.

Likhachev, G. N. Okhotnich'e khozyaistvo Verkhne-Obskogo lesnogo massiva (Hunting in the Upper Ob Forest Area).— Izvestiya Sibirskoi Kraevoi Nauchnoi Okhotnich'e-Promyslovoi Stantsii, No. 1, Novosibirsk. 1930.

Likhachev, G. N. Nekotorye cherty ekologii barsuka v shirokolistvennom lesu Tul'skikh zasek (Features of the Badger Ecology in the Broadleaf Forests of Tul'skaya Abatis).— In: Sbornik materialov po rezul'tatam mlekopitayushchikh v gosudarstvennykh zapovednikakh, Moskva. 1956.

Linnik, T. G. Nekotorye nablyudeniya nad manulom v nevole (Observations on Otocolobus manul in Captivity).— Izvestiya Gosudarstvennogo Protivochumnogo Instituta Sibiri i Dal'nevostochnogo Kraya, Vol. 3. 1936.

Lobachev, S. V. Okhota na medvedya (Bear Hunting).— Moskva, Voenizdat. 1951.

Lyalin, A. N. Okhoty v Sibiri. Tri nedeli v Bakcharskom bolote zimoi 1903 goda (Hunting in Siberia. Three Weeks in the Bakchar Swamp in Winter 1903).— Priroda i Okhota, No. 5. 1903.

Maak, R. Puteshestvie na Amur, sovershennoe po rasporyazheniyu Sibirskogo otdela Imperatorskogo russkogo geograficheskogo obshchestva v 1855 godu (A Journey to the Amur Carried out according to Instructions of the Siberian Section of the Imperial Russian Geographical Society in 1855). Sankt-Peterburg. 1859.

Maak, R. Puteshestvie po doline reki Ussuri (A Journey through the Ussuri River Valley), Vol. 1, Sankt-Peterburg. 1861.

Maak, R. Vilyuskii okrug Yakutskoi oblasti (The Vilyui Range of the Yakut Region), Sankt-Peterburg. 1886.

Maidel', G. Puteshestvie po severo-vostochnoi chasti Yakutskoi oblasti 1863— 1870 gg. (A Journey through the Northeastern Part of the Yakut Region in 1863—1870), Sankt-Peterburg. 1894.

Manteifel', P. A. Nashi lesnye zhivotnye i okhota za nimi (Russian Forest Animals and their Hunting). 1927.

Manteifel', P. A. Nashi lesnye zhivotnye i okhota za nimi (Russian Forest Animals and their Hunting), Moskva. 1934.

Manteifel', P. A. Zhizn' pushnykh zverei (Life of Fur-Bearing Animals).— Moskva, Gosudarstvennoe Izdatel'stvo. 1948.

Mel'nitskii, N. A. Medved' i okhota na nego (The Bear and its Hunting), Petrograd. 1915.

Middendorf, A. Puteshestvie na sever i vostok Sibiri, ch. 2. Sever i vostok Sibiri v estestvenno-istoricheskom otnoshenii. Otdel 5,

Sibirskaya fauna (A Journey to the North and East of Siberia, Part 2. Natural and Historical Aspects of North and East Siberia, Sec. 5, Siberian Fauna), Sankt-Peterburg. 1869.

M i g u l i n, A. A. Novyi podvid stepnogo khor'ka iz nogaiskikh stepei Dagestanskoi respubliki (A New Subspecies of the Siberian Polecat (M. p u t o r i u s e v e r s m a n n i Lesson) from the Nogaiskie Steppes of the Dagestan Republic). — Ukrayins'ke Myslyvstvo ta Rybalka, No. 9, Khar'kov. 1928.

M i k h e l', N. M. Promyslovye zveri Severo-Vostochnoi Yakutii (Commercial Animals of Northeast Yakutia), Leningrad. 1938.

M i k h e l', N. M. Promyslovye zveri Severo-Vostochnoi Yakutii (Commercial Animals of Northeast Yakutia). — Trudy Nauchno-Issledovatel'skogo Instituta Polyarnogo Zemledeliya, Zhivotnovodstva i Promyslovogo Khozyaistva. 1939.

N a d e e v, V. N. and V. V. T i m o f e e v. Sobol' (The Sable). — Moskva, Izd. tekhnicheskoi i ekonomicheskoi literatury po voprosam zagotovok. 1955.

N a n s e n, F. Vo mrake nochi i vo l'dakh (Translation of "Fram over Polhaver," Vol. II). — Sankt-Peterburg. 1897.

N a s i m o v i c h, A. A. Sezonnye migratsii i nekotorye drugie osobennosti burogo medvedya na Zapadnom Kavkaze (Seasonal Migrations and Some Other Peculiarities of the European Brown Bear (U r s u s a r c t o s L.) in the Western Caucasus). — Nauchno-Metodicheskie Zapisi Glavnogo Upravleniya po Zapovednikam, No. 7. Moskva.

N a s i m o v i c h, A. A. Ocherk ekologii gornostaya v Laplandskom zapovednike (An Essay on the Ecology of the Ermine (M u s t e l a e r m i n e a L.) in the Lapland Reserve). — Trudy Laplandskogo Gosudarstvennogo Zapovednika, No. 3, Moskva. 1948.

N a s i m o v i c h, A. A. Promyslovye zveri Tsentral'nogo Altaya (Commercial Animals of the Central Altai). — Pushnye Bogatstva SSSR, No. 1, Moskva, Zagotizdat. 1949.

N a s i m o v i c h, A. A. K biologii korsaka v Daurskikh stepyakh (Biology of the Corsac Fox (V u l p e s c o r s a c L.) in the Dauria Steppes). — Priroda, No. 1. 1951.

N a u m o v, S. P. Mlekopitayushchie i ptitsy Gydanskogo poluostrova (Severo-Zapadnaya Sibir) (Mammals and Birds of the Gyda Peninsula (Northwestern Siberia)). — Trudy Polyarnoi Komissii AN SSSR, No. 4, Leningrad. 1931.

N a u m o v, N. P. Mlekopitayushchie Tungusskogo okruga (Mammals of the Tunguska District). — Trudy Polyarnoi Komissii AN SSSR, No. 17, Leningrad. 1934.

N a u m o v, S. P. and N. P. L a v r o v. Osnovy biologii promyslovykh zverei (Fundamentals of Biology of Commercial Animals), Moskva. 1941.

N a u m o v, S. P. and N. P. L a v r o v. Biologiya promyslovykh zverei i ptits SSSR (Biology of Commercial Animals and Birds of the USSR). Moskva, Zagotizdat. 1948.

N i k o l' s k i i, A. M. Puteshestvie v Altaiskie gory (A Journey to the Altai Mountains). — Trudy Sankt-Peterburgskogo Obshchestva Estestvoispytatelei, Vol. 11. 1884.

Nikol'skii, A. M. Ostrov Sakhalin i ego fauna pozvonochnykh zhivotnykh
    (Sakhalin and its Vertebrate Fauna), Supplement to Vol. 9. —
    Zapiski Imperatorskoi Akademii Nauk, No. 5, Sankt-Peterburg. 1889
Novikov, G. A. Evropeiskaya norka (The European Mink, M. lutreola
    L.). — Leningrad, Izd. LGU. 1939.
Novikov, G. A. Khishchnye mlekopitayushchie fauny SSSR (Carnivorous
    Mammals of the Fauna of the USSR). — Moskva-Leningrad, Izdatel'stvo
    AN SSSR. 1956.
Ognev, S. I. O kollektsii mlekopitayushchikh iz Ussuriiskogo kraya
    (Collecting Mammals from the Ussuri Area). — Ezhegodnik
    Zoologicheskogo Muzeya Akademii Nauk. 1911.
Ognev, S. I. Materialy po sistematike russkikh mlekopitayushchikh.
    Novyi podvid gornostaya (Data on the Systematics of Russian
    Mammals. A New Subspecies of Ermine (Mustela
    erminea L.)). — Byulleten' Izvestii Gosudarstvennogo Nauchno-
    Issledovatel'skogo Instituta im. Timiryazeva, Vol. 1. 1922.
Ognev, S. I. O medvedyakh vodyashchikhsya v Rossii (On Bears Inhabiting
    Russia). — Priroda i Okhota na Ukraine, Nos. 1—2. 1924.
Ognev, S. I. Mlekopitayushchie Severo-Vostochnoi Sibiri (Mammals of
    Northeastern Siberia), Vladivostok. 1926.
Ognev, S. I. Mlekopitayushchie Shantarskikh ostrovov (Mammals of the
    Shantar Islands). — Izvestiya Tikhookeanskoi Nauchno-Promyslovoi
    Stantsii, Vol. 2, No. 5, Vladivostok. 1929.
Ognev, S. I. Sobol' (The Sable). — Trudy po Lesnomu Opytnomu Delu
    Tsentral'noi Lesnoi Opytnoi Stantsii i Otdela Biologii i Promyslovoi
    Okhoty, No. 14. 1931.
Ognev, S. I. Zveri Vostochnoi Evropy i Severnoi Azii, Vol. 2, Moskva-
    Leningrad. 1931; Vol. 3. 1935.
Ognev, S. I. Mlekopitayushchie Tsentral'nogo Tyan'-Shanya (Zailiiskogo i
    Kungei Alatau) (Mammals of the Central Tien Shan (Trans-Ili and
    Kungei Ala-Tau)). — Materialy k Poznaniyu Fauny i Flory SSSR, otdel'
    zoologicheskii, novaya seriya, No. 3 (18), Moskva. 1940.
Ognev, S. I. Zametki po sistematike anadyrskikh mlekopitayushchikh
    (Notes on the Systematics of Anadyr Mammals). — In: L. A. Portenko.
    Fauna Anadyrskogo Kraya, Part 3, mlekopitayushchie, Leningrad-
    Moskva. 1941.
Ognev, S. I. Ekologiya mlekopitayushchikh (Ecology of Mammals). —
    Moskva, Izd. MOIP. 1951.
Okhotnik i pushnik Sibiri (Hunter and Fur Trader of Siberia). No. 1. 1926.
Okhotnik i pushnik Sibiri (Hunter and Fur Trader of Siberia). No. 2. 1926.
Okhotnik i rybak Sibiri (Hunter and Fisherman of Siberia). No. 3. —
    Tri medvedya v odnoi berloge. 1933.
Orlov, S. I. and M. D. Zverev. Perevyazka v Pribaltiiskikh stepyakh
    (Mottled Polecat (Putorius sarmatius) in the Steppes of the
    Baltic Area). No. 4. — Novosibirsk, Izd. Sibirskoi Kraistazry. 1930.
Osmolovskaya, V. I. Ekologiya khishchnykh ptits poluostrova Yamala
    (Ecology of Birds of Prey of the Yamal Peninsula). — Trudy Instituta
    Geografii AN SSSR, No. 16. 1948.
Paramonov, A. A. Pesets i pestsovyi promysel v SSSR (Arctic Fox
    (Alopex lagopus L.) and Arctic Fox Trade in the USSR). —
    Leningrad, Izdatel'stvo AN SSSR. 1920.

Paramonov, A. A.   Materialy po vozrastnoi kraniologii mleko-
pitayushchikh (Data on the Age Craniology of Mammals). — In: Sbornik
Pamyati akademika Mikhaila Aleksandrovicha Menzbira, Moskva-
Leningrad, Izdatel'stvo AN SSSR. 1937.

Pavlov, E.   Ptitsy i zveri Chitinskoi oblasti (Birds and Animals of the
Chita Region), Chita. 1948.

Pereleshin, S. D.   Svoeobraznyi zverek Yuzhnogo Sakhalina — itatsi (A
Peculiar Animal of Family Mustelidae — Itatsi of Southern Sakhalin). —
Byulleten' MOIP, otdel biologicheskii, Vol. 63, No. 6. 1957.

Peshkov, B. I.   Dannye o chislennosti khishchnikov v Yugo-Vostochnom
Zabaikal'e (The Population of Carnivora in the Southeast of
Transbaikalia). — Izvestiya Irkutskogo Gosudarstvennogo Nauchno-
Issledovatel'skogo Protivochumnogo Instituta Sibiri i Dal'nego Vostoka,
Vol. 12, Irkutsk. 1954.

Petri, B. E.   Opisanie okhotnich'ei territorii tuturskikh tungusov
(Description of the Hunting Area of Tutura Evens). — Izvestiya Biologo-
Geograficheskogo Nauchno-Issledovatel'skogo Instituta pri Irkutskom
Gosudarstvennom Universitete, Vol. 5, No. 2, Irkutsk. 1930.

Pfitsenmaier, E. V.   V Sibir' za mamontom (Mammoth Hunting in
Siberia). — Moskva-Leningrad, Gosudarstvennoe Izdatel'stvo. 1928.

Plotnikov, A. F.   Narymskii krai (The Narym Territory),   Sankt-
Peterburg. 1901.

Plyater-Plokhotskii, K.   Vrednye i poleznye mlekopitayushchie v
sel'skom khozyaistve DVK (Harmful and Useful Mammals in
Agriculture of the Far East), Khabarovsk. 1936.

Podarel'skii, V. B.   Problemy sel'skokhozyaistvennoi akklimatizatsii
v Vostochnoi Sibiri (Problems of Agricultural Acclimatization in
Eastern Siberia), Irkutsk. 1936.

Podkovyrkin, B. A.   Nazemnye mlekopitayushchie ozera Shumshu
(Terrestrial Mammals of Lake Shumshu). — Byulleten' MOIP,
Vol. 63, No. 4, Moskva. 1958.

Pogudin, A. A.   Ocherk okhotnich'ego promysla Kirenskogo okruga
(Hunting in the Kirensk District). — Trudy po Lesnomu Optynomu Delu
Tsentral'noi Lesnoi Opytnoi Stantsii, No. 7, Moskva. 1930.

Polikevich, P.   Kratkii ocherk promyslovoi okhoty v Minusinskom uezde
i Uryankhaiskom krae (A Brief Survey of Commercial Hunting in
the Minusinsk County and the Uryankhai Territory). — Okhotnich'e
Delo, Nos. 8 — 9, Moskva, Izd. TsK. Vserossiiskogo soyuza
okhotnikov. 1923.

Polyakov, I. S.   Geograficheskoe rasprostranenie zhivotnykh v yugo-
vostochnoi chasti Lenskogo basseina (Geographical Distribution of
Animals in the Southeastern Part of the Lena Basin). — Zapiski
Imperatorskogo Geograficheskogo Obshchestva, 3. 1873.

Polyakov, I. S.   Zhizn' cheloveka i zhivotnykh v doline reki Obi (Human and
Animal Life in the Ob River Valley). — Izvestiya Russkogo
Geograficheskogo Obshchestva. 1877.

Polyakov, I. S.   Otchet ob issledovaniyakh na ostrove Sakhaline i v
Yuzhno-Ussuriiskom krae (A Report on the Investigations of
Sakhalin and the Southern Ussuri Territory). — Zapiski Akademii
Nauk, Vol. 48, Appendix No. 6. 1884.

Polyakov, G. I. Poezdka na ozerakh Zaisan-Nor i Marka-Kul' (A Trip on the Zaisan-Nor and Marka-Kul Lakes), Moskva. 1914.

Popov, L. N. Promyslovye mlekopitayushchie vostochnogo poberezh'ya Taimyrskogo poluostrova (Commercial Mammals of the Eastern Shore of the Taimyr Peninsula).— In: Sbornik "Promyslovye mleko-pitayushchie poberezh'ya Taimyrskogo poluostrova," edited by Prof. G. G. Doppel'maier, Leningrad, Izd. Glavsevmorputi. 1939.

Popov, V. A. Materialy po ekologii norki (Mustela vison Br.) i rezul'taty akklimatizatsii ee v Tatarskoi ASSR (Data on the Ecology of the Mink (Mustela vison Br.) and Results of its Acclimatization in the Tatar ASSR).— Trudy Kazanskogo Filiala AN SSSR, No. 2. 1949.

Portenko, L. A. Medvezhii ochag na ostrove Vrangelya (Bear Ground on Wrangel Island).— Sovetskii Okhotnik, No. 3. 1941_1.

Portenko, L. A. Fauna Anadyrskogo kraya. Chast' 3 (Fauna of the Anadyr Territory. Part 3).— Mlekopitayushchie, Moskva-Leningrad, Izd. Glavsevmorputi. 1941_2.

Przheval'skii, N. M. Puteshestvie v Ussuriiskom krae 1867—1869 gg. (A Journey through the Ussuri Territory in 1867—1869), Sankt-Peterburg. 1870.

Raevskii, V. V. Kolichestvennyi uchet sobolei (Mustela zibellina L.) po zimnim gnezdam (Quantitative Assessment of Sables (Mustela zibellina L.) according to Winter Nests).— Zoologicheskii Zhurnal, Vol. 25, No. 2. 1947.

Razorenova, A. P. Nekotorye dannye o rasprostranenii mleko-pitayushchikh na Altae (Some Data on the Distribution of Mammals in the Altai).— Sbornik Trudov Gosudarstvennogo Zoologicheskogo Muzeya pri MGU, No. 5, Moskva. 1939.

Reshetkin, V. V. and N. N. Shidlovskaya. Akklimatizatsiya morskoi vydry ili kalana (Acclimatization of the Sea Otter (Enhydra lutris L.).— In Sbornik Kalan, Glavnoe upravlenie po zapovednikam, Moskva. 1947.

Romanov, A. A. Pushnye zveri Leno-Khatangskogo kraya i ikh promysel (Fur-Bearing Animals of the Lena-Khatanga Territory and their Trade).— Moskva-Leningrad, Izd. Glavsevmorputi. 1941.

Rutilevskii, G. L. Promyslovye mlekopitayushchie poluostrova Chelyuskina i proliva Vil'kitskogo (Commercial Mammals of Cape Chelyuskin and the Vilkitski Strait).— In: Sbornik "Promyslovye mlekopitayushchie poberezh'ya Taimyrskogo poluostrova," edited by G. G. Doppel'maier, Leningrad, Izd. Glavsevmorputi. 1939.

Sabaneev, L. P. Pozvonochnye Srednego Urala i geograficheskoe rasprostranenie ikh v Permskoi i Orenburgskoi gubernii (Vertebrates of the Central Urals and their Geographical Distribution in the Perm and Orenburg [Chkalov] Provinces), Moskva. 1874.

Sabaneev, L. P. Sobol' i sobolinyi promysel (Sable and Sable Hunting), Moskva. 1875.

Sabaneev, L. P. Katalog zverei i ptits, gadov i ryb Srednego Urala (Lists of Animals and Birds, Reptiles and Fishes of the Central Urals), Moskva. 1878_1.

Sabaneev, L. P. Medved' i medvezhii promysel na Urale (Bears and Bear Hunting in the Urals).— Priroda i Okhota, Vol. 4, No. 12. 1878_2.

Sadovnikov, N. S.   Reki Vakha Surgutskogo uezda (The Vakh River in the Surgut County). — Ezhegodnik Tobol'skogo Gubernskogo Muzeya, No. 19, p. 1909. Tobol'sk. 1911.

Salmin, Yu. A.   K rasprostraneniyu, biologii i promyslu amurskogo tigra Felis tigris longipilis Fitzin. v gornoi strane Sikhote-Alin' (On the Distribution, Biology and Trade of the Amur Tiger (Felis tigris longipilis Fitzin.) on the Heights of Sikhote-Alin). — Nauchno-Metodicheskie Zapiski Glavnogo Upravleniya po Zapovednikam, No. 7. 1940.

Samorodov, A. V.   K faune mlekopitayushchikh zemli olyutorskikh koryak (The Fauna of Terrestrial Mammals of the Olyutorskie Koryaks). — Sbornik Trudov Gosudarstvennogo Zoologicheskogo Muzeya pri MGU, No. 5, Moskva. 1939.

Satunin, K. A.   Altaiskaya rys' (The Altai Lynx). — Priroda i Okhota, Nos. 2—3. 1906.

Satunin, K. A.   Opredelitel' mlekopitayushchikh Rossiiskoi Imperii (Key to Mammals of the Russian Empire), Tiflis. 1914.

Satunin, K. A.   Koreiskii tigr (The Korean Tiger). — Nasha Okhota, No. 5. 1915.

Sdobnikov, V. M.   Raspredelenie mlekopitayushchikh i ptits po tipam mestoobitanii v Bol'shezemel'skoi tundre i na Yamale (Distribution of Mammals and Birds according to Types of Habitat in the Bol'shezemel'skaya Tundra and the Yamal). — Trudy Arkticheskogo Instituta, Vol. 92. 1937.

Sdobnikov, V. M.   Bor'ba s khishchnikami. Kratkie svedeniya po biologii, rasprostraneniyu i obrazu zhizni severnogo volka (Control of Carnivores. Brief Information on the Biology, Distribution and Way of Life of the Northern Wolf). — In: Severnoe olenevodstvo, OGIZ, Sel'khozgiz. 1948.

Selevin, V. K.   K rasprostraneniyu snezhnogo barsa na Altae (On the Distribution of the Snow-Leopard (P. uncia Schreber) in the Altai). — Okhotnik, No. 8. 1929.

Severtsov, N. A.   Tigr (The Tiger). — Vestnik Estestvennykh Nauk, Nos. 15, 16, 17, 19. 1855.

Shaposhnikov, F. D.   K ekologii sobolya Severo-Vostochnogo Altaya (On the Ecology of Sable of the Northwest Altai). — In: Sbornik materialov po rezul'tatam izucheniya mlekopitayushchikh v gosudarstvennykh zapovednikakh, Moskva. 1956.

Sharleman, E. V.   Mlekopitayushchie okrestnosti goroda Kieva (Mammals in the Vicinity of Kiev). — Izd. Kievskogo ornitologicheskogo obshchestva im. Kesslera. 1915.

Shastin, L. P.   Nazemnye mlekopitayushchie severo-zapadnoi chasti Taimyrskogo poluostrova (Terrestrial Mammals of the Northwestern Part of the Taimyr Peninsula). — In: "Promyslovye mlekopitayushchie poberezh'ya Taimyrskogo poluostrova"; Trudy Nauchno-Issledovatel'skogo Instituta Polyarnogo Zemledeliya, Zhivotnovodstva i Promyslovogo Khozyaistva, Seriya Promyslovoe Khozyaistvo, No. 8, Leningrad, Izd. Glavsevmorputi. 1939.

Shilova- Krassova, S. A. O pitanii barsuka v Buzulukskom boru
    (Diet of the Badger (Meles meles L.) in the Buzuluk Pine
    Forest). — Zoologicheskii Zhurnal, Vol. 30, No. 3. 1951.

Shirinskii-Shikhmatov, A. A. Po medvezh'im sledam (Following Bear
    Tracks). 1900.

Shmidt, P. Yu. — Kamchatskaya ekspeditsiya F. P. Ryabushinskogo,
    zoologicheskii otdel, No. 1, Moskva. 1916.

Shmidt, F. Otchet nachal'nika fizicheskogo otdela Sibirskoi ekspeditsii
    (A Report by the Head of the Physics Division of the Siberian
    Expedition). — Zapiski Geograficheskogo Obshchestva, Vol. 1. 1862.

Shmidt, F. B. Puteshestvie v Amurskuyu oblast' i na ostrov Sakhalin
    (A Journey to the Amur Region and Sakhalin). 1868.

Shnitnikov, V. N. Mlekopitayushchie Semirech'ya (Mammals of
    Semirech'e). — Moskva- Leningrad, Izdatel'stvo AN SSSR. 1936.

Shukhov, I. N. Materialy k poznaniyu okhotnich'ego dela v Eniseiskoi
    gubernii (Contribution to the Studies of Hunting in the Yenisei
    Province) — Priroda i Okhota, No. 1. 1925.

Shukhov, I. N. Okhotnichii promysel v severnoi chasti Tarskogo okruga
    (Hunting in the Northern Part of the Tarskoe District). — Materialy k
    Poznaniyu Okhotnich'ego Dela v Sibiri, No. 2. 1928.

Shvetsov, S. Ocherk Surgutskogo kraya (A Survey of the Surgut Area). —
    Zapiski Sibirskogo Otdeleniya Russkogo Geograficheskogo
    Obshchestva, No. 10, Omsk. 1888.

Silant'ev, A. A. Obzor promyslovykh okhot v Rossii (A Survey of
    Commercial Hunting in Russia), Sankt-Peterburg. 1898.

Simashko, Yu. Russkaya fauna (Russian Fauna). 1. 1850.

Simashko, Yu. Russkaya fauna (Russian Fauna). 2. 1851.

Skalon, V. N. Pesets na Tomskom severe (Arctic Fox (Alopex
    lagopus L.) in the Tomsk North). — Okhotnik. 1928.

Skalon, V. N. Olenevodstvo v basseine r. Taza (Reindeer Breeding in the
    Taz River Basin). — Sovetskii Sever, Nos. 3 — 4. 1931.

Skalon, V. N. Materialy k poznaniyu fauny yuzhnykh granits Sibiri
    (Contribution to the Study of the Southern Siberia Fauna). — Izvestiya
    Gosudarstvennogo Protivochumnogo Instituta Sibiri i Dal'nego
    Vostoka. 1936.

Skalon, V. N., V. V. Raevskii, and E. S. Zhdanov. Svoevremennoe
    rasprostranenie sobolya i kunitsy v Severo- Vostochnom Priural'e i
    ikh vzaimootnosheniya (Timely Distribution of Sable and Marten
    and their Relationships in the Northeastern Urals Area). — Nauchno-
    Metodicheskie Zapiski Glavnogo Upravleniya Zapovednikov, No. 7.
    Moskva. 1940.

Skalon, V. N. and P. P. Tarasov. O roli kedra v zhizni taezhnykh zverei
    i ptits v Mongolii i Sibiri (On the Role of the Siberian Pine in
    the Life of Taiga Animals and Birds in Mongolia and Siberia). —
    Uchenye Zapiski Mongol'skogo Universiteta, Ulan Bator. 1946.

Slovtsov, I. Ya. Pozvonochnye Tyumenskogo okruga i ikh rasprostranenie
    v Tobol'skoi gubernii (Vertebrates of the Tyumen District in the
    Tobol'sk Province). — Materialy k Poznaniyu Fauny i Flory Rossiiskoi
    Imperii, otdel zoologicheskii, No. 1. Moskva. 1892.

Sludskii, A. A.   Massovoe poyavlenie korsaka v Barabinskoi stepi (Mass Occurrence of the Corsac Fox (Vulpes corsac L.) in the Baraba Steppe).— Trudy Sibirskoi Okhotnich'e-Promyslovoi Stantsii, Novosibirsk. 1930.

Sludskii, A. A.   Tigr v SSSR (The Tiger in the USSR).— Izvestiya Akademii Nauk Kazakhskoi SSR, Seriya Biologicheskaya, 1, No. 8. 1953.

Slyunin, N. V.   Okhotsko-Kamchatskii krai. Estestvenno-istoricheskoe opisanie (Okhotsk-Kamchatka Area.   Natural and Historical Description). Vol. 1, Sankt-Peterburg. 1900.

Smirnov, N. A.   Buryi medved' v kollektsiyakh Kavkazskogo muzeya (European Brown Bear (Ursus arctos L.) in the Collections of the Caucasus Museum).— Zapiski Kavkazskogo Muzeya, seriya A, No. 4. 1916.

Sokol'nikov, N. P.   Okhotnich'i i promyslovye zveri Anadyrskogo kraya (Game and Commercial Animals of the Anadyr Area).— Byulleten' MOIP, Vol. 36, Nos. 1—2. 1927.

Solov'ev, D. K.   Zapovedniki, ikh vozniknovenie, znachenie, organizatsiya etc. (Reserves, their Origin, Importance, Organization, etc.).— Trudy ekspeditsii po izucheniyu sobolya i issledovaniyu sobolinogo promysla, seriya, 2, Sayanskaya ekspeditsiya. 1920_1.

Solov'ev, D. K.   Sayanskii promyslovo-okhotnichii raion i sobolinyi promysel v nem (Sayan Commercial and Hunting District and its Sable Trade), Peterburg. 1920_2.

Solov'ev, D. K.   Osnovy okhotovedeniya (Fundamentals of the Hunting Trade). Part 3, Moskva. 1925.

Solov'ev, D. K. and V. N. Belousov.   Sobol' i sobolinyi promysel (Sable and Sable Trade).— In: Sayanskii promyslovo-okhotnichii raion i sobolinyi promysel v nem, Peterburg. 1920.

Spangenberg, E. P. and A. M. Sudilovskaya.   Irbisy v Kirgizskom Ala-Tau (Snow Leopards (Panthera uncia Schreber) in Kirghiz Ala-Tau).— Priroda, No. 9. 1954.

Spasskii, G.   Izvestie ob ubitom v Sibiri nepodaleku ot Zmeinogorskogo rudnika tigre i o kamennom shchegle (Report on the Killing of a Tiger near the Zmeinogorsk Mine and on the Siberian Gray-Headed Goldfinch (Carduelis carduelis L.)).— Umozritel'nye Issledovaniya Sankt-Peterburgskoi Akademii Nauk, Vol. 4, Sankt-Peterburg. 1815.

Stepanov, P.   Putevye zametki, vedennye vo vremya poezdki letom 1885 goda v verkhov'yakh rr. Tartasa i Tary, i zoogeograficheskii ocherk lesisto-bolotistoi polosy, lezhashchei mezhdu rr. Om'yu, Taroi i Irtyshom (Travel Observations of Summer 1885 a Trip into the Upper Reaches of the Tartas and Tara Rivers. Zoogeographical Survey of the Forest-Swamp Belt between the Om, Tara, and Irtysh Rivers).— Zapiski Sibirskogo Otdeleniya Russkogo Geograficheskogo Obshchestva No. 8, Issue 1, Omsk. 1886.

Stroganov, S. U.   Novye dannye po sistematike perevyazki (Vormela peregusna Gueldenstaedt) (New Data on the Systematics of Vormela peregusna Gueldenstaedt).— Trudy Zoologicheskogo Instituta Akademii Nauk SSSR, Vol. 7. 1948.

Suprunenko, N. I. Fauna pozvonochnykh zhivotnykh Sakhalina (Vertebrate Fauna of Sakhalin). — In: Katalog mezhdunarodnoi vystavki, Sankt-Peterburg. 1890.

Sviridenko, P. A. Stepnoi khorek i ego sel'skokhozyaistvennoe znachenie v bor'be s gryzunami (The Steppe Polecat (Putorius eversmannii) and its Agricultural Importance in the Control of Rodents). — Moskva-Leningrad, Izdatel'stvo VASKhNIL. 1935.

Sysoev, V. P. Okhota v Khabarovskom krae (Hunting in the Khabarovsk Area), Khabarovsk. 1952.

Tel', G. Puteshestvie v Sibiri sukhim putem i plavanie po Eniseyu (A Journey to Siberia by Land and on the Yenisei). — In: A. E. Nordenshel'd. Ekspeditsiya k ust'yu Eniseya 1875 i 1876 godov, Sankt-Peterburg. 1880. [Russian translation from Swedish.]

Telishchev, I. Zametka o nekotorykh promyslovykh mlekopitayushchikh basseina reki Obi (A Note on Some Commercial Mammals from the Ob River Basin). — Ural'skii Okhotnik, No. 2. 1931.

Teplov, P. and E. N. Teplova. Mlekopitayushchie Pechero-Ylychskogo zapovednika (Mammals of the Pechora-Ilych Preserve). — Trudy Pechero-Ylychskogo Gosudarstvennogo Zapovednika, No. 5, Moskva. 1947.

Ternovskii, D. V. Biologiya i akklimatizatsiya amerikanskoi norki (Lutreola vison Brisson) na Altae (Biology and Acclimatization of the American Mink (Putorius vison Brisson) on the Altai)), Novosibirsk. 1958.

Timofeev, V. V. Zveri nashei oblasti (Animals of the Irkutsk Region), Irkutsk. 1949.

Tolstov, S. I. K faune promyslovykh mlekopitayushchikh Turukhanskogo kraya (On the Fauna of Commercial Mammals of the Turukhansk Area). — Nasha Okhota, No. 18. 1916.

Tret'yakov, P. I. Turukhanskii krai (The Turukhansk Area). — Zapiski Russkogo Geograficheskogo Obshchestva po Obshchei Geografii, Vol. 2. 1869.

Troitskii, V. N. Zametki lesnogo i okhotnich'ego khozyaistva raiona r. Any. Abakanskaya ekspeditsiya 1927 — 1928 gg. (Notes on the Forestry and Hunting in the Ana River District, the Abakan Expedition of 1927 — 1928). — Trudy Obshchestva Izucheniya Sibiri, Novosibirsk. 1930_1.

Troitskii, V. N. Okhotnichii promysel v Chuno-Angarskom raione (byvshego Kanskogo okruga) (Hunting in the Chuna-Angarsk District (former Kansk District)). — Izvestiya Sibirskoi Kraevoi Nauchnoi Okhotnich'e-Promyslovoi Stantsii, No. 1, Novosibirsk. 1930_2.

Tsalkin, V. I. K biologi belogo medvedya arkhipelaga Frantsa Iosifa (On the Biology of the White Polar Bear (Ursus maritimus) of the Franz Josef Archipelago). — Byulleten' MOIP, Vol. 14. 1936.

Tsetsevinskii, L. M. Amerikanskaya norka v lesakh Zaural'ya (The American Mink Putorius vison in the Forests of the Transurals).— Sovetskii Okhotnik, No. 10. 1939.

Tsetsevinskii, L. M. Materialy po ekologii pestsa Severnogo Yamala (Data on the Ecology of the Arctic Fox Alopex lagopus L. of Northern Yamal). — Zoologicheskii Zhurnal, Vol. 19, No. 1. 1940.

Tugarinov, A. Ya.   Promyslovye zveri Zasayanskogo kraya (Commercial Animals of the Sayan Area). — Nasha Okhota, No. 6. 1916.

Tugarinov, A. Ya., N. A. Smirnov, and A. I. Ivanov. Ptitsy i mlekopitayushchie Yakutii (Birds and Mammals of Yakutia). — Trudy po izucheniyu proizvoditel'nykh sil Sibiri. 1934.

Turov, S. S.   O faune pozvonochnykh zhivotnykh severo-vostochnogo poberezh'ya ozera Baikal (On the Vertebrate Fauna of the Northeastern Shore of Lake Baikal). — Doklady AN SSSR, Seriya A, Nos. 7—9. 1924.

Turov, S. S.   Okhotnichii promysel u tungusov Severnogo Baikala (Hunting of the Northern Baikal Inhabited by the Tungus). — Okhotnik, No. 8. 1925.

Turov, S. S.   Zoologicheskaya ekspeditsiya v Yugo-Zapadnye Sayany (Zoological Expedition to the Southwest Sayans). — Boets-Okhotnik, No. 1. 1936.

Turov, S. S.   Materialy po mlekopitayushchim severo-vostochnogo poberezh'ya Baikala i Burguzinskogo khrebta (Data on Mammals of the Northeastern Coast of the Baikal and Burguzin Range). — Sbornik Trudov Gosudarstvennogo Zoologicheskogo Muzeya pri MGU, No. 3, Moskva. 1939.

Tyulin, A.   Promyslovaya fauna ostrova Belogo (Commercial Fauna of Bely Island). — Leningrad, Izd. Glavsevmorputi. 1938.

Tyushev, V. N.   Po zapadnomu beregu Kamchatki (Along the Western Coast of Kamchatka). — Zapiski Russkogo Geograficheskogo Obshchestva, Vol. 37, No. 2. 1906.

Urvantsev, N. N.   Noril'skoe kamennougol'noe mestorozhdenie (The Norilsk Coal-Bearing Deposit). — Trudy G. R. U. 1931.

Ushakov, V. E.   K biologii medvedya (The Biology of the Bear). — Ural'skii Okhotnik, No. 8. 1926.

Ushakov, V. E.   Unichtozhili khishchnika (Extermination of Beasts of Prey). — Okhotnik i Pushnik Sibiri, No. 8. 1928.

Vasenova, A.   Norka v Khabarovskom krae (The Mink (Putorius) in the Khabarovsk Area). — Okhota i Okhotnich'e Khozyaistvo, No. 4. 1957.

Vasil'ev, V. V.   Reka Dem'yanovka (The Dem'yanovka River), Tobol'sk. 1929.

Vasil'ev, V. V., V. V. Raevskii, and Z. I. Georgievskaya.   Rechnye bobry i soboli v Kondo-Sosvinskom gosudarstvennom zapovednike (European Beavers (Castor fiber L.) and Sables in the Konda-Sosva State Reserve). — Trudy Kondo-Sosvinskogo Gosudarstvennogo Zapovednika, Vol. 1, Moskva. 1941.

Velizhanin, G. A.   Zoo-ekologicheskoe obsledovanie khor'kovskogo zakaznika Sibirskogo otdeleniya Instituta zashchity rastenii (Zoo-Ecological Investigation of the Khor Forest Reserve in the Siberian Section of the Institute for Plant Protection). — Trudy Instituta Zashchity Rastenii Sibiri, No. 1(8). 1931.

Vereshchagin, V. I.   Ot Barnaula do Mongolii.   Altaiskii sbornik (From Barnaul to Mongolia.   Altai Collection). 9. 1908.

Vershinin, A. A. and E. M. Dolgorukov.   Materialy po biologii sobolya i sobolinomu promyslu Kamchatskoi oblasti (Data on Sable Biology and Sable Hunting). — Trudy Vsesoyuznogo Nauchno-Issledovatelskogo Instituta Okhotnich'ego Promysla, No. 8. 1948.

Vladimirov, K. A.   Amerikanskaya norka v Irkutskoi oblasti (The American Mink (Putorius vison) in the Irkutsk Region), Irkutsk. 1940.

Vrangel' [Wrangel], F.   Puteshestvie po severnym beregam Sibiri i po Ledovitomu okeanu, ch. 1, 2 (A Journey along the Northern Coasts of Siberia and on the Arctic Ocean, Parts 1, 2), Sankt-Peterburg. 1841.

Vrangel' [Wrangel], F.   Puteshestviya k severynym beregam Sibiri i po Ledovitomu moryu, sovershennye v 1820, 21, 22, 23 i 1824 godakh ekspeditseyu, sostoyashchego pod nachal'stvom flota-leitenanta Ferdinanda fon-Vrangelya (Journeys to the Northern Coasts of Siberia and the Arctic Ocean Conducted in 1820, 1821, 1822, 1823 and 1824 by the Expedition under the Command of Navy Lieutenant Ferdinand von Wrangel).   Part 2 and Appendix, Sankt-Peterburg. 1841.

Yablonskii, N. I.   Na Altae (In the Altai).— Priroda i Okhota, Nos. 10—12. 1901; Nos. 1—12. 1902; Nos. 1—12. 1903.

Yablonskii, N. I.   Okhotnich'i i promyslovye ptitsy i zveri Yuzhnogo Altaya (Game and Commercial Birds and Animals of the Southern Altai).— Priroda i Okhota, Nos. 2, 8, 9. 1904.

Yachmen', V.   Nashestvie medvedei (Bear Invasion).— Okhotnik i Pushnik Sibiri, No. 12. 1927.

Yakovlev, E. O.   K granitsam rasprostraneniya promyslovykh zverei i ptits v Turu-Khanskom krae (Distribution Limits of the Commercial Animals and Birds in the Turukhan Area).— Trudy Zoologicheskoi Sektsii Sredne-Sibirskogo Otdeleniya Russkogo Geograficheskogo Obshchestva, Zoologicheskii Sbornik, Krasnoyarsk. 1930.

Yankovskii, M. N.   Pyatnistye oleni, barsy i tigry Ussuriiskogo kraya (Axis Deer (Cervus nippon hortulorum Swinthoe), Leopards (Panthera pardus tulliana Valenciennes) and Tigers (Panthera tigris L.) of the Ussuri Territory).— Izvestiya Vostochno-Sibirskogo Otdeleniya Geograficheskogo Obshchestva, Vol. 13, No. 3. 1882.

Yanushevich, A. I.   Promyslovye zveri i ptitsy Zapadnoi Sibiri (Commercial Animals and Birds of Western Siberia), Novosibirsk. 1952.

Yanushevich, A. I.   Fauna pozvonochnykh Tuvinskoi oblasti (Vertebrate Fauna of the Tuva Region), Novosibirsk. 1952.

Yanushevich, A. I. and K. T. Yurlov.   Vertikal'noe rasprostranenie mlekopitayushchikh i ptits v Zapadnom Sayane (Vertical Distribution of Mammals and Birds in the Western Sayans).— Izvestiya zapadno-Sibirskogo Filiala Akademii Nauk SSSR, seriya biologicheskaya, Vol. 3, No. 2, Novosibirsk. 1949.

Yudin, B. S.   Teriofauna yuzhnoi chasti Tomskoi oblasti (Theriofauna of the Southern Part of the Tomsk Region).   Synopsis of Report.— X otchetnaya sessiya Zapadno-Sibirskogo filiala Akademii Nauk SSSR, Novosibirsk. 1956.

Yurgenson, P. B.   O gornostayakh Dal'nevostochnogo kraya (Far Eastern Ermines (Mustela erminea L.)).— Byulleten' MOIP, otdel biologicheskii, Vol. 45, No. 3. 1936.

Yurgenson, P. B.   Materialy po ekologii i pitanii burogo medvedya
(Data on Ecology and Nutrition of the European Brown Bear (Ursus
arctos L.)). — Trudy Tsentral'nogo Gosudarstvennogo Zapovednika,
No. 2. 1937.

Yurgenson, P. B.   Materialy k poznaniyu mlekopitayushchikh
priteletskogo uchastka Altaiskogo gosudarstvennogo zapovednika
(Contribution to Studies of Mammals of the Teletskoe Area Section of
the Altai State Reserve). — Trudy Altaiskogo Gosudarstvennogo
Zapovednika, No. 1, Moskva. 1938.

Yurgenson, P. B.   Kidus — gibrid sobolei i kunits ("Kidus," a Hybrid of
Sable and Marten). — Trudy Pechero-Ylychskogo Zapovednika,
No. 5. 1947.

Zharkov, I. V. and V. P. Teplov.   Materialy po pitaniyu barsuka v
Tatarskoi respublike (Data on Nutrition of the Badger (Meles
meles L.) in the Tatar Republic). — Raboty Volzhsko-Kamskoi
Zonal'noi Okhotnich'e-Promyslovoi Biologicheskoi Stantsii, No. 2.
1932.

Zhitkov, B. M.   Poluostrov Yamal (The Yamal Peninsula). — Zapiski
Russkogo Geograficheskogo Obshchestva, 19. 1913.

Zhitkov, B. M.   O kollektsii mlekopitayushchikh sobrannykh Kolymskoi
ekspeditsiei 1905 goda (Collection of Mammals of the 1905 Kolyma
Expedition). — Dnevnik Zoologicheskogo Otdeleniya Obshchestva
Lyubitelei Estestvoznaniya, Antropologii i Etnografii, novaya seriya,
Vol. 1, No. 5, Moskva. 1913.

Zolotarev, N. T.   Promyslovaya fauna i okhotnichii promysel Udskogo i
Verkhne-Selemdzhinskogo raionov (Commercial Fauna and Hunting
in the Uda and Verkhne-Selemdzha Districts). — Trudy Soveta po
izucheniyu proizvoditel'nykh sil, Izdatel'stvo AN SSSR. 1934.

Zolotarev, N. T.   Mlekopitayushchie basseina reki Imana (Mammals of
the Iman River Basin). — Leningrad, Izdatel'stvo AN SSSR. 1936.

Zubarovskii, M. I.   Dal'nevostochnyi lesnoi kot Felis
(Prionaelurus) euptilura microtis Milne-Edwards
(1868—1874) (The Far Eastern Wildcat Felis (Prionaelurus)
euptilura microtis Milne-Edwards (1868—1874)). — Byulleten'
MOIP, otdel biologicheskii, Vol. 48, Nos. 2—3. 1939.

Zverev, M. D.   Materialy po biologii i sel'skokhozyaistvennomu
znacheniyu v Sibiri khor'kov i drugikh khishchnikov iz semeistva
Mustelidae (Data on the Biology and Agricultural Significance of
Polecats and Other Carnivora of Family Mustelidae in Siberia). —
Trudy po Zashchite Rastenii Sibiri, Vol. 1(8). 1931.

Zverev, M. D.   Mlekopitayushchie v raione severnogo uchastka Turkestano-
Sibirskoi zheleznoi dorogi (Mammals in the District of the Northern
Section of the Turkestan-Siberian Railroad). — Trudy po Zashchite
Rastenii, Seriya 4, No. 2. Novosibirsk. 1932.

Zverev, M. D.   Mlekopitayushchie Novosibirskogo raiona (Mammals of the
Novosibirsk District). — Trudy Novosibirskogo Zooparka, Vol. 1.
Novosibirsk. 1937.

Zverev, M. D. and I. M. Zalesskii.   Kolonok i ego dobyvanie (The
Siberian Weasel (Mustela sibirica Pallas) and Ways of Trapping
it). — KOIZ. 1935.

Allen, J. A. Report of the Mammals Collected in Northeastern Siberia by the Jesup. North Pacific Expedition with Itinerary and Field Notes by N. G. Buxton. — Bull. Amer. Museum Natur. History, Vol. 19. 1903.

Allen, G. M. — Proc. New Engl. Zool. Club, Vol. 5. 1914.

Allen, G. Mustelids from the Asiatic Expeditions. — Amer. Museum Novitates, No. 358. 1929.

Allen, G. M. The Mammals of China and Mongolia, P. 1. 1938.

Bechstein, I. M. Uebersicht der vierfüssigen Thiere, 2, Weimar, p. 408. 1800.

Blanford, W. T. Scientific Results of the Second Jarkand Mission. — Mammalia. 1879.

Blasius, J. N. — Säugethiere Deutschlands. p. 222. 1857.

Blasius, W. XIII Bericht der naturforsch. Gesellsch. Bamberg. 1884.

Brandt, F. Observations sur le Manul. — Bull. Sci. publié par l'Acad. Imp. des Scienc. de St. Pétersb., 9. 1841.

Brandt, F. Considérations sur les animaux vertebreés de la Sibérie occidentale, Paris. 1845.

Brandt, J. F. Untersuchungen über die Verbreitung des Tiger und seine Beziehungen zur Menschheit. — Mem. Acad. Petersb. 6. 1856.

Brandt, J. F. Mitteilungen über die verschiedenen Kleider der Seeotter. — Melanges biol. Bull. Acad. Imp. St. Petersb., 13. 1881.

Buffon, G. Hist. nat. 9, p. 151. 1761. tab. 13.

Bunge, A. Naturhistorische Beobachtungen und Fahrten im Lena-Delta. — Mel. biologiques. t. 12. 1834.

Bunge, A. Naturhistorische Nachrichten aus der Polarstation an der Lena Mündung. — Bull. Acad. Imper. St. Petersb., 28. 1883.

Bunge, A. Bericht über die im Jana Gebiet im Sommer 1885 ausgeführten Reisen, nebst einem Verzeichniss der daselbst beobachteten oder erkundeten Säugetiere und Vögel. — Beitr. z. Kenntn. des Russ. Reichs., Bd. 13, Sankt-Peterburg. 1887.

Desmarest, A. G. Mammalogie ou description des espèces des mammifères, Paris. 1820.

Dode, E. — Proc. Zool. Soc., London, p. 480. 1871.

Domaniewski, J. Neue Säugetiere aus Nordasien. — Ann. Zool. Mus. Polon. Hist. Nat., 5. 1926.

Dybowski, B. — Arch. towar. nauk we Lwowie, 3. 1922.

Ellerman, J. R. and T. C. S. Morrison-Scott. Checklist of Palaearctic and Indian Mammals, 1758 to 1946, London. 1951.

Elliot, D. G. Remarks on Various Species of Felidae, with a Description of a Species from North-Western Siberia. — Proc. Zool. Soc. London, pp. 758—761. 1871.

Elliot, D. G. Monograph on Felidae, pl. 26 and text (Lapsus calomi instead of Felis microtis). 1883.

Erxleben, Ch. Systema regni animalis de classes, ordines, genera, etc. — Mammalia, 1. 1777.

Eversmann, E. — Bull. Soc. Imp. not. Moscou. 1840.

Finch, O. and A. Bren. Voyage to Western Siberia [Russian translation, 1882].

Fitzinger, L. — Sitzungsber. Kaiser. Akad. Wissensch, 58. p. 455. Wien. 58. 1868.

Gebler, Fr. Le putois des Alpes.— Mem. Soc. Imp. Nat., Mosc. 6. 1823.

Gebler, F. von. Uebersicht des Katunischen Gebirges, der höchsten Spitze des russischen Altai.— Mem. pres. Acad. Imp. Sci. de St.-Petersb., t. 3. 1837.

Gebler, F. von. Über das Vorkommen des Tigers im Altai.— Bull. Sci. Acad., t. 6. St.-Petersb. 1840.

Glehn. Reisebericht von der Insel Sachalin.— Trudy Sibirskoi Ekspeditsii Russkogo Geograficheskogo Obshchestva, fizicheskii otdel, Vol. 1. 1868.

Gmelin, J. G.— Nov. Comment. Acad. Petrop., 5. 1760.

Goodwin, G. G. Mammals Collected in the Maritime Province of Siberia by the Modern Graves North Asiatic Expedition, with the Description of a New Hare from the Amur River.— Amer. Musem Novitates, No. 681. 1933.

Hensel, R. Craniologische Studien.— Nova Acta Kaiserl. Leop. Carol. Deutsch. Acad. der Naturforsch., Bd. 42, No. 4. 1881.

Heptner, W. G.— Z. Säugetiere, 15, p. 224. 1940.

Heude, P. M. Mémoires concernant l'histoire naturelle de l'Empire Chinois par des pères de la compagnie de Jésus. 4, Chang-Hai. 1898.

Heude, P. M. Notes sur quelques ursides peu ou point connus.— Mém. concern. l'Hist. Nat. de l'Emp. Chin., 5, pt. 1. 1901.

Hollister, N. New Mammals from the Highland of Siberia.— Smiths. Misc. Collect. Vol. 63, No. 14. 1912.

Hollister, N.— Proc. Biol. Soc. Washington. 26. 1913.

Jurgenson [Yurgenson], P. B. Das Hermelin aus dem Turuchansk-Gebiet.— Zool. Anz., Bd. 98, h. 1/2. 1932.

Karelin, G. S. Lettres de M. Kareline Voyageur de la Société.— Bull. Soc. Natur. Moscou, t. 14. 1841; t. 17. 1844.

Keyserling, A. U. and J. N. Blasius. Die Wirbeltiere Europas, p. 66 (type Mustela putorius L.). 1840.

Kerr, R.— Animal Kingdom, No. 381. 1792.

Kischida.— Zool. Mag. Tokyo, Vol. 42. 1930.

Knottnerus-Meyer, Th. Ueber den Eisbären und seine geographischen Formen.— Sitzber. Gesellsch. Naturforsch. Freunde zu Berlin. 1903.

Krumbiegel, I. Biologie der Tiere Deutschlands, Berlin. 1930.

Krusenstern, I. F. Reise um die Welt. H. 2. 1811.

Kuroda. On New Mamm. from Riu Kin and Vicinity, 10, Tokyo. 1924.

Kuroda.— Bull. Biogeogr. Soc. 13, Tokyo. 1943.

Lataste, F. Le vison du Japon (Putorius itatsi Temm.) etc.— Bull. Sci. depart. du Nord. Vol. 10 (2 ser.). 1887.

Lönnberg, E. Remarks on Some Palearctic Bears.— Proc. Zool. Soc. London. 1923.

Lowkaschkin.— China J. Sci. a. Arts, 20. 1934.

Lydekker. Note on the Wild Ass of Mongolia.— Proc. Zool. Soc. London, 5, 1. 1904.

Merriam, H. Review of the Grizzly and Brown Bears of North America (gen. Ursus).— North Americ. Fauna, No. 14. 1918.

Middendorf, A. Sibirische Reise. Säugethiere, Vögel und Amphibien, Bd. 2, St.-Petersb., 1853.

Middendorf, A. Sibirische Reise, Bd. 4, Theil 2. Die Thierwelt Sibiriens, St.-Petersb. 1867.

Middendorf, A.   Übersicht der Natur Nord- und Ost-Sibiriens, Bd. 4. 1875. pt. 2.

Miller, G. S.   List of North American Land Mammals in the United States Nat. Mus.— Bul. 79, U. S. Nat. Mus. 1912.

Milne-Edwards, A.   Recherches pour servir à l'Histoire Naturelle des Mammifères 1868.— Ann. Nat., Zool. Ser., 5, Vol. 8. 1867.

Milne-Edwards, A.   Recherches pour servir à l'Histoire Naturelle des mammifères, p. 221, Paris. 1867—1874.

Miller, G. S.   Catalogue of the Mammals of Western Europe, London. 1912.

Mori, T.— Ann. Mag. Nat. Hist., X, p. 609. 1922.

Noack, Th.   Füchse und Wölfe des Altai.— Zool. Anz., Bd. 31. 1910.

Osgood, W. H.   Mammals of the Kelley-Roosvelts and Delacour Asiatic Expedition.— Publ. Field Mus. Nat. Hist., Zool. Ser., 18. 1932.

Pallas, P. S.   Reise durch verschiedene Provinzen des Russischen Reichs, 3. 1776.

Pallas, P. S.   Zoographia Rosso-Asiatica, t. 1, Petropoli. 1811.

Pallas, P. S.   Zoographia Rosso-Asiatica, t. 1, Petropoli. 1831.

Pocock, R. I.— Proc. Zool. Soc. London, p. 302. 1907.

Pocock, R. I.— Ann. Mag. Nat. Hist. 1918.

Pocock, R. I.— Proc. Zool. Soc. London, p. 543. 1921.

Pocock, R. I.— Bombay Nat. Hist. Soc., 33, p. 527. 1929.

Pocock, R. I.   The Polecats of the Genera Putorius and Vormela in British Museum.— Proc. Zool. Soc. London. 1936.

Radde, G.   Reisen im Süden von Ost-Sibirien in Jahren 1855—1859, St.-Petersb. 1862.

Satunin, K. A.   Neue Katzenarten aus Central-Asien.— Ezhegodnik Zoologicheskogo Muzeya Imperatorskoi Akademii Nauk, 9, pp. 528—532, Sankt-Peterburg. 1904.

Satunin, K.   Der Amur-Tiger.— Neue Baltische Wildmannsblätter, No. 4, p. 73. 1907.

Simpson, G. G.   The Principles of Classification and Classification of Mammals.— Bull. Amer. Museum Nat. Hist., Vol. 85, N. Y. 1945.

Scalon, W. N.   Ueber einige interessante Säugetiere des Narymgebietes.— Zool. An., Bd. 77, H. 11/12. 1928.

Schmidt, Fr.   Historischer Bericht über die Tätigkeit der physikalischen Abteilung der sibirischen Expedition der Kaiserlichen Geographischen Gesellschaft.— Trudy Sibirskoi Ekspeditsii Russkogo Geograficheskogo Obshchestva, Vol. 1, Sankt-Peterburg. 1868.

Schmidt, Fr.   Wissenschaftliche Resultate der zur Aufsuchung eines angekündeten Mammuthkadavers an dem unteren Jenissei ausgesandten Expedition.— Memm. de l'Acad. Sci. St.-Petersb., t. 28. 1872.

Schreber, C. L.— Die Säugetiere, Vol. 3, p. 386. 1777. tabl. 100. (1776, Figure from Buffon and Text).

Schrenck, L.   Reisen und Forschungen im Amur-Lande in den Jahren 1854—1856, St.-Petersb. 1858.

Schrenk, L.   Bemerkungen über die Säugetierfauna Süd-Sachalins und der südlichen Kurilien auf Veranlassung brieflicher Mitteilungen des Hrn. Fr. Schmidt.— Bull. Acad. imper. Sci., t. 4, St.-Petersb. 1862.

Sowerby, A.   Notes On Heude's Bears in the Sikawei Museum and on the Bears of Palaearctic Eastern Asia.— J. of Mammalogy, 1. 1920.

Temminck, C. J.   Fauna Japonica.— Mamm., 34. 1844. pl. 7, fig. 2.

Thomas, O.   On Mammals from Central Asia, Collected by Mr. Douglas Carruthers.— Ann. and Mag. Nat. Hist., Ser. 8, Vol. 9. 1912.

Thomas, O.   On Small Mammals from Djarkent. — Ann. Mag. Nat. Hist.,
    Ser. 8, Vol. 13. 1914.
Toll, E.   Die russische Polarfahrt der "Sarja," Berlin. 1909.
Trouessart, E. L.   Catalogus Mammalium, 1. 1897.
Trouessart, E. L.   Catalogus Mammalium, 1, p. 278. 1898.
Trouessart, E. L.   Catalogus Mammalium tam viventium quam
    fossilium. — Quinquennale Supplementum, Berolini. 1904.
Trouessart, E. L.   Faune Mamm. d'Europe, p. 75. 1910.

EXPLANATORY LIST OF ABBREVIATED NAMES OF USSR INSTITUTIONS, PERIODICALS, ETC., APPEARING IN THIS TEXT

Abbreviation	Full name (transliterated)	Translation
AN SSSR	Akademiya nauk SSSR	Academy of Sciences of the USSR
GRU	Glavnoe razvedyvatel'noe upravlenie	Central Exploration Administration
Izd.	Izdatel'stvo	Publishing House
KOIZ	Vsesoyuznoe kooperativnoe izdatel'stvo	All-Union Cooperative Publishing House
LGU	Leningradskii gosudarstvennyi universitet	Leningrad State University
MGU	Moskovskii gosudarstvennyi universitet	Moscow State University
MOIP	Moskovskoe obshchestvo ispytatelei prirody	Moscow Society of Naturalists
OGIZ	Ob"edinenie gosudarstvennykh izdatel'stv	State United Publishing Houses
RGO	Russkoe geograficheskoe obshchestvo	Russian Geographical Society
SGU	Severnoe geodezicheskoe upravlenie	Northern Geodetic Administration
TsK	Tsentral'nyi komitet	Central Committee
VASKhNIL	Vsesoyuznaya akademiya sel'skokhozyaistvennykh nauk im. V.I. Lenina	V. I. Lenin All-Union Academy of Agricultural Sciences

[5106]   Printed in Jerusalem, Israel   TT 68-50349